Math 1

An Incremental Development

Home Study Teacher's Edition

Nancy Larson

with

Linda Mathews
Dee Dee Wescoatt

Saxon Publishers, Inc.

Math 1: An Incremental Development

Home Study Teacher's Edition

Copyright © 1994 by Saxon Publishers, Inc. and Nancy Larson

Printed in the United States of America

ISBN 13: 978-1-56577-014-0
ISBN 10: 1-56577-014-5

Production Supervisor: David Pond
Graphic Artists: Scott Kirby, John Chitwood, Gary Skidmore, Tim Maltz, and Chad Threet

28 0877 21

4500833528

┌─── *Reaching us via the Internet* ───┐

www.saxonpublishers.com

E-mail: info@saxonpublishers.com

MATH 1 HOME STUDY OVERVIEW

The *Math 1 Home Study Teacher's Edition* contains all the information you will need to teach first grade math concepts to your child. The scripted lessons provide language and techniques that have proven effective for teachers in a variety of settings.

The program is designed so that four lessons are taught each week with the fifth day of the week used for review, if necessary. Each *Math 1* lesson has four components. These components are The Meeting, The Lesson, Class Practice, and Written Practice. Every fifth lesson includes a Written Assessment and every tenth lesson includes an Oral Assessment.

The Meeting occurs at the beginning of each day. During The Meeting your child will use a Meeting Book and a Meeting Strip. The chart on the next page shows the calendar patterns used each month in the Meeting Book. A Meeting Strip master is included at the end of the overview. Thirty-three copies of this master will provide enough meeting strips for the year.

Read each day's lesson before teaching it to become familiar with the lesson activity, the materials needed, and the important questions to ask. While teaching The Lesson, you may read the script exactly as it is written. During The Lesson, encourage your child to discuss observations and discoveries and to ask questions. The "doing" part of this program is very important and leads to concept understanding.

The Student Workbook includes masters used in lessons, written practice sheets for each lesson (Sides A and B), fact sheets, assessments, and color-coded fact cards. Give your child the appropriate master, written practice sheet, fact sheet, assessment, or fact card page when it is described in a lesson. It is suggested that you keep the workbook and give your child the pages as they are needed.

Each written practice sheet includes a short practice of the new objective and a review of previous concepts. Your child completes Side A with your assistance during the lesson. Side B, which mirrors the problems on Side A, is completed later in the day. This time delay between practice improves retention.

A fact sheet is completed each day. The fact cards and fact sheets provide an opportunity for your child to practice the number facts that have been introduced in previous lessons. All number facts are introduced in groups. Your child is encouraged to use the fact strategies presented in the lessons to find the answers. Automatic fact recall is expected by the end of *Math 3*.

Certain manipulative materials used in the lessons will need to be purchased from an educational supply house. These are pattern blocks, rulers, geoboards, linking cubes, hundred number chart, demonstration clocks, and balance. Other materials you will need during the year include the following:

Chalkboard or whiteboard
Scrap paper
Construction paper (1 package, multicolored)
3" × 5" cards (about 250)
Crayons
Scissors
Tape and glue
Small plastic bags
Coins (650 pennies, 10 nickels, 20 dimes, and 20 quarters)

CALENDAR PATTERNS

Month	Shape Pattern Used	Shape Pattern
August	circle, square	○ □
September	square, circle	□ ○
October	rectangle, circle, circle	▭ ○ ○
November	triangle, square, circle	△ □ ○
December	rectangle, triangle, circle, circle	▭ △ ○ ○
January	hexagon, triangle, triangle, rectangle	⬡ △ △ ▭
February	parallelogram, square, hexagon	▱ □ ⬡
March	hexagon, parallelogram, parallelogram, circle	⬡ ▱ ▱ ○
April	rectangle, square, parallelogram, hexagon	▭ □ ▱ ⬡
May	trapezoid, rectangle, parallelogram	⬭ ▭ ▱
June	hexagon, trapezoid, trapezoid, parallelogram	⬡ ⬭ ⬭ ▱

TABLE OF CONTENTS

LIST OF MATERIALS

Lesson 1   Math 1 Meeting Book
            meeting strip
            piece of paper

Lesson 2   Master 1-2
            linking cubes, unsnapped (at least
                30)
            crayons

Lesson 3   1–5 number strips from Lesson 2
            collection of 5 objects (pencils)
            handwriting paper
            penny

Lesson 4   Master 1-2 (bottom half)
            1–5 number strips from Lesson 2
            small plastic bag
            scissors

Lesson 5   number cards 0–9 (from
                Master 1-2)
            handwriting paper
            7 objects (pencils)
            penny

Lesson 6   construction paper
            tower of 10 linking cubes

Lesson 7   3" paper squares
            crayons
            graphing grid
            glue stick

Lesson 8   number cards 0–9
            handwriting paper
            9 objects (pencils)
            penny
            2 towers of 10 linking cubes

Lesson 9   linking cubes in a container (6 red,
                7 yellow, 9 green, and 8 blue)
            0–9 number cards
            2 towers of 10 linking cubes

Lesson 10   Written Assessment #1
            Oral Assessment #1
            individual number cards 1–5

Lesson 11   tag board circle and brass fastener
                for morning/afternoon clock
            1 red, 1 yellow, and 1 blue linking
                cube
            6 stuffed animals, dolls, action
                figures, or other toys

Lesson 12   5 stuffed animals, dolls, or other
                toys

Lesson 13   7 construction paper shapes
            10–15 stuffed animals, dolls, action
                figures, small trucks, or other
                collection of toys

Lesson 14   2 geoboards and geobands
            10 stuffed animals, dolls, or action
                figures

Lesson 15   Written Assessment #2
            10 apples
            bowl or container for the apples
            10–15 stuffed animals, dolls, action
                figures, or other toys

Lesson 16   container of 50–75 pennies
            hundred number chart

Lesson 17   10 pennies
            1 piece of paper
            Meeting Book
            camera (optional)

Lesson 18   1 apple
            cutting board and knife
            paper towels or napkins
            2 envelopes or small plastic bags

Lesson 19   envelopes of seeds from Lesson 18
            Master 1-19 and Master 1-19A
            fifteen 3" × 5" cards
            crayon

Lesson 20   Written Assessment #3
            Oral Assessment #2
            individual number cards (from
                Lesson 2)

Lesson 21   Master 1-19 (from Lesson 19)
            7 linking cubes
            Master 1-21

Lesson 22   6 linking cubes (one each of red,
                green, yellow, blue, orange, and
                black)
            6 toys (toy cars, stuffed animals,
                dolls, or action figures)

Lesson 23   10 linking cubes (all the same color)
            six 3" × 5" cards

Lesson 24   8 construction paper shapes
            geoboard and geoband
            large fact cards (from Lesson 23)

Lesson 25   Written Assessment #4
            10 stuffed animals, dolls, action
                figures, or other toys
            7 crayons
            large fact cards

Lesson 26   pattern blocks
            large fact cards

Lesson 27   balance
            6 identical containers with different
                contents (see **the night before**)
            Master 1-27
            large fact cards

Lesson 28   ten 3" × 5" cards
            large fact cards (from Lesson 23)
            tower of 10 red linking cubes
            tower of 10 blue linking cubes
            addition fact cards — tan
            bag or storage container for fact
                cards

Lesson 29   large fact cards
            tan individual fact cards
            Fact Sheet AA 1.0

Lesson 30   Written Assessment #5
            Oral Assessment #3
            linking cubes (6 red, 9 blue,
                4 yellow)
            individual number cards

Lesson 31   Master 1-31
            pattern blocks
            large fact cards
            Fact Sheet AA 1.0

Lesson 32   Master 1-32
            envelope or plastic bag for storing
                the number cards
            2 towers of 10 linking cubes
            large fact cards
            Fact Sheet AA 1.1

Lesson 33   10 stuffed animals, dolls, action
                figures, or other toys
            7 crayons
            large fact cards
            Fact Sheet AA 1.1

Lesson 34   hundred number chart
            cup of 20 pennies
            large fact cards
            Fact Sheet AA 1.1

Lesson 35   Written Assessment #6
            4 pieces of paper
            4 magazine pictures
            magazines
            glue
            scissors
            large fact cards

Lesson 36   tag board circle and brass fastener
                for morning/afternoon/evening/
                night clock
            100 linking cubes in towers of 10
                each
            individual fact cards
            Fact Sheet A 1.2

Lesson 37   twenty-seven 3" × 5" cards
            tower of 10 linking cubes
            addition fact cards — peach
            Fact Sheet AA 2.0

Lesson 38   Master 1-38
            basket of pattern blocks
            large fact cards (doubles)
            Fact Sheet A 1.2

Lesson 39   balance
            100 pennies
            eraser, crayon, and pencil

            8 small objects of different weights
            Master 1-39
            individual fact cards
            Fact Sheet A 1.2

Lesson 40   Written Assessment #7
            Oral Assessment #4
            9 yellow and 9 blue linking cubes

Lesson 41   9 pennies
            addition fact cards — lavender
            sixteen 3" × 5" cards
            Fact Sheet AA 3.0

Lesson 42   pattern blocks
            Master 1-42
            crayons
            large fact cards (adding one facts)
            Fact Sheet AA 2.0

Lesson 43   hundred number chart
            tower of 10 linking cubes
            Meeting Book
            Fact Sheet A 3.0

Lesson 44   2 towers of 10 linking cubes
            0–20 number cards (from Master
                1-32)
            subtraction fact cards (peach)
            ten 3" × 5" cards
            Fact Sheet S 2.0

Lesson 45   Written Assessment #8
            cup of 10 dimes
            piece of paper
            plastic bag with 80 pennies
            plastic bag with 8 dimes
            large fact cards (adding one facts)
            Fact Sheet AA 2.0

Lesson 46   1-cup liquid measuring cup
                (preferably plastic)
            5 empty containers
            basin, funnel, and newspaper
            water (approximately 3 gallons)
            food coloring (optional)
            masking tape
            marker
            linking cubes (10 each of red,
                green, blue, yellow, and black)
            large fact cards (subtracting one
                facts)
            Fact Sheet S 2.0

Lesson 47   5 dolls, stuffed animals, or action
                figures
            individual fact cards
            Fact Sheet A 1.2

Lesson 48   demonstration clock
            individual clocks
            small bell
            individual fact cards
            Fact Sheet A 2.0

Lesson 49   16 pennies
            Meeting Book
            large fact cards
            Fact Sheet A 3.0

Lesson 50   Written Assessment #9
            Oral Assessment #5

Lesson 51   hundred number chart
            4 linking cubes (red, yellow, green,
               blue)
            large fact cards (adding one facts)
            Fact Sheet A 2.0

Lesson 52   hundred number chart
            1 cup of 23 pennies and 1 cup of
               10 dimes
            large fact cards
            Fact Sheet A 2.2

Lesson 53   large bag of unshelled peanuts
            10 cups or bowls
            Master 1-53
            brown crayon
            1 sheet of newspaper
            large fact cards (subtracting one
               facts)
            Fact Sheet S 2.0

Lesson 54   chart paper and marker
            1 cup shelled peanuts
            blender or food processor
            vegetable oil
            measuring cup and teaspoon
            cutting board and knife
            1 cracker that can be divided in half
            1 celery stalk
            napkins
            individual fact cards
            Fact Sheet A 2.2

Lesson 55   Written Assessment #10
            Meeting Book
            large fact cards
            Fact Sheet A 3.2

Lesson 56   2 demonstration clocks
            Master 1-56
            large fact cards
            Fact Sheet A 3.2

Lesson 57   1 tower of 10 linking cubes
            yellow crayon
            Master 1-57
            individual fact cards
            Fact Sheet A 3.2

Lesson 58   1 tower of 10 linking cubes
            Master 1-57 (from Lesson 57)
            orange crayon
            addition fact cards — green
            Fact Sheet AA 4.0

Lesson 59   fourteen 3" × 5" cards
            pattern blocks
            Masters 1-59A and 1-59B
            Fact Sheet AA 4.0

Lesson 60   Written Assessment #11
            Oral Assessment #6
            individual clock

Lesson 61   5 pencils of differing lengths (include
               1 new pencil)
            linking cubes in towers of 10

Lesson 62   twenty 3" × 5" cards
            cup of 10 pennies
            subtraction fact cards — lavender
            Fact Sheet S 3.2

Lesson 63   piece of paper
            large fact cards (adding two facts)
            Fact Sheet A 4.0

Lesson 64   4 cups of pennies (7, 12, 15, 18
               pennies)
            4 pieces of paper
            large fact cards (subtracting zero
               and subtracting a number from
               itself)
            Fact Sheet S 3.2

Lesson 65   Written Assessment #12
            Meeting Book
            crayons
            large fact cards (adding two facts)
            Fact Sheet A 4.0

Lesson 66   cup of 10 pennies
            cup of 10 dimes
            piece of paper
            6 empty food cans or boxes
            6 paper tags
            tape
            individual fact cards
            Fact Sheet A 4.0

Lesson 67   sharp knife and cutting board
            two slices of bread (trim to square)
            two 6" paper squares
            scissors
            large fact cards (subtraction facts)
            Fact Sheet S 3.2

Lesson 68   ten 3" × 5" cards
            cup of 20 pennies
            subtraction fact cards — tan
            Fact Sheet S 1.2

Lesson 69   Masters 1-69A and 1-69B
            pattern blocks
            crayons
            large fact cards (addition facts)
            Fact Sheet A 4.2

Lesson 70   Written Assessment #13
            Oral Assessment #7
            cup of 10 pennies
            9 dimes and 9 pennies

Lesson 71   20–30 toys in a box
            paper
            20 pennies and container
            large fact cards (subtracting half of
               a double facts)
            Fact Sheet S 1.2

Lesson 72   Master 1-72
            ruler
            crayons

large fact cards (adding two facts)
Fact Sheet A 4.0

Lesson 73 paper (12–16 pieces)
marker
25–30 empty food cans or boxes
large fact cards (addition facts)
Fact Sheet A 4.2

Lesson 74 price tags for the store items
sorted store items from Lesson 73
sales receipt from a grocery store
Master 1-74
piece of paper
cup of 10 dimes and cup of 10
pennies
large fact cards (subtraction facts)
Fact Sheet S 3.4

Lesson 75 Written Assessment #14
sorted store items
Master 1-75
cup of 10 dimes and cup of 10
pennies
large fact cards (addition facts)
Fact Sheet A 4.2

Lesson 76 Master 1-76
2 towers of 10 linking cubes
(different colors)
large fact cards (addition facts)
Fact Sheet A 4.2

Lesson 77 2 towers of 10 linking cubes
Meeting Book
Master 1-77
large fact cards (subtraction facts)
Fact Sheet S 3.4

Lesson 78 sixteen 3" × 5" cards
Master 1-77 (from Lesson 77)
large fact cards (various)
Fact Sheet S 3.4

Lesson 79 addition fact cards — pink
Fact Sheet AA 5.1

Lesson 80 Written Assessment #15
Oral Assessment #8

Lesson 81 2 towers of 10 linking cubes (use a
different color for each tower)
large fact cards (doubles plus one
facts)
Fact Sheet AA 5.1

Lesson 82 graphing grid
fifteen 3" square tags for the graph
crayons
10 linking cubes
glue stick
large fact cards (doubles plus one
facts)
Fact Sheet A 5.1

Lesson 83 2 geoboards
8 geobands
large fact cards (doubles plus one
facts)
Fact Sheet A 5.1

Lesson 84 3 bags with 60–100 objects each
Masters 1-84A and 1-84B
large fact cards (doubles plus one
facts)
Fact Sheet A 5.1

Lesson 85 Written Assessment #16
plastic bag of 25 pennies
plastic bag of 42 pennies
cup of 40 pennies
cup of 4 dimes
Master 1-84B
large fact cards (addition facts)
Fact Sheet A 5.2

Lesson 86 new price tags for the store items
sorted store items
Master 1-86
cup of 10 dimes and cup of
20 pennies
large fact cards (addition facts)
Fact Sheet A 5.2

Lesson 87 demonstration clocks
large fact cards (addition facts)
Fact Sheet A 5.2

Lesson 88 four 6" white paper squares
crayons
Master 1-88
optional: 1 slice of bread, peanut
butter, napkins, knife
large fact cards (addition facts)
Fact Sheet A 5.2

Lesson 89 hundred number chart
cup of 10 pennies
Fact Sheet A 5.2

Lesson 90 store items priced at 32¢ and 14¢
10 dimes
20 pennies
Written Assessment #17
Oral Assessment #9

Lesson 91 hundred number chart
Master 1-91
large fact cards (subtraction facts)
Fact Sheet S 3.4

Lesson 92 10 dimes and 10 pennies
small cup
6" × 9" piece of white construction
paper
6" × 9" piece of yellow construction
paper
individual fact cards (subtraction)
Fact Sheet S 3.4

Lesson 93 twenty-five 3" × 5" cards
individual fact cards (addition)
Fact Sheet A 5.2

Lesson 94 four 3" × 5" cards
cup of 10 pennies
piece of paper
addition fact cards — blue
Fact Sheet MA 6.0

Lesson 95 Written Assessment #18
5 bags of 100 pennies (save for
    Lesson 111)
Masters 1-84A and 1-84B (from
    Lesson 84)
Meeting Book
Fact Sheet MA 6.0

Lesson 96 2 geoboards
7 geobands
Master 1-96A (2 copies)
Fact Sheet MA 6.0

Lesson 97 ruler
Master 1-97
ribbon or string
one 3" × 5" card
tape
Fact Sheet MA 6.0

Lesson 98 11 linking cubes
subtraction fact cards — green
Fact Sheet S 4.0

Lesson 99 ten 3" × 5" cards
cup of 40 pennies
cup of 8 nickels
piece of paper
Fact Sheet S 4.0

Lesson 100 100 pennies
small covered container
2 geoboards
4 geobands
Written Assessment #19
Oral Assessment #10

Lesson 101 cup of 10 pennies
cup of 8 nickels
piece of paper
large fact cards (subtracting two
    facts)
Fact Sheet S 4.0

Lesson 102 ball
ice-cream cone
1 large piece of construction paper
scissors
stapler or tape
large fact cards (subtraction facts)
Fact Sheet S 4.4

Lesson 103 21 wrapped chocolate candies in a
    small bag (other objects can be
    substituted)
4 small plastic bags
5 small plates
15 linking cubes
large fact cards (subtraction facts)
Fact Sheet S 4.4

Lesson 104 2 egg cartons
6 red and 6 blue linking cubes
2 towers of 10 linking cubes (2
    different colors)
large fact cards (subtraction facts)
Fact Sheet S 4.4

Lesson 105 Written Assessment #20
six 3" × 5" cards

cup of 10 pennies
Master 1-105
subtraction fact cards — blue
Fact Sheet S 6.0

Lesson 106 2 rulers
large fact cards (subtracting a
    number from ten facts)
Fact Sheet S 6.0

Lesson 107 pattern blocks
large fact cards (subtracting a
    number from ten facts)
Fact Sheet S 6.0

Lesson 108 ten 3" × 5" cards
addition fact cards — yellow
Master 1-108
Fact Sheet AA 7.1

Lesson 109 unbreakable liter (soda or pop
    bottle), quart (milk, juice, or
    cream), and gallon (milk or juice)
    containers
labels for containers
waterproof marker
unbreakable measuring cup (1 cup)
funnel (optional)
newspapers or plastic drop cloth
large containers for water
food coloring (optional)
Master 1-109
3 plastic containers
large fact cards (adding nine facts)
Fact Sheet AA 7.1

Lesson 110 2 quarters, 3 dimes, 4 nickels, and
    5 pennies
graphing grid (Master 1-38)
Written Assessment #21
Oral Assessment #11

Lesson 111 1 bag of 100 pennies
Masters 1-84A and 1-84B (from
    Lesson 84)
1 one-dollar bill
scrap paper
large fact cards (adding nine facts)
Fact Sheet A 7.1

Lesson 112 one-dollar bill
13 small envelopes
13 1" construction paper tags in 6
    different colors
6 cherry tomatoes, 3 mushrooms,
    2 celery stalks, 2 carrots,
    2 cucumbers, and 4 green beans
6 paper plates
cutting board and knife
napkins
large fact cards (adding nine facts)
Fact Sheet A 7.1

Lesson 113 graphing grid (see *the night before*)
1 tag of each color from
    Lesson 112
envelopes with tags (from
    Lesson 112)
glue stick

paper
large fact cards (addition facts)
Fact Sheet A 7.2

Lesson 114 1 cup of 5 dimes, 8 nickels, and 10 pennies
piece of paper
Fact Sheet A 7.2

Lesson 115 Written Assessment #22
Meeting Book
crayons
large fact cards (addition facts)
Fact Sheet A 7.2

Lesson 116 2 towers of linking cubes (10 each of two colors)
Master 1-116
crayons
addition fact cards — white
sixteen 3" × 5" cards
Fact Sheet A 8.1

Lesson 117 ruler
Master 1-117
Fact Sheet A 8.1

Lesson 118 1 linking cube (other cubes can be used as models)
2 cans of food
scissors
two 6" × 9" pieces of construction paper
tape
Fact Sheet A 8.1

Lesson 119 scrap paper
large fact cards (oddball addition facts)
Fact Sheet A 8.2

Lesson 120 50 pennies
5 dimes
Written Assessment #23
Oral Assessment #12

Lesson 121 Master 1-121
cup of 20 pennies
large fact cards (oddball addition facts)
Fact Sheet A 8.2

Lesson 122 seven 3" × 5" cards
1 tower of 10 linking cubes
subtraction fact cards — yellow
large fact cards (subtraction facts)
Fact Sheet S 2.2

Lesson 123 Master 1-123
large fact cards (subtraction facts)
Fact Sheet S 2.2

Lesson 124 25 pennies, 6 nickels, and 2 dimes
3 small plastic bags
16–20 quarters
5 small cups
large fact cards (oddball addition facts)
Fact Sheet A 8.2

Lesson 125 Written Assessment #24
eight 3" × 5" cards
11 linking cubes
subtraction fact cards — pink
Fact Sheet S 5.0

Lesson 126 5 bags of 100 pennies plus 50 extra pennies
Masters 1-84A and 1-84B (from Lesson 84)
Master 1-126 (2 copies)
1 small plastic bag
scissors
large fact cards (subtraction using the doubles plus one facts)
Fact Sheet S 5.0

Lesson 127 bag of pieces from Master 1-126
cup of 10 pennies
1 piece of paper
large fact cards (subtraction using the doubles plus one facts)
Fact Sheet S 5.0

Lesson 128 eight 3" × 5" cards
1 tower of 10 linking cubes
subtraction fact cards — white
Fact Sheet S 9.1

Lesson 129 crayons
large fact cards (leftover subtraction facts)
Fact Sheet S 9.1

Lesson 130 individual clock
Written Assessment #25
Oral Assessment #13

Meeting Strip

Coin Cup

Today's date is _____

Today's pattern is _____

Coin Cup

Today's date is _____

Today's pattern is _____

Coin Cup

Today's date is _____

Today's pattern is _____

Coin Cup

Today's date is _____

Today's pattern is _____

Lesson 1

identifying today's date

---

lesson preparation ——————————————————

materials

Math 1 Meeting Book (This will be used for all lessons.)

meeting strip (This will be used for all lessons. A master is included in the overview.)

piece of paper

the night before

• Write the year on each month of the calendar in your child's Math 1 Meeting Book.

• Fill in the shape patterns and dates through yesterday's date on this month's calendar. (Use the monthly shape pattern described in the overview.) Each day's shape pattern and date will be added during The Meeting. Add Saturday's and Sunday's shape pattern and date prior to Monday's meeting.

in the morning

• Use a green crayon to draw and color the next shape on the calendar. Do this carefully so that the shape can be clearly identified.

THE MEETING

———————————————————————————

• Show your child the Math 1 Meeting Book.

"Each morning, we will be doing some activities using this Math Meeting Book."

"Let's look though the book."

"What do you see?"

• Spend 2–3 minutes looking through the book together.

"Write your name on the first page."

"Now I will show you how we will use this book."

"We will begin each day with a Math Meeting."

"Today you will learn about parts of the Math Meeting."

"You will also learn how to read today's date."

calendar

• Open your child's Meeting Book to this month's calendar.

"What do we call this?"   **a calendar**

"Why do we use a calendar?"   **to tell us the month, date, year, and day of the week**

"We use the calendar to tell us the month, date, year, and day of the week."

• Point to each on the calendar.

"What year is it?"

• Point to the year.

"What month is it?"

• Point to the month.

"Yesterday was the (twenty-eighth of August)."

• Point to the date.

"What do you think today's date is?"   **(twenty-ninth of August)**

"We write the (twenty-ninth) using the number (twenty-nine)."

"We write it like this."

• Write the digits on the calendar without discussing the shape pattern.

"What day of the week is it today?"

"How do you know?"

"It's (Thursday) because we wrote today's date under (Thursday)."

• Point to the date and move your finger up to (Thursday).

"Let's read the names of the days of the week together."

• Point as you say the days of the week with your child.

"Each day we will write today's full date on a meeting strip."

• Show your child a meeting strip.

"We will write the month, the date, and the year."

"What will we write first?"   **the month**

"What month is it?"

"Tell me the letters we use to spell (month)."

• Write the month on the meeting strip.

"What is the date?"

"What digit will we write first?"

"What digit will we write next?"

• Write the date on the meeting strip.

"What is the year?"

"What digits will we use to write the year?"

- Record the year on the meeting strip.

"Let's say the full date together."

- Point to the words on the meeting strip as you say the following with your child: "Today's date is (month, date, year)."

"Each morning, we will write the date on the calendar, write the full date on a meeting strip, and read the names of the days of the week."

counting

- Point to the hundred number chart on the inside back cover of the Meeting Book.

"This is a hundred number chart."

"We will use it to help us count."

"Let's read the numbers together as I point to them."

- Slowly move your finger from 1 to 30 as you count with your child.
- Turn to pages 46 and 47 in the Meeting Book.

"This year we are going to make a number line."

"Where do you think we will start our number line?"

- Point to the square in the upper left-hand corner of page 46.

"We will write the number one in the first square."

"Each day we will add one more number."

- Write the number 1 in the first square.
- Other information on the meeting strip is not used today.

THE LESSON

Identifying Today's Date

"This year you will start to become a mathematician."

"What do you think mathematicians do?" they study numbers, patterns, form, arrangements, and relationships

- Use your child's language when recording his/her ideas on a piece of paper.

<table>
<tr><td>What do mathematicians do?

</td></tr>
</table>

"We will save this paper so that we can add new ideas as we learn more about mathematics this year."

esson 2

making towers for the numbers 1–5

---

lesson preparation

materials

Master 1-2

linking cubes, unsnapped (at least 30)

crayons

the night before

• Cut Master 1-2 (number card strips) in half along the dotted line. Do not cut apart individual cards.

in the morning

• Use a green crayon to draw and color the next shape on the calendar. Do this carefully so that the shape can be clearly identified.

THE MEETING

"Let's begin the Math Meeting."

calendar

• Open your child's Meeting Book to this month's calendar.

"What do we call this?" **a calendar**

"Why do we use a calendar?" **to tell us the month, date, year, and day of the week**

"What year is it?"

• Point to the year.

"What month is it?"

• Point to the month.

"Yesterday was the (twenty-eighth of August)."

• Point to the date.

"What do you think today's date is?" **(twenty-ninth of August)**

"We write the (twenty-ninth) using the number (twenty-nine)."

"We write it like this."

• Write the digits on the calendar without discussing the shape pattern.

"What day of the week is it today?"

"How do you know?"

"It's (Thursday) because we wrote today's date under (Thursday)."

- Point to the date and move your finger up to (Thursday).

"Let's read the names of the days of the week together."

- Point as you say the days of the week with your child.

"Now we will write today's full date on a meeting strip."

"We will write the month, the date, and the year."

"What will we write first?" **the month**

"What month is it?"

"Tell me the letters we use to spell (month)."

- Write the month on the meeting strip.

"What is the date?"

"What digit will we write first?"

"What digit will we write next?"

- Write the date on the meeting strip.

"What is the year?"

"What digits will we use to write the year?"

- Record the year on the meeting strip.

"Let's say the full date together."

- Point to the words on the meeting strip as you say the following with your child: "Today's date is (month, date, year)."

weather graph

"What is it like outside this morning?"

"Is it _____ every day?"

"What else could it be?" **sunny, cloudy, rainy, snowy**

"Each morning we will look outside to see if it is sunny, cloudy, rainy, or snowy."

"We are going to make a graph to keep track of the weather each day."

- Open the Meeting Book to this month's weather graph.
- Point to the symbol of the sun at the bottom of the graph.

"What kind of day would it be if we used this symbol?"

"How do you know?"

"Which symbol shows today's weather?"

- Repeat with each symbol.

> *"Draw a (sun, cloud, raindrop, snowflake) above this symbol to show today's weather."*

- Allow time for your child to draw and color the symbol.

counting

- Point to the hundred number chart on the inside back cover of the Meeting Book.

  "Let's use our hundred number chart to help us count."

  "Let's read the numbers together as I point to them."

- Slowly move your finger from 1 to 30 as you count together.

- Turn to pages 46 and 47 in the Meeting Book.

  "Now we will add one more number to our number line."

  "Yesterday we started our number line with the number one."

  "What number will we add today?"

  "Where will we write the number two?"

- Write the number 2 on the number line.

  "We have finished The Meeting."

- Other information on the meeting strip is not used today.

THE LESSON

Making Towers for the Numbers 1–5

"Today we will use a math material called linking cubes (multilinks)."

"You will learn how to use linking cubes to make towers."

"When we build a tower, we will start at the bottom and build up."

- Give your child a basket of 30 or more linking cubes.

  "Let's build some towers."

  "As I say each number, take one cube and snap it on."

- Do this with your child.

  "One, two, three."

  "Let's count the cubes together."

  "Start at the bottom."

  "Point to each cube as we count."   *one, two, three*

  "Let's break off one cube at a time and count."   *one, two, three*

- Do this with your child.

"Now let's make another tower."

"As I say each number, take one cube and snap it on."

• Do this with your child.

"One, two, three, four, five."

"How many cubes are in this tower?"

"Let's count the cubes together to check."

"Start at the bottom."

"Point to each cube as we count."   one, two, three, four, five

"Let's break off one cube at a time and count."   one, two, three, four, five

• Repeat with a tower of four cubes, if desired.

• Give your child the 1–5 number strip from **Master 1-2**.

"What do you see?"   *the numbers 1–5*

"Put your number strip on the table in front of you."

"Let's read these numbers together."

"Point to each number as we say it together."

• Count with your child.

"Now we will make towers to match each of these numbers."

"How do you think we will do that?"

"Make a tower for 1."

"How many cubes did you use?"   *1*

"Stand your tower on the number 1."

• Repeat with numbers 2–5. Leave each tower standing.

"What do you see?"   *steps, each tower is one taller*

"We will use the linking cubes again."

"Unsnap the cubes from your towers and put them in the basket."

• Save the number card strips from **Master 1-2**.

WRITTEN PRACTICE

"Almost every day we will have a practice sheet at the end of our math lesson."

- Give your child **Worksheet 2A/2B**. (Side A is completed after the lesson and Side B is completed later in the day.)

"Put your finger below the 2A."

"We will do side A now."

"Write your name on the top line."

- Allow time for your child to do this.

"Look at the first problem on Side A."

"The directions say to color the towers."

"When you color the towers, you begin at the bottom."

"Use your crayons to color the towers."

- Allow time for your child to do this.

"The second problem tells you to circle one of the tower numbers and then draw that number of animals in the box."

"What kinds of animals could you draw?"

"Circle one of your tower numbers."

"Now draw that number of animals in the box."

- Allow time for your child to do this.

"Turn your paper over to the other side."

"Point to the 2B at the end of the top line."

"We will do this side later in the day."

- Complete Side B with your child later in the day.

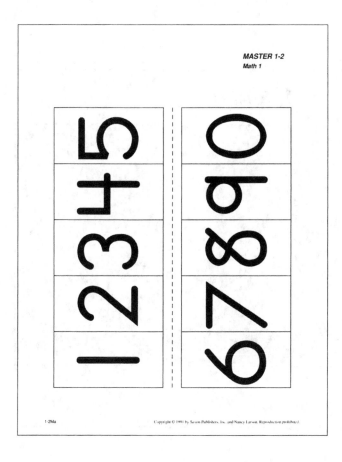

MASTER 1-2
Math 1

Name _____ *LESSON 2A*
Math 1

1. Color the towers. Start from the bottom.

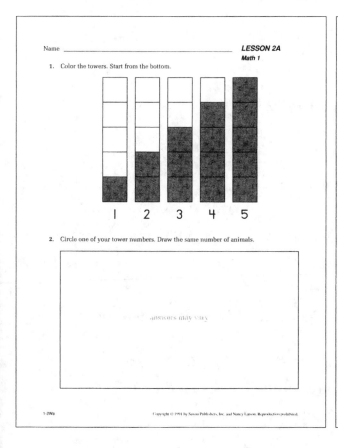

2. Circle one of your tower numbers. Draw the same number of animals.

answers may vary

Name _____ *LESSON 2B*
Math 1

1. Color the towers. Start from the bottom.

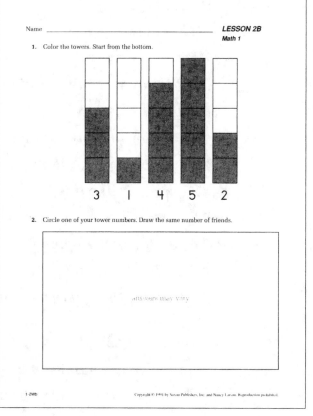

2. Circle one of your tower numbers. Draw the same number of friends.

answers may vary

esson 3

writing the numbers 1, 4, and 5

---

lesson preparation

materials

1–5 number strips from Lesson 2

collection of 5 objects (pencils)

handwriting paper

penny

in the morning

• Use a green crayon to draw and color the next shape on the calendar.

THE MEETING

calendar

• Open your child's Meeting Book to this month's calendar.

"What year is it?"

• Point to the year.

"What month is it?"

• Point to the month.

"Yesterday was the _____th of (month)."

• Point to the date.

"What do you think today's date is?" _____th of (month)

"We write the _____th using the number _____."

"We write it like this."

• Write the digits on the calendar without discussing the shape pattern.

"What day of the week is it today?"

"How do you know?"

"It's (day of the week) because we wrote today's date under (day of the week)."

• Point to the date and move your finger up to (day of the week).

"Let's read the names of the days of the week together."

• Point as you say the days of the week with your child.

"Now we will write today's full date on a meeting strip."

"We will write the month, the date, and the year."

"What will we write first?"   **the month**

"What month is it?"

"Tell me the letters we use to spell (month)."

• Write the month on the meeting strip.

"What is the date?"

"What digit will we write first?"

"What digit will we write next?"

• Write the date on the meeting strip.

"What is the year?"

"What digits will we use to write the year?"

• Record the year on the meeting strip.

"Let's say the full date together."

• Point to the words on the meeting strip as you say the following with your child: "Today's date is (month, date, year)."

weather graph

• Open the Meeting Book to this month's weather graph.

"What is it like outside this morning?"

"What symbol will we use to show today's weather on our graph?"

"Where do you think we should draw today's symbol?"

"Draw a (sun, cloud, raindrop, snowflake) above this symbol to show today's weather."

• Allow time for your child to draw and color the symbol.

counting

• Point to the hundred number chart on the inside back cover of the Meeting Book.

"Let's use our hundred number chart to help us count."

"What number did we stop at yesterday?"   **30**

"Today we will stop at 40."

"Let's read the numbers together as I point to them."

• Slowly move your finger from 1 to 40 as you count together.

• Turn to pages 46 and 47 in the Meeting Book.

"Yesterday we added the number two to our number line."

"What number will we add today?" three

- Add this number to the number line.

"We have finished The Meeting."

- Other information on the meeting strip is not used today.

THE LESSON

Writing the Numbers 1, 4, and 5

- Give your child handwriting paper, a pencil, and a penny.

"Today you will learn how to write the numbers 1, 4, and 5."

"Mathematicians have special symbols they use when they want to tell someone in writing how many things they have."

- Hold up 1 object (pencil).

"How many (pencils) do I have in my hand?" 1

"How do we write the number 1?"

- Draw a large 1 on the chalkboard.

"Let's practice drawing a 1 in the air using our finger."

"On our handwriting paper there are lines: a top line, a middle line, and a bottom line."

- Point to each.

"When we write the number 1, we start at the top line and draw a line straight down."

"We cross the middle line and stop at the bottom line."

"Now you will practice making 1's on your paper."

- Point to the upper left-hand corner of your child's paper.

"This is where you will start."

"Put your pencil point on the top line."

"Now begin to draw a line straight down."

"Cross the middle line and stop at the bottom line."

"Now make some more 1's next to your first 1."

"Leave a penny space between your numbers."

- Allow time for your child to practice making 1's.

"Let's try writing another number."

- Give your child the 1–5 number strip from **Master 1-2**.
- Hold up 4 objects (pencils).

"How many (pencils) do I have in my hand?" **4**

"Let's count them together to check."

"Point to the number 4 on your number strip."

"Watch as I write the number 4."

• Draw a large 4 on the chalkboard.

"The 4 begins the same way as the 1."

"I draw a line down."

"Next I draw a line across."

"Now I lift up the chalk and make a line just like a 1 to finish the 4."

"When we make a 4, we go down, across, and down."

• Retrace the 4 as you say the steps.

"Let's practice tracing a 4 on the number card using our finger."

"The 4 begins the same way as the 1."

"We go down to the middle and across."

"Now we lift up our finger and make a line just like a 1 to finish the 4."

"Let's practice tracing it with our finger a few more times."

"Down, across, down."

"Let's practice drawing a 4 in the air using our finger."

"We go down part way, across, and down."

"Now you will practice making 4's on your paper."

• Point to the left margin of the second line on your child's paper.

"This is where you will start to make your 4's."

"Put your pencil point on the top line."

"Draw a line straight down to the middle line."

• Demonstrate on writing paper.

"Draw a line across, just like you moved your finger."

"Lift your pencil."

"Now draw a line like a 1 to finish the 4."

"Make some more 4's next to your first 4."

"Remember to leave a penny space between your numbers."

• Allow time for your child to practice making 4's.

"Let's try writing another number."

• Hold up 5 objects (pencils).

"How many (pencils) do I have in my hand?" **5**

"Let's count them together to check."

"Point to the number 5 on your number strip."

"Watch as I draw a 5."

- Draw a large 5 on the chalkboard.

"The 5 begins the same way as the 4."

"I draw a line down, and instead of going across like the 4, I go around like this."

"Now I lift up the chalk to draw the line across the top of the 5."

"When we make a 5, we go down, around, and across."

- Retrace the 5 as you say the steps.

"Let's practice tracing a 5 on the number card using our finger."

"The 5 begins the same way as the 4."

"We go down to the middle."

"Next we go around."

"Now we lift up our finger and make a line across the top to finish the 5."

"Let's practice tracing it with our finger a few more times."

"Down, around, across."

"Let's practice drawing a 5 in the air using our finger."

"We go down part way, around, and across."

"Now you will practice making 5's on your paper."

- Point to the left margin of the third line on your child's paper.

"This is where you will start to make your 5's."

"Put your pencil point on the top line."

"Draw a line straight down to the middle line."

- Demonstrate on writing paper.

"Draw a line around, just like you moved your finger."

"Lift your pencil."

"Now draw a line across the top to finish the 5."

"Make some more 5's next to your first 5."

"Remember to leave a penny space between your numbers."

- Allow time for your child to practice making 5's.

- Save the number card strip.

WRITTEN PRACTICE

- •Give your child **Worksheet 3A/3B**.

  "Put your finger below the 3A."

  "We will do Side A now."

  "Write your name on the top line."

  "The first problem on Side A tells you to write the numbers."

- •Allow time for your child to do this.

  "The second problem asks you how many squares are in the train."

  "Count the squares."

  "Write the number next to the train."

- •Allow time for your child to do this.

  "Now color one square green."

  "Color the others orange."

- •Allow time for your child to do this.

  "The next question asks how many squares are orange."

  "Write the answer in the space."

  "The directions for the third problem tell you to trace the numbers and color the squares to match the numbers."

- •Allow time for your child to do this.

- •Complete Side 3B with your child later in the day.

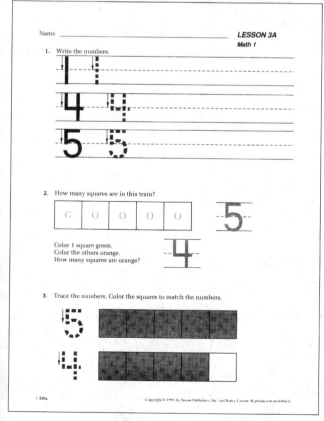

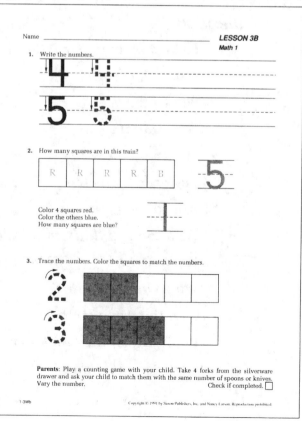

L esson 4

making towers for the numbers 1–9
ordering the numbers 0–9

---

lesson preparation

materials

Master 1-2 (bottom half)

1–5 number strips from Lesson 2

small plastic bag

scissors

the night before

• Cut the zero off the Master 1-2 number strip. Trim and save the zero.

in the morning

• Use a green crayon to draw and color the next shape on the calendar.

THE MEETING

calendar

> *"Let's start with our calendar."*

> *"What year is it?"*

• Point to the year.

> *"What month is it?"*

• Point to the month.

> *"Yesterday was the _____ th of (month)."*

• Point to the date.

> *"What do you think today's date is?"*   _____ th of (month)

> *"We write the _____ th using the number _____."*

> *"We write it like this."*

• Write the digits on the calendar without discussing the shape pattern.

> *"What day of the week is it today?"*

> *"How do you know?"*

"It's (day of the week) because we wrote today's date under (day of the week)."

- Point to the date and move your finger up to (day of the week).

"Let's read the names of the days of the week together."

- Point as you say the days of the week with your child.

"Now we will write today's full date on a meeting strip."

"What will we write first?"   **the month**

"What month is it?"

"Tell me the letters we use to spell (month)."

- Write the month on the meeting strip.

"What is the date?"

"What digit will we write first?"

"What digit will we write next?"

- Write the date on the meeting strip.

"What is the year?"

"What digits will we use to write the year?"

- Record the year on the meeting strip.

"Let's say the full date together."

weather graph

- Open the Meeting Book to this month's weather graph.

"What is it like outside this morning?"

"What symbol will we use to show today's weather on our graph?"

"Where do you think we should draw today's symbol?"

"Draw a (sun, cloud, raindrop, snowflake) above this symbol to show today's weather."

- Allow time for your child to draw and color the symbol.

counting

- Point to the hundred number chart on the inside back cover of the Meeting Book.

"Let's use our hundred number chart to help us count."

"What number did we stop at yesterday?"   **40**

"We will stop at 40 again today."

"Let's read the numbers together as I point to them."

- Slowly move your finger from 1 to 40 as you count together.

- Turn to pages 46 and 47 in the Meeting Book.

"Yesterday we added the number three to our number line."

"What number will we add today?"   **four**

- Add this number to the number line.

"We have finished The Meeting."

- Other information on the meeting strip is not used today.

THE LESSON

Making Towers for the Numbers 1–9
Ordering the Numbers 0–9

"Today you will learn how to make towers for the numbers 1 to 9."

"You will also learn how to order the numbers 0 to 9."

"A few days ago, we used linking cubes."

"What did we do with them?"   **made towers**

"How many cubes high were the towers?"   **5**

"Today we will make some more towers using the cubes."

- Give your child a basket of 50 or more unsnapped linking cubes.

"Let's build some towers."

"As I say each number, take one cube and snap it on."

- Do this with your child.
- Count to seven.

"Let's count the cubes together."

"Point to each cube as we count."

"Stand your tower next to mine on the table."

"Are they the same size?"

"Break off one cube."

"How many cubes do you think we have now?"   **6**

"Let's break off one cube at a time and count to check."   **one, two, three, four, five, six**

"Let's make another tower."

"As I say each number, take one cube and snap it on."

- Do this with your child.
- Count to nine.

"How many cubes are in this tower?"

"Let's count the cubes together to check."

"Point to each cube as we count."

"Break off one cube from the top."

"How many cubes do you think we have now?" **8**

"Let's break off one cube at a time and count." **one, two, three, four, five, six, seven, eight**

- Give your child the 1–5 and 6–9 number strips from **Master 1-2.**

"Put your number strips on the table in front of you."

"Which number strip should you put first?" **1–5**

"Why?" **because these numbers come first when we count**

"Let's read the numbers on the number strips together."

"We will start with the number 1."

"Point to each number as we say it."

- Count with your child.

"Now you will make towers for each of these numbers."

- Assist your child, if necessary. It may be necessary to lay the towers on the table if they will not stand upright.

- When your child finishes, continue.

"What do you see?" **steps, each tower is taller**

"Unsnap the cubes from your towers and put them in the basket."

- Cut apart the number cards as your child unsnaps the cubes.

"Now you will put these number cards in order on the table so they look just like the numbers on the hundred number chart in your Meeting Book."

- Open the Meeting Book to the hundred number chart.

"What number will you put first?"

"What number will you put next?"

"Put your number cards in order."

- When your child finishes, continue.

"Point to each number as we count from one to nine."

- Count from 1 to 9.

"Let's count backward together."

"Point to each number card as we count from nine to one."

- Count from 9 to 1.

"When do people count backward?" **astronauts and people who launch rockets**

"When a rocket or spacecraft is launched, they count down for liftoff."

"They count down just like we did and say liftoff after the one."

"Now I will give you another number card."

- Give your child the zero number card.

"What number is this?"

"Put the zero where you think it belongs."

- Allow your child to position the zero. If your child places the zero correctly, skip the next five lines.

"Let's count to see if this sounds correct."

- Count with your child.

"What number comes after nine when we count?"   **ten**

"Is that the correct place for the zero?"   **no**

"Let's put the zero before the one."

"Let's count backward to see if this sounds correct."

- Count backward with your child.

"When mathematicians count, they say zero instead of liftoff."

- Give your child a small plastic bag.

"Put your cards in this bag."

WRITTEN PRACTICE

- Give your child **Worksheet 4A/4B**.

"Put your finger below the 4A."

"Write your name on the top line."

"The first problem on Side A tells you to write the numbers."

"What numbers do you see?"

"Let's read the numbers together."

"What number do you think will come next?"   **1**

"What number do you think will come after that?"   **4**

"Let's write some more ones and fours."

- Repeat with 1, 5, 1, 5.

"Problem number two tells you to color the towers to match the numbers."

"Start from the bottom when you color the towers."

- Complete Side 4B with your child later in the day.

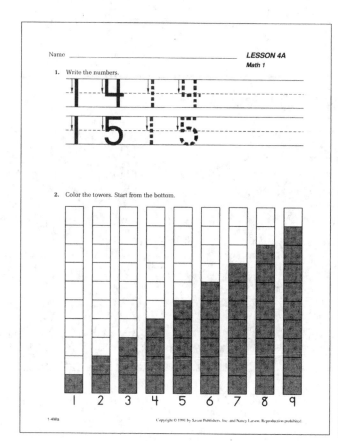

Name _____ **LESSON 4A**
Math 1

1. Write the numbers.

2. Color the towers. Start from the bottom.

1 2 3 4 5 6 7 8 9

1-4Wa   Copyright © 1991 by Saxon Publishers, Inc. and Nancy Larson. Reproduction prohibited.

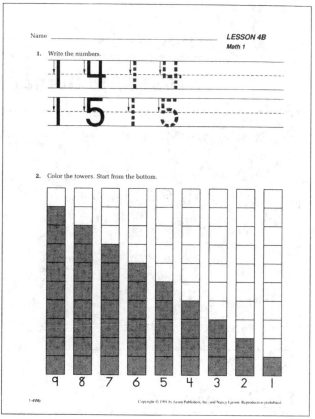

Name _____ **LESSON 4B**
Math 1

1. Write the numbers.

2. Color the towers. Start from the bottom.

9 8 7 6 5 4 3 2 1

1-4Wb   Copyright © 1991 by Saxon Publishers, Inc. and Nancy Larson. Reproduction prohibited.

esson 5

writing the numbers 2, 3, and 7

---

lesson preparation

materials

number cards 0–9 (from Master 1-2)

handwriting paper

7 objects (pencils)

penny

in the morning

• Use a green crayon to draw and color the next shape on the calendar.

THE MEETING

calendar

> *"Let's start with our calendar."*
>
> *"What year is it?"*

• Point to the year.

> *"What month is it?"*

• Point to the month.

> *"Yesterday was the _____ th of (month)."*

• Point to the date.

> *"What do you think today's date is?"*   *_____ th of (month)*
>
> *"We write the _____ th using the number _____."*
>
> *"We write it like this."*

• Write the digits on the calendar without discussing the shape pattern.

> *"What day of the week is it today?"*
>
> *"How do you know?"*
>
> *"It's (day of the week) because we wrote today's date under (day of the week)."*

• Point to the date and move your finger up to (day of the week).

> *"Let's read the names of the days of the week together."*

• Point as you say the days of the week with your child.

"Now we will write today's full date on a meeting strip."

"What will we write first?"   the month

"What month is it?"

"Tell me the letters we use to spell (month)."

• Write the month on the meeting strip.

"What is the date?"

"What digit will we write first?"

"What digit will we write next?"

• Write the date on the meeting strip.

"What is the year?"

"What digits will I use to write the year?"

• Record the year on the meeting strip.

"Let's say the full date together."

weather graph

"What is it like outside this morning?"

"What symbol will we use to show today's weather on our graph?"

"Where do you think we should draw today's symbol?"

"Draw a (sun, cloud, raindrop, snowflake) above this symbol to show today's weather."

• Allow time for your child to draw and color this symbol.

"How many sunny days have we had?"

"Let's count them together."

• Repeat with cloudy, rainy, and snowy.

counting

"Let's use our hundred number chart to help us count."

"What number did we stop at yesterday?"   40

"We will stop at 40 again today."

"Let's read the numbers together as I point to them."

• Slowly move your finger from 1 to 40 as you count together.

• Turn to pages 46 and 47 in the Meeting Book.

"What number did we add to our number line yesterday?"

"What number will we add today?"

"We have finished The Meeting."

• Other information on the meeting strip is not used today.

THE LESSON

Writing the Numbers 2, 3, and 7

- Give your child handwriting paper, a pencil, a penny, and the bag of number cards.

  "Put your number cards in order on the table."

- Allow time for your child to do this.

  "What numbers did we practice writing before?" **1, 4, 5**

  "Today you will learn how to write the numbers 2, 3, and 7."

  "Put the 2, 3, and 7 number cards in front of you."

  "Put all of the other cards back into the bag."

- Hold up two objects (pencils).

  "How many (pencils) do I have in my hand?" **2**

  "Let's count them together to check."

  "Point to the number card for two."

  "Watch as I write the number two."

- Draw a large 2 on the chalkboard.

  "The 2 begins the same way as the part that goes around in the 5."

  "I draw a line around and down."

  "Next I draw a line across the bottom."

  "When we make a 2, we go around, down, and across."

- Retrace the 2 as you say the steps.

  "Let's practice tracing a 2 on the number card using our finger."

  "We go around, down, and across."

  "Let's practice tracing it with our finger a few more times."

  "Around, down, and across."

  "Let's practice drawing a 2 in the air using our finger."

  "We go around, down, and across."

- Use handwriting paper to demonstrate the following:

  "When we write the number 2 on writing paper, we start just below the top line and draw a line around, then down."

  "We cross the middle line and stop at the bottom line."

  "At the bottom line, we draw a line across."

  "Now you will practice making 2's on your paper."

- Point to the upper left-hand corner on your child's paper.

"This is where you will start to make your 2's."

"Put your pencil point just below the top line."

"Draw a line around."

• Demonstrate on writing paper.

"Cross the middle line and keep going down to the bottom line."

"When you reach the bottom line, draw a line across."

"Make some more 2's next to your first 2."

"Remember to leave a penny space between your numbers."

• Allow time for your child to practice making 2's.

"Let's try writing another number."

• Hold up three objects (pencils).

"How many (pencils) do I have in my hand?"   **3**

"Let's count them to check."

"Point to the number card for 3."

"Watch as I write the number 3."

• Draw a large 3 on the chalkboard.

"The 3 begins the same way as the 2."

"I will go around part way and stop on the middle line."

"Now I go around again."

"When we make a 3, we start just below the top line, go around, stop at the middle line, and go around again."

• Retrace the 3 as you say the steps.

"Let's practice tracing a 3 on the number card using our finger."

"The 3 begins the same way as the 2."

"We go around and stop."

"Now we go around again to finish the 3."

"Let's practice tracing it with our finger a few more times."

"Around, stop, and around."

"Let's practice drawing a 3 in the air using our finger."

"We go around, stop, and around."

"Now you will practice making 3's on your paper."

• Point to the left margin of the second line on your child's paper.

"This is where you will start to make your 3's."

"Put your pencil point just below the top line."

"Draw a line around to the middle line and stop."

- Demonstrate on writing paper.

  "Draw the next line around just like you moved your finger."

  "Make some more 3's next to the first 3 you made."

  "Remember to leave a penny space between your numbers."

- Allow time for your child to practice making 3's.

  "Let's try writing another number."

- Hold up seven objects (pencils).

  "How many (pencils) do I have in my hand?"   **7**

  "Let's count them together to check."

  "Point to the number card for 7."

  "Watch as I write the number 7."

- Draw a large 7 on the chalkboard.

  "The 7 begins the same way as the top of the 5."

  "I go across the top line like the top of the 5."

  "Now I go down and stop at the bottom line like I did for the 2."

  "When we make a 7, we go across and down."

- Retrace the 7 as you say the steps.

  "Let's practice tracing a 7 on the number card using our finger."

  "The 7 begins the same way as the top of the 5."

  "We go across."

  "Next we go down like the 2 and stop at the bottom line."

  "Let's practice tracing it with our finger a few more times."

  "Across and down."

  "Let's practice drawing a 7 in the air using our finger."

  "We go across and down."

  "Now you will practice making 7's on your paper."

- Point to the left margin of the third line on your child's paper.

  "This is where you will start to make your 7's."

  "Put your pencil point on the top line."

  "Draw a line across."

- Demonstrate on writing paper.

  "Now draw a line down like we did for the 2 and stop at the bottom line."

  "Make some more 7's next to the first 7 you made."

  "Remember to leave a penny space between your numbers."

- Allow time for your child to practice making 7's.

WRITTEN PRACTICE

- Give your child **Worksheet 5A/5B**.

  "Put your finger below the 5A."

  "Write your name on the top line."

- Read the directions for each problem. Allow time for your child to complete each problem before continuing.

- Complete Side 5B with your child later in the day.

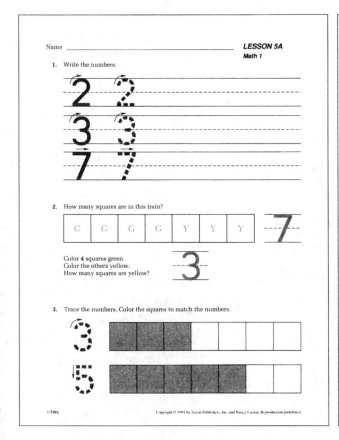

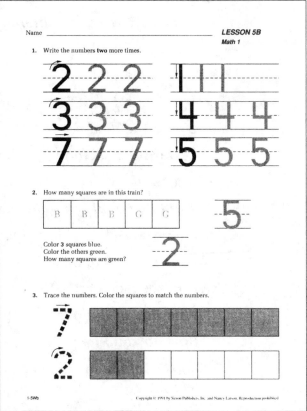

esson 6

identifying a circle and a square
identifying the number of sides and angles of a square

---

lesson preparation

materials
construction paper
tower of 10 linking cubes

the night before
• Cut out a construction paper square, circle, and rectangle.

in the morning
• Use a green crayon to draw and color the next shape on the calendar.

THE MEETING

calendar

> *"Let's start with our calendar."*

> *"What year is it?"*

• Point to the year.

> *"What month is it?"*

• Point to the month.

> *"Yesterday was the _____th of (month)."*

• Point to the date.

> *"What do you think today's date is?"*

> *"We write the _____th using the number _____."*

> *"We write it like this."*

• Write the digits on the calendar without discussing the shape pattern.

> *"What day of the week is it today?"*

> *"How do you know?"*

> *"It's (day of the week) because we wrote today's date under (day of the week)."*

- Point to the date and move your finger up to (day of the week).

  "Let's read the names of the days of the week together."

- Point as you say the days of the week with your child.

  "Now we will write today's full date on a meeting strip."

  "What will we write first?" **the month**

  "What month is it?"

  "Tell me the letters we use to spell (month)."

- Write the month on the meeting strip.

  "What is the date?"

  "What digit will we write first?"

  "What digit will we write next?"

- Write the date on the meeting strip.

  "What is the year?"

  "What digits will I use to write the year?"

- Record the year on the meeting strip.

  "Let's say the full date together."

weather graph

  "What is it like outside this morning?"

  "What symbol will we use to show today's weather on our graph?"

  "Where do you think we should draw today's symbol?"

  "Draw a (sun, cloud, raindrop, snowflake) above this symbol to show today's weather."

- Allow time for your child to draw and color this symbol.

  "How many sunny days have we had?"

  "Let's count them together."

- Repeat with cloudy, rainy, and snowy.

counting

  "Let's use our hundred number chart to help us count."

  "What number did we stop at yesterday?" **40**

  "Today we will stop at 50."

  "Let's read the numbers together as I point to them."

- Slowly move your finger from 1 to 50 as you count together.

- Turn to pages 46 and 47 in the Meeting Book.

  "What number did we add to our number line yesterday?"

"What number will we add today?"

"We have finished The Meeting."

• Other information on the meeting strip is not used today.

THE LESSON

Identifying a Circle and a Square
Identifying the Number of Sides and Angles of a Square

"Today you will learn about two shapes."

• Hold up the circle.

"What do we call this shape?"   **circle**

"Let's find something in this room that has the same shape as this paper circle."

"Look around the room."

"What do you see?"

• Ask your child to identify as many circles as possible.

"Where do you think the center of my circle is?"

• Ask your child to point to the center of the paper circle.

"Does my circle have any points or corners?"   **no**

"Does my circle have sides?"   **no**

• Hold up the paper square.

"What do we call this shape?"   **square**

"Try to find something in this room that has the same shape as this paper square."

"Look around the room."

"What do you see?"

• Ask your child to identify as many squares as possible.

"Where do you think the center of my square is?"

• Ask your child to point to the center of the paper square.

"Does my square have any corners?"

"How many corners do you think it has?"

"Let's count to check."

• Hold the shape by one corner.

"Count with me as I point to each corner."

"We will count this corner first."

• Point to each corner as you count with your child.

"Mathematicians use another word for corners."

"They call the corners angles."

"How many angles does a square have?"   4

"How many sides does a square have?"

"Let's count to check."

• Hold the square by one side.

"Count with me as I point to each side."

"We will count this side first."

• Point to each side as you count with your child.

"How many sides does a square have?"

"What do you notice about the sides of a square?"   *they are all the same length*

• Hold up a construction paper rectangle.

"Is this a square?"

"Why not?"   *the sides are not all the same length*

CLASS PRACTICE

making towers for the numbers 6–9

"Today you will practice making towers with your linking cubes."

• Give your child a tower of ten linking cubes.

"I will write a number on the chalkboard."

"Make a tower with that number of cubes."

• Write the number 4 on the chalkboard.

"Hold up your tower."

"Let's count the cubes together."

"Point to each cube as we count."

• Write the number 5 on the chalkboard.

"Now let's see how quickly you can make a tower with this number of cubes."

"Is there a fast way to make a tower with 5 cubes?"

• Ask your child to point to and count the cubes, if necessary.

• Write the number 6 on the chalkboard.

"Now let's see how quickly you can make a tower with this number of cubes."

"Is there a fast way to make a tower with 6 cubes?"

- Repeat with 7, 8, 9, 8, 7, 6, 5, 4, 3, 2, 1, and 0.

- Watch to see if your child breaks apart the links and counts again or if he/she just adds on or breaks off one link each time. Allow your child to do this activity in the way he/she is most comfortable.

"Make a tower with all your linking cubes."

WRITTEN PRACTICE

- Complete **Worksheet 6A** with your child.

- Complete **Worksheet 6B** with your child later in the day.

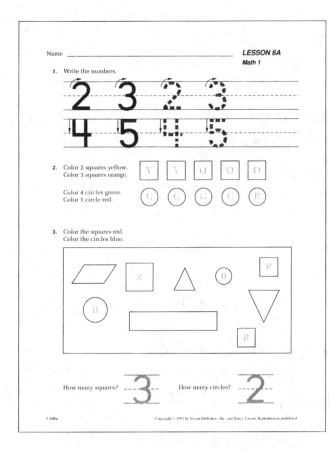

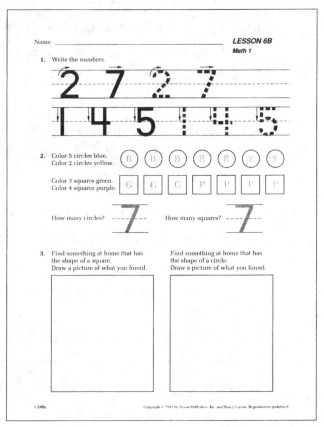

Lesson 7

graphing a picture on a pictograph
identifying the most and the fewest on a graph
identifying right and left

lesson preparation

materials

3" paper squares

crayons

graphing grid

glue stick

the night before

• Prepare the following graphing grid:

Cars, Trucks, and Bikes

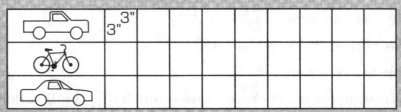

• Cut out squares for the pictures for the graph.

THE MEETING

calendar

> *"Let's start with our calendar."*

> *"What year is it?"*

• Point to the year.

> *"What month is it?"*

• Point to the month.

> *"Each day I have been drawing a shape on the calendar."*

• Point to the shapes on the calendar.

> *"What do you notice about the shapes?"*

> *"Did I draw the same shape each day?"*   **no**

"What shapes did I draw on our calendar this month?"

"Let's read the shapes together."

- Point as you read each shape with your child.

"We have a shape pattern on our calendar."

"It is a (1st shape, 2nd shape) pattern."

"What shape do you think I will draw today?"

"How do you know?"

- Draw the suggested shape on the calendar using a pencil.

"Let's read our shape pattern again to see if we are correct."

- Point as you read each shape with your child.

- Ask your child to color the shape.

"Yesterday was the _____th of (month)."

- Point to the date.

"What do you think today's date is?"

"We write the _____th using the number _____."

"We write it like this."

- Write the date on the calendar.

"What day of the week is it today?"

"How do you know?"

"It's (day of the week) because we wrote today's date under (day of the week)."

- Point to the date and move your finger up to (day of the week).

"Let's read the names of the days of the week together."

- Point as you say the days of the week with your child.

"Now we will write today's full date on a meeting strip."

"What will we write first?" **the month**

"What month is it?"

"Tell me the letters we use to spell (month)."

- Write the month on the meeting strip.

"What is the date?"

"What digit will we write first?"

"What digit will we write next?"

- Write the date on the meeting strip.

"What is the year?"

"What digits will we use to write the year?"

• Record the year on the meeting strip.

"Let's say the full date together."

weather graph

"What is it like outside this morning?"

"What symbol will we use to show today's weather on our graph?"

"Where do you think we should draw today's symbol?"

• Ask your child to draw the symbol on the graph.

"How many sunny days have we had?"

"Let's count them together."

• Repeat with cloudy, rainy, and snowy.

counting

"Let's use our hundred number chart to help us count."

"What number did we stop at yesterday?"   **50**

"We will stop at 50 again today."

"Let's read the numbers together as I point to them."

• Slowly move your finger from 1 to 50 as you count together.

• Turn to pages 46 and 47 in the Meeting Book.

"What number did we add to our number line yesterday?"

"What number will we add today?"

"We have finished The Meeting."

• Other information on the meeting strip is not used today.

THE LESSON

Graphing a Picture on a Pictograph
Identifying the Most and the Fewest on a Graph

"Today you will learn how to graph a picture on a pictograph."

"You will also learn how to find the most and the fewest on a graph."

"We will make a graph to show the number of cars, trucks, and bikes we have at our house."

"We will also show the cars, trucks, and bikes of some of our friends and family."

"Whose cars, trucks, and bikes should we show on our graph?"

• Ask your child to name 3–5 families. Your child will need 10–15 vehicles for the graph.

"First you will draw pictures of the cars, trucks, and bikes at our house on paper tags."

"Each car, truck, and bike will have its own tag."

- Give your child tags on which to draw the vehicles. Discuss with your child the vehicles to be drawn.

- Allow time for your child to draw the vehicles.

"Now let's draw _____'s cars, trucks, and bikes."

- Give your child tags on which to draw the vehicles. Discuss with your child the vehicles to be drawn.

- Allow time for your child to draw the vehicles.

- Repeat with 1–3 more families or until 10–15 vehicles are drawn.

"Let's make a graph of your pictures so we can find out how many cars, trucks, and bikes you drew."

- Point to the symbols on the graph.

"What do you think these symbols mean?"

"How will you know where to put your tags?"

- Ask your child to place the tags on the graph.

- Make sure your child does not skip spaces when he/she graphs the tags.

- Use a glue stick to attach the pictures to the graph.

"Let's count together to find out how many cars you drew."

- Point and count together.

"Let's count together to find out how many trucks you drew."

- Point and count together.

"Let's count together to find out how many bikes you drew."

- Point and count together.

"Which row has the greatest number of pictures?"

"How do you know?"

"Instead of saying the words 'greatest number,' we can say the word 'most.' "

"Which row has the most pictures?"

"Which row has the smallest number of pictures?"

"How do you know?"

"Instead of saying the words 'smallest number,' we can say the word 'fewest.' "

"Which row has the fewest pictures?"

"Do any of the rows have the same number of pictures?"

Identifying Right and Left

"If we wanted to tell someone how to go from our home to the store, we would need to give them directions to follow."

"We would need to tell them which way to go when they come to a corner."

"Sometimes we go straight ahead when we come to a corner."

"Other times we turn when we come to a corner."

"There are special words we use to tell people in which direction to turn."

"Do you know these words?"   *right, left*

• Stand with your back to your child.

"When we want someone to turn this way, we say 'turn right.' "

• Demonstrate.

"When we want someone to turn this way, we say 'turn left.' "

• Demonstrate.

"Today you will learn about right and left."

• Open the Meeting Book to the inside back cover.

"Find the hands on this page."

"These show a right hand and a left hand."

"Everyone has a right hand and a left hand."

"We will use clues to help us remember which is our right hand and which is our left hand."

"Color the right hand red."

• Allow time for your child to do this.

• Write the word "right" below the right hand.

"The right hand is red and is on the right-hand side."

"When you face the Meeting Book, your hand on that side is your right hand."

"Raise your right hand."

"Color the left hand lime green."

• Allow time for your child to do this.

• Write the word "left" below the left hand.

"The left hand is lime green and is on the left-hand side."

"When you face the Meeting Book, your hand on that side is your left hand."

"Raise your left hand."

"Let's practice using left and right."

"Stand facing the Meeting Book."

"Hold up your left hand."

"Hold up your right hand."

"Hold up your left thumb."

"Hold up your right thumb."

• Repeat with foot, elbow, and knee.

"Point to your right ear."

"Point to your left ear."

"Turn to the left."

"Face the Meeting Book."

"Turn to the right."

"Face the Meeting Book."

• Optional: The Hokey Pokey is a fun way to practice left and right. When doing this, face the same direction as your child.

WRITTEN PRACTICE

• Complete **Worksheet 7A** with your child.

• Complete **Worksheet 7B** with your child later in the day.

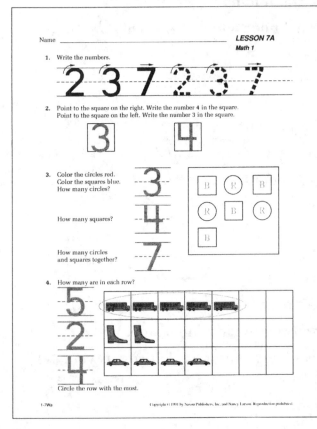

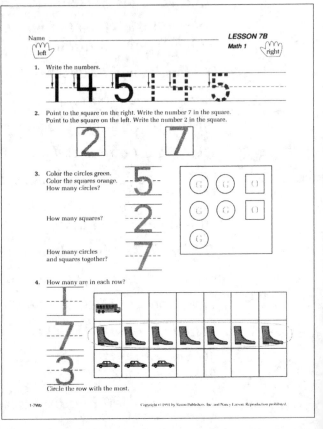

 Lesson 8

writing the numbers 0, 6, 8, and 9

---

lesson preparation ————————————————————————

materials

number cards 0–9

handwriting paper

9 objects (pencils)

penny

2 towers of 10 linking cubes

THE MEETING

calendar

> *"Let's start with our calendar."*

> *"What year is it?"*

- Point to the year.

> *"What month is it?"*

- Point to the month.

> *"What shapes are we using on our calendar this month?"*

> *"Let's read our shapes together."*

- Point as you read the shapes with your child.

> *"What shape do you think we will draw today?"*

> *"How do you know?"*

- Draw the suggested shape on the calendar using a pencil.

> *"Let's read our shape pattern again to see if we are correct."*

- Point as you read the shapes with your child.

- Ask your child to color the shape.

> *"What is our shape pattern this month?"* (1st shape, 2nd shape)

> *"Yesterday was the _____th of (month)."*

- Point to the date.

> *"What do you think today's date is?"*

> *"We write the _____th using the number _____."*

"We write it like this."

• Write the date on the calendar.

"What day of the week is it today?"

"How do you know?"

"It's (day of the week) because we wrote today's date under (day of the week)."

• Point to the date and move your finger up to (day of the week).

"Let's read the names of the days of the week together."

• Point as you say the days of the week with your child.

"Now we will write the month, the date, and the year on a meeting strip."

"What will we write first?"   the month

"What month is it?"

"Tell me the letters we use to spell (month)."

• Write the month on the meeting strip.

"What is the date?"

"What digit will we write first?"

"What digit will we write next?"

• Write the date on the meeting strip.

"What is the year?"

"What digits will we use to write the year?"

• Record the year on the meeting strip.

"Let's say the full date together."

weather graph

"What is it like outside this morning?"

"What symbol will we use to show today's weather on our graph?"

"Where do you think we should draw today's symbol?"

• Ask your child to draw the symbol on the graph.

"How many sunny days have we had?"

"Let's count them together."

• Repeat with cloudy, rainy, and snowy.

"What type of weather have we had most often?"

"How can you tell?"

counting

"Let's use our hundred number chart to help us count."

"What number did we stop at yesterday?" **50**

"We will stop at 50 again today."

"Let's read the numbers together as I point to them."

- Slowly move your finger from 1 to 50 as you count together.

- Turn to pages 46 and 47 in the Meeting Book.

"What number did we add to our number line yesterday?"

"What number will we add today?"

right/left

- Put the Meeting Book, open to the inside back cover, on the table in front of your child.

"We will end The Meeting by practicing right and left."

"Face the Meeting Book."

"Hold up your left hand."

"Hold up your right hand."

"Hold up your left thumb."

"Hold up your right thumb."

- Repeat with foot, elbow, and knee.

"Point to your right ear."

"Point to your left ear."

"Turn to the left."

"Face the Meeting Book."

"Turn to the right."

"Face the Meeting Book."

"We have finished The Meeting."

- Other information on the meeting strip is not used today.

THE LESSON

Writing the Numbers 0, 6, 8, and 9

- Give your child handwriting paper, a penny, and the bag of number cards.

"Put your number cards in order on the table."

"What numbers did we practice writing before?" **1, 2, 3, 4, 5, and 7**

"Today you will learn how to write the numbers 0, 6, 8, and 9."

"Put the 0, 6, 8, and 9 number cards in front of you."

"Put all of the other cards back into the bag."

- Hold up an empty hand.

  "How many (pencils) do I have in my hand?"   **0**

  "Point to the number card for zero."

  "Watch as I write the number zero."

- Draw a large zero on the chalkboard.

  "To make a zero, we start at the top, make a curved line like a C, and when we get to the bottom make a curved line back to the top."

- Retrace the O as you say the steps.

  "Let's practice tracing a zero on the number card using our finger."

  "To make a zero, we start at the top, make a curved line like a C, and when we get to the bottom make a curved line back to the top."

  "Let's practice tracing it with our finger a few more times."

- Repeat the steps.

  "Now let's practice drawing a zero in the air using our finger."

  "We start at the top, make a curved line like a C, and when we get to the bottom make a curved line back to the top."

- Use handwriting paper to demonstrate the following:

  "When we write the number zero on writing paper, we start at the top line, make a curved line like a C, go through the middle line, touch the bottom line, and make a curved line back to the top."

  "Now you will practice making zeros on your paper."

- Point to the upper left-hand corner on your child's paper.

  "This is where you will start to make your zeros."

  "Put your pencil point on the top line."

  "When we write the number zero, we make a curved line like a C."

  "Go through the middle line, touch the bottom line, and make a curved line back to the top."

  "Make some more zeros next to the first zero."

  "Remember to leave a penny space between your numbers."

- Allow time for your child to practice writing zeros.

  "Let's try writing another number."

- Hold up 6 objects (pencils).

  "How many (pencils) do I have in my hand?"   **6**

  "Let's count them to check."

  "Point to the number card for 6."

  "Watch as I write the number 6."

- Draw a large 6 on the chalkboard.

"To write the number 6, we draw a line down like a 0, go down to the bottom, come up to the middle, and close the circle."

• Retrace the 6 as you say the steps.

"Let's practice tracing a 6 on the number card using our finger."

"The 6 begins at the top."

"Draw a line down like a 0, come up to the middle, and close the circle."

"Let's practice tracing it with our finger a few more times."

• Repeat the steps.

"Let's practice drawing a 6 in the air using our finger."

• Repeat the steps.

"Now you will practice making 6's on your paper."

• Point to the left margin of the second line on your child's paper.

"This is where you will start to make your 6's."

"Put your pencil point on the top line."

"When we write a 6, we draw a line down like a 0, touch the bottom, come up to the middle, and close the circle."

• Demonstrate on writing paper.

"We start at the top, draw a line down like a 0, reach the bottom, come up to the middle, and close the circle."

"Make some more 6's next to the first 6 you made."

"Remember to leave a penny space between your numbers."

• Allow time for your child to practice making 6's.

"Let's try writing another number."

• Hold up 9 objects (pencils).

"How many (pencils) do I have in my hand?" 9

"Let's count them to check."

"Point to the number card for 9."

"Watch as I write the number 9."

• Draw a large 9 on the chalkboard.

"The 9 begins the same way as the top of the zero."

"We make a small circle that looks like a balloon."

"Now we lift the pencil and make a line like a 1 that touches the right side of the circle."

"When we make a 9, we make a small circle that sits on the middle line and a line like a 1 next to it."

• Retrace the 9 as you say the steps.

"Let's practice tracing the 9 on the number card using our finger."

"The 9 begins the same way as the top of the zero."

"First we go left and make a small circle."

"Now we lift our finger and make a line like a 1 that touches the right side of the circle."

"Let's practice tracing it with our finger a few more times."

- Repeat the steps.

"Let's practice drawing a 9 in the air using our finger."

- Repeat the steps.

"Now you will practice making 9's on your paper."

- Point to the left margin on your child's paper.

"This is where you will start to make your 9's."

"Put your pencil point just below the top line."

"The 9 begins the same way as the top of the zero."

- Demonstrate on writing paper.

"We start just below the top line, go left, and make a small circle that sits on the middle line."

"Now we lift the pencil and make a line like a 1 that touches the right side of the circle."

"Make some more 9's next to the first 9 you made."

"Remember to leave a penny space between your numbers."

- Allow time for your child to practice making 9's.

"Let's try writing another number."

- Hold up 8 objects (pencils).

"How many (pencils) do I have in my hand?" **8**

"Let's count them to check."

"Point to the number card for 8."

"Watch as I write the number 8."

- Draw a large 8 on the chalkboard.

"The curve for the 8 begins just like the 9."

"We go up and touch the top line and continue the curve to the middle."

"Now curve the other way until we touch the bottom line."

"Now we are going to finish our 8 by drawing a line to where we started."

- Retrace the 8 as you say the steps.

"Let's practice tracing the 8 on the number card using our finger."

"The curve for the 8 begins just below the top line."

"We curve to the left and reach the top, then continue the curve until we get to the middle."

"Now curve the other way until we reach the bottom."

"Now we are going to finish our 8 by drawing a line to where we started."

"Let's practice tracing it with our finger a few more times."

- Repeat the steps.

"Let's practice drawing an 8 in the air using our finger."

- Repeat the steps.

"Now you will practice making 8's on your paper."

- Point to the left margin of the fourth line on your child's paper.

"This is where you will start to make your 8's."

"The curve for the 8 begins just below the top line."

"Put your pencil point below the top line."

"We curve to the left and touch the top line, then continue the curve until we get to the middle line."

- Demonstrate on writing paper.

"Now curve the other way until we touch the bottom line."

"Now we are going to finish our 8 by drawing a line to where we started."

"Make some more 8's next to the first 8 you made."

"Remember to leave a penny space between your numbers."

- Allow time for your child to practice writing 8's.

CLASS PRACTICE

- You and your child will each need one tower of 10 linking cubes.

"Yesterday we made a graph."

"Which row had the most?"

"Which row had the fewest?"

"Our graph tells us that our family and friends have _____ cars."

"Let's make a tower with _____ cubes."

- Make your tower as your child makes his/her tower.

"Stand your tower next to mine."

"Are they the same size?"

"Let's count the number of cubes in our tower."

"Point to each cube as we count together."

"Our graph tells us that family and friends have _____ bikes."

"What can we do to our towers so that we will have a tower of _____ cubes?"

"Make your tower have _____ cubes."

• Do this with your child.

"Let's count the number of cubes in our tower."

"Point to each cube as we count together."

"Our graph tells us that our family and friends have _____ trucks."

"What can we do to our towers so that we will have a tower of _____ cubes?"

"Make your tower have _____ cubes."

"Let's count the number of cubes in our tower."

"Point to each cube as we count together."

WRITTEN PRACTICE

• Complete **Worksheet 8A** with your child.

• Complete **Worksheet 8B** with your child later in the day.

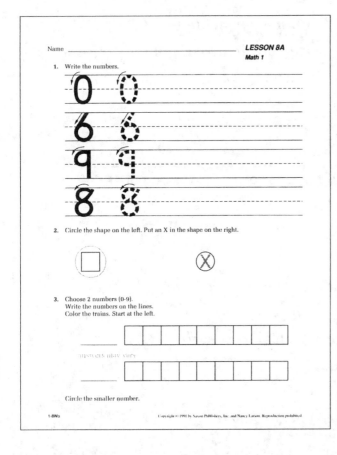

esson 9

ordering sets from smallest to largest
ordering numbers from least to greatest
identifying fewest, most

---

lesson preparation

materials

linking cubes in a container (6 red, 7 yellow, 9 green, and 8 blue)

0–9 number cards

2 towers of 10 linking cubes

THE MEETING

calendar

> *"Let's start with our calendar."*

> *"What year is it?"*

• Point to the year.

> *"What month is it?"*

• Point to the month.

> *"What shapes are we using on our calendar this month?"*

> *"Let's read our shapes together."*

• Point as you read the shapes with your child.

> *"What shape do you think we will draw today?"*

> *"How do you know?"*

• Draw the suggested shape on the calendar using a pencil.

> *"Let's read our shape pattern again to see if we are correct."*

• Point as you read the shapes with your child.

> *"What is our shape pattern this month?"* **(1st shape, 2nd shape)**

• Ask your child to color the shape.

> *"Yesterday was the _____th of (month)."*

• Point to the date.

> *"What do you think today's date is?"*

> *"We write the _____th using the number _____."*

"We write it like this."

- Write the date on the tag.

"What day of the week is it today?"

"How do you know?"

"It's (day of the week) because we wrote today's date under (day of the week)."

- Point to the date and move your finger up to (day of the week).

"Let's read the names of the days of the week together."

- Point as you say the days of the week with your child.

"Now we will write the month, the date, and the year on a meeting strip."

"What will we write first?" **the month**

"What month is it?"

"Tell me the letters we use to spell (month)."

- Write the month on the meeting strip.

"What is the date?"

"What digit will we write first?"

"What digit will we write next?"

- Write the date on the meeting strip.

"What is the year?"

"What digits will we use to write the year?"

- Record the year on the meeting strip.

"Let's say the full date together."

weather graph

"What is it like outside this morning?"

"What symbol will we use to show today's weather on our graph?"

"Where do you think we should draw today's symbol?"

- Ask your child to draw the symbol on the graph.

"How many sunny days have we had?"

"Let's count them together."

- Repeat with cloudy, rainy, and snowy.

"What type of weather have we had most often?"

"How can you tell?"

counting

> *"Let's use our hundred number chart to help us count."*
>
> *"What number did we stop at yesterday?"* **50**
>
> *"Today we will stop at 60."*
>
> *"Let's read the numbers together as I point to them."*

- Slowly move your finger from 1 to 60 as you count together.
- Turn to pages 46 and 47 in the Meeting Book.

> *"What number did we add to our number line yesterday?"*
>
> *"What number will we add today?"*

right/left

- Put the Meeting Book, open to the inside back cover, on the table in front of your child.

> *"We will end The Meeting by practicing right and left."*
>
> *"Face the Meeting Book."*
>
> *"Hold up your left hand."*
>
> *"Hold up your right hand."*
>
> *"Hold up your left thumb."*
>
> *"Hold up your right thumb."*

- Repeat with foot, elbow, and knee.

> *"Point to your right ear."*
>
> *"Point to your left ear."*

- Repeat as desired with eyebrow, cheek, shoulder, ankle, or hip.

> *"Turn to the left."*
>
> *"Face the Meeting Book."*
>
> *"Turn to the right."*
>
> *"Face the Meeting Book."*
>
> *"We have finished The Meeting."*

- Other information on the meeting strip is not used today.

THE LESSON

Ordering Sets from Smallest to Largest
Ordering Numbers from Least to Greatest
Identifying Fewest, Most

"Today you will learn how to put towers in order from smallest to largest."

"You will learn how to use the words 'fewest' and 'most.'"

"You also will learn how to order numbers from least to greatest."

- Give your child the container of 7 yellow, 8 blue, 6 red, and 9 green unsnapped linking cubes.

"There are four colors of linking cubes in this container."

"What colors do we have?"

"Which color do you think we have the most of?"

"Which color do you think we have the fewest of?"

"Is it hard to tell?"

"Let's sort the cubes and compare them."

- Allow time for your child to sort the cubes.

"Snap the cubes to make a tower for each color."

- Allow time for your child to do this.

"Stand the towers next to each other on the table."

"Is it easier to tell which has the most now?"

"Why?"

"Let's count to see how many cubes are in the yellow tower."

- Ask your child to hold up the tower and point to each cube as you count together.

- Give your child the set of number cards.

"Find the number card to match this tower."

- Ask your child to label the tower with a number card.

- Leave the tower standing on the table with the number card label.

- Repeat with green, red, and blue.

"Which tower has the fewest or least number of cubes?"

- Remove the tower and place the tower and card in a nearby location.

"Now which tower has the fewest or least number of cubes?"

- Remove the tower and place the tower and card to the right of the first tower.

"Which tower has the fewest or least number of cubes now?"

- Remove the tower and place the tower and card to the right of the second tower.
- Point to the remaining tower.

  "This tower has the most or greatest number of cubes."

- Place the tower and card to the right of the other towers.

  "What do you notice about our towers now?"   they make steps

  "Which color did we have the most of?"

- Remove the towers and give your child the number cards.

  "Now you will use linking cubes to make some more towers."

- Give your child two towers of 10 linking cubes.

  "Make a tower using four cubes."

- Allow time for your child to make the tower.

  "Find the number card for the tower."

  "Put the number card in front of the tower."

  "Now make a new tower using seven cubes."

- Allow time for your child to make the tower.

  "Find the number card for the tower."

  "Put the number card in front of the tower."

- Repeat with three and six.

  "Hold up the tower that has the fewest cubes."

  "How many cubes are in this tower?"

  "Now hold up the tower that has the most cubes."

  "How many cubes are in this tower?"

  "Put your towers and their number cards in order from smallest to largest."

- Allow time for your child to do this.

  "Read the numbers from least to greatest."

  "Now snap the cubes into towers of ten."

- Allow time for your child to make the towers.

  "Put your number cards in order from least to greatest."

- Allow time for your child to do this.

  "Point to each card as we read the numbers from least to greatest."

  "Put each number card in the bag as I say the number."

- Say the numbers 0–9 in random order.
- Save the number cards.

WRITTEN PRACTICE

- Complete **Worksheet 9A** with your child.
- Complete **Worksheet 9B** with your child later in the day.

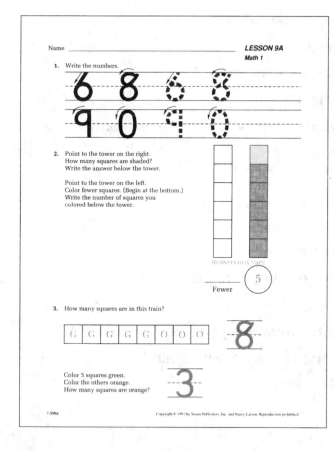

Name _____

LESSON 9A
Math 1

1. Write the numbers.

6 8 6 8

9 0 9 0

2. Point to the tower on the right.
   How many squares are shaded?
   Write the answer below the tower.

   Point to the tower on the left.
   Color fewer squares. (Begin at the bottom.)
   Write the number of squares you
   colored below the tower.

   _____ Fewer   (5)

3. How many squares are in this train?

   | G | G | G | G | G | O | O | O |

   8

   Color 5 squares green.
   Color the others orange.
   How many squares are orange?

   3

1-9Wa

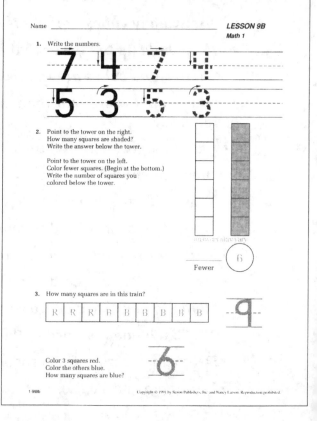

Name _____

LESSON 9B
Math 1

1. Write the numbers.

7 4 7 4

5 3 5 3

2. Point to the tower on the right.
   How many squares are shaded?
   Write the answer below the tower.

   Point to the tower on the left.
   Color fewer squares. (Begin at the bottom.)
   Write the number of squares you
   colored below the tower.

   _____ Fewer   (6)

3. How many squares are in this train?

   | R | R | R | R | B | B | B | B | B |

   9

   Color 3 squares red.
   Color the others blue.
   How many squares are blue?

   6

1-9Wb

Lesson 10

assessment

---

lesson preparation ————————————————————

materials

Written Assessment #1

Oral Assessment #1

individual number cards 1–5

THE MEETING

calendar

> *"Let's start with our calendar."*
>
> *"What year is it?"*

- Point to the year.

> *"What month is it?"*

- Point to the month.

> *"What shapes are we using on our calendar this month?"*
>
> *"Let's read our shapes together."*

- Point as you read the shapes with your child.

> *"What shape do you think we will draw today?"*
>
> *"How do you know?"*

- Draw the suggested shape on the calendar using a pencil.

> *"Let's read our shape pattern again to see if we are correct."*

- Point as you read the shapes with your child.

> *"What is our shape pattern this month?"*   (1st shape, 2nd shape)

- Ask your child to color the shape.

> *"Yesterday was the ____th of (month)."*

- Point to the date.

> *"What do you think today's date is?"*
>
> *"We write the ____th using the number ____."*
>
> *"We write it like this."*

- Write the date on the tag.

"What day of the week is it today?"

"How do you know?"

"It's (day of the week) because we wrote today's date under (day of the week)."

• Point to the date and move your finger up to (day of the week).

"Let's read the names of the days of the week together."

• Point as you say the days of the week with your child.

"Now we will write the month, the date, and the year on a meeting strip."

"What will we write first?"   the month

"What month is it?"

"Tell me the letters we use to spell (month)."

• Write the month on the meeting strip.

"What is the date?"

"What digits will we use to write the date?"

• Write the date on the meeting strip.

"What is the year?"

"What digits will we use to write the year?"

• Write the year on the meeting strip.

"Let's say the full date together."

weather graph

"What is it like outside this morning?"

"What symbol will we use to show today's weather on our graph?"

"Where do you think we should draw today's symbol?"

• Ask your child to draw the symbol on the graph.

"How many sunny days have we had?"

"Let's count them together."

• Repeat with cloudy, rainy, and snowy.

"What type of weather have we had most often?"

"How can you tell?"

counting

"Let's use our hundred number chart to help us count."

"What number did we stop at yesterday?"   60

"We will stop at 60 again today."

"Let's read the numbers together as I point to them."

- Slowly move your finger from 1 to 60 as you count together.

- Turn to pages 46 and 47 in the Meeting Book.

"What number did we add to our number line yesterday?"

"What number will we add today?"

"Every ten numbers we will color the square orange."

- Ask your child to use an orange crayon to color the number square for 10.

right/left

- Put the Meeting Book, open to the inside back cover, on the table in front of your child.

"We will end The Meeting by practicing right and left."

"Face the Meeting Book."

"Hold up your left _____."

"Hold up your right _____."

"Point to your right _____."

"Point to your left _____."

"Turn to the left."

"Face the Meeting Book."

"Turn to the right."

"Face the Meeting Book."

"We have finished The Meeting."

- Other information on the meeting strip is not used today.

ASSESSMENT

Written Assessment

- There is a written assessment every fifth lesson. All of the questions on the assessment are based on concepts and skills presented at least five lessons ago. If your child is having difficulty with a concept, reteach the concept the following day.

"Today, I would like to see what you remember from what you have been practicing."

- Give your child **Written Assessment #1**.

"Write your name at the top of the paper."

"I will read the directions for each problem."

- Read the directions for each problem. Allow time for your child to complete each problem before continuing.
- Correct the paper, noting your child's mistakes on the **Individual Recording Form.** Review the errors with your child.

Oral Assessment

- An oral assessment occurs every ten lessons.
- Record your child's response to the oral interview questions on the interview sheet.
- Materials needed for the oral assessment are listed at the top of the **Oral Assessment Recording Form.**

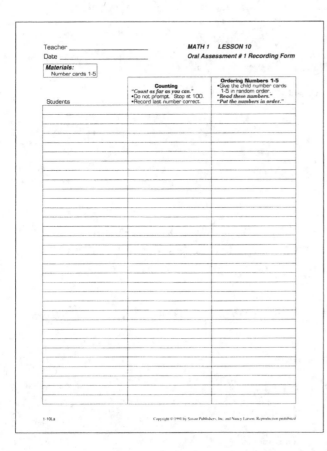

Teacher _____

Date _____

Materials:
Number cards 1-5

MATH 1   LESSON 10
Oral Assessment # 1 Recording Form

Students

	Counting *"Count as far as you can."* •Do not prompt. Stop at 100. •Record last number correct.	Ordering Numbers 1-5 •Give the child number cards 1-5 in random order. *"Read these numbers." "Put the numbers in order."*

1-10La

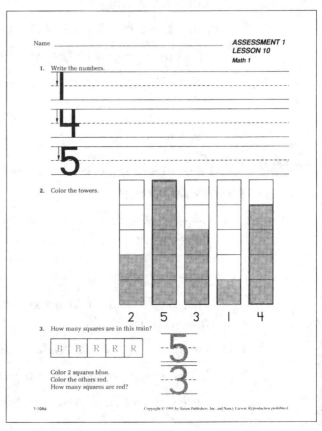

Name _____

ASSESSMENT 1
LESSON 10
Math 1

1. Write the numbers.

2. Color the towers.

2   5   3   1   4

3. How many squares are in this train?

| B | B | R | R | R |

Color 2 squares blue.
Color the others red.
How many squares are red?

1-10Aa

esson 11

writing the number 10
identifying morning and afternoon
identifying first, last, between
identifying first, second, third

---

lesson preparation

materials

tag board circle and brass fastener for morning/afternoon clock

1 red, 1 yellow, and 1 blue linking cube

6 stuffed animals, dolls, action figures, or other toys

the night before

• Make a tag board clock that looks like the following:

THE MEETING

calendar

> *"Let's begin with the calendar."*
>
> *"What year is it?"*

• Point to the year.

> *"What month is it?"*

• Point to the month.

> *"What shapes are we using on our calendar this month?"*
>
> *"Let's read our shapes together."*

• Point as you read the shapes with your child.

> *"What shape do you think we will draw today?"*

"How do you know?"

- Draw the suggested shape on the calendar.

"Let's read our shape pattern again to see if we are correct."

- Point as you read the shapes with your child.

"What is our shape pattern this month?" **(1st shape, 2nd shape)**

- Ask your child to color the shape.

"Yesterday was the _____th of (month)."

- Point to the date.

"What do you think today's date is?"

"We write the _____th using the number _____."

"Now you will have a chance to write the date on the calendar."

"Where will you write the date?"

- Ask your child to write the date on the calendar. If your child is unable to do this, write the number on another piece of paper and let your child copy your number.

"What day of the week is it today?"

"How do you know?"

"Let's read the names of the days of the week together."

- Point as you say the days of the week with your child.

"Now we will write the month, the date, and the year on a meeting strip."

"What will we write first?" **the month**

"What month is it?"

"Tell me the letters we use to spell (month)."

- Write the month on the meeting strip.

"What is the date?"

"What digits will we use to write the date?"

- Write the date on the meeting strip.

"What is the year?"

"What digits will we use to write the year?"

- Write the year on the meeting strip.

"Let's say the full date together."

weather graph

"What is it like outside this morning?"

"What symbol will we use to show today's weather on our graph?"

- Ask your child to draw the symbol on the graph.

  "How many sunny days have we had?"

  "Let's count them together."

- Repeat with cloudy, rainy, and snowy.

  "What type of weather have we had most often?"

  "How can you tell?"

counting

"Let's use our hundred number chart to help us count."

"What number did we stop at yesterday?" **60**

"We will stop at 60 again today."

"Let's read the numbers together as I point to them."

- Slowly move your finger from 1 to 60 as you count together.

  "What number did we add to our number line yesterday?"

  "What number will we add today?"

  "Let's count to check."

right/left

- Put the Meeting Book, open to the inside back cover, on the table in front of your child.

  "We will end The Meeting by practicing right and left."

  "Face the Meeting Book."

  "Hold up your left _____."

  "Hold up your right _____."

  "Point to your right _____."

  "Point to your left _____."

  "Turn to your left."

  "Face the Meeting Book."

  "Turn to the right."

  "Face the Meeting Book."

  "We have finished The Meeting."

- Other information on the meeting strip is not used today.

THE LESSON

Writing the Number 10

"We practiced writing the numbers 0, 1, 2, 3, 4, 5, 6, 7, 8, and 9."

• Write 0, 1, 2, 3, 4, 5, 6, 7, 8, and 9 on the chalkboard.

"Today we are going to learn how to write a new number."

"What number do you think we will write today?" **ten**

• Write the number 10 on the chalkboard.

"What digits do you see in the number ten?" **the digits 1 and 0**

"How would you tell someone how to write the number ten?"

"When we write the number ten, we write the digit 1 on the left and the digit 0 on the right."

Identifying Morning and Afternoon

"Today you will learn how to identify morning and afternoon."

• Show your child the morning/afternoon clock.

"When we start our school work, is it morning or afternoon?"

"Each day we eat breakfast in the morning."

"After lunch it is afternoon."

"We _____ in the afternoon."

"Each morning, you will set our clock to show that it is morning."

"After lunch, you will set our clock to show that it is afternoon."

Identifying First, Last, Between
Identifying First, Second, Third

• Arrange 3 chairs like cars in a train. Dolls, stuffed animals, or other toys will be used as passengers.

"Today you will learn how to identify first, last, and between."

"You will also learn how to identify first, second, and third."

"We will pretend that these chairs are cars in a train."

"Each car will have only one seat."

"(Name three stuffed animals, dolls, action figures, or other toys) will be the passengers."

"_____ will sit on the seat in the first car."

"Which chair should _____ sit on?"

• Ask your child to place the (animal, doll, action figure, or toy) on the chair.

"_____ will sit on the seat in the last car."

"Which chair should _____ sit on?"

- Ask your child to place the (animal, doll, action figure, or toy) on the chair.

"_____ will sit on the seat in the middle car."

"Which chair should _____ sit on?"

- Ask your child to place the (animal, doll, action figure, or toy) on the chair.

- Ask your child the following questions:

"Who (what) is sitting in the first car of the train?"

"Who (what) is sitting in the last car of the train?"

"Who (what) is sitting in the car between the first and the last car?"

- Repeat with 3 other stuffed animals, dolls, action figures, or toys.

"We can also say first, second, and third."

"Who (what) is sitting on the seat in the first car?"

"Who (what) is sitting on the seat in the second car?"

"Who (what) is sitting on the seat in the third car?"

- Point to the second chair.

"Which chair is this?"

- Repeat with the first and third chairs.

CLASS PRACTICE

- Give your child one red, one blue, and one yellow linking cube.

"We will pretend that these cubes are the cars in a train."

"Point to the left side of the table."

"We will put the first cube on the left side of the table."

"Put the blue cube first."

"Put the yellow cube second."

"Put the red cube third."

"What color is the first car of the train?"

"What color is the third car of the train?"

"What color is the second car of the train?"

"Point to the cube in the middle."

"Pick up the middle cube."

"Make it last."

"What color is the second car of the train now?"   red

"Snap the cubes together."

WRITTEN PRACTICE

- Complete **Worksheet 11A** with your child.

- Complete **Worksheet 11B** with your child later in the day.

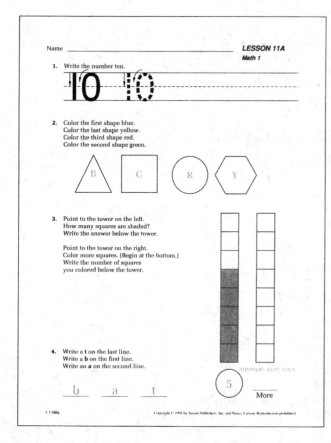

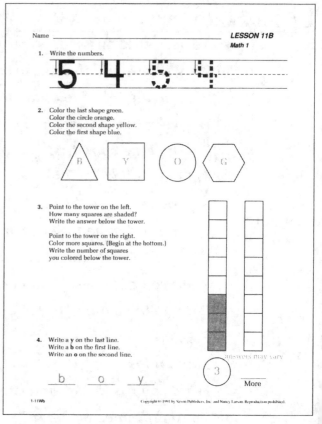

Copyright © 1994 by Saxon Publishers, Inc. and Nancy Larson. Reproduction prohibited.

Lesson 12

writing the number 11
acting out some, some more and some, some went away stories

---

lesson preparation ————————————————————————

materials

5 stuffed animals, dolls, or other toys

THE MEETING

calendar

> *"Let's begin with the calendar."*
>
> *"What year is it?"*

• Point to the year.

> *"What month is it?"*

• Point to the month.

> *"What shapes are we using on our calendar this month?"*
>
> *"Let's read our shapes together."*

• Point as you read the shapes with your child.

> *"What shape do you think we will draw today?"*
>
> *"How do you know?"*

• Draw the suggested shape on the calendar.

> *"Let's read our shape pattern again to see if we are correct."*

• Point as you read the shapes with your child.

> *"What is our shape pattern this month?"*   (1st shape, 2nd shape)

• Ask your child to color the shape.

> *"Yesterday was the _____th of (month)."*
>
> *"What do you think today's date is?"*
>
> *"We write the _____th using the number _____."*
>
> *"Write the date on the calendar."*
>
> *"Where will you write the date?"*

- Ask your child to write the date on the calendar. If your child is unable to do this, write the number on another piece of paper and let your child copy your number.

  "What day of the week is it today?"

  "How do you know?"

  "Let's read the names of the days of the week together."

- Point as you say the days of the week with your child.

  "Now we will write the month, the date, and the year on a meeting strip."

  "What will we write first?"   **the month**

  "What month is it?"

  "Tell me the letters we use to spell (month)."

- Write the month on the meeting strip.

  "What is the date?"

  "What digits will we use to write the date?"

- Write the date on the meeting strip.

  "What is the year?"

  "What digits will we use to write the year?"

- Write the year on the meeting strip.

  "Let's say the full date together."

weather graph

  "What is it like outside this morning?"

  "What symbol will we use to show today's weather on our graph?"

- Ask your child to draw the symbol on the graph.

  "How many sunny days have we had?"

  "Let's count them together."

- Repeat with cloudy, rainy, and snowy.

  "What type of weather have we had most often?"

  "How can you tell?"

counting

  "Let's use our hundred number chart to help us count."

  "What number did we stop at yesterday?"   **60**

  "We will stop at 60 again today."

  "Let's read the numbers together as I point to them."

- Slowly move your finger from 1 to 60 as you count together.

  "What number did we add to our number line yesterday?"

  "What number will we add today?"

  "Let's count to check."

clock

"Each morning you will set our clock to show that it is morning."

"After lunch, you will set our clock to show that it is afternoon."

- Ask your child to set the clock to show morning or afternoon.

right/left

- Put the Meeting Book, open to the inside back cover, on the table in front of your child.

  "We will end The Meeting by practicing right and left."

  "Face the Meeting Book."

  "Hold up your left _____."

  "Hold up your right _____."

  "Point to your right _____."

  "Point to your left _____."

  "Turn to your left."

  "Face the Meeting Book."

  "Turn to the right."

  "Face the Meeting Book."

- Other information on the meeting strip is not used today.

THE LESSON

Writing the Number 11

"Yesterday we practiced writing the number ten."

"Today we are going to learn how to write a new number."

"What number do you think we will write today?"   **eleven**

- Write the number 11 on the chalkboard.

  "What digits do you see in the number eleven?"   **the digit 1**

  "How would you tell someone how to write the number eleven?"

  "When we write the number eleven, we write the digit 1 on the left and another digit 1 on the right."

Acting Out Some, Some More and Some, Some Went Away Stories

"Today you will learn about some, some more and some, some went away stories."

- Arrange 5 chairs like the cars on a train. Stuffed animals, dolls, or other toys will be used as passengers.

"We will pretend that this is a train."

"Your (stuffed animals, dolls, or toys) will be the passengers."

"Each passenger will have its own seat."

- Place 2 _____ on the train.

"There are some _____ on the train."

"How many _____ are on the train?"

"Now some more _____ will get on the train."

"I will put three more _____ on the train."

- Place 3 more _____ on the train.

"This is a some, some more story."

"Some _____ got on the train and then some more _____ got on the train."

"How many _____ are on the train now?"

"Who (What) is sitting in the second car?"

"Who (What) is sitting in the first car?"

"Who (What) is sitting in the last car?"

"Who (What) is sitting in the third car?"

"Now the train is coming to the next stop."

"The _____ in the first, last, and middle cars are going to get off at this stop."

- Ask your child to remove these _____ from the train.

"This is a some, some went away story."

"There were some _____ on the train and then some _____ went away."

"How many _____ got off the train?" 3

"How many _____ are on the train now?" 2

"There are two _____ on the train."

"Now two more _____ will get on the train."

"Which _____ will get on the train?"

"_____ will sit in the third car and _____ will sit in the last car."

"How many _____ are on the train now?"   **4**

"This is a some, some more story."

"There were two _____ on the train and then two more _____ got on the train."

"Now the train is coming to the next stop."

"How many _____ are on the train?"   **4**

"All of the _____ are going to get off at this stop."

"How many _____ will get off the train?"   **4**

• Remove the _____ from the train.

"How many _____ are on the train now?"   **0**

"This is a some, some went away story."

"There were some _____ on the train and then some _____ went away."

• Act out one or two additional some, some more and some, some went away stories with your child.

WRITTEN PRACTICE

• Complete **Worksheet 12A** with your child.

• Complete **Worksheet 12B** with your child later in the day.

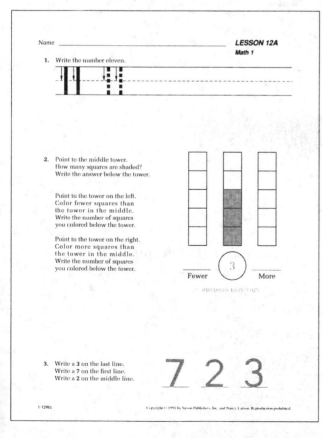

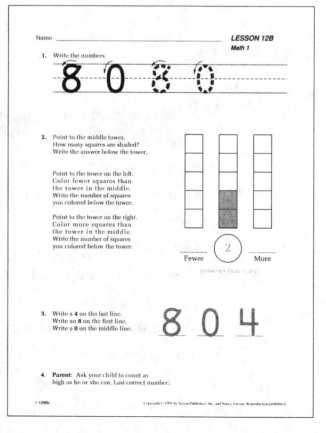

Lesson 13

writing the number 12
identifying a triangle
identifying the number of sides and angles of a triangle
sorting by one attribute

---

lesson preparation

materials

7 construction paper shapes

10–15 stuffed animals, dolls, action figures, small trucks, or other collection of toys

the night before

- Cut out the following construction paper shapes:

THE MEETING

calendar

"Let's begin with the calendar."

"What year is it?"

- Point to the year.

"What month is it?"

- Point to the month.

"What shapes are we using on our calendar this month?"

"Let's read our shapes together."

- Point as you read the shapes with your child.

"What shape do you think we will draw today?"

"How do you know?"

- Draw the suggested shape on the calendar.

"Let's read our shape pattern again to see if we are correct."

• Point as you read the shapes with your child.

"What is our shape pattern this month?"　**(1st shape, 2nd shape)**

• Ask your child to color the shape.

"Yesterday was the _____th of (month)."

"What do you think today's date is?"

"We write the _____th using the number _____."

"Write the date on the calendar."

"Where will you write the date?"

• Ask your child to write the date on the calendar. If your child is unable to do this, write the number on another piece of paper and let your child copy your number.

"What day of the week is it today?"

"How do you know?"

"Let's read the names of the days of the week together."

• Point as you say the days of the week with your child.

"Now we will write the month, the date, and the year on a meeting strip."

"What will we write first?"　**the month**

"What month is it?"

"Tell me the letters we use to spell (month)."

• Write the month on the meeting strip.

"What is the date?"

"What digits will we use to write the date?"

• Write the date on the meeting strip.

"What is the year?"

"What digits will we use to write the year?"

• Write the year on the meeting strip.

"Let's say the full date together."

weather graph

"What is it like outside this morning?"

"What symbol will we use to show today's weather on our graph?"

• Ask your child to draw the symbol on the graph.

"How many sunny days have we had?"

"Let's count them together."

- Repeat with cloudy, rainy, and snowy.

"What type of weather have we had most often?"

"How can you tell?"

counting

"Let's use our hundred number chart to help us count."

"What number did we stop at yesterday?" **60**

"Today we will stop at 70."

"Let's read the numbers together as I point to them."

- Slowly move your finger from 1 to 70 as you count together.

"What number did we add to our number line yesterday?"

"What number will we add today?"

"Let's count to check."

clock

"Each morning you will set our clock to show that it is morning."

"After lunch, you will set our clock to show that it is afternoon."

- Ask your child to set the clock to show that it is morning or afternoon.

right/left

- Put the Meeting Book, open to the inside back cover, on the table in front of your child.

"We will end The Meeting by practicing right and left."

"Face the Meeting Book."

"Hold up your left _____."

"Hold up your right _____."

"Point to your right _____."

"Point to your left _____."

"Turn to your left."

"Face the Meeting Book."

"Turn to the right."

"Face the Meeting Book."

- Other information on the meeting strip is not used today.

THE LESSON

Writing the Number 12

>*"Yesterday we practiced writing the number eleven."*

>*"Today we are going to learn how to write a new number."*

>*"What number do you think we will write today?"*   **twelve**

- Write the number 12 on the chalkboard.

>*"What digits do you see in the number twelve?"*   **the digits 1 and 2**

>*"How would you tell someone how to write the number twelve?"*

>*"When we write the number twelve, we write the digit 1 on the left and the digit 2 on the right."*

Identifying a Triangle
Identifying the Number of Sides and Angles of a Triangle

>*"Today you will learn about another shape."*

>*"You will also learn how to sort."*

- Show your child the construction paper triangle.

>*"What do we call this shape?"*

>*"We call this shape a triangle."*

>*"Let's try to find something in our house that has the same shape as this paper triangle."*

- Walk through the house, identifying as many triangles as possible.

- Return to the teaching area.

- Point to an angle on the paper triangle.

>*"Do you know what we call these?"*

>*"Some people call them corners."*

>*"Mathematicians call them angles."*

>*"How many angles does a triangle have?"*   **3**

>*"Let's count to check."*

- Hold the shape by one angle.

>*"Count with me as I point to each angle."*

>*"We will count this angle first."*

- Count the angles with your child.

>*"How many sides does a triangle have?"*   **3**

>*"Let's count to check."*

- Hold the shape by one side.

"Count with me as I point to each side."

"We will count this side first."

- Count the sides with your child.

"How many sides does a triangle have?" **3**

- Show your child all the construction paper shapes.

"I have some shapes that are triangles and some that are not."

"Let's sort our shapes into two piles."

- Hold up the construction paper shapes one at a time. Hold up the rectangle first.

"Is this a triangle?"

"How do you know?"

"Let's check by counting the sides and angles."

- Repeat with each shape. Put the triangles in one pile and the other shapes in another pile.

- Point to the pile of triangles.

"These are triangles."

- Point to the other shapes.

"These are not triangles."

Sorting by One Attribute

- For the following activity, use only one kind of toy (for example, stuffed animals, dolls, or trucks).

"We just sorted our shapes into two groups."

"One group has triangles and the other group does not have triangles."

"Now we will find ways to sort your (stuffed animals, dolls, or trucks)."

"Which have _____?"

- Name a characteristic shared by some of the toys but not others. For example, "Which have 'ears'?" or "Which are red?"

- Have your child remove these _____ from the group.

"Which do not have _____?"

- Use the same characteristic named above.

"We have sorted the _____ into two groups."

"In this group are all the _____ that have _____ and in this group are all the _____ that do not have _____."

"_____ is the sorting rule."

- Put the toys together in one group.

"Find the (stuffed animals wearing clothes)."

"Put these together in one group."

"What is the same about all of these _____?" they are (wearing clothes)

"What is the same about all of the _____ that are not in this group?" they are not (wearing clothes)

"(Wearing clothes) is the sorting rule."

• Put the toys together in one group.

"Now I will sort the _____ in a different way."

"See if you can discover my sorting rule."

• Sort the toys using a rule that will be obvious to your child.

"What is the same about all of these _____?"

"What is the same about all of the other _____?"

"What is my sorting rule?"

• Put the toys together in one group.

"Now I will sort the _____ in a different way."

"See if you can discover my sorting rule."

• Use a different sorting rule.

"Try to guess my sorting rule."

"We are trying to find something that is the same about all of these _____."

"What is the same about all of these _____?"

"What is the same about all of the other _____?"

"What is my sorting rule?"

• Write the following on the chalkboard:

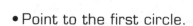

• Point to the first circle.

"What is the same about all of these numbers?" curves

"How are they different from the other numbers?"

"What is my sorting rule?" curves and no curves

WRITTEN PRACTICE

• Complete **Worksheet 13A** with your child.

• Complete **Worksheet 13B** with your child later in the day.

Name _____   *LESSON 13A*
                                          Math 1

1. Write the number twelve.

    12 12 _____

2. Trace each side of the triangle
    with a different color crayon.

    How many sides
    does a triangle have? ___3___

3. How many shapes are in each row of the graph?
    Write the number next to each row.
    Color the row with the most.

    5
    6
    3

4. Use the weather graph to answer this question.

    What type of weather have we had most often?

    Draw the symbol.

    answers may vary

1-13Wa   Copyright © 1991 by Saxon Publishers, Inc. and Nancy Larson. Reproduction prohibited.

Name _____   *LESSON 13B*
                                          Math 1

1. Write the numbers.

    2 7 2 7 _____

2. Trace each side of the square
    with a different color crayon.

    How many sides
    does a square have? ___4___

3. How many shapes are in each row of the graph?
    Write the number next to each row.
    Color the row with the most.

    5
    4
    7

4. **Parent**: Play a sorting game with your child.
        Collect 10–15 objects.
        Decide on a sorting rule. For example, the objects could be sorted into a pile
        of blue objects and a pile of not blue objects.
        Ask your child to identify how the objects are sorted.

1-13Wb   Copyright © 1991 by Saxon Publishers, Inc. and Nancy Larson. Reproduction prohibited.

Lesson 14

writing the number 13
making a shape on the geoboard
identifying inside and outside

lesson preparation

materials

2 geoboards and geobands
10 stuffed animals, dolls, or action figures

THE MEETING

calendar

> *"Let's begin with the calendar."*

> *"What year is it?"*

• Point to the year.

> *"What month is it?"*

• Point to the month.

> *"What shapes are we using on our calendar this month?"*

> *"Let's read our shapes together."*

• Point as you read the shapes with your child.

> *"What shape do you think we will draw today?"*

> *"How do you know?"*

• Draw the suggested shape on the calendar.

> *"Let's read our shape pattern again to see if we are correct."*

• Point as you read the shapes with your child.

> *"What is our shape pattern this month?"*   *(1st shape, 2nd shape)*

• Ask your child to color the shape.

> *"Yesterday was the _____th of (month).*

> *"What do you think today's date is?"*

> *"We write the _____th using the number _____."*

> *"Write the date on the calendar."*

> *"Where will you write the date?"*

- Ask your child to write the date on the calendar. If your child is unable to do this, write the number on another piece of paper and let your child copy your number.

  "What day of the week is it today?"

  "How do you know?"

  "Let's read the names of the days of the week together."

- Point as you say the days of the week with your child.

  "Now we will write the month, the date, and the year on a meeting strip."

  "What will we write first?"   the month

  "What month is it?"

  "Tell me the letters we use to spell (month)."

- Write the month on the meeting strip.

  "What is the date?"

  "What digits will we use to write the date?"

- Write the date on the meeting strip.

  "What is the year?"

  "What digits will we use to write the year?"

- Write the year on the meeting strip.

  "Let's say the full date together."

weather graph

  "What is it like outside this morning?"

  "What symbol will we use to show today's weather on our graph?"

- Ask your child to draw the symbol on the graph.

  "How many sunny days have we had?"

  "Let's count them together."

- Repeat with cloudy, rainy, and snowy.

  "What type of weather have we had most often?"

  "How can you tell?"

counting

  "Let's use our hundred number chart to help us count."

  "What number did we stop at yesterday?"   70

  "Today we will stop at 80."

  "Let's read the numbers together as I point to them."

- Slowly move your finger from 1 to 80 as you count together.

"What number did we add to our number line yesterday?"

"What number will we add today?"

"Let's count to check."

clock

"Each morning you will set our clock to show that it is morning."

"After lunch you will set our clock to show that it is afternoon."

- Ask your child to set the clock to show that it is morning or afternoon.

right/left

"We will end The Meeting by practicing right and left."

"Face the Meeting Book."

"Hold up your left _____."

"Hold up your right _____."

"Point to your right _____."

"Point to your left _____."

"Turn to the left."

"Face the Meeting Book."

"Turn to the right."

"Face the Meeting Book."

- Other information on the meeting strip is not used today.

THE LESSON

Writing the Number 13

"Yesterday we practiced writing the number twelve."

"Today we are going to learn how to write a new number."

"What number do you think we will write today?" *thirteen*

- Write the number 13 on the chalkboard.

"What digits do you see in the number thirteen?" *the digits 1 and 3*

"How would you tell someone how to write the number thirteen?"

"When we write the number thirteen, we write the digit 1 on the left and the digit 3 on the right."

Making a Shape on the Geoboard
Identifying Inside and Outside

"Today you will learn how to use a geoboard and how to make a shape on the geoboard."

"You will also learn how to identify the inside and the outside of a shape."

• Show your child a geoboard.

"This is called a geoboard."

"What do you notice about it?"

• Allow time for your child to offer observations.

"We use geobands on a geoboard."

"They look like rubber bands, but when we use them on a geoboard, we call them geobands."

"When we use a geoboard and geobands, we will want to use them in a safe way."

"What do you think is a safe way to use a geoboard and geoband?"

"I will show you a safe way to put a geoband on the geoboard and take it off the geoboard."

• Demonstrate as you say the following steps:

"To put a geoband on the geoboard, put it over a peg."

"Put your finger on that peg."

"Now carefully stretch the band to another peg."

"Test it before you take your finger off the first peg."

"When you take the geoband off the geoboard, put your finger on one peg and carefully lift the other end of the band."

"We want to try not to lose or break our geobands or hit ourselves or someone else."

• Give your child a geoboard and geoband.

"Show me how to put a geoband on the geoboard."

• Repeat the steps as your child puts the geoband on the geoboard.

"Show me how to take the geoband off the geoboard."

• Repeat the steps as your child takes the geoband off the geoboard.

"Make something with your geoband."

• Allow time for your child to make a shape or design on the geoboard.

• Make a 1 on your geoboard.

"I made a 1 on my geoboard."

"Try to make a 1 on your geoboard."

- Allow time for your child to do this.

  "Let's make a triangle on our geoboards."

  "How many sides does a triangle have?"

  "Make a triangle on your geoboard."

- Allow time for your child to do this.

  "How will we check to make sure that we have made a triangle?"

  "Let's count the angles together."

  "Let's count the sides together."

  "Put your finger inside the triangle."

  "How do you know that this is the inside?"

  "Put your finger outside the triangle."

  "How do you know that this is the outside?"

  "Let's make a different triangle on our geoboard."

- Allow time for your child to do this.

  "How will we check to make sure that we have made a triangle?"

  "Let's count the angles together."

  "Let's count the sides together."

  "Put your finger inside the triangle."

  "Put your finger outside the triangle."

CLASS PRACTICE

acting out some, some more and some, some went away stories

"Today we will act some, some more and some, some went away stories."

- Arrange 5 chairs like the seats on a bus.

  "We will pretend that this is a bus and the (stuffed animals or dolls) are the passengers."

  "Today two passengers can sit on each seat."

- Place 5 (stuffed animals or dolls) on seats.

  "There are some _____ on the bus."

  "How many _____ are on the bus?" **5**

  "Now some more _____ will get on the bus."

- Place 3 more (stuffed animals or dolls) on seats.

  "How many _____ are on the bus now?" **8**

- Point to each _____ on the bus as you count with your child.

"This is a some, some more story."

"Some _____ got on the bus and then some more _____ got on the bus."

"Who (What) is sitting in the second row?"

"Who (What) is sitting in the first row?"

"Who (What) is sitting in the last row?"

"Who (What) is sitting in the third row?"

"Who (What) is sitting between the first and third rows?"

"Now the bus is coming to the next stop."

"The _____ in the first, last, and middle rows are going to get off at this stop."

"Which _____ will get off the bus?"

- Remove the (stuffed animals or dolls) from the bus.

"How many _____ got off the bus?"

"How many _____ are on the bus now?"

"This is a some, some went away story."

"There were some _____ on the bus and some _____ went away."

- Repeat, using different numbers of (stuffed animals or dolls).

WRITTEN PRACTICE

- Complete **Worksheet 14A** with your child.

- Complete **Worksheet 14B** with your child later in the day.

Name _____   **LESSON 14A**
                                          Math 1

1. Write the number thirteen.

   13 13

2. Circle each angle of the triangle using a different color crayon.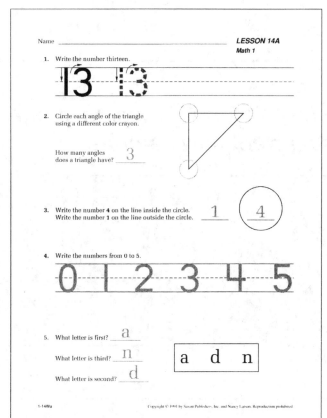

   How many angles does a triangle have? __3__

3. Write the number **4** on the line inside the circle.
   Write the number **1** on the line outside the circle. __1__ __4__

4. Write the numbers from 0 to 5.

   0 1 2 3 4 5

5. What letter is first? __a__

   What letter is third? __n__

   What letter is second? __d__

   | a | d | n |

1-14Wa

Name _____   **LESSON 14B**
                                          Math 1

1. Write the numbers.

   9 6   9 6

2. Circle each angle of the square using a different color crayon.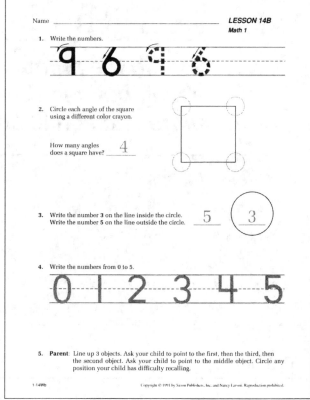

   How many angles does a square have? __4__

3. Write the number **3** on the line inside the circle.
   Write the number **5** on the line outside the circle. __5__ __3__

4. Write the numbers from 0 to 5.

   0 1 2 3 4 5

5. **Parent**: Line up 3 objects. Ask your child to point to the first, then the third, then the second object. Ask your child to point to the middle object. Circle any position your child has difficulty recalling.

1-14Wb

L esson 15

writing the number 14
acting out and drawing pictures for some, some more and some, some went away stories

---

lesson preparation

materials

Written Assessment #2

10 apples

bowl or container for the apples

10 –15 stuffed animals, dolls, action figures, or other toys

THE MEETING

calendar

> *"Let's begin with the calendar."*
>
> *"What year is it?"*

• Point to the year.

> *"What month is it?"*

• Point to the month.

> *"What shapes are we using on our calendar this month?"*
>
> *"Let's read our shapes together."*

• Point as you read the shapes with your child.

> *"What shape do you think we will draw today?"*
>
> *"How do you know?"*

• Draw the suggested shape on the calendar.

> *"Let's read our shape pattern again to see if we are correct."*

• Point as you read the shapes with your child.

> *"What is our shape pattern this month?"*   *(1st shape, 2nd shape)*

• Ask your child to color the shape.

> *"Yesterday was the _____th of (month)."*
>
> *"What do you think today's date is?"*
>
> *"We write the _____th using the number _____."*

"Write the date on the calendar."

• Ask your child to write the date on the calendar.

"What day of the week is it today?"

"How do you know?"

"Let's read the names of the days of the week together."

"Now we will write the month, the date, and the year on a meeting strip."

"What will we write first?" **the month**

"What month is it?"

"Tell me the letters we use to spell (month)."

• Write the month on the meeting strip.

"What is the date?"

"What digits will we use to write the date?"

• Write the date on the meeting strip.

"What is the year?"

"What digits will we use to write the year?"

• Write the year on the meeting strip.

"Let's say the full date together."

weather graph

"What is it like outside this morning?"

"What symbol will we use to show today's weather on our graph?"

• Ask your child to draw the symbol on the graph.

"How many sunny days have we had?"

"Let's count them together."

• Repeat with cloudy, rainy, and snowy.

"What type of weather have we had most often?"

"How can you tell?"

counting

"Let's use our hundred number chart to help us count."

"What number did we stop at yesterday?" **80**

"Today we will stop at 80 again."

"Let's read the numbers together as I point to them."

• Slowly move your finger from 1 to 80 as you count together.

"What number did we add to our number line yesterday?"

"What number will we add today?"

"Let's count to check."

clock

- Ask your child to set the clock to show that it is morning.

- After lunch, remind your child to change the clock to show afternoon.

right/left

"We will end The Meeting by practicing right and left."

"Face the Meeting Book."

"Hold up your left _____."

"Hold up your right _____."

"Point to your right _____."

"Point to your left _____."

"Turn to the left."

"Face the Meeting Book."

"Turn to the right."

"Face the Meeting Book."

- Other information on the meeting strip is not used today.

ASSESSMENT

- All of the questions on the assessment are based on concepts and skills presented at least five lessons ago. If your child is having difficulty with a specific concept, reteach the concept the following day.

Written Assessment

"Today I would like to see what you remember from what we have been practicing."

- Pass out **Written Assessment #2**.

"Write your name at the top of the paper."

"I will read the directions for each problem."

- Read the directions for each problem. Allow time for your child to complete each problem before continuing.

- Correct the paper, noting your child's mistakes on the **Individual Recording Form**. Review the errors with your child.

THE LESSON

Writing the Number 14

"Yesterday we practiced writing the number thirteen."

"Today we are going to learn how to write a new number."

"What number do you think we will write today?"   *fourteen*

- Write the number 14 on the chalkboard.

"What digits do you see in the number fourteen?"   *the digits 1 and 4*

"How would you tell someone how to write the number fourteen?"

"Which digit is on the left?"

"Which digit is on the right?"

Acting Out and Drawing Pictures for Some, Some More and Some, Some Went Away Stories

"We have been acting out some, some more and some, some went away stories."

"Today you will learn how to draw pictures to show these stories."

"Today we will use apples for our stories instead of (stuffed animals or dolls)."

- Place a bowl on the table.

- Put 3 apples in the bowl.

"I put some apples in this bowl."

"How many apples are in the bowl?"   *3*

"Now I will put some more apples in the bowl."

"How many apples should I put in the bowl?"

- Limit the number to five.

"What happened in my story?"   *there were some apples in the bowl and you put some more apples in the bowl*

"This is a some, some more story."

"Let's count to see how many apples are in the bowl now."

- Have your child count as you remove the apples from the bowl one at a time. Replace them when you finish counting.

"How many apples are in the bowl?"

"I will draw a picture on the chalkboard to show what happened in this story."

- Draw a bowl.

"This is the bowl."

"What happened first?"

"I put some apples in the bowl."

"How many apples did I put in the bowl?" **3**

- Draw the apples in the bowl.

"What happened next?"

"I put some more apples in the bowl."

"How many apples did I put in the bowl?"

- Draw the apples in the bowl.

"Let's count the apples in the picture to see how many apples are in the bowl altogether."

- Count the apples in the picture with your child.

"Now I will give you two apples."

- Do not remove the apples from the bowl yet.

"How many apples do I have in the bowl?"

"How many apples will I give away?" **2**

- Remove the 2 apples from the bowl and put them on the table.

"What happened in my story?"   **there were some apples in the bowl and you gave some apples away**

"This is a some, some went away story."

"Let's count to see how many apples are in the bowl now."

- Have your child count as you remove the apples from the bowl one at a time. Replace them when you finish counting.

"How many apples are in the bowl now?"

"Let's draw a picture on the chalkboard to show what happened in this story."

- Draw the bowl and apples on the chalkboard.

"This is the bowl."

"How many apples were in the bowl at the beginning?"

"What happened in this story?"

"I gave away two apples."

"Instead of erasing my apples, I will cross them out to show that they were the apples I gave to you."

"How many apples are in the bowl now?"

"Now we will act out some, some more and some, some went away stories about apples together."

- Put 10 apples on the table next to the empty bowl.

  "Let's pretend you went to the store and bought four apples."

  "When you got home, you put them in a bowl."

  "How many apples will you put in the bowl?" **4**

- Ask your child to put 4 apples in the bowl.

  "Then I gave you one more apple to put in the bowl."

- Ask your child to put another apple in the bowl.

  "How many apples are in the bowl now?" **5**

  "How will I draw a picture on the chalkboard to show what happened in this story?"

- Draw a bowl.

  "This is the bowl. How many apples did we put in the bowl first?"

- Draw the 4 apples in the bowl.

  "What happened next?"

- Draw another apple in the bowl.

  "How many apples are in the bowl now?"
  5

  "Take two apples out of the bowl."

- Ask your child to do this.

  "How will I show what happened in my picture?"

  "Instead of erasing the apples, I will cross them out to show that these were the apples you took out of the bowl."

- Cross out 2 apples.

  "How many apples are in the bowl now?"

- Repeat the story several times using different numbers of apples.

- Ask your child to make up a story to act out.

CLASS PRACTICE

sorting by one attribute

"A few days ago we played the game where I sorted the _____ and you tried to guess the sorting rule."

"Let's play that game again today."

"Today I will sort the _____ in a different way."

"See if you can discover my sorting rule."

- Sort the toys.

"What is the same about all of these _____?"

"What is the same about all of the other _____?"

"What is my sorting rule?"

"Now I will sort the _____ in a different way."

"See if you can discover my sorting rule."

- Sort the toys a different way.

"Try to guess my sorting rule."

"We are trying to find something that is the same about all of these _____."

"What is the same about all of these _____?"

"What is the same about all of the other _____?"

"What is my sorting rule?"

WRITTEN PRACTICE

- Complete **Worksheet 15A** with your child.
- Complete **Worksheet 15B** with your child later in the day.

Name _____

1. Color the circles red.

   Color the squares blue.

   How many circles are there? _____ 4

   How many squares are there? _____ 3

2. How many are in each row?
   Write the number next to each row.

   4

   3

   6

   Color the row with the most.

3. Point to the shape on the right. Write the number 2 in the shape.
   Point to the shape on the left. Write the number 4 in the shape.

   (4) [2]

Name _____

1. Write the number fourteen.

   14 14

2. Alex had three crackers. His sister gave him two more crackers.
   Draw a picture to show what happened.

3. Write the numbers from 6 to 9.

   6 7 8 9

4. Color the shape with 4 sides blue.
   Color the shape with 3 angles green.
   Color the shape on the right yellow.

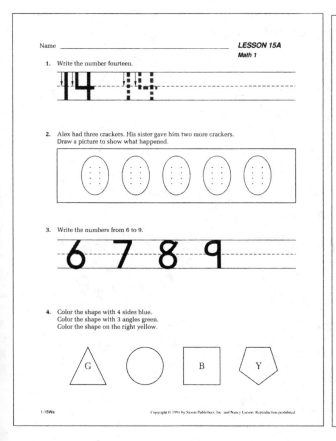

Name _____

1. Write the numbers.

   2 5 2 5

2. Janis had four pencils. Her brother gave her one more pencil.
   Draw a picture to show what happened.

3. Write the numbers from 6 to 9.

   6 7 8 9

4. Color the shape with 3 sides orange.
   Color the shape with 4 angles red.
   Color the shape on the right blue.

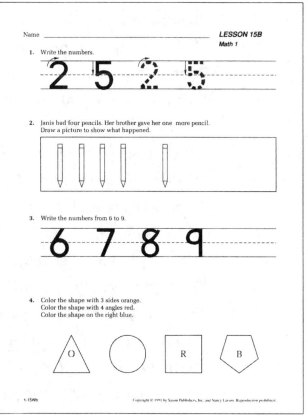

Lesson 16

*writing the number 15
counting pennies*

lesson preparation —————————————————————

materials
container of 50–75 pennies
hundred number chart

THE MEETING

calendar

> *"Let's begin with the calendar."*

> *"What year is it?"*

• Point to the year.

> *"What month is it?"*

• Point to the month.

> *"What shapes are we using on our calendar this month?"*

> *"Let's read our shapes together."*

• Point as you read the shapes with your child.

> *"What shape do you think we will draw today?"*

> *"How do you know?"*

• Draw the suggested shape on the calendar.

> *"Let's read our shape pattern again to see if we are correct."*

• Point as you read the shapes with your child.

> *"What is our shape pattern this month?"* **(1st shape, 2nd shape)**

• Ask your child to color the shape.

> *"Yesterday was the _____th of (month)."*

> *"What do you think today's date is?"*

> *"We write the _____th using the number _____."*

> *"Write the date on the calendar."*

• Ask your child to write the date on the calendar.

"What day of the week is it today?"

"How do you know?"

"Let's read the names of the days of the week together."

"Now we will write the month, the date, and the year on a meeting strip."

"What will we write first?"   **the month**

"What month is it?"

"Tell me the letters we use to spell (month)."

- Write the month on the meeting strip.

"What is the date?"

"What digits will we use to write the date?"

- Write the date on the meeting strip.

"What is the year?"

"What digits will we use to write the year?"

- Write the year on the meeting strip.

"Let's say the full date together."

weather graph

"What is it like outside this morning?"

"What symbol will we use to show today's weather on our graph?"

- Ask your child to draw the symbol on the graph.

"How many sunny days have we had?"

"Let's count them together."

- Repeat with cloudy, rainy, and snowy.

"What type of weather have we had most often?"

"How can you tell?"

counting

"Let's use our hundred number chart to help us count."

"What number did we stop at yesterday?"   **80**

"Today we will stop at 90."

"Let's read the numbers together as I point to them."

- Slowly move your finger from 1 to 90 as you count together.

"What number did we add to our number line yesterday?"

"What number will we add today?"

"Let's count to check."

clock

- Ask your child to set the clock to show that it is morning.
- After lunch, remind your child to change the clock to show afternoon.

right/left

"We will end The Meeting by practicing right and left."

"Face the Meeting Book."

"Hold up your left _____."

"Hold up your right _____."

"Point to your right _____."

"Point to your left _____."

"Turn to the left."

"Face the Meeting Book."

"Turn to the right."

"Face the Meeting Book."

- Other information on the meeting strip is not used today.

THE LESSON

Writing the Number 15

"Yesterday we practiced writing the number fourteen."

"Today we are going to learn how to write a new number."

"What number do you think we will write today?"   fifteen

- Write the number 15 on the chalkboard.

"What digits do you see in the number fifteen?"   the digits 1 and 5

"How would you tell someone how to write the number fifteen?"

"Which digit is on the left?"

"Which digit is on the right?"

Counting Pennies

"Today you will learn how to count pennies."

"Each morning we have been using the hundred number chart to help us count."

"Today we will read our numbers to 100 in a different way."

- Give your child a hundred number chart.

"Point to each number on your hundred number chart as we count to 100 together."

- Read the numbers from 11 to 20 in the following way: "10 and 1 is 11, 10 and 2 is 12, 10 and 3 is 13, 10 and 4 is 14," etc. Read the numbers from 21 to 30 in the following way: "20 and 1 is 21, 20 and 2 is 22, 20 and 3 is 23," etc. Continue to 50. Count from 50 to 100 in the usual way.

"We talked about writing the number 15 today."

"Point to the number 15 on your hundred number chart."

"Point to 8."

- Repeat with 3, 11, 9, and 20.

"Today I will give you some pennies to use."

"How much is one penny worth?"

"Each penny is worth one cent."

"When we count pennies, we count by ones."

"I will give you a handful of pennies."

"When I give you the pennies, put the pennies on the hundred number chart."

"Start at the number one and cover as many numbers as you can."

"Put one penny on each number."

"Do not skip any numbers."

- Give your child a handful of pennies.

- Allow time for your child to cover the numbers.

"Let's count the pennies on your hundred number chart."

"Point to each penny as we count."

- Count the pennies with your child.

"Lift up your last penny."

"What number is underneath?"

"Slide the pennies off your chart."

"Let's try this again."

- Repeat this activity several times.

- Optional: Play the "Grab a Penny" game. The game is played using a container of pennies and a hundred number chart. Ask your child to grab a handful of pennies and put them in the middle of the hundred number chart. You each predict how many pennies are on the chart. To check the predictions, ask your child to put a penny on each number on the hundred number chart, beginning at 1.

WRITTEN PRACTICE

- Complete **Worksheet 16A** with your child.
- Complete **Worksheet 16B** with your child later in the day.

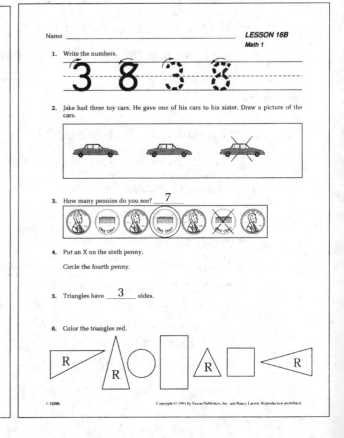

Name _____   LESSON 16A
                                 Math 1

1. Write the number fifteen.

15 15

2. The children in Room 2 have five balls to play with. They gave one of their balls to the children in Room 3 to use. Draw a picture of the balls.

3. How many pennies do you see? 6

4. Put an X on the fourth penny.

   Circle the fifth penny.

5. Triangles have ___3___ sides.

6. Color the triangles red.

1-16Wa   Copyright © 1991 by Saxon Publishers, Inc. and Nancy Larson. Reproduction prohibited.

Name _____   LESSON 16B
                                 Math 1

1. Write the numbers.

3 8 3 8

2. Jake had three toy cars. He gave one of his cars to his sister. Draw a picture of the cars.

3. How many pennies do you see? 7

4. Put an X on the sixth penny.

   Circle the fourth penny.

5. Triangles have ___3___ sides.

6. Color the triangles red.

1-16Wb   Copyright © 1991 by Saxon Publishers, Inc. and Nancy Larson. Reproduction prohibited.

Lesson 17

writing the number 16
identifying the season—fall

lesson preparation ─────────────────────

materials

10 pennies

1 piece of paper

Meeting Book

camera (optional)

THE MEETING

calendar

> "*Let's begin with the calendar.*"

> "*What year is it?*"

- Point to the year.

> "*What month is it?*"

- Point to the month.

> "*What shapes are we using on our calendar this month?*"

> "*Let's read our shapes together.*"

- Point as you read the shapes with your child.

> "*What shape do you think we will draw today?*"

> "*How do you know?*"

- Draw the suggested shape on the calendar.

> "*Let's read our shape pattern again to see if we are correct.*"

- Point as you read the shapes with your child.

> "*What is our shape pattern this month?*"   *(1st shape, 2nd shape)*

- Ask your child to color the shape.

> "*Yesterday was the _____th of (month).*"

> "*What do you think today's date is?*"

> "*We write the _____th using the number _____.*"

> "*Write the date on the calendar.*"

• Ask your child to write the date on the calendar.

"What day of the week is it today?"

"How do you know?"

"Let's read the names of the days of the week together."

"Now we will write the month, the date, and the year on a meeting strip."

"What will we write first?"   the month

"What month is it?"

"Tell me the letters we use to spell (month)."

• Write the month on the meeting strip.

"What is the date?"

"What digits will we use to write the date?"

• Write the date on the meeting strip.

"What is the year?"

"What digits will we use to write the year?"

• Write the year on the meeting strip.

"Let's say the full date together."

weather graph

"What is it like outside this morning?"

"What symbol will we use to show today's weather on our graph?"

• Ask your child to draw the symbol on the graph.

"How many sunny days have we had?"

"Let's count them together."

• Repeat with cloudy, rainy, and snowy.

"What type of weather have we had most often?"

"How can you tell?"

counting

"Let's use our hundred number chart to help us count."

"What number did we stop at yesterday?"   90

"Today we will stop at 100."

"Let's read the numbers together as I point to them."

• Slowly move your finger from 1 to 100 as you count together.

"What number did we add to our number line yesterday?"

"What number will we add today?"

"Let's count to check."

clock

- Ask your child to set the clock to show that it is morning.
- After lunch, remind your child to change the clock to show afternoon.

right/left

"We will end The Meeting by practicing right and left."

"Face the Meeting Book."

"Hold up your left _____."

"Hold up your right _____."

"Point to your right _____."

"Point to your left _____."

"Turn to the left."

"Face the Meeting Book."

"Turn to the right."

"Face the Meeting Book."

- Other information on the meeting strip is not used today.

THE LESSON

Writing the Number 16

"Yesterday we practiced writing the number fifteen."

"Today we are going to learn how to write a new number."

"What number do you think we will write today?"   **sixteen**

- Write the number 16 on the chalkboard.

"What digits do you see in the number sixteen?"   **the digits 1 and 6**

"How would you tell someone how to write the number sixteen?"

"Which digit is on the left?"

"Which digit is on the right?"

Identifying the Season — Fall

"Today you will learn about one of the seasons."

"There are four natural parts of a year."

"These are called seasons."

"In different seasons the weather is different and plants, trees, and animals change."

"We are going to choose a tree (or other plant) and watch how it changes during different seasons."

"What season do you think it is now?"

"This is the beginning of the season we call fall."

- Open the Meeting Book to page 6.

"You will use this page to show how our tree looks in the fall."

"At the bottom of the page you will write about what you have noticed about our tree in the fall."

- Choose a tree or plant that changes noticeably with the change of seasons.

- Go outside to observe the tree (plant). Take the Meeting Book.

"What do you notice about the tree (plant)?"

"Draw the tree in the fall."

- Allow time for your child to draw a picture of the tree (plant). This can be done outside while observing the tree.

  Optional: Take a picture of the child next to the tree (plant).

- Encourage your child to write about the tree (plant) using approximate spelling. Do not correct your child's writing; rather let this be documentation of how your child's writing develops during the year.

  Optional: This can be expanded into a science lesson. "What type of tree is this? How can we find out?" Introduce your child to tree (plant) identification books and allow him/her to try to match and identify the tree or leaf. This research can be expanded to other trees or plants as well.

CLASS PRACTICE

acting out some, some more and some, some went away stories

"Today we will act out some story problems using pennies."

- Give your child 10 pennies and a piece of paper.

"Slide and count your pennies to make sure that you have ten pennies."

- Draw a large circle on the paper.

"Let's pretend that the circle on this paper is a pocket in your shirt."

"Put three pennies in the paper pocket."

"Now put three more pennies in the pocket."

"How many pennies are in the pocket now?"

"How will I draw a picture on the chalkboard to show what happened in this story?"

- Draw a circle and 3 pennies on the chalkboard.

"This is your pocket and three pennies."

"Then you put three more pennies in the pocket."

• Draw 3 more pennies on the chalkboard.

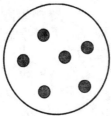

"How many pennies are in the pocket now?"

"Let's pretend you spent four pennies."

"Take four pennies out of the pocket."

"Instead of erasing the pennies, I will cross them out to show that these were the pennies you spent."

• Cross out 4 pennies.

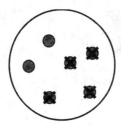

"How many pennies are in the pocket now?"

• Repeat, using several different stories.

"Make up a story about the pennies for us to act out."

• Draw a picture of the pennies on the chalkboard as your child acts out the story using pennies.

WRITTEN PRACTICE

• Complete **Worksheet 17A** with your child.

• Complete **Worksheet 17B** with your child later in the day.

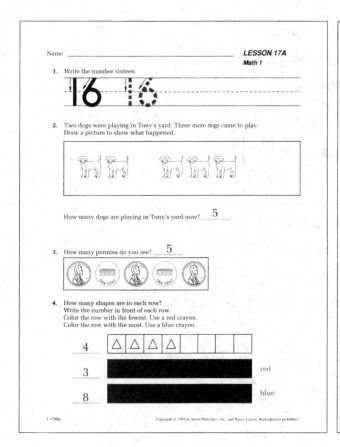

Name _____

1. Write the number sixteen.

2. Two dogs were playing in Tony's yard. Three more dogs came to play.
Draw a picture to show what happened.

How many dogs are playing in Tony's yard now? __5__

3. How many pennies do you see? __5__

4. How many shapes are in each row?
Write the number in front of each row.
Color the row with the fewest. Use a red crayon.
Color the row with the most. Use a blue crayon.

4
3   red
8   blue

1-17Wa

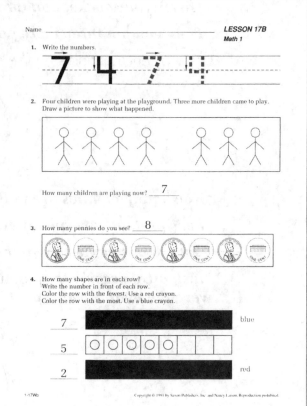

Name _____

1. Write the numbers.

2. Four children were playing at the playground. Three more children came to play.
Draw a picture to show what happened.

How many children are playing now? __7__

3. How many pennies do you see? __8__

4. How many shapes are in each row?
Write the number in front of each row.
Color the row with the fewest. Use a red crayon.
Color the row with the most. Use a blue crayon.

7   blue
5
2   red

1-17Wb

L esson 18

writing the number 17
dividing a solid in half

---

lesson preparation

materials

1 apple

cutting board and knife

paper towels or napkins

2 envelopes or small plastic bags

THE MEETING

calendar

"Let's begin with the calendar."

"What year is it?"

• Point to the year.

"What month is it?"

• Point to the month.

"What shapes are we using on our calendar this month?"

"Let's read our shapes together."

• Point as you read the shapes with your child.

"What shape do you think we will draw today?"

"How do you know?"

• Draw the suggested shape on the calendar.

"Let's read our shape pattern again to see if we are correct."

• Point as you read the shapes with your child.

"What is our shape pattern this month?"   **(1st shape, 2nd shape)**

• Ask your child to color the shape.

"Yesterday was the _____th of (month)."

"What do you think today's date is?"

"We write the _____th using the number _____."

"Write the date on the calendar."

- Ask your child to write the date on the calendar.

"What day of the week is it today?"

"How do you know?"

"Let's read the names of the days of the week together."

"Now we will write the month, the date, and the year on a meeting strip."

"What will we write first?"   the month

"What month is it?"

"Tell me the letters we use to spell (month)."

- Write the month on the meeting strip.

"What is the date?"

"What digits will we use to write the date?"

- Write the date on the meeting strip.

"What is the year?"

"What digits will we use to write the year?"

- Write the year on the meeting strip.

"Let's say the full date together."

weather graph

"What is it like outside this morning?"

"What symbol will we use to show this type of weather on our graph?"

- Ask your child to draw the symbol on the graph.

"How many sunny days have we had?"

"Let's count them together."

- Repeat with cloudy, rainy, and snowy.

"What type of weather have we had most often?"

"How can you tell?"

counting

"Let's use our hundred number chart to help us count."

"What number did we stop at yesterday?"   *100*

"We will stop at 100 again today."

"Let's read the numbers together as I point to them."

- Slowly move your finger from 1 to 100 as you count together.

"What number did we add to our number line yesterday?"

"What number will we add today?"

"Let's count to check."

clock

- Ask your child to set the clock to show that it is morning.

- After lunch, remind your child to change the clock to show afternoon.

right/left

"We will end The Meeting by practicing right and left."

"Face the Meeting Book."

"Hold up your left _____."

"Hold up your right _____."

"Point to your right _____."

"Point to your left _____."

"Turn to the left."

"Face the Meeting Book."

"Turn to the right."

"Face the Meeting Book."

- Other information on the meeting strip is not used today.

THE LESSON

Writing the Number 17

"Yesterday we practiced writing the number sixteen."

"Today we are going to learn how to write a new number."

"What number do you think we will write today?"   **seventeen**

- Write the number 17 on the chalkboard.

"What digits do you see in the number seventeen?"   **the digits 1 and 7**

"How would you tell someone how to write the number seventeen?"

"Which digit is on the left?"

"Which digit is on the right?"

Dividing a Solid in Half

"Today you will learn how to divide a solid in half."

"We will do this using an apple."

- Show your child an apple.

"What do we know about apples?"   **they are red (green); they are good to eat; they have seeds**

"You and I will share this apple."

"How can I divide the apple so that it will be fair?"   **cut the apple in half**

"I will cut the apple in half."

"How should I do this?"

• Cut the apple in half.

"When I cut the apple in half, how many pieces did I get?"

"How many halves are in one whole apple?"

• Put the apple together to show the whole. Separate to show the halves.

"Now I will give you half of the apple."

• Put each half on a napkin or paper towel.

"Look at your apple half very carefully without touching it."

"What do you see?"

• Allow time for your child to share observations.

"What do you notice in the center of the apple?"

"What do we call these small things?"   **seeds**

"Why do you think apples have seeds?"

"I wonder if all apples have the same number of seeds."

"What do you think?"

"Both halves of our apple look the same."

"I wonder if both halves of our apple have the same number of seeds."

"Let's try to find the answers to these questions."

"To do this, we will need to take the seeds out of our apple halves."

"How can we do this?"

"We will eat our apple halves very carefully."

"Most of the seeds are near the center, or the core."

"When you find a seed in your apple, put it in this envelope."

• Give your child an envelope.

• Eat your half of the apple and save the seeds in another envelope.

"We will find the answers to our questions during the next few days."

• Save the envelopes of seeds for Lesson 19.

• Optional: Your child can continue to explore seeds using reference books from the library. He/She can collect and compare seeds from different fruits, vegetables, and other plants.

WRITTEN PRACTICE

- Complete **Worksheet 18A** with your child.
- Complete **Worksheet 18B** with your child later in the day.

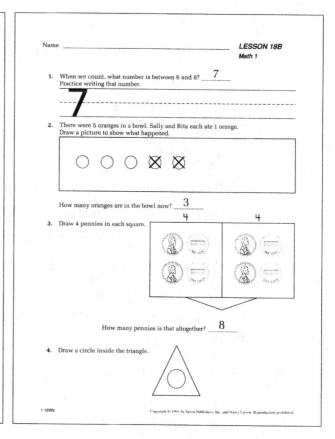

Name _____ **LESSON 18A**
Math 1

1. Write the number seventeen.

2. There were 6 apples in a bowl. Tramel and Victor each ate 1 apple.
Draw a picture to show what happened.

How many apples are in the bowl now? __4__

3. Draw 3 pennies in each square.

How many pennies is that altogether? __6__

4. Draw a triangle inside the circle.

Name _____ **LESSON 18B**
Math 1

1. When we count, what number is between 6 and 8? __7__
Practice writing that number.

2. There were 5 oranges in a bowl. Sally and Rita each ate 1 orange.
Draw a picture to show what happened.

How many oranges are in the bowl now? __3__

3. Draw 4 pennies in each square.

How many pennies is that altogether? __8__

4. Draw a circle inside the triangle.

Lesson 19

writing the number 18
picturing and combining sets
graphing a picture on a pictograph

---

lesson preparation

materials

envelopes of seeds from Lesson 18

Master 1-19 and Master 1-19A

fifteen 3" × 5" cards

crayon

the night before

• Draw apples similar to those on Master 1-19A on ten 3" × 5" cards.

• Cut five 3" × 5" cards in half. Write the numbers 1–10 on these cards.

THE MEETING

calendar

> *"Let's begin with the calendar."*

> *"What year is it?"*

• Point to the year.

> *"What month is it?"*

• Point to the month.

> *"What shapes are we using on our calendar this month?"*

> *"Let's read our shapes together."*

• Point as you read the shapes with your child.

> *"What shape do you think we will draw today?"*

> *"How do you know?"*

• Draw the suggested shape on the calendar.

> *"Let's read our shape pattern again to see if we are correct."*

• Point as you read the shapes with your child.

> *"What is our shape pattern this month?"*   *(1st shape, 2nd shape)*

• Ask your child to color the shape.

"Yesterday was the _____th of (month)."

"What do you think today's date is?"

"We write the _____th using the number _____."

"Write the date on the calendar."

- Ask your child to write the date on the calendar.

"What day of the week is it today?"

"How do you know?"

"Let's read the names of the days of the week together."

"Now we will write the month, the date, and the year on a meeting strip."

"What will we write first?"   the month

"What month is it?"

"Tell me the letters we use to spell (month)."

- Write the month on the meeting strip.

"What is the date?"

"What digits will we use to write the date?"

- Write the date on the meeting strip.

"What is the year?"

"What digits will we use to write the year?"

- Write the year on the meeting strip.

"Let's say the full date together."

weather graph

"What is it like outside this morning?"

"What symbol will we use to show this type of weather on our graph?"

- Ask your child to draw the symbol on the graph.

"How many sunny days have we had?"

"Let's count them together."

- Repeat with cloudy, rainy, and snowy.

"What type of weather have we had most often?"

"How can you tell?"

counting

"Let's use our hundred number chart to help us count."

"What number did we stop at yesterday?"   100

"We will stop at 100 again today."

"Let's read the numbers together as I point to them."

• Slowly move your finger from 1 to 100 as you count together.

"What number did we add to our number line yesterday?"

"What number will we add today?"

"Let's count to check."

clock

• Ask your child to set the clock to show that it is morning.

• After lunch, remind your child to change the clock to show afternoon.

right/left

"We will end The Meeting by practicing right and left."

"Face the Meeting Book."

"Hold up your left _____."

"Hold up your right _____."

"Point to your right _____."

"Point to your left _____."

"Turn to the left."

"Face the Meeting Book."

"Turn to the right."

"Face the Meeting Book."

• Other information on the meeting strip is not used today.

THE LESSON

Writing the Number 18

"Yesterday we practiced writing the number seventeen."

"Today we are going to learn how to write a new number."

"What number do you think we will write today?"   **eighteen**

• Write the number 18 on the chalkboard.

"What digits do you see in the number eighteen?"   **the digits 1 and 8**

"How would you tell someone how to write the number eighteen?"

"Which digit is on the left?"

"Which digit is on the right?"

Picturing and Combining Sets
Graphing a Picture on a Pictograph

"Today you will learn how to picture and combine sets."

"Yesterday we used an apple in our math lesson."

"What did we do with our apple?"   cut it in half, took out the seeds, ate it

"Today we will try to find out if both halves of our apple had the same number of seeds."

"We will also try to find how many seeds were in the whole apple."

- Give your child **Master 1-19**.

"We will pretend that this is our apple."

"I will give you your envelope of seeds from yesterday."

"Open your envelope carefully and put your seeds on your half of the apple."

"I will put the seeds from my half of the apple on the other side."

- Give your child his/her envelope of seeds.

"Let's count your seeds."

- Count your child's seeds together.

"Now let's count my seeds."

- Count your seeds together.

"Do we have the same number of seeds?"

"Who has more?"

"We will leave our apple seeds on this paper."

"Now you will draw a picture of our apple seeds."

- Give your child a crayon and a 3" × 5" card with a picture of an apple.

"Draw a picture of the seeds in our apple on this card."

- Allow time for your child to do this.

"Count all the seeds in our apple."

- Count the seeds with your child.

"Write the number of seeds below the picture of the apple."

"During the next few days, we will count and draw pictures of the seeds in nine more apples."

- Other family members and friends can participate by eating an apple and saving the seeds, or you and your child can eat 1 or 2 apples each day. Ask your child to draw the pictures of the seeds from these apples on 9 more cards. When the seeds from 10 apples have been counted and drawn, complete this lesson.

"Now we will make a graph to try to find how many apples have the same number of seeds."

"We will make a graph like the graph we make for our weather each morning."

"We will put all the apples with _____ seeds in a column, all the apples with _____ seeds in a column, all the apples with _____ seeds in a column, and so forth."

• Use the floor or a large table for the graph. Place the number cards in a row on the table or the floor.

• Hand your child 1 apple card.

"Where will you put this apple?"

"How do you know?"

• Repeat until all the cards are graphed. Make sure that the columns of apples are in one–to–one correspondence.

"Did all of our apples have the same number of seeds?"

"What do you notice about our apple seed graph?"

"I will write the things you notice about our graph."

• Record your child's observations.

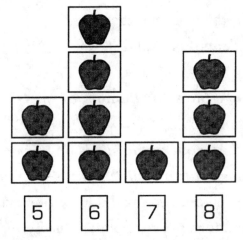

"How many seeds did most of our apples have?"

"What was the fewest number of seeds we had?"

"How many apples had _____ seeds?"

"What was the greatest number of seeds we had?"

"How many apples had _____ seeds?"

• Continue with other questions, if appropriate.

• Save **Master 1-19** for use in Lesson 21.

WRITTEN PRACTICE

• Complete **Worksheet 19A** with your child.

• Complete **Worksheet 19B** with your child later in the day.

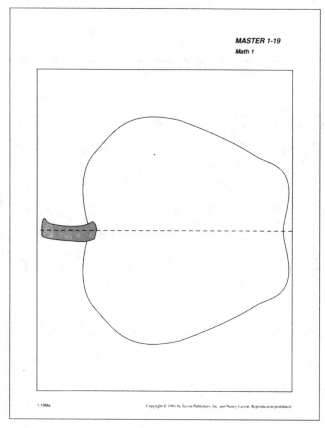

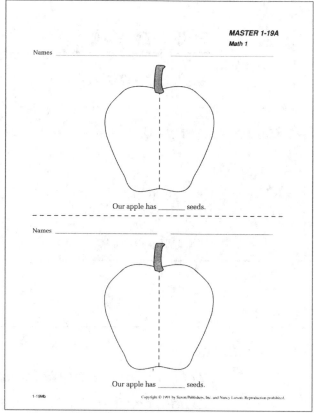

Names _____ _____

Our apple has _____ seeds.

Names _____ _____

Our apple has _____ seeds.

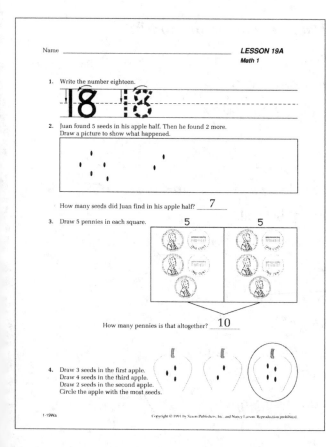

Name _____   LESSON 19A
Math 1

1. Write the number eighteen.

2. Juan found 5 seeds in his apple half. Then he found 2 more.
   Draw a picture to show what happened.

   How many seeds did Juan find in his apple half? ___7___

3. Draw 5 pennies in each square.

   How many pennies is that altogether? ___10___

4. Draw 3 seeds in the first apple.
   Draw 4 seeds in the third apple.
   Draw 2 seeds in the second apple.
   Circle the apple with the most seeds.

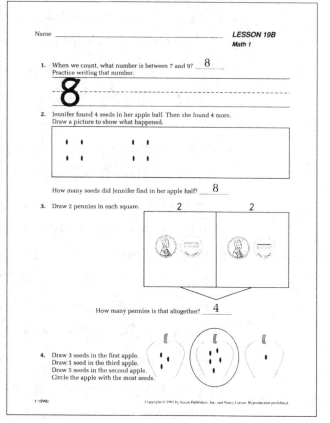

Name _____   LESSON 19B
Math 1

1. When we count, what number is between 7 and 9? ___8___
   Practice writing that number.

2. Jennifer found 4 seeds in her apple half. Then she found 4 more.
   Draw a picture to show what happened.

   How many seeds did Jennifer find in her apple half? ___8___

3. Draw 2 pennies in each square.

   How many pennies is that altogether? ___4___

4. Draw 3 seeds in the first apple.
   Draw 1 seed in the third apple.
   Draw 5 seeds in the second apple.
   Circle the apple with the most seeds.

Lesson 20

assessment

---

lesson preparation

materials

Written Assessment #3

Oral Assessment #2

individual number cards (from Lesson 2)

THE MEETING

calendar

> *"Let's begin with the calendar."*
>
> *"What year is it?"*

- Point to the year.

> *"What month is it?"*

- Point to the month.

> *"What shapes are we using on our calendar this month?"*
>
> *"Let's read our shapes together."*

- Point as you read the shapes with your child.

> *"What shape do you think we will draw today?"*
>
> *"How do you know?"*

- Draw the suggested shape on the calendar.

> *"Let's read our shape pattern again to see if we are correct."*

- Point as you read the shapes with your child.

> *"What is our shape pattern this month?"*   **(1st shape, 2nd shape)**

- Ask your child to color the shape.

> *"Yesterday was the _____th of (month)."*
>
> *"What do you think today's date is?"*
>
> *"We write the _____th using the number _____."*
>
> *"Write the date on the calendar."*

- Ask your child to write the date on the calendar.

> *"What day of the week is it today?"*

"How do you know?"

"Let's read the names of the days of the week together."

"Now we will write the month, the date, and the year on a meeting strip."

"What will we write first?"   **the month**

"What month is it?"

"Tell me the letters we use to spell (month)."

- Write the month on the meeting strip.

"What is the date?"

"What digits will we use to write the date?"

- Write the date on the meeting strip.

"What is the year?"

"What digits will we use to write the year?"

- Write the year on the meeting strip.

"Let's say the full date together."

weather graph

"What is it like outside this morning?"

"What symbol will we use to show this type of weather on our graph?"

- Ask your child to draw the symbol on the graph.

"How many sunny days have we had?"

"Let's count them together."

- Repeat with cloudy, rainy, and snowy.

"What type of weather have we had most often?"

"How can you tell?"

counting

"Let's use our hundred number chart to help us count."

"What number did we stop at yesterday?"   **100**

"We will stop at 100 again today."

"Let's read the numbers together as I point to them."

- Slowly move your finger from 1 to 100 as you count together.

"What number did we add to our number line yesterday?"

"What number will we add today?"

"Let's count to check."

"Every ten numbers, we will color the square orange."

• Ask your child to use an orange crayon to color the number square for 20.

clock

• Ask your child to set the clock to show that it is morning.

• After lunch, remind your child to change the clock to show afternoon.

right/left

"We will end The Meeting by practicing right and left."

"Face the Meeting Book."

"Hold up your left _____."

"Hold up your right _____."

"Point to your right _____."

"Point to your left _____."

"Turn to the left."

"Face the Meeting Book."

"Turn to the right."

"Face the Meeting Book."

• Other information on the meeting strip is not used today.

ASSESSMENT

• All of the questions on the assessment are based on concepts and skills presented at least five lessons ago. If your child is having difficulty with a specific concept, reteach the concept the following day.

Written Assessment

"Today I would like to see what you remember from what we have been practicing."

• Give your child **Written Assessment #3**.

"Write your name at the top of the paper."

"I will read the directions for each problem."

• Read the directions for each problem. Allow time for your child to complete each problem before continuing.

• Correct the paper, noting your child's mistakes on the **Individual Recording Form**. Review the errors with your child.

Oral Assessment

• Record your child's responses to the oral interview on the interview sheet.

Teacher _____

Date _____

Materials:
Number cards 0-9

MATH 1   LESSON 20
Oral Assessment # 2 Recording Form

Ordering Numbers 0-9
•Give the child number cards 0-9 in random order.
"Read these numbers."
"Put the numbers in order."

Students

Name _____

1. Color the second shape red.
    Color the last shape yellow.
    Color the third shape blue.
    Color the first shape green.

G   R   B   Y

2. Choose three numbers (0-9).
    Write the numbers on the lines.   answers may vary
    Color the trains.

Circle the smallest number.

3. Trace each side of the triangle
    with a different color crayon.

    How many sides
    does a triangle have? ___3___

    Circle each angle of the square
    with a different color crayon.

    How many angles
    does a square have? ___4___

Lesson 21

writing the number 19
writing addition number sentences

---

lesson preparation

materials

Master 1-19 (from Lesson 19)

7 linking cubes

Master 1-21

THE MEETING

- Refer to Lesson 20, if necessary, for specific questions in The Meeting. New questions are included in the script.

calendar

- Ask your child to identify the following:

    year

    month

    shapes on the calendar

    today's shape

    shape pattern for the month

- Ask your child to write the date on the calendar.

- Ask your child to do the following:

    identify today's day of the week

    read the days of the week

- Write the full date on the meeting strip as your child spells the name of the month and names the digits for the date and year.

weather graph

- Ask your child to report and graph the weather.

- Ask questions about the graph.

counting

- Count from 1 to 100 using the hundred number chart.

- Add another number to the number line.
- Count to check.

clock

- Your child sets the morning/afternoon clock.

right/left

- Continue to practice left and right.
- Other information on the meeting strip is not used today.

THE LESSON

Writing the Number 19

"The last number we practiced writing was the number eighteen."

"What number do you think we will learn how to write today?"

- Write the number 19 on the chalkboard.

"What digits do you see in the number nineteen?"

"How would you tell someone how to write the number nineteen?"

"Which digit is on the left?"

"Which digit is on the right?"

Writing Addition Number Sentences

"We have been using apples for our math lessons."

"What did we do with our apples?"

"We counted our apple seeds and drew pictures of the seeds."

"Today you will learn how to write addition number sentences to show the number of seeds in an apple."

- Give your child **Master 1-19** and a cup of 7 linking cubes.

"We will pretend that these cubes are apple seeds."

"Take four apple seeds out of the cup."

"Put them in your apple."

- Draw a picture of the apple on the chalkboard.

"How many seeds are in the left half of your apple?"

"How many seeds are in the right half of your apple?"

- Draw the seeds.

"How many seeds did you use altogether?" 4

• Record the number of seeds in the following way:

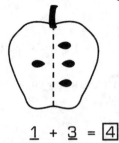

$$\underline{1} + \underline{3} = \boxed{4}$$

"Put your seeds in the apple a different way."

"I will draw a picture on the chalkboard."

"How many seeds are in the left half of your apple?"

"How many seeds are in the right half of your apple?"

• Draw the seeds.

"How many seeds did you use altogether?" **4**

• Record the number of seeds in the following way:

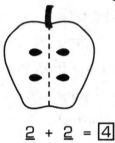

$$\underline{2} + \underline{2} = \boxed{4}$$

• Repeat until all combinations for 4 are included. If your child did not include 0 + 4 = 4 or 4 + 0 = 4, tell your child to put all the seeds in one half of the apple and repeat the questions above.

"Take another apple seed from your cup."

"Put all the seeds on the left side of the big apple."

"Now you will have a chance to draw pictures and write addition number sentences to show five pretend seeds in the apple."

• Give your child **Master 1-21** and a crayon.

"Write your name on the top line."

"Point to the apple in the top left-hand corner of the paper."

"Draw a picture to show how you put the seeds in the big apple."

• Allow time for your child to draw the seeds.

• Draw a picture on the chalkboard as your child draws the seeds.

"How many seeds are on the left side?" **5**

"Write the number below the left side."

• Demonstrate on the chalkboard.

"How many seeds are on the right side?" **0**

"Write the number below the right side."

• Demonstrate on the chalkboard.

"How many seeds did we use altogether?"   **5**

"Write this number in the square."

"Now move one seed to the right side of the big apple."

"Point to the apple in the top right-hand corner of the paper."

"Draw a picture to show how you put the seeds in the big apple."

• Draw a model on the chalkboard.

"How many seeds are on the left side?"   **4**

"Write the number below the left side."

• Demonstrate on the chalkboard.

"How many seeds are on the right side?"   **1**

"Write the number below the right side."

• Demonstrate on the chalkboard.

"How many seeds did we use altogether?"   **5**

"Write this number in the square."

• Repeat moving one seed at a time to the right side until your child has completed six apples.

"Now I will draw a picture of some apple seeds on the chalkboard."

• Draw the following on the chalkboard:

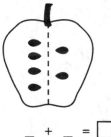

_ + _ = ☐

"Use the linking cubes to show these seeds on the large apple."

"What number sentence will we write to show these seeds?"

• Ask your child to write the number sentence on the chalkboard.

• Repeat with the following:

 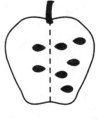

_ + _ = ☐   _ + _ = ☐

WRITTEN PRACTICE

- Complete **Worksheet 21A** with your child.

- Complete **Worksheet 21B** with your child later in the day.

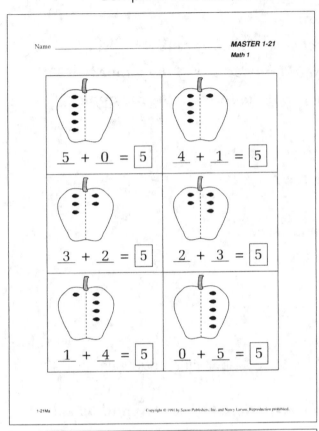

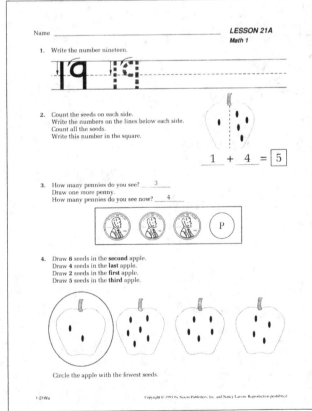

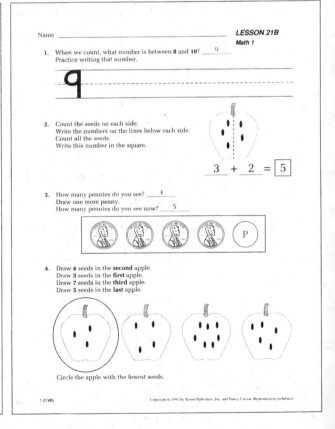

esson 22

writing the number 20
identifying ordinal position to sixth

---

lesson preparation ———————————

materials

6 linking cubes (one each of red, green, yellow, blue, orange, and black)

6 toys (toy cars, stuffed animals, dolls, or action figures)

THE MEETING

- Refer to Lesson 20, if necessary, for specific questions in The Meeting. New questions are included in the script.

calendar

- Ask your child to identify the following:

    year

    month

    shapes on the calendar

    today's shape

    shape pattern for the month

- Ask your child to write the date on the calendar.

- Ask your child to do the following:

    identify today's day of the week

    read the days of the week

- Write the full date on the meeting strip as your child spells the name of the month and names the digits for the date and year.

weather graph

- Ask your child to report and graph the weather.

- Ask questions about the graph.

counting

- Count from 1 to 100 using the hundred number chart.

- Add another number to the number line.

- Count to check.

clock

- Your child sets the morning/afternoon clock.

right/left

- Continue to practice left and right.

- Other information on the meeting strip is not used today.

THE LESSON

Writing the Number 20

"The last number we practiced writing was the number nineteen."

"What number do you think we will learn how to write today?"

- Write the number 20 on the chalkboard.

"What digits do you see in the number twenty?"

"How would you tell someone how to write the number twenty?"

"Which digit is on the left?"

"Which digit is on the right?"

Identifying Ordinal Position to Sixth

"Today you will learn how to identify ordinal position to sixth."

"We will use six (toys)."

- Show your child the 6 (toys).

- Arrange the (toys) in a line.

"Who (What) is first in line?"

"Who (What) is second in line?"

"Who (What) is third in line?"

- Point to the fourth (toy) in line.

"What do we call this (toy)?" *fourth*

- Repeat with the fifth and sixth (toy).

"Now the second (toy) will be last."

- Move the second (toy) to the end.

"Who (What) is third now?"

"Who (What) is fifth?"

"Move the fourth (toy) so that it will be second."

"Is _____ second now?"

"Now we will use linking cubes and pretend that they are (toys)."

- Give your child a red, yellow, blue, green, orange, and black linking cube.

"Point to the left side of the table."

"This is where you will put the first cube."

"Put the black cube first."

"Put the red cube second."

"Put the green cube third."

"Put the orange cube fourth."

"Put the blue cube fifth."

"Put the yellow cube sixth."

"In which place is the yellow cube?" sixth

"In which place is the orange cube?" fourth

"In which place is the black cube?" first

"In which place is the blue cube?" fifth

"Point to the second cube."

"Pick it up."

"Put it last."

"Point to the third cube now."

- Repeat with all positions.

"Point to the fourth cube."

"Pick it up."

"Put it second."

"Point to the third cube now."

- Repeat with all positions.

WRITTEN PRACTICE

- Complete **Worksheet 22A** with your child.

- Complete **Worksheet 22B** with your child later in the day.

Math 1 · Lesson 22

Name _____ **LESSON 22A**
Math 1

1. Write the number twenty.

20 20

2. Carlos had 7 baseball cards. He gave 3 cards to his friend.
Draw a picture to show what happened.

How many baseball cards does Carlos have now? ___ cards

3. How many apples are in each row?

4
1
5
_

Color the apples in the row with the most. Use a red crayon.
Color the apples in the row with the fewest. Use a green crayon.

4. Color the squares red. How many squares did you color? ___

R O △ ⊠ Y (R)

5. Circle the sixth shape.
Put an X on the fourth shape.
Color the fifth shape yellow.

1-22Wa   Copyright © 1991 by Saxon Publishers, Inc. and Nancy Larson. Reproduction prohibited.

Name _____ **LESSON 22B**
Math 1

1. When we count, what number is between 1 and 3? ___
Practice writing that number.

2

2. Michelle had 10 baseball cards. She gave her friend 2 cards.
Draw a picture to show what happened.

How many baseball cards does Michelle have now? ___ cards

3. How many apples are in each row?

3
6
5
2

Color the apples in the row with the most. Use a red crayon.
Color the apples in the row with the fewest. Use a green crayon.

4. Color the triangles blue. How many triangles did you color? ___

△ □ △ G ⊘ □

5. Circle the last shape.
Put an X on the fifth shape.
Color the fourth shape green.

1-22Wb   Copyright © 1991 by Saxon Publishers, Inc. and Nancy Larson. Reproduction prohibited.

124   Copyright © 1994 by Saxon Publishers, Inc. and Nancy Larson. Reproduction prohibited.

Lesson 23

writing the number 21
addition facts—doubles to 10

---

lesson preparation ——————————————————————

materials

10 linking cubes (all the same color)

six 3" × 5" cards

the night before

• Write the following on the 3" × 5" cards:

| 0 + 0 | 1 + 1 | 2 + 2 | 3 + 3 | 4 + 4 | 5 + 5 |

THE MEETING

• Refer to Lesson 20, if necessary, for specific questions in The Meeting. New questions are included in the script.

calendar

• Ask your child to identify the following:

> year
>
> month
>
> shapes on the calendar
>
> today's shape
>
> shape pattern for the month

• Ask your child to write the date on the calendar.

• Ask your child to do the following:

> identify today's day of the week
>
> read the days of the week

• Write the full date on the meeting strip as your child spells the name of the month and names the digits for the date and year.

weather graph

• Ask your child to report and graph the weather.

• Ask questions about the graph.

counting

- Count from 1 to 100 using the hundred number chart.
- Add another number to the number line.
- Count to check.

clock

- Your child sets the morning/afternoon clock.

right/left

- Continue to practice left and right.
- Other information on the meeting strip is not used today.

THE LESSON

Writing the Number 21

"The last number we practiced writing was the number twenty."

"What number do you think we will learn how to write today?"

- Write the number 21 on the chalkboard.

"What digits do you see in the number 21?"

"How would you tell someone how to write the number 21?"

"Which digit is on the left?"

"Which digit is on the right?"

Addition Facts — Doubles to 10

"Today you will learn the addition facts called the doubles."

- Give your child 10 linking cubes.

"Make a tower of one and another tower of one."

- Write "1 + 1" on the chalkboard.

"Put your towers together."

"How many cubes do you have now?"   2

"One and one is two."

- Write "1 + 1 = 2."

"Make a tower of two and another tower of two."

- Write "2 + 2" on the chalkboard below 1 + 1 = 2.

"Put your towers together."

"How many cubes do you have now?"

"Two and two is four."

- Write "2 + 2 = 4."

- Repeat with 3 + 3, 4 + 4, and 5 + 5.

- Point to each number sentence as you say the following:

  "We read these number sentences like this: one and one is two, or one plus one equals two."

- Repeat with each number fact.

- Write "0 + 0 =" above 1 + 1 = 2.

  "What do you think is the answer for zero plus zero?"

  "How do you know?"

  "Put zero cubes in your left hand."

  "Put zero cubes in your right hand."

  "How many cubes do you have in your hands now?"

- Write "0 + 0 = 0."

  "Let's read each of our number sentences."

  "We will read each one in two ways."

- Read them first as "_____ and _____ is _____."

- Read them next as "_____ plus _____ equals _____."

  "Put your cubes together in a tower."

- Allow time for your child to do this.

  "I have written these addition facts on cards without the answers."

  "I will hold up a card for one of our addition facts."

  "Let's say the problem and the answer together when I hold up the card."

- Hold up the fact cards one at a time. Repeat several times with the cards in random order.

WRITTEN PRACTICE

- Complete **Worksheet 23A** with your child.

- Complete **Worksheet 23B** with your child later in the day.

Name _____ **LESSON 23A**
Math 1

1. Write the number twenty-one.

2. There are 4 ants on the table. Three more ants climbed onto the table.
   Draw a picture to show what happened.

How many ants are on the table now? ___7___ ants

3. Write number sentences for these apples.

$\underline{3} + \underline{3} = \boxed{6}$ $\underline{2} + \underline{5} = \boxed{7}$

4. Write the answers.

$0 + 0 = \underline{0}$ $1 + 1 = \underline{2}$ $2 + 2 = \underline{4}$

$3 + 3 = \underline{6}$ $4 + 4 = \underline{8}$ $5 + 5 = \underline{10}$

5. Fill in the missing numbers.

1	2	3	4	5	6	7	8	9	10
11	12	13	14	15	16	17	18	19	20

1-23Wa

Name _____ **LESSON 23B**
Math 1

1. When we count, what number is between 2 and 4? ___3___
   Practice writing that number.

2. There are 6 ants on the table. Four more ants climbed onto the table.
   Draw a picture to show what happened.

How many ants are on the table now? ___10___ ants

3. Write number sentences for these apples.

$\underline{2} + \underline{2} = \boxed{4}$ $\underline{4} + \underline{1} = \boxed{5}$

4. Write the answers.

$5 + 5 = \underline{10}$ $2 + 2 = \underline{4}$ $3 + 3 = \underline{6}$

$0 + 0 = \underline{0}$ $4 + 4 = \underline{8}$ $1 + 1 = \underline{2}$

5. Fill in the missing numbers.

1	2	3	4	5	6	7	8	9	10
11	12	13	14	15	16	17	18	19	20

1-23Wb

esson 24

writing the number 22
identifying a rectangle
identifying the number of sides and angles of a rectangle

---

lesson preparation

materials

8 construction paper shapes
geoboard and geoband
large fact cards (from Lesson 23)

the night before

• Cut out the following construction paper shapes:

THE MEETING

• Refer to Lesson 20, if necessary, for specific questions in The Meeting. New questions are included in the script.

calendar

• Ask your child to identify the following:

    year

    month

    shapes on the calendar

    today's shape

    shape pattern for the month

• Ask your child to write the date on the calendar.

- Ask your child to do the following:

    identify today's day of the week

    read the days of the week

- Write the full date on the meeting strip as your child spells the name of the month and names the digits for the date and year.

weather graph

- Ask your child to report and graph the weather.

- Ask questions about the graph.

counting

- Count from 1 to 100 using the hundred number chart.

- Add another number to the number line.

- Count to check.

clock

- Your child sets the morning/afternoon clock.

right/left

- Continue to practice left and right.

- Other information on the meeting strip is not used today.

THE LESSON

Writing the Number 22

"The last number we practiced writing was the number 21."

"What number do you think we will learn how to write today?"

- Write the number 22 on the chalkboard.

"What digits do you see in the number 22?"

"How would you tell someone how to write the number 22?"

"Which digit is on the left?"

"Which digit is on the right?"

Identifying a Rectangle
Identifying the Number of Sides and Angles of a Rectangle

"Today you will learn about another shape."

- Show your child the construction paper rectangle.

"What do we call this shape?"

"We call this shape a rectangle."

"Let's try to find something in this room that has the same shape as this paper rectangle."

"Look around the room."

"What do you see?"

- Ask your child to identify as many rectangles as possible.

- Point to an angle on the paper rectangle.

"What do we call this?"   **angle**

"How many angles does a rectangle have?"   **4**

- Hold the shape by one angle.

"Count with me as I point to each angle."

- Count the angles with your child.

"These angles look just like the corners of a piece of paper."

"How many sides does a rectangle have?"   **4**

- Hold the shape by one side.

"Count with me as I point to each side."

- Count the sides with your child.

"How many sides does a rectangle have?"   **4**

- Show your child all of the construction paper shapes.

"I have some shapes that are rectangles and some that are not."

"Let's sort these shapes into two piles."

- Hold up the construction paper shapes (except the square) one at a time.

"Is this a rectangle?"

"How do you know?"

"Let's check by counting the sides and angles."

"Do the angles look like the corners of a piece of paper?"

- Hold up the square.

"What is the name of this shape?"   **square**

"We can also call this shape a rectangle because it has four sides and four angles like the corners of a piece of paper."

"Squares are special rectangles."

"What do you notice about the square that makes it special?"   **4 equal sides**

- Put the square in the pile of rectangles.

- Note: All squares are rectangles. Do not spend time emphasizing this because class inclusion is very difficult for young children to understand.

- Point to the pile of rectangles.

  "These are rectangles."

- Point to the other shapes.

  "These are not rectangles."

  "Now you will use a geoboard to make rectangles."

- Give your child a geoboard and geoband.

  "How many sides does a rectangle have?"

  "How many angles does a rectangle have?"

  "The angles look like the corners of a piece of paper."

  "Make a rectangle on your geoboard."

- Allow time for your child to do this.

  "Now make a different rectangle on your geoboard."

- Allow time for your child to do this.

  "Make a triangle on your geoboard."

  "How many sides does a triangle have?"

  "How many angles does a triangle have?"

CLASS PRACTICE

"Let's practice the doubles facts."

"I will hold up a card for one of the doubles facts."

"Say the problem and the answer when I hold up the card."

- Hold up the large fact cards one at a time. Repeat several times with the cards in random order.

WRITTEN PRACTICE

- Complete **Worksheet 24A** with your child.
- Complete **Worksheet 24B** with your child later in the day.

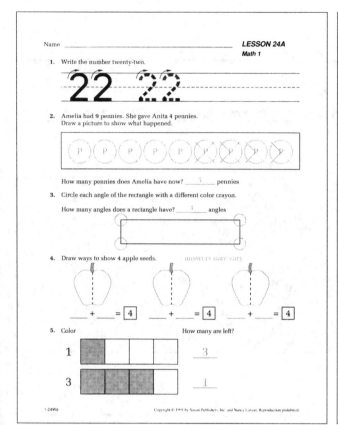

LESSON 24A
Math 1

1. Write the number twenty-two.

22 22

2. Amelia had 9 pennies. She gave Anita 4 pennies.
   Draw a picture to show what happened.

   How many pennies does Amelia have now? ____5____ pennies

3. Circle each angle of the rectangle with a different color crayon.

   How many angles does a rectangle have? ____4____ angles

4. Draw ways to show 4 apple seeds.   answers may vary

   ____ + ____ = 4   ____ + ____ = 4   ____ + ____ = 4

5. Color   How many are left?

   1 [▨][ ][ ][ ]   3

   3 [▨][▨][▨][ ]   1

1-24Wa   Copyright © 1991 by Saxon Publishers, Inc. and Nancy Larson. Reproduction prohibited.

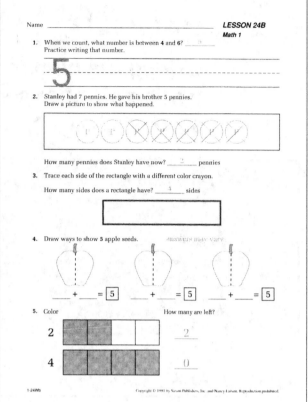

LESSON 24B
Math 1

1. When we count, what number is between 4 and 6? ____5____
   Practice writing that number.

   5

2. Stanley had 7 pennies. He gave his brother 5 pennies.
   Draw a picture to show what happened.

   How many pennies does Stanley have now? ____2____ pennies

3. Trace each side of the rectangle with a different color crayon.

   How many sides does a rectangle have? ____4____ sides

4. Draw ways to show 5 apple seeds.   answers may vary

   ____ + ____ = 5   ____ + ____ = 5   ____ + ____ = 5

5. Color   How many are left?

   2 [▨][▨][ ][ ]   2

   4 [▨][▨][▨][▨]   0

1-24Wb   Copyright © 1991 by Saxon Publishers, Inc. and Nancy Larson. Reproduction prohibited.

Lesson 25

writing the number 23
writing number sentences for some, some more stories

lesson preparation

materials

Written Assessment #4

10 stuffed animals, dolls, action figures, or other toys

7 crayons

large fact cards

THE MEETING

- Refer to Lesson 20, if necessary, for specific questions in The Meeting. New questions are included in the script.

calendar

- Ask your child to identify the following:

  year

  month

  shapes on the calendar

  today's shape

  shape pattern for the month

- Ask your child to write the date on the calendar.

- Ask your child to do the following:

  identify today's day of the week

  read the days of the week

- Write the full date on the meeting strip as your child spells the name of the month and names the digits for the date and year.

weather graph

- Ask your child to report and graph the weather.

- Ask questions about the graph.

counting

- Count from 1 to 100 using the hundred number chart.
- Add another number to the number line.
- Count to check.

clock

- Your child sets the morning/afternoon clock.

right/left

- Continue to practice left and right.
- Other information on the meeting strip is not used today.

ASSESSMENT

- All of the questions on the assessment are based on concepts and skills presented at least five lessons ago. If your child is having difficulty with a specific concept, reteach the concept the following day.

Written Assessment

"Today, I would like to see what you remember from what we have been practicing."

- Give your child **Written Assessment #4.**

"Write your name at the top of the paper."

"I will read the directions for each problem."

- Read the directions for each problem. Allow time for your child to complete each problem before continuing.

- Correct the paper, noting your child's mistakes on the **Individual Recording Form.** Review the errors with your child.

THE LESSON

Writing the Number 23

"The last number we practiced writing was the number 22."

"What number do you think we will learn how to write today?"

- Write the number 23 on the chalkboard.

"What digits do you see in the number 23?"

"How would you tell someone how to write the number 23?"

"Which digit is on the left?"

"Which digit is on the right?"

Writing Number Sentences for Some, Some More Stories

"We have been acting out and drawing pictures for some, some more stories."

"Today you will learn how to write number sentences for some, some more stories."

"Let's act out a story together."

"We will use (toys) to do this."

• Use stuffed animals, dolls, or action figures.

"We will pretend that our _____ are going for a ride in the car."

• Designate an area to be the car.

"Four _____ got in the car."

• Ask your child to put 4 _____ in the pretend car.

"Now one more _____ got in the car."

• Ask your child to put 1 more _____ in the pretend car.

"Let's count to see how many _____ are in the car now."

• Point to each _____ as your child counts.

"Now we will draw a picture to show what happened in this story."

• Quickly draw a sketch of a car on the chalkboard.

"What happened first in this story?"

• Draw 4 _____ in the car.

"I will write the number four under the car to show that four _____ got in the car first."

"What happened next?"   one more _____ got in the car

• Draw 1 more _____ in the car.

"I will write the plus sign and the number one under the car to show that one more _____ got in the car."

"What did we do next?"   counted how many _____ were in the car altogether

"Let's count the number of _____ in the car altogether."

• Point to each _____ in the picture as your child counts.

"I will write the equal sign and the number five under the car to show that now there are five _____ in the car."

"Let's read our number sentence together."   four plus one equals five

"Let's act out another car story together."

"Six _____ got in the car."

• Ask your child to put 6 _____ in the pretend car.

"Now three more _____ got in the car."

• Ask your child to put 3 more _____ in the pretend car.

"Let's count to see how many _____ are in the car now."

• Point to each _____ as your child counts.

"Let's draw a picture of what happened in this story."

• Quickly draw a sketch of a car.

"What happened first in this story?"

• Draw 6 _____ in the car.

"I will write the number six under the car to show that six _____ got in the car first."

"What happened next?"

• Draw 3 more _____ in the car.

"I will write the plus sign and the number three under the car to show that three more _____ got in the car."

"What did we do next?"   *counted how many _____ were in the car altogether*

"Let's count the number of _____ in the car altogether."

• Point to each _____ in the picture as your child counts.

"I will write the equal sign and the number nine under the car to show that now there are nine _____ in the car."

"Let's read our number sentence together."   *six plus three equals nine*

"Let's act out a different story."

• Give your child 5 crayons.

"How many crayons did I give you?"

• Give your child 2 more crayons.

"Now I gave you two more crayons."

"Let's count to see how many crayons you have now."

• Encourage your child to count on from five.

"Now we will draw a picture to show what happened in this story."

"What happened first in this story?"

• Draw 5 crayons.

"I will write the number five under the crayons to show that I gave you five crayons first."

"What happened next?"

- Draw 2 more crayons.

   "I will write the plus sign and the number two under the crayons to show that I gave you two more crayons."

   "What did we do next?"　**counted all the crayons**

   "Let's count the number of crayons."

- Point to each crayon in the picture as you count with your child.

   "I will write the equal sign and the number seven under the crayons to show that now you have seven crayons."

   "Let's read our number sentence together."　**five plus two equals seven**

   "Altogether, how many crayons did I give you?"

- Repeat with 4 crayons plus 3 crayons.

CLASS PRACTICE

   "Let's practice the doubles facts."

   "I will hold up a card for one of the doubles facts."

   "Say the problem and the answer when I hold up the card."

- Hold up the large fact cards one at a time. Repeat several times with the cards in random order.

WRITTEN PRACTICE

- Complete **Worksheet 25A** with your child.
- Complete **Worksheet 25B** with your child later in the day.

Name _____

1. Sammy had five pencils. He gave his brother two pencils. Draw a picture to show what happened.

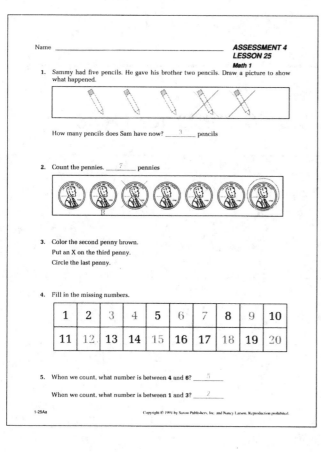

How many pencils does Sam have now? ___3___ pencils

2. Count the pennies. ___7___ pennies

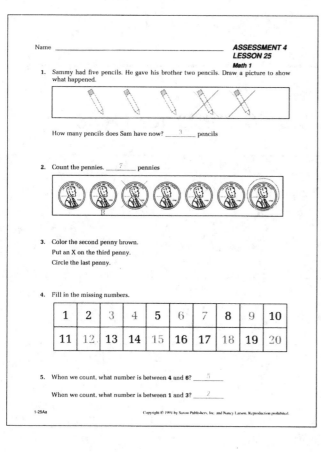

3. Color the second penny brown.
Put an X on the third penny.
Circle the last penny.

4. Fill in the missing numbers.

1	2	3	4	5	6	7	8	9	10
11	12	13	14	15	16	17	18	19	20

5. When we count, what number is between **4** and **6**? ___5___

When we count, what number is between **1** and **3**? ___2___

1-25Aa

Name _____
LESSON 25A
Math 1

1. Write the number twenty-three.

23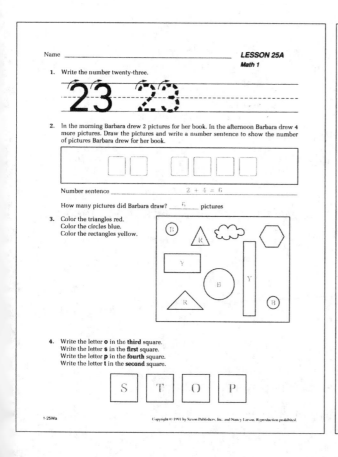

2. In the morning Barbara drew 2 pictures for her book. In the afternoon Barbara drew 4 more pictures. Draw the pictures and write a number sentence to show the number of pictures Barbara drew for her book.

Number sentence _____ $2 + 4 = 6$

How many pictures did Barbara draw? ___6___ pictures

3. Color the triangles red.
Color the circles blue.
Color the rectangles yellow.

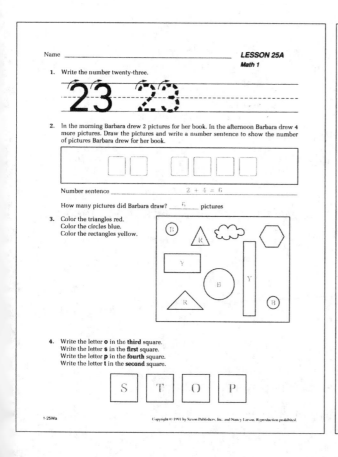

4. Write the letter **o** in the **third** square.
Write the letter **s** in the **first** square.
Write the letter **p** in the **fourth** square.
Write the letter **t** in the **second** square.

S	T	O	P

1-25Wa

Name _____
LESSON 25B
Math 1

1. Fill in the missing numbers.

1	2	3	4	5	6	7	8	9	10

2. In the morning John drew 5 pictures for his book. In the afternoon John drew 5 more pictures for his book. Draw the pictures and write a number sentence to show the number of pictures John drew for his book.

Number sentence _____ $5 + 5 = 10$

How many pictures did John draw? ___10___ pictures

3. Find something at home that has the shape of a triangle.
Draw a picture of what you found.

   Find something at home that has the shape of a rectangle.
Draw a picture of what you found.

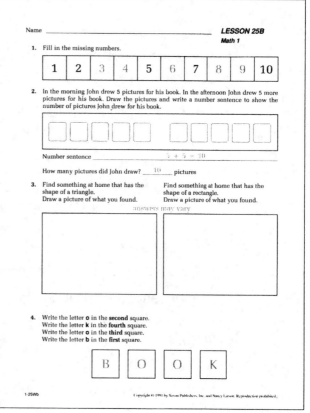

answers may vary

4. Write the letter **o** in the **second** square.
Write the letter **k** in the **fourth** square.
Write the letter **o** in the **third** square.
Write the letter **b** in the **first** square.

B	O	O	K

1-25Wb

Lesson 26

writing the number 24
identifying the attributes of pattern blocks

---

lesson preparation

materials

pattern blocks

large fact cards

THE MEETING

- Refer to Lesson 20, if necessary, for specific questions in The Meeting. New questions are included in the script.

calendar

- Ask your child to identify the following:

    year

    month

    shapes on the calendar

    today's shape

    shape pattern for the month

- Ask your child to write the date on the calendar.

- Ask your child to do the following:

    identify today's day of the week

    read the days of the week

- Write the full date on the meeting strip as your child spells the name of the month and names the digits for the date and year.

weather graph

- Ask your child to report and graph the weather.

- Ask questions about the graph.

counting

- Count from 1 to 100 using the hundred number chart.

- Add another number to the number line.

- Count to check.

clock

- Your child sets the morning/afternoon clock.

right/left

- Continue to practice left and right.

- Other information on the meeting strip is not used today.

THE LESSON

Writing the Number 24

"The last number we practiced writing was the number 23."

"What number do you think we will learn how to write today?"

- Write the number 24 on the chalkboard.

"What digits do you see in the number 24?"

"How would you tell someone how to write the number 24?"

"Which digit is on the left?"

"Which digit is on the right?"

Identifying the Attributes of Pattern Blocks

"Today you will learn about pattern blocks."

- Give your child a double handful of pattern blocks.

"What do you notice about pattern blocks?"

- Encourage your child to offer observations.

"How many different pattern blocks are there?"   **6**

"We can name the pieces by their color or by their shape."

"What colors are the pattern blocks?"   **yellow, red, blue, green, orange, tan**

"Do you know the names of any of the shapes?"

"What are they?"

"The green block is a triangle, the orange block is a square, the yellow block is a hexagon, the red block is a trapezoid, and the blue and tan pieces are parallelograms." (The blue and tan pieces are also rhombuses; a rhombus is a parallelogram with equal sides.)

- Allow your child to refer to the pieces by color or shape. Whenever possible, refer to the pieces by shape or by shape and color to help your child learn the shape names.

"Now you will have a chance to make a design using the pattern blocks."

• Allow time for your child to make a design.

"Tell me about your design."

"It is time to put away the pattern blocks now."

"Carefully put your pattern blocks in the container."

• Optional: Encourage your child to use the pattern blocks to make designs during free time.

CLASS PRACTICE

"Let's practice the doubles facts."

"I will hold up a card for one of the doubles facts."

"Say the problem and the answer when I hold up the card."

• Hold up the large fact cards one at a time. Repeat several times with the cards in random order.

WRITTEN PRACTICE

• Complete **Worksheet 26A** with your child.

• Complete **Worksheet 26B** with your child later in the day.

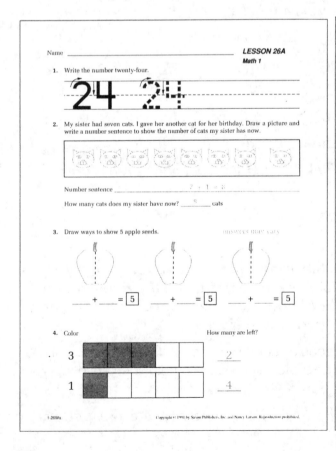

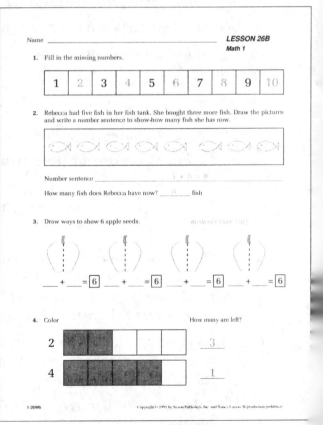

L esson 27

writing the number 25
identifying lighter and heavier using a balance

---

lesson preparation

materials

balance

6 identical containers with different contents (see *the night before*)

Master 1-27

large fact cards

the night before

- Fill six identical containers (margarine tubs, yogurt containers, paper or styrofoam cups with covers, etc.) with objects of differing weights. For example, nails, counters, rice, paper clips, cotton balls, nuts, sand, stones, and/or cereal could be used. Try to fill each container to minimize identification of the objects by sound. If the cover is transparent, put a piece of paper inside the cover so that your child cannot identify the objects by sight. Label the containers with the letters A, B, C, D, E, and F.

THE MEETING

- Refer to Lesson 20, if necessary, for specific questions in The Meeting. New questions are included in the script.

calendar

- Ask your child to identify the following:

    year

    month

    shapes on the calendar

    today's shape

    shape pattern for the month

- Ask your child to write the date on the calendar.

- Ask your child to do the following:

    identify today's day of the week

    read the days of the week

- Write the full date on the meeting strip as your child spells the name of the month and names the digits for the date and year.

---

weather graph

- Ask your child to report and graph the weather.

- Ask questions about the graph.

counting

- Count from 1 to 100 using the hundred number chart.

- Add another number to the number line.

- Count to check.

clock

- Your child sets the morning/afternoon clock.

right/left

- Continue to practice left and right.

- Other information on the meeting strip is not used today.

THE LESSON

Writing the Number 25

"The last number we practiced writing was the number 24."

"What number do you think we will learn how to write today?"

- Write the number 25 on the chalkboard.

"What digits do you see in the number 25?"

"How would you tell someone how to write the number 25?"

"Which digit is on the left?"

"Which digit is on the right?"

Identifying Lighter and Heavier Using a Balance

"Today you will learn how to compare the weight of two containers."

- Show your child the balance.

"Do you know what this is called?"   **balance**

"This is called a balance."

"What do you think we use a balance for?"   **to find out which object is heavier or lighter**

- Place the 6 containers on the floor or table in front of you.

"I have some containers."

- Hold up 2 containers of distinctly different weights.

"We will try to find out which of these containers is heavier and which is lighter."

"I'm going to put these two containers on the balance."

- Put the 2 containers on the balance.

"What happened?"

"Why do you think that happened?"

"Let's feel our containers."

- Ask your child to hold the 2 containers.

"What do you notice about them?"

"Which one is heavier?"

"What do you think is going to happen when we put these back on the balance?"

"Let's put them on the balance again."

- Ask your child to put the containers on the balance.

"What happened?"

"Which container is heavier?"

"Which container is lighter?"

"I will draw a picture of our balance on the chalkboard."

- Draw a picture of the balance on the chalkboard.

- Write the letters of the containers on the appropriate sides.

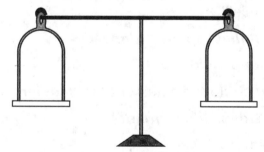

"Let's circle the side of the balance that went down."

"Which side of the balance went down?"

"This is the heaviest container."

- Circle that side.

"Let's try this with two different containers."

"I'm going to put two containers on the balance."

- Put 2 containers on the balance. Choose 2 with distinctly different weights.

"What happened?"

"Why do you think that happened?"

"Let's feel our containers."

- Ask your child to hold the containers.

    "What do you notice about them?"

    "Which one is heavier?"

    "What do you think is going to happen when we put these back on the balance?"

    "Let's put them on the balance again."

    "What happened?"

    "Which container is heavier?"

    "Which container is lighter?"

    "I will draw a picture of our balance on the chalkboard."

- Draw a picture of the balance on the chalkboard.

- Write the letters of the containers on the appropriate sides.

    "Let's circle the side of the balance that went down."

    "Which side of the balance went down?"

    "This is the heavier container."

- Draw another picture of the balance on the chalkboard.

    "Choose two containers and tell me which one feels heavier."

- Ask your child to hold the containers.

- Write the letters on the chalkboard balance.

    "What do you think is going to happen when we put the containers on the balance?"

    "Let's put them on the balance."

    "What happened?"

    "We will circle the side with the heavier container."

    "Which side will we circle?"

- Repeat several times.

    "Now you will have a chance to compare these containers."

- Use **Master 1-27** to record the results.

CLASS PRACTICE

"Let's practice the doubles facts."

"I will hold up a card for one of the doubles facts."

"Say the problem and the answer when I hold up the card."

- Hold up the large fact cards one at a time. Repeat several times with the cards in random order.

WRITTEN PRACTICE

• Complete **Worksheet 27A** with your child.

• Complete **Worksheet 27B** with your child later in the day.

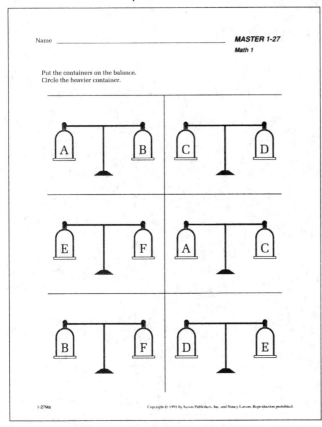

Name _____ **MASTER 1-27**
                                    Math 1

Put the containers on the balance.
Circle the heavier container.

1-27Ma   Copyright © 1991 by Saxon Publishers, Inc. and Nancy Larson. Reproduction prohibited.

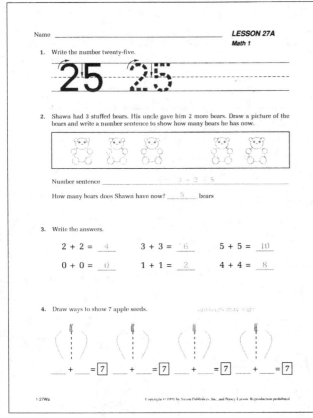

Name _____ **LESSON 27A**
                                    Math 1

1. Write the number twenty-five.

   25 25

2. Shawn had 3 stuffed bears. His uncle gave him 2 more bears. Draw a picture of the bears and write a number sentence to show how many bears he has now.

   Number sentence _____ 3 + 2 = 5

   How many bears does Shawn have now? ___5___ bears

3. Write the answers.

   $2 + 2 =$ __4__ $3 + 3 =$ __6__ $5 + 5 =$ __10__

   $0 + 0 =$ __0__ $1 + 1 =$ __2__ $4 + 4 =$ __8__

4. Draw ways to show 7 apple seeds.   answers may vary

   ___ + ___ = 7   ___ + ___ = 7   ___ + ___ = 7   ___ + ___ = 7

1-27Wa   Copyright © 1991 by Saxon Publishers, Inc. and Nancy Larson. Reproduction prohibited.

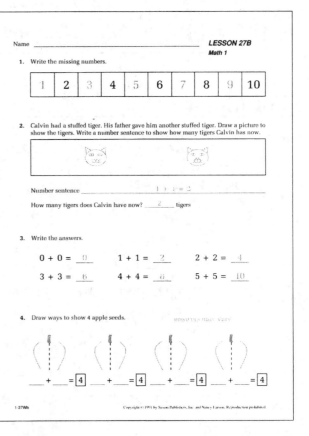

Name _____ **LESSON 27B**
                                    Math 1

1. Write the missing numbers.

   | 1 | 2 | 3 | 4 | 5 | 6 | 7 | 8 | 9 | 10 |

2. Calvin had a stuffed tiger. His father gave him another stuffed tiger. Draw a picture to show the tigers. Write a number sentence to show how many tigers Calvin has now.

   Number sentence _____ 1 + 1 = 2

   How many tigers does Calvin have now? ___2___ tigers

3. Write the answers.

   $0 + 0 =$ __0__ $1 + 1 =$ __2__ $2 + 2 =$ __4__

   $3 + 3 =$ __6__ $4 + 4 =$ __8__ $5 + 5 =$ __10__

4. Draw ways to show 4 apple seeds.   answers may vary

   ___ + ___ = 4   ___ + ___ = 4   ___ + ___ = 4   ___ + ___ = 4

1-27Wb   Copyright © 1991 by Saxon Publishers, Inc. and Nancy Larson. Reproduction prohibited.

esson 28

writing the number 26
addition facts—doubles to 18

---

lesson preparation

materials

ten 3" × 5" cards

large fact cards (from Lesson 23)

tower of 10 red linking cubes

tower of 10 blue linking cubes

addition fact cards — tan

bag or storage container for fact cards

the night before

- Use the 3" × 5" cards to make a set of large fact cards for the doubles facts with the answer on the back of each card. Write them in the following way:

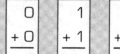

0	1	2	3	4	5	6	7	8	9
+ 0	+ 1	+ 2	+ 3	+ 4	+ 5	+ 6	+ 7	+ 8	+ 9

- Separate the tan addition fact cards.

THE MEETING

- Refer to Lesson 20, if necessary, for specific questions in The Meeting. New questions are included in the script.

calendar

- Ask your child to identify the following:

    year

    month

    shapes on the calendar

    today's shape

    shape pattern for the month

- Ask your child to write the date on the calendar.

- Ask your child to do the following:

    identify today's day of the week

read the days of the week

• Write the full date on the meeting strip as your child spells the name of the month and names the digits for the date and year.

weather graph

• Ask your child to report and graph the weather.

• Ask questions about the graph.

counting

• Count from 1 to 100 using the hundred number chart.

• Add another number to the number line.

• Count to check.

clock

• Your child sets the morning/afternoon clock.

right/left

• Continue to practice left and right.

• Other information on the meeting strip is not used today.

THE LESSON

Writing the Number 26

"The last number we practiced writing was the number 25."

"What number do you think we will learn how to write today?"

• Write the number 26 on the chalkboard.

"What digits do you see in the number 26?"

"How would you tell someone how to write the number 26?"

"Which digit is on the left?"

"Which digit is on the right?"

Addition Facts — Doubles to 18

"Each day we have been practicing our fact cards."

"Let's read our problems and say the answers."

• Hold up the fact cards (from Lesson 23) as your child reads the problems and says the answers.

"Some people write their fact cards another way."

"Today you will learn another way to write number facts."

"You will also learn some more doubles facts."

"We usually write one plus one equals two like this."

- Write "1 + 1 = 2" on the chalkboard.

"This is called a number sentence."

"We read it from left to right like a word sentence."

- Write the following on the chalkboard:

$$\begin{array}{r} 1 \\ + 1 \\ \hline 2 \end{array}$$

"When we write our number facts this way, we will call them problems."

"We read our problems from top to bottom."

"We read this problem as 'one plus one equals two.' "

- Point to each number as you read.

"We write the addition symbol in front of the second number."

"The line in a problem is like the equal sign."

- Put the horizontal fact cards in a row on the table.

- Hold up the following fact card:

"Find the fact card on the table that matches this number fact."

- Repeat with the remaining fact cards.

"Now we will use linking cubes to make towers for these fact cards and some new fact cards."

- Give your child red and blue towers of 10 cubes each.

"How many cubes are in the red tower?"

"How many cubes are in the blue tower?"

- Hold up the following fact card:

"Make a tower for the first number using red cubes."

"Make a tower for the second number using the same color."

"Stand the towers next to each other on the table."

"What do you notice about the towers?"   *they are the same height*

"Put the towers together."

"Lay the towers down on the table to make a train."

"How many cubes do you think are in the train?"

"Let's count to check."

"Take apart your train."

- Repeat with 3 + 3 and 5 + 5.
- Hold up the following fact card:

"Make a tower for the first number using red cubes."

"Try to make a tower for the second number using the same color."

"What happened?"

"Use some of the blue cubes to finish the second tower."

"Stand the towers next to each other on the table."

"Are they the same height?"

"Put the towers together."

"Lay the towers down on the table to make a train."

"How many cubes do you think are in the train?"

"Let's count to check."

- Count the cubes with your child.

"How many red cubes do you have?"

"How many blue cubes do you have?"

"Take apart your train."

- Repeat with the following fact cards: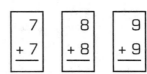

"All of these facts are called the doubles because both of the numbers are the same."

"Today I will give you your own set of fact cards."

- Give your child the tan addition fact cards.

"Write the answer for each fact on the back of the card."

"Use your cubes to help you find the answers."

- Check the answers on the cards.
- Give your child a plastic bag or container in which to store his/her cards.

WRITTEN PRACTICE

- Complete **Worksheet 28A** with your child.
- Complete **Worksheet 28B** with your child later in the day.

1. Write the number twenty-six.

$$26 \quad 26$$

2. Steven put 5 glasses on the table. Then he put 1 more glass on the table. Draw a picture and write a number sentence to show the glasses on the table.

Number sentence _____ 5 + 1 = 6

How many glasses are on the table now? _____ glasses

3. Point to the one that is different. Put an X on it.

4. Point to the square at the top left.
   Color it red.
   Point to the square at the bottom left.
   Color it blue.
   Point to the square at the top right.
   Color it green.
   Point to the square at the bottom right.
   Color it yellow.

R	G
B	Y

1-28Wa

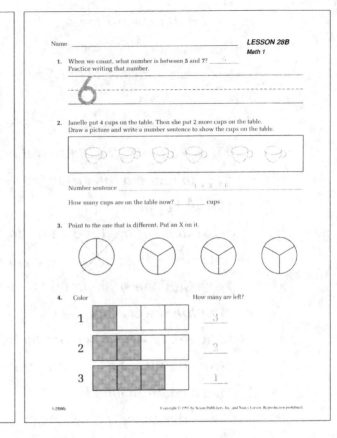

1. When we count, what number is between 5 and 7? _____
   Practice writing that number.

$$6$$

2. Janelle put 4 cups on the table. Then she put 2 more cups on the table. Draw a picture and write a number sentence to show the cups on the table.

Number sentence _____ 4 + 2 = 6

How many cups are on the table now? _____ cups

3. Point to the one that is different. Put an X on it.

4. Color   How many are left?

   1 ▢▢▢▢   3

   2 ▢▢▢▢   2

   3 ▢▢▢▢   1

1-28Wb

esson 29

writing the number 27
addition facts—doubles

---

lesson preparation

materials

large fact cards

tan individual fact cards

Fact Sheet AA 1.0

THE MEETING

calendar

- Ask your child to identify the following:

    year

    month

    shapes on the calendar

    today's shape

    shape pattern for the month

- Ask your child to write the date on the calendar.

- Ask your child to do the following:

    identify today's day of the week

    read the days of the week

- Write the full date on the meeting strip as your child spells the name of the month and names the digits for the date and year.

weather graph

- Ask your child to report and graph the weather.

- Ask questions about the graph.

counting

- Count from 1 to 100 using the hundred number chart.

- Add another number to the number line.

- Count to check.

clock

- Your child sets the morning/afternoon clock.

right/left

- Continue to practice left and right.

- Other information on the meeting strip is not used today.

THE LESSON

Writing the Number 27

"The last number we practiced writing was the number 26."

"What number do you think we will learn how to write today?"

- Write the number 27 on the chalkboard.

"What digits do you see in the number 27?"

"How would you tell someone how to write the number 27?"

"Which digit is on the left?"

"Which digit is on the right?"

Addition Facts—Doubles

"Today you will learn how to use your fact cards to practice the doubles facts."

"You will also learn how to write the answers for the doubles facts on a fact sheet."

"I will show you how you will use the fact cards to practice the doubles facts."

- Demonstrate, using your large (vertical) fact cards.

"First I will make sure all my fact cards are face up."

"Next I will make sure they are mixed up."

"Now I will put them in a pile and hold them in one hand."

"I will look at the first fact card and say the number fact softly to myself."

"Now I will check to make sure I am right."

- Show your child how to turn the card over to check the answer.

"I was right, so now I will put that fact card on the table in front of me."

- Repeat with 2 or 3 more fact cards.

"Now I will show you what to do if you say the wrong answer."

- Answer the next fact card incorrectly.

"I checked the answer and saw that it was wrong."

"I will put this fact card under the pile of fact cards in my hand so that I can practice it again."

• Continue practicing the fact cards, making 1–2 mistakes. After you make each mistake, ask your child what you should do with that fact card.

"Now you will have a chance to practice the doubles facts using your own fact cards."

"Take your fact cards out of the bag."

"Put your fact cards in a pile in your hand."

"Make sure that they are face up."

"Say each fact and the answer quietly to yourself."

"Check the answer on the back of the card."

"What will you do if you say the correct answer?"

"What will you do if you make a mistake?"

• Allow time for your child to practice the fact cards independently.

"Put your fact cards back in the bag."

"Now you will have a chance to see how many number facts you remember."

• Give your child **Fact Sheet AA 1.0**.

"Write your name at the top of the paper using a pencil."

"What number facts do you see?"

"Try to answer these problems using your mind only."

"Say each problem and the answer to yourself."

"Write the answer below the problem."

"Try to answer as many problems as you can."

• Allow time for your child to complete the fact sheet.

"Now you will correct your paper using a crayon."

"I will read the problems and the answers for each row."

"If the answer is correct, put a dot next to the answer."

"If the answer is wrong, circle the problem and write the correct answer."

• Demonstrate on the chalkboard.

• Read the problems and the answers slowly.

WRITTEN PRACTICE

- • Complete **Worksheet 29A** with your child.
- • Complete **Worksheet 29B** with your child later in the day.

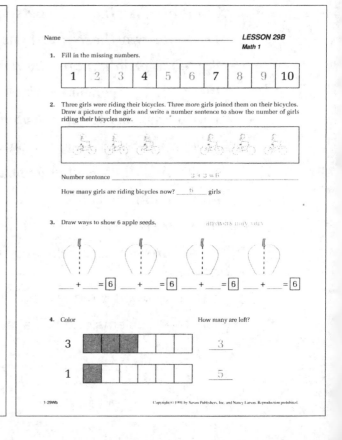

Name _____ **LESSON 29A**
Math 1

1. Write the number twenty-seven.

   27 27

2. Four boys were playing soccer. Four more boys joined them to play soccer.
   Draw a picture of the boys and write a number sentence to show the number of boys playing soccer now.

   Number sentence _____ 4 + 4 = 8

   How many boys are playing soccer now? ___8___ boys

3. Draw ways to show 8 apple seeds.   answers may vary

   ___ + ___ = 8   ___ + ___ = 8   ___ + ___ = 8   ___ + ___ = 8

4. Color   How many are left?

   4   4

   1   7

1-29Wa   Copyright © 1991 by Saxon Publishers, Inc. and Nancy Larson. Reproduction prohibited.

Name _____ **LESSON 29B**
Math 1

1. Fill in the missing numbers.

   | 1 | 2 | 3 | 4 | 5 | 6 | 7 | 8 | 9 | 10 |

2. Three girls were riding their bicycles. Three more girls joined them on their bicycles.
   Draw a picture of the girls and write a number sentence to show the number of girls riding their bicycles now.

   Number sentence _____ 3 + 3 = 6

   How many girls are riding bicycles now? ___6___ girls

3. Draw ways to show 6 apple seeds.   answers may vary

   ___ + ___ = 6   ___ + ___ = 6   ___ + ___ = 6   ___ + ___ = 6

4. Color   How many are left?

   3   3

   1   5

1-29Wb   Copyright © 1991 by Saxon Publishers, Inc. and Nancy Larson. Reproduction prohibited.

Lesson 30

assessment

lesson preparation

materials

Written Assessment #5

Oral Assessment #3

linking cubes (6 red, 9 blue, 4 yellow)

individual number cards

THE MEETING

calendar

- Ask your child to identify the following:

    year

    month

    shapes on the calendar

    today's shape

    shape pattern for the month

- Ask your child to write the date on the calendar.

- Ask your child to do the following:

    identify today's day of the week

    read the days of the week

- Write the full date on the meeting strip as your child spells the name of the month and names the digits for the date and year.

weather graph

- Ask your child to report and graph the weather.

- Ask questions about the graph.

counting

- Count from 1 to 100 using the hundred number chart.

- Add another number to the number line.

- Count to check.

- Use an orange crayon to color the square for 30.

clock

- Your child sets the morning/afternoon clock.

right/left

- Continue to practice left and right.

- Other information on the meeting strip is not used today.

ASSESSMENT

- All of the questions on the assessment are based on concepts and skills presented at least five lessons ago. If your child is having difficulty with a specific concept, reteach the concept the following day.

Written Assessment

"Today, I would like to see what you remember from what we have been practicing."

- Give your child **Written Assessment #5.**

"Write your name at the top of the paper."

"I will read the directions for each problem."

- Read the directions for each problem. Allow time for your child to complete each problem before continuing.

- Correct the paper, noting your child's mistakes on the **Individual Recording Form.** Review the errors with your child.

Oral Assessment

- Record your child's responses to the oral interview on the interview sheet.

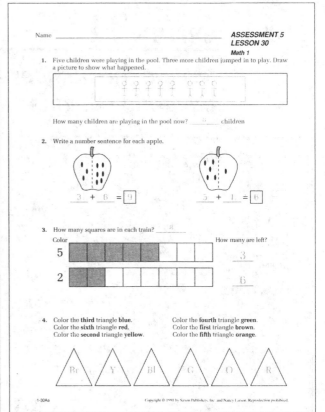

Teacher _____

Date _____

Materials:
Linking cubes (6 red, 9 blue, 4 yellow)
number cards 0-9
pencil

•Make towers of red, yellow, and blue cubes.
A. *"Which tower has the most?"*
B. *"Which tower has the fewest?"*
C. *"Find the number card that matches each tower."*
D. *"Put your towers and number cards in order from smallest to largest."*

•Position a pencil vertically on the desk.
"Put a blue cube on the right side of the pencil."
"Put a yellow cube on the left side of the pencil."

Students

A. most	B. fewest	C. matches cards	D. orders	right	left

1-30La

Name _____

1. Five children were playing in the pool. Three more children jumped in to play. Draw a picture to show what happened.

How many children are playing in the pool now? _____ children

2. Write a number sentence for each apple.

$3 + 6 = \boxed{9}$ $5 + 1 = \boxed{6}$

3. How many squares are in each train? _____ 8
    Color   How many are left?

    5   3

    2   6

4. Color the **third** triangle **blue**.   Color the **fourth** triangle **green**.
    Color the **sixth** triangle **red**.   Color the **first** triangle **brown**.
    Color the **second** triangle **yellow**.   Color the **fifth** triangle **orange**.

Br   Y   Bl   G   O   R

1-30Aa

Lesson 31

writing the number 28
covering designs with pattern blocks

---

lesson preparation

materials

Master 1-31

pattern blocks

large fact cards

Fact Sheet AA 1.0

in the morning

• Write the following number pattern on the meeting strip:

> 3, 4, 5, ___, ___, ___

Answer: 3, 4, 5, 6, 7, 8

• Put **7 pennies** in the coin cup.

THE MEETING

calendar

• Ask your child to identify the following:

  year

  month

  shapes on the calendar

  today's shape

  shape pattern for the month

• Ask your child to write the date on the calendar.

• Ask your child to do the following:

  identify today's day of the week

  read the days of the week

"Today you will write the date on the meeting strip."

• Assist your child as he/she writes the full date on the meeting strip.

weather graph

- Ask your child to report and graph the weather.
- Ask questions about the graph.

counting

- Count from 1 to 100 using the hundred number chart.
- Add another number to the number line.
- Count to check.

number pattern

"Each day we have been counting from 1 to 100."

- Point to the number pattern on the meeting strip.

"I started a counting pattern and left out some numbers."

"Let's read the numbers we see."

"What numbers do you think are missing?"

"Why?"

"I will write one number on each line."

- Fill in the missing numbers.

"Let's read our number pattern together."

clock

- Your child sets the morning/afternoon clock.

coin cup

"Each day there will be some coins in a coin cup for you to count."

- Show your child the coins.

"What do we call these coins?"   *pennies*

"Let's count the money together as you slide and count the pennies."

- Count the money with your child.

"How much money was in the coin cup?"

"We write seven cents like this."

- Write "7¢" in the coin cup box on the meeting strip.

"When we write 'cents,' we use a cents symbol."

right/left

- Continue to practice left and right.

THE LESSON

Writing the Number 28

"The last number we practiced writing was the number 27."

"What number do you think we will learn how to write today?"

• Write the number 28 on the chalkboard.

"What digits do you see in the number 28?"

"How would you tell someone how to write the number 28?"

"Which digit is on the left?"

"Which digit is on the right?"

Covering Designs with Pattern Blocks

"We used pattern blocks before."

"What did we do with them?"

"Today you will use pattern blocks to cover designs that someone else made."

"How many different pattern blocks are there?"   **6**

"We can name the pieces by their color or by their shape."

"What colors are the pattern blocks?"   **yellow, red, blue, green, orange, tan**

"Do you remember the names of any of the shapes?"

"The green block is a triangle, the orange block is a square, the yellow block is a hexagon, the red block is a trapezoid, and the blue and tan pieces are parallelograms." (The blue and tan pieces are also rhombuses; a rhombus is a parallelogram with equal sides.)

• Allow your child to refer to the pieces by color or shape. Whenever possible, refer to them by shape or by shape and color to help your child learn the shape names.

• Give your child **Master 1-31**.

"We will use pattern blocks to cover these designs."

"When we cover something, what do we do to it?"   **cover it completely without pieces hanging over or areas left uncovered**

"When we cover a design, we make sure that each piece is inside the lines and that there are no spaces between the blocks in the design."

• Put a basket of pattern blocks on the table.

"Use the pattern blocks to cover the design at the top of this paper."

"After you cover the design, count the number of pattern blocks you used."

"Write that number on the line next to the design."

• Allow time for your child to do this.

"How many pattern blocks did you use?"

"Now cover the design in the middle of the paper."

"After you cover the design, count the number of pattern blocks you used."

"Write that number on the line next to the design."

• Allow time for your child to do this.

"How many pattern blocks did you use?"

• Repeat with the design at the bottom of the paper.

"Which design was the easiest to cover?"

"Why?"

"Which design was the hardest to cover?"

"Why?"

"It is time to put away the pattern blocks now."

"Carefully put your pattern blocks in the container."

• Optional: Ask your child to cover the designs using different pieces.

CLASS PRACTICE

"Let's review the number facts called the doubles."

"I will hold up one of my fact cards."

"Read each problem and say the answer."

• Hold up the large (vertical) fact cards one at a time in order.

• Repeat several times with the cards in random order.

"Now you will have a chance to write the answers for these number facts."

• Give your child **Fact Sheet AA 1.0**.

"Write your name at the top of the paper."

"What number facts do you see?"

"Try to answer these problems using your mind only."

"Say each problem and answer to yourself."

"Write the answer below the problem."

"Try to answer as many problems as you can."

• Allow time for your child to complete the fact sheet.

"Now you will correct your paper using a crayon."

"I will read the problems and the answers for each row."

"If the answer is correct, put a dot next to the answer."

"If the answer is wrong, circle the problem and write the correct answer."

- Demonstrate on the chalkboard, if necessary.
- Read the problems and the answers slowly.

WRITTEN PRACTICE

- Complete **Worksheet 31A** with your child.
- Complete **Worksheet 31B** with your child later in the day.

Name _____ **MASTER 1-31**
Math 1

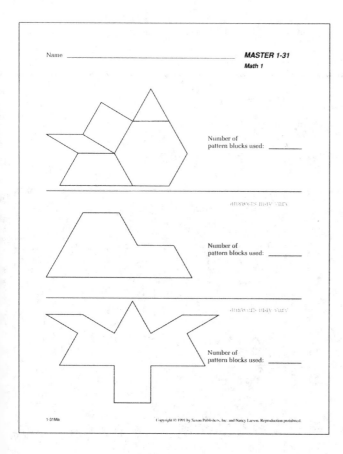

Number of
pattern blocks used: _____

Number of
pattern blocks used: _____

Number of
pattern blocks used: _____

1-31Ma   Copyright © 1991 by Saxon Publishers, Inc. and Nancy Larson. Reproduction prohibited.

Name _____ **LESSON 31A**
Math 1

1. Write the number twenty-eight.

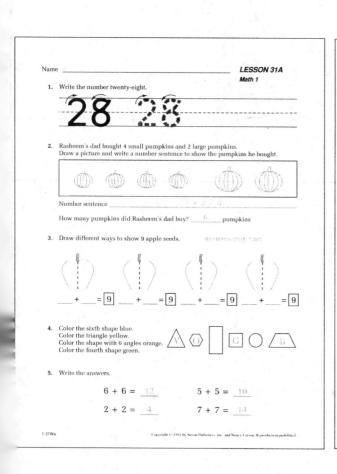

2. Rasheem's dad bought 4 small pumpkins and 2 large pumpkins.
   Draw a picture and write a number sentence to show the pumpkins he bought.

   Number sentence _____

   How many pumpkins did Rasheem's dad buy? _____ pumpkins

3. Draw different ways to show 9 apple seeds.

   ___ + ___ = 9   ___ + ___ = 9   ___ + ___ = 9   ___ + ___ = 9

4. Color the sixth shape blue.
   Color the triangle yellow.
   Color the shape with 6 angles orange.
   Color the fourth shape green.

5. Write the answers.

   6 + 6 = ____   5 + 5 = ____

   2 + 2 = ____   7 + 7 = ____

1-31Wa   Copyright © 1991 by Saxon Publishers, Inc. and Nancy Larson. Reproduction prohibited.

Name _____ **LESSON 31B**
Math 1

1. Write the next 3 numbers.

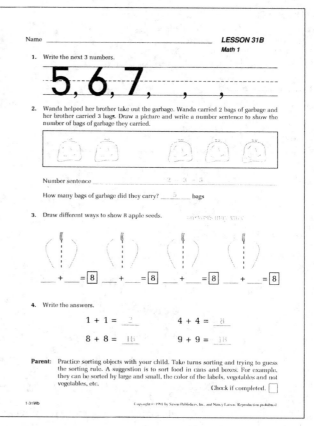

2. Wanda helped her brother take out the garbage. Wanda carried 2 bags of garbage and
   her brother carried 3 bags. Draw a picture and write a number sentence to show the
   number of bags of garbage they carried.

   Number sentence _____

   How many bags of garbage did they carry? _____ bags

3. Draw different ways to show 8 apple seeds.

   ___ + ___ = 8   ___ + ___ = 8   ___ + ___ = 8   ___ + ___ = 8

4. Write the answers.

   1 + 1 = ____   4 + 4 = ____

   8 + 8 = ____   9 + 9 = ____

Parent: Practice sorting objects with your child. Take turns sorting and trying to guess
the sorting rule. A suggestion is to sort food in cans and boxes. For example,
they can be sorted by large and small, the color of the labels, vegetables and not
vegetables, etc.

Check if completed. ☐

1-31Wb   Copyright © 1991 by Saxon Publishers, Inc. and Nancy Larson. Reproduction prohibited.

Lesson 32

writing the number 29
ordering numbers to 20
adding one to a number

lesson preparation ————————————————————————

materials

Master 1-32

envelope or plastic bag for storing the number cards

2 towers of 10 linking cubes

large fact cards

Fact Sheet AA 1.1

the night before

• Cut apart the number cards on Master 1-32 and put them in an envelope.

in the morning

• Write the following number pattern on the meeting strip:

> 7, 8, 9, __, __, __

Answer: 7, 8, 9, 10, 11, 12

• Put **9 pennies** in the coin cup.

THE MEETING

calendar

• Ask your child to identify the following:

year

month

shapes on the calendar

today's shape

shape pattern for the month

• Ask your child to write the date on the calendar.

• Ask your child to do the following:

identify today's day of the week

read the days of the week

"Today you will write the date on the meeting strip."

• Assist your child as he/she writes the full date on the meeting strip.

weather graph

• Ask your child to report and graph the weather.

• Ask questions about the graph.

counting

• Count from 1 to 100 using the hundred number chart.

• Add another number to the number line.

• Count to check.

number pattern

• Point to the number pattern on the meeting strip.

"I started a counting pattern and left out some numbers."

"Let's read the numbers we see."

"What numbers do you think are missing?"

"Why?"

• Fill in the missing numbers.

"Let's read our number pattern together."

clock

• Your child sets the morning/afternoon clock.

coin cup

"Each day there will be some coins in the coin cup for you to count."

• Show your child the coins.

"What do we call these coins?"

"Slide and count these pennies."

• Count the money with your child.

"How much money was in the coin cup?"

"How do we write nine cents?"

• Ask your child to write "9¢" on the meeting strip.

right/left

• Continue to practice left and right.

THE LESSON

Writing the Number 29

"The last number we practiced writing was the number 28."

"What number do you think we will learn how to write today?"

• Write the number 29 on the chalkboard.

"What digits do you see in the number 29?"

"How would you tell someone how to write the number 29?"

"Which digit is on the left?"

"Which digit is on the right?"

Ordering Numbers to 20
Adding One to a Number

"Today you will learn how to order numbers to 20."

"You will also learn how to add one to a number."

• Give your child the number cards from **Master 1-32**.

"Put these number cards in order from smallest to largest."

• Allow time for your child to do this.

"Point to the smallest number."

"Point to the largest number."

"Point to the number that comes after seven."

"What number is it?"

• Repeat with 11, 5, 17, and 4.

• Give your child 2 towers of 10 linking cubes.

"Make a train of six linking cubes."

"Hold up the number card that matches this number of cubes."

"Put the card down."

"Add one more cube to the train."

"Hold up the number card that matches the number of cubes in the train now."

"How many is six cubes and one more?"   **7**

"Make a train of four linking cubes."

"Hold up the number card that matches this number of cubes."

"Put the card down."

"Add one more cube to the train."

"Hold up the number card that matches the number of cubes in the train now."

- Repeat with 8, 11, 15, and 2 cubes.

  "What happened when we added one linking cube to a train?"

  "How did you know what number card to hold up?"

  "Now we will practice adding one without using the cubes."

  "Hold up the number card for nine."

  "Now hold up the number card for one more than nine."

  "Put the number cards back in order."

- Repeat with 5, 7, 16, and 19.

  "Put your number cards in the envelope."

- Save the envelope of number cards.

  "Snap together your cubes to make two trains with ten cars in each train."

CLASS PRACTICE

"Let's review the number facts called the doubles."

"I will hold up one of my fact cards."

"Read each problem and say the answer."

- Hold up the large (vertical) fact cards one at a time in order.

- Repeat several times with the cards in random order.

  "Now you will have a chance to write the answers for these number facts."

- Give your child **Fact Sheet AA 1.1**.

  "Write your name at the top of the paper."

  "What number facts do you see on this paper?"

  "Say each problem and answer to yourself."

  "Write the answer below the problem."

- Allow time for your child to complete the fact sheet.

  "Now you will correct your paper using a crayon."

- Read the problems and the answers slowly.

WRITTEN PRACTICE

- Complete **Worksheet 32A** with your child.

- Complete **Worksheet 32B** with your child later in the day.

MASTER 1-32
Math 1

6	13	20
5	12	19
4	11	18
3	10	17
2	9	16
1	8	15
0	7	14

1-32Ma   Copyright © 1991 by Saxon Publishers, Inc. and Nancy Larson. Reproduction prohibited.

Name _____

LESSON 32A
Math 1

1. Write the number twenty-nine.

29   29

2. Sabrina had 7 stickers in her sticker book. Mrs. Ahern gave her 3 more stickers for her sticker book.
Draw a picture and write a number sentence to show the stickers Sabrina has now.

Number sentence _____ 7 + 3 = 10

How many stickers does Sabrina have now? ___10___ stickers

3. Finish the pattern.

○ △ ○ △ ○ △ ○

4. How many squares are in each train? ___10___

Color   How many are left?

| 1 | ■ | | | | | | | | | | 9
| 9 | ■ ■ ■ ■ ■ ■ ■ ■ ■ | | 1

5. Put an X in the top left-hand corner of this paper.

6. Write the answers.

$3 + 3 = 6$ $9 + 9 = 18$ $7 + 7 = 14$

1-32Wa   Copyright © 1991 by Saxon Publishers, Inc. and Nancy Larson. Reproduction prohibited.

Name _____

LESSON 32B
Math 1

1. Write the next 3 numbers.

7, 8, 9, ___, ___, ___

2. Ross has 5 purple jelly beans and 6 green jelly beans. Draw a picture and write a number sentence to show the number of jelly beans Ross has.

Number sentence _____ 5 + 6 = 11

How many jelly beans does Ross have? ___11___ jelly beans

3. Continue the pattern.

□ ○ □ ○ □ ○ □

4. How many squares are in each train? ___10___

Color   How many are left?

| 4 | ■ ■ ■ ■ | | | | | | | 6
| 6 | ■ ■ ■ ■ ■ ■ | | | | 4

5. Put an O in the bottom right-hand corner of this paper.

6. Write the answers.

$2 + 2 = 4$ $6 + 6 = 12$ $8 + 8 = 16$

                                                                    O

1-32Wb   Copyright © 1991 by Saxon Publishers, Inc. and Nancy Larson. Reproduction prohibited.

Lesson 33

writing the number 30
writing number sentences for some, some went away stories

---

lesson preparation

materials

10 stuffed animals, dolls, action figures, or other toys

7 crayons

large fact cards

Fact Sheet AA 1.1

in the morning

• Write the following number pattern on the meeting strip:

> 12, 13, 14, ___, ___, ___

Answer: 12, 13, 14, 15, 16, 17

• Put **10 pennies** in the coin cup.

THE MEETING

calendar

- • Ask your child to identify the following:

    year

    month

    shapes on the calendar

    today's shape

    shape pattern for the month

- • Ask your child to write the date on the calendar.

- • Ask your child to do the following:

    identify today's day of the week

    read the days of the week

- • Ask your child to write the full date on the meeting strip.

---

weather graph

- Ask your child to report and graph the weather.
- Ask questions about the graph.

counting

- Count from 1 to 100 using the hundred number chart.
- Add another number to the number line.
- Count to check.

number pattern

- Point to the number pattern on the meeting strip.

   "Let's read the numbers in our pattern."

   "What numbers do you think are missing?"

   "Why?"

- Fill in the missing numbers.

   "Let's read our number pattern together."

clock

- Your child sets the morning/afternoon clock.

coin cup

   "Let's find how much money is in the coin cup."

   "What do we call these coins?" pennies

   "Slide and count these pennies."

   "How much money was in the coin cup?"

   "How do we write ten cents?"

- Ask your child to write "10¢" on the meeting strip.

right/left

- Continue to practice left and right.

THE LESSON

Writing the Number 30

   "The last number we practiced writing was the number 29."

   "What number do you think we will learn how to write today?"

- Write the number 30 on the chalkboard.

"What digits do you see in the number 30?"

"How would you tell someone how to write the number 30?"

"Which digit is on the left?"

"Which digit is on the right?"

Writing Number Sentences for Some, Some Went Away Stories

"We have been acting out and drawing pictures for some, some went away stories."

"Today you will learn how to write number sentences for some, some went away stories."

"Let's act out a story together."

"We will use (toys) to do this."

- Use stuffed animals, dolls, or action figures.

"We will pretend that our _____ are going to ride in the car."

- Designate an area to be the car.

"Four _____ got in the car."

- Ask your child to put 4 _____ in the pretend car.

"Then one _____ got out of the car."

- Ask your child to remove 1 _____ from the pretend car.

"Let's count to see how many _____ are in the car now."

- Point to each _____ as your child counts.

"Now we will draw a picture to show what happened in this story."

- Quickly draw a sketch of a car.

"What happened first in this story?"

- Draw 4 _____ in the car.

"I will write the number four under the car to show that four _____ got in the car first."

"What happened next?"

- Put an X on 1 _____ in the car.

"I will write the minus sign and the number one under the car to show that one _____ got out of the car."

"What did we do next?" counted how many _____ were still in the car

"Let's count the number of _____ in the car now."

- Point to each _____ in the picture as your child counts.

"I will write the equal sign and the number three under the car to show that now there are three _____ in the car."

"Let's read our number sentence together." **four minus one equals three**

"Let's act out another car story together."

"Six _____ got in the car."

• Ask your child to put 6 _____ in the pretend car.

"Then three _____ got out of the car."

• Ask your child to remove 3 _____ from the pretend car.

"Let's count to see how many _____ are in the car now."

• Point to each _____ as your child counts.

"Let's draw a picture to show what happened in this story."

• Quickly draw a sketch of a car.

"What happened first in this story?"

• Draw 6 _____ in the car.

"I will write the number six under the car to show that six _____ got in the car first."

"What happened next?"

• Put an X on 3 _____ in the car.

"I will write the minus sign and the number three under the car to show that three _____ got out of the car."

"What did we do next?" **counted how many _____ were still in the car**

"Let's count the number of _____ in the car now."

• Point to each _____ in the picture as your child counts.

"I will write the equal sign and the number three under the car to show that now there are three _____ in the car."

"Let's read our number sentence together." **six minus three equals three**

"Let's act out a different story together."

• Pick up 7 crayons.

"I have seven crayons."

"Now I will give you two of my crayons."

• Hand your child 2 crayons.

"How many crayons do I have left?"

"Let's count to see how many crayons I have now."

• Hold up 1 crayon at a time as your child counts.

"Now we will draw a picture to show what happened in this story."

"What happened first in this story?"   **you had 7 crayons**

• Draw 7 crayons.

"I will write the number seven under the crayons to show how many crayons I have."

"What happened next?"   **you gave two crayons to me**

"How can I show that I gave away two crayons?"   **put an X on two crayons**

"I will write a minus sign and the number two under the crayons to show that I gave away two crayons."

"What did we do next?"   **counted the crayons that were left**

"Let's count the number of crayons I have left."

• Point to each crayon in the picture as your child counts.

"I will write the equal sign and the number five under the crayons to show that now I have five crayons."

"Let's read our number sentence together."   **seven minus two equals five**

"The answer to our story is five crayons."

"We will always use a minus sign when we write number sentences for some, some went away stories."

CLASS PRACTICE

"Let's review the number facts called the doubles."

"I will hold up one of my fact cards."

"Read each problem and the answer."

• Hold up the large (vertical) fact cards one at a time in order.

• Repeat several times with the cards in random order.

• Give your child **Fact Sheet AA 1.1**.

"Write your name at the top of the paper."

"What number facts do you see on this paper?"

"Say the problem and answer to yourself."

"Write the answer below the problem."

• Allow time for your child to complete the fact sheet.

"Now you will correct your paper using a crayon."

• Read the problems and the answers slowly.

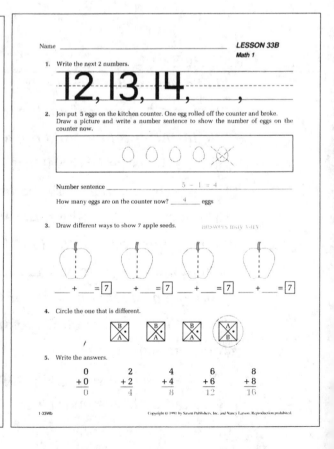

WRITTEN PRACTICE

- Complete **Worksheet 33A** with your child.
- Complete **Worksheet 33B** with your child later in the day.

Name _____   **LESSON 33A**
   Math 1

1. Write the number thirty.

$$30 \quad 30$$

2. Jill put 4 crayons on her desk. One crayon rolled off the desk.
Draw a picture and write a number sentence to show the number of crayons on the desk now.

Number sentence _____ 4 − 1 = 3 _____

How many crayons are on the desk now? _____ crayons

3. Draw different ways to show 10 apple seeds.   answers may vary

___ + ___ = 10   ___ + ___ = 10   ___ + ___ = 10   ___ + ___ = 10

4. Circle the one that is different.

5. Write the answers.

1	3	5	7	9
+1	+3	+5	+7	+9
2	6	10	14	18

1-33Wa   Copyright © 1991 by Saxon Publishers, Inc. and Nancy Larson. Reproduction prohibited.

Name _____   **LESSON 33B**
   Math 1

1. Write the next 2 numbers.

$$12, 13, 14, \quad , \quad$$

2. Jon put 5 eggs on the kitchen counter. One egg rolled off the counter and broke.
Draw a picture and write a number sentence to show the number of eggs on the counter now.

Number sentence _____ 5 − 1 = 4 _____

How many eggs are on the counter now? _____4_____ eggs

3. Draw different ways to show 7 apple seeds.   answers may vary

___ + ___ = 7   ___ + ___ = 7   ___ + ___ = 7   ___ + ___ = 7

4. Circle the one that is different.

5. Write the answers.

0	2	4	6	8
+0	+2	+4	+6	+8
0	4	8	12	16

1-33Wb   Copyright © 1991 by Saxon Publishers, Inc. and Nancy Larson. Reproduction prohibited.

Lesson 34

writing the number 31
counting backward from 10 to 1
adding one to a number

---

lesson preparation

materials

hundred number chart
cup of 20 pennies
large fact cards
Fact Sheet AA 1.1

in the morning

• Write the following number pattern on the meeting strip:

> 15, 16, 17, ___, ___, ___

Answer: 15, 16, 17, 18, 19, 20

• Put **12 pennies** in the coin cup.

THE MEETING

calendar

• Ask your child to identify the following:

   year

   month

   shapes on the calendar

   today's shape

   shape pattern for the month

• Ask your child to write the date on the calendar.

• Ask your child to do the following:

   identify today's day of the week

   read the days of the week

• Ask your child to write the full date on the meeting strip.

weather graph

- Ask your child to report and graph the weather.
- Ask questions about the graph.

counting

- Count from 1 to 100 using the hundred number chart.
- Add another number to the number line.
- Count to check.

number pattern

- Point to the number pattern on the meeting strip.

  "Let's read the numbers in our pattern."

  "What numbers do you think are missing?"

  "Why?"

- Fill in the missing numbers.

  "Let's read our number pattern together."

clock

- Your child sets the morning/afternoon clock.

coin cup

  "Let's find how much money is in the coin cup."

  "What do we call these coins?"   pennies

  "Slide and count these pennies."

  "How much money was in the coin cup?"

  "How do we write twelve cents?"

- Ask your child to write "12¢" on the meeting strip.

right/left

- Continue to practice left and right.

THE LESSON

Writing the Number 31

  "The last number we practiced writing was the number 30."

  "What number do you think we will learn how to write today?"

- Write the number 31 on the chalkboard.

"What digits do you see in the number 31?"

"How would you tell someone how to write the number 31?"

"Which digit is on the left?"

"Which digit is on the right?"

Counting Backward From 10 to 1
Adding One to a Number

"Today you will learn how to count backward from 10 to 1."

"You will also learn how to add one to a number."

• Give your child a hundred number chart and a cup of 20 pennies.

"Begin at the number one and put one penny on each number on your number chart."

• Allow time for your child to do this.

"Count your pennies."

• Allow time for your child to do this.

"How many pennies did you count?"

"What number do you think is under the last penny?"

"Lift up the last penny to check."

"Leave the top row of pennies on your number chart."

"Take all the extra pennies off your chart."

"How many pennies are on the chart now?"

"Let's count to check."

"Take the last penny in the row off the chart."

"What number do you see?" **10**

"How many pennies are on the chart now?" **9**

"Let's count to check."

"Take the last penny in the row off the chart."

"What number do you see?" **9**

"How many pennies are on the chart now?" **8**

• Repeat until all the pennies have been removed from the chart.

"When we take pennies off the chart, we are counting backward."

"Let's start at ten and count backward to one."

"Point to each number as we say it."

• Count backward with your child.

"Each morning we will practice counting backward from 10 by 1's."

"Put five pennies on the number chart."

"Begin at one."

- Write the number 5 on the chalkboard.

"Add one more penny to your number chart."

- Write "+ 1" next to the 5 on the chalkboard.

"How many pennies are on the number chart now?"

"Lift up the last penny to check."

"We can write a number sentence to show what we did like this."

- Write "5 + 1 = 6" on the chalkboard.

- Point to each symbol as you say the following:

"Five pennies plus one penny equals six pennies."

"Take the pennies off the chart."

- Repeat with 8 pennies, 12 pennies, and 3 pennies.

- Write the number 6 on the chalkboard.

"Put this number of pennies on the number chart."

- Write "+ 1" after the 6.

"Now put one more penny on the number chart."

"How many pennies are on the number chart now?"

"Lift up the last penny to check."

- Record "= 7" on the chalkboard.

"Take the pennies off the chart."

- Write "4 + 1" on the chalkboard.

"What will we do first?"   *put 4 pennies on the chart*

"What will we do next?"   *put 1 more penny on the chart*

"How many pennies are on the number chart now?"

- Record "= 5" on the chalkboard.

"Take the pennies off the chart."

- Repeat with 11 + 1 and 5 + 1.

"How many pennies would we have if we put 23 + 1 pennies on the chart?"

"How do you know?"

- Repeat with 17 + 1 and 25 + 1.

"Put the pennies in the cup."

CLASS PRACTICE

"Let's review the number facts called the doubles."

"Read each problem and say the answer."

• Hold up the large (vertical) fact cards one at a time in order.

• Repeat several times with the cards in random order.

• Give your child **Fact Sheet AA 1.1.**

"Write your name at the top of the paper."

"What number facts do you see on this paper?"

"Say each problem and answer to yourself."

"Write the answer below the problem."

• Allow time for your child to complete the fact sheet.

"Now you will correct your paper using a crayon."

• Read the problems and the answers slowly.

WRITTEN PRACTICE

• Complete **Worksheet 34A** with your child.

• Complete **Worksheet 34B** with your child later in the day.

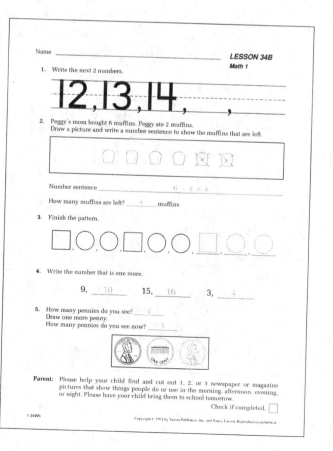

esson 35

writing the number 32
identifying morning, afternoon, evening, and night

lesson preparation

materials

Written Assessment #6

4 pieces of paper

4 magazine pictures

magazines

glue

scissors

large fact cards

the night before

• Cut 4 pictures from magazines. Each picture should show something people do in the morning, afternoon, evening, or night. Try to select one picture for each time of day.

• Tape the 4 pieces of paper together. Label each quarter in the following way:

Morning	Afternoon
Night	Evening

in the morning

• Write the following number pattern on the meeting strip:

22, 23, 24, __, __, __

Answer: *22, 23, 24, 25, 26, 27*

• Put **8 pennies** in the coin cup.

THE MEETING

calendar

- Ask your child to identify the following:

  year

  month

  shapes on the calendar

  today's shape

  shape pattern for the month

- Ask your child to write the date on the calendar.

- Ask your child to do the following:

  identify today's day of the week

  read the days of the week

- Ask your child to write the full date on the meeting strip.

weather graph

- Ask your child to report and graph the weather.

- Ask questions about the graph.

counting

- Count from 1 to 100 using the hundred number chart.

- Add another number to the number line.

- Count to check.

number pattern

- Point to the number pattern on the meeting strip.

  "Let's read the numbers in our pattern."

  "What numbers do you think are missing?"

  "Why?"

- Fill in the missing numbers.

  "Let's read our number pattern together."

clock

- Your child sets the morning/afternoon clock.

coin cup

  "Let's find how much money is in the coin cup."

  "Slide and count the pennies."

"How much money was in the coin cup?"

"How do we write eight cents?"

- Ask your child to write "8¢" on the meeting strip.

right/left

- Continue to practice left and right.

ASSESSMENT

- All of the questions on the assessment are based on concepts and skills presented at least five lessons ago. If your child is having difficulty with a specific concept, reteach the concept the following day.

Written Assessment

"Today, I would like to see what you remember from what we have been practicing."

- Give your child **Written Assessment #6**.

"Write your name at the top of the paper."

"I will read the directions for each problem."

- Read the directions for each problem. Allow time for your child to complete each problem before continuing.

- Correct the paper, noting your child's mistakes on the **Individual Recording Form**. Review the errors with your child.

THE LESSON

Writing the Number 32

"The last number we practiced writing was the number 31."

"What number do you think we will learn how to write today?"

- Write the number 32 on the chalkboard.

"What digits do you see in the number 32?"

"How would you tell someone how to write the number 32?"

"Which digit is on the left?"

"Which digit is on the right?"

Identifying Morning, Afternoon, Evening, and Night

"Each day we have been setting our morning and afternoon clock."

"What do we call the time of day when we wake up?"

"What do we call the time of day after lunch?"

"Today you will learn about two other names we use for times of the day."

"The time of day when many people eat dinner (supper) is called evening."

"Evening is the time of day when the sun is setting."

"Most people say that it is night when it is dark outside."

"Today we are going to make a collage of pictures to show morning, afternoon, evening, and night."

• Point to each section of the chart as you say the following:

"In this space we will put morning pictures."

"What happens in the morning?"

"In this space we will put afternoon pictures."

"What happens in the afternoon?"

"In this space we will put evening pictures."

"What happens in the evening?"

"In this space we will put night pictures."

"What happens at night?"

• Hold up one of your magazine pictures.

"What is happening in this picture?"

"When is this happening?"

"Is it morning, afternoon, evening, or night?"

"How do you know?"

"Where do you think this picture belongs on our chart?"

• Ask your child to place the picture in the correct location on the chart.

• Repeat with your three other magazine pictures.

"Now you will have a chance to find more pictures for our chart."

"We will use these magazines to find pictures."

• Show your child the magazines that can be cut.

"When you find a picture in a magazine that shows something that is done in the morning, afternoon, evening, or night, cut it out."

"When you finish, we will glue your pictures on this chart to make a collage."

• When your child has cut out 15–20 pictures, continue.

• Hold up one of your child's pictures.

"What is happening in this picture?"

"When is this happening?"

"Is it morning, afternoon, evening, or night?"

"How do you know?"

"Where do you think this picture belongs on our chart?"

- Ask your child to place the picture in the correct location on the chart.

"Now we will glue the pictures on the chart to make a collage."

- Assist your child with gluing.

CLASS PRACTICE

"Let's review the number facts called the doubles."

"I will hold up one of my fact cards."

"Read each problem and say the answer."

- Hold up the large (vertical) fact cards one at a time in order.
- Repeat several times with the cards in random order.

WRITTEN PRACTICE

- Complete **Worksheet 35A** with your child.
- Complete **Worksheet 35B** with your child later in the day.

Name _____

1. Robert counted three red cars and four blue cars in the parking lot. Draw a picture and write a number sentence to show the cars Robert saw.

Number sentence _____ 3 + 4 = 7 _____

How many cars did Robert see? ____7____ cars

2. How many apples are in each row?

   2

   7

   5

   Find the row with the most. Using a red crayon, color the apples in the row with the most. Find the row with the fewest. Using a green crayon, color the apples in the row with the fewest.

3. Draw ways to show 5 apple seeds.   answers may vary

   ____ + ____ = 5   ____ + ____ = 5   ____ + ____ = 5

4. Point to the circle at the bottom left. Color it yellow.
   Point to the circle at the top right. Color it red.
   Point to the circle at the top left. Color it green.
   Point to the circle at the bottom right. Color it blue.

   G   R

   Y   B

1-35Aa

Name _____

1. Write the number thirty-two.

   32 32

2. Six girls and four boys rode their bicycles to school.
   Draw a picture and write a number sentence to show the number of children who rode their bicycles to school.

   Number sentence _____ 6 + 4 = 10 _____

   How many children rode their bicycles to school? ____10____ children

3. How many squares are in each train? ____5____

   Color   How many are left?

   5   0

   4   1

   3   2

   2   3

1-35Wa

Name _____

1. Write the next 2 numbers.

   22,23,24,____,____,

2. One child sat in the front seat of the car and three children sat in the back seat.
   Draw a picture and write a number sentence to show the number of children in the car.

   Number sentence _____ 1 + 3 = 4 _____

   How many children are in the car? ____4____ children

3. Draw pictures of yourself.

Morning	Afternoon
answers may vary	
Night	Evening

1-35Wb

esson 36

writing the number 33
measuring length and width using nonstandard units

---

lesson preparation ─────────────────────

materials

tag board circle and brass fastener for morning/afternoon/evening/night clock

100 linking cubes in towers of 10 each

individual fact cards

Fact Sheet A 1.2

the night before

• Make a tag board clock that looks like the following:

in the morning

• Write the following number pattern on the meeting strip:

> 25, 26, 27, __, __, __

Answer: 25, 26, 27, 28, 29, 30

• Put **14 pennies** in the coin cup.

THE MEETING

calendar

• Ask your child to identify the following:

year

month

shapes on the calendar

today's shape

shape pattern for the month

- Ask your child to write the date on the calendar.
- Ask your child to do the following:

    identify today's day of the week

    read the days of the week

- Ask your child to write the full date on the meeting strip.

weather graph

- Ask your child to report and graph the weather.
- Ask questions about the graph.

counting

- Count from 1 to 100 using the hundred number chart.
- Count backward from 10 to 1.
- Add another number to the number line.
- Count to check.

number pattern

- Point to the number pattern on the meeting strip.

    "Let's read the numbers in our pattern."

    "What numbers do you think are missing?"

    "Why?"

- Fill in the missing numbers.

    "Let's read our number pattern together."

clock

"Yesterday we made a collage to show different parts of the day."

"What do we do in the morning?"

"What do we do in the afternoon?"

"What do we do in the evening?"

"What do we do at night?"

"Today we have a new clock."

"Each morning you will set the clock to show that it is morning."

"When will you change the clock to show that it is afternoon?"

"When will you change the clock to show that it is evening?"

"When will you change it to show that it is night?"

• Remind your child to set the clock during the day.

coin cup

• Ask your child to slide and count the pennies in the coin cup.

• Ask your child to write the money amount on the meeting strip.

right/left

• Continue to practice left and right.

THE LESSON

Writing the Number 33

"The last number we practiced writing was the number 32."

"What number do you think we will learn how to write today?"

• Write the number 33 on the chalkboard.

"What digits do you see in the number 33?"

"How would you tell someone how to write the number 33?"

"Which digit is on the left?"

"Which digit is on the right?"

Measuring Length and Width Using Nonstandard Units

"Sometimes we need to tell someone how long or wide something is."

"This is called measuring."

"Today you will learn how to use linking cubes to measure this table."

"Our unit of measure will be a linking cube."

• Give your child 10 towers of ten linking cubes each.

"Let's measure the length of the table."

• Indicate the longer dimension.

"Make a train that goes from the left side of this table to the right side of this table."

"Put the first cube at the left edge of the table."

"When we measure, we always start at the edge."

• Demonstrate.

• Allow time for your child to measure the length of the table using the cubes.

"How many cubes did you use to measure the length of the table?"

- Count with your child, if necessary.

    "Our table is _____ cubes long."

    "Now we will measure the width of our table."

- Indicate the shorter dimension.

    "Make a train that goes from the top edge of the table to the edge in front of you (bottom of the table)."

- Point to the appropriate edges.

    "Put the first cube at the top edge of the table."

    "When we measure, we always start at the edge."

- Demonstrate, if necessary.

- Allow time for your child to measure the width of the table.

    "How many cubes did you use to measure the width of the table?"

    "Our table is _____ cubes wide."

- Optional: Ask your child to use the linking cubes to measure the length and width of another table in your home.

CLASS PRACTICE

"Let's review the number facts called the doubles."

"Take out your bag of fact cards."

"Put your fact cards in order on the table."

"Read each fact card to yourself."

"Turn over the card and check the answer."

"Now mix up your fact cards and read each card to yourself."

"Turn over the card and check the answer."

"Put your fact cards back in the bag."

- Give your child **Fact Sheet A 1.2**.

    "Write your name at the top of the paper."

    "What number facts do you see on this paper?"

    "Say each problem and answer to yourself."

    "Write the answer below the problem."

- Allow time for your child to complete the fact sheet.

    "Now you will correct your paper using a crayon."

- Read the problems and the answers slowly.

WRITTEN PRACTICE

- Complete **Worksheet 36A** with your child.
- Complete **Worksheet 36B** with your child later in the day.

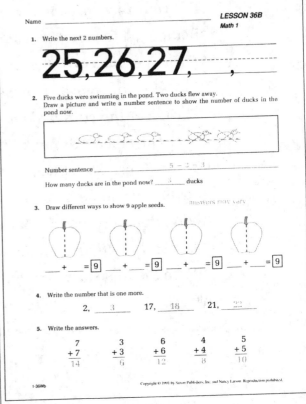

Name _____ **LESSON 36A**
Math 1

1. Write the number thirty-three.

33 33

2. Eight children were in line. Three returned to their seats.
Draw a picture and write a number sentence to show the number of children in line now.

Number sentence _____ 8 − 3 = 5 _____

How many children are in line now? ___5___ children

3. Draw different ways to show 10 apple seeds.   answers may vary

___ + ___ = 10   ___ + ___ = 10   ___ + ___ = 10   ___ + ___ = 10

4. Write the number that is one more.

4, __5__   13, __14__   22, __23__

5. Write the answers.

0	9	1	8	2
+0	+9	+1	+8	+2
0	18	2	16	4

1-36Wa

Copyright © 1991 by Saxon Publishers, Inc. and Nancy Larson. Reproduction prohibited.

Name _____ **LESSON 36B**
Math 1

1. Write the next 2 numbers.

25, 26, 27, ___ , ___

2. Five ducks were swimming in the pond. Two ducks flew away.
Draw a picture and write a number sentence to show the number of ducks in the pond now.

Number sentence _____ 5 − 2 = 3 _____

How many ducks are in the pond now? ___3___ ducks

3. Draw different ways to show 9 apple seeds.   answers may vary

___ + ___ = 9   ___ + ___ = 9   ___ + ___ = 9   ___ + ___ = 9

4. Write the number that is one more.

2, __3__   17, __18__   21, __22__

5. Write the answers.

7	3	6	4	5
+7	+3	+6	+4	+5
14	6	12	8	10

1-36Wb

Copyright © 1991 by Saxon Publishers, Inc. and Nancy Larson. Reproduction prohibited.

esson 37

writing the number 34
adding one to a number

---

lesson preparation

materials

twenty-seven 3" × 5" cards

tower of 10 linking cubes

addition fact cards — peach

Fact Sheet AA 2.0

the night before

• Use twenty-seven 3" × 5" cards. Make a set of large cards for the adding 1 facts with the answer on the back of each card.

| 0 + 1 | | 2 + 1 | | 3 + 1 | | 4 + 1 |

| 5 + 1 | | 6 + 1 | | 7 + 1 | | 8 + 1 | | 9 + 1 |

| 0
+ 1 | 2
+ 1 | 3
+ 1 | 4
+ 1 | 5
+ 1 | 6
+ 1 | 7
+ 1 | 8
+ 1 | 9
+ 1 |

| 1
+ 0 | 1
+ 2 | 1
+ 3 | 1
+ 4 | 1
+ 5 | 1
+ 6 | 1
+ 7 | 1
+ 8 | 1
+ 9 |

• Separate the peach addition fact cards.

in the morning

• Write the following number pattern on the meeting strip:

$$19, 20, 21, \_\_, \_\_, \_\_$$

Answer: 19, 20, 21, 22, 23, 24

• Put **16 pennies** in the coin cup.

THE MEETING

calendar

- Ask your child to identify the following:

    year

    month

    shapes on the calendar

    today's shape

    shape pattern for the month

- Ask your child to write the date on the calendar.

- Ask your child to do the following:

    identify today's day of the week

    read the days of the week

- Ask your child to write the full date on the meeting strip.

weather graph

- Ask your child to report and graph the weather.

- Ask questions about the graph.

counting

- Count from 1 to 100 using the hundred number chart.

- Count backward from 10 to 1.

- Add another number to the number line.

- Count to check.

number pattern

- Point to the number pattern on the meeting strip.

    "Let's read the numbers in our pattern."

    "What numbers do you think are missing?"

    "Why?"

- Fill in the missing numbers.

    "Let's read our number pattern together."

clock

- Remind your child to set the morning/afternoon/evening/night clock.

coin cup

- Ask your child to slide and count the pennies in the coin cup.

• Ask your child to write the money amount on the meeting strip.

right/left

• Ask your child to do several quick physical motions to practice right and left. An activity such as "Simon Says" can be used.

THE LESSON

Writing the Number 34

"The last number we practiced writing was the number 33."

"What number do you think we will learn how to write today?"

• Write the number 34 on the chalkboard.

"What digits do you see in the number 34?"

"How would you tell someone how to write the number 34?"

"Which digit is on the left?"

"Which digit is on the right?"

Adding One to a Number

• Give your child a tower of ten linking cubes.

"Each day we have been practicing our number facts called the doubles."

"Today you will learn the answers for number facts called the adding one number facts."

• Hold up the following fact card: $\boxed{2 + 1}$

• Cover "+ 1" with your hand.

"Show me this number of cubes."

• Uncover and point to "+ 1."

"What does this tell us to do?"   **add one more cube**

"Add one cube to the tower."

"How many linking cubes do you have in your tower now?"

• Repeat with 4–6 different fact cards.

"We can write our cards another way."

• Hold up the following fact card:

• Cover "+ 1" with your hand.

"Show me this number of cubes."

• Point to "+ 1."

"*What does this tell us to do?*"   **add one more cube**

"*Add one cube to the tower.*"

"*How many linking cubes do you have in your tower now?*"

• Hold up the horizontal and vertical cards for 4 + 1.

"*These cards say the same thing.*"

• Repeat with 6 + 1, 9 + 1, and 3 + 1.

"*Today I will give you your own set of adding one fact cards.*"

• Give your child the peach addition fact cards.

"*Use your linking cubes to find each answer.*"

"*Write the answer on the back of each card.*"

• When your child finishes, continue.

"*Snap your cubes together to make a tower of ten cubes.*"

"*Put your cards in a pile.*"

"*Now read each problem to yourself.*"

"*See if you can remember the answer.*"

"*Turn over the card to check the answer.*"

"*Practice saying the answers to yourself.*"

• Allow time for your child to practice independently.

"*Now let's try to match the cards with the same answer.*"

"*Put together the cards that have the same answer.*"

• Allow time for your child to do this.

"*Did you find two cards with the same answer?*"

"*What cards are they?*"

"*Let's look at these cards.*"

"*What is the same about these cards?*"

"*What is different about these cards?*"

• Repeat until your child sees the pattern.

"*We will call these our adding one number facts.*"

"*Why do you think we will call them that?*"

"*How can we remember these answers?*"

"*When we are adding one, we look for the larger number and add one more.*"

"*Adding one is just like counting up.*"

"*Each day, we will practice our adding one facts and our doubles facts.*"

"*Put your fact cards in your fact card bag.*"

CLASS PRACTICE

- • Give your child **Fact Sheet AA 2.0**.

  "Write your name at the top of the paper."

  "What number facts do you see on this paper?"

  "Adding one is like counting up."

  "Say each problem and answer to yourself."

  "Write the answer below the problem."

- • Allow time for your child to complete the fact sheet.

  "Now you will correct your paper using a crayon."

- • Read the problems and the answers slowly.

WRITTEN PRACTICE

- • Complete **Worksheet 37A** with your child.
- • Complete **Worksheet 37B** with your child later in the day.

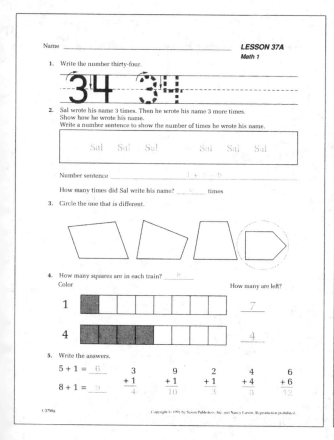

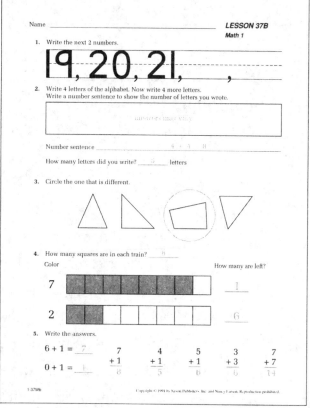

Lesson 38

writing the number 35
sorting items and creating a graph

---

lesson preparation ————————————————————

materials

Master 1-38

basket of pattern blocks

large fact cards (doubles)

Fact Sheet A 1.2

the night before

• Remove the yellow pattern blocks.

in the morning

• Write the following number pattern on the meeting strip:

> 10, 9, 8, __, __, __

Answer: 10, 9, 8, 7, 6, 5

• Put **11 pennies** in the coin cup.

THE MEETING

calendar

• Ask your child to identify the following:

  year

  month

  shapes on the calendar

  today's shape

  shape pattern for the month

• Ask your child to write the date on the calendar.

• Ask your child to do the following:

  identify today's day of the week

  read the days of the week

• Ask your child to write the full date on the meeting strip.

weather graph

- Ask your child to report and graph the weather.
- Ask questions about the graph.

counting

- Count from 1 to 100 using the hundred number chart.
- Count backward from 10 to 1.
- Add another number to the number line.
- Count to check.

number pattern

- Point to the number pattern on the meeting strip.

  "Let's read the numbers in our pattern."

  "What numbers do you think are missing?"

  "Why?"

- Fill in the missing numbers.

  "Let's read our number pattern together."

clock

- Remind your child to set the morning/afternoon/evening/night clock.

coin cup

- Ask your child to slide and count the pennies in the coin cup.
- Ask your child to write the money amount on the meeting strip.

right/left

- Ask your child to do several quick physical motions to practice right and left. An activity such as "Simon Says" can be used.

THE LESSON

Writing the Number 35

"The last number we practiced writing was the number 34."

"What number do you think we will learn how to write today?"

- Write the number 35 on the chalkboard.

"What digits do you see in the number 35?"

"How would you tell someone how to write the number 35?"

"Which digit is on the left?"

"Which digit is on the right?"

Sorting Items and Creating a Graph

"Today we will use pattern blocks for our math lesson."

"We have used pattern blocks before."

"What did we do with them?"

"Today you will learn how to sort and graph pattern blocks."

"What is a graph?"

"What graphs have we made?"

"Let's make a pattern block graph together."

"First I will reach into the basket of pattern blocks and take a double handful."

• Put the double handful of pattern blocks on the table.

"Now we will sort these pattern blocks."

"How will we do this?"

• Ask your child to sort the pattern blocks.

"What is the sorting rule?"　**color and/or shape**

"Now we will stack the pattern blocks."

"We will put all the blocks that are the same color in a stack."

• Ask your child to stack the pattern blocks.

"Which stack is the tallest?"

"Which stack is the shortest?"

"Are any stacks the same height?"

"Now we will use these pattern blocks to make a graph."

"We will graph the pattern blocks just like we graph the weather each day."

"How do you think we will do this?"

• Use a copy of **Master 1-38.**

"What do we have to remember when we make a graph?"　**start at one end of the graph, do not skip spaces, one block per box**

"Graph one stack of pattern blocks."

• Take turns graphing the other stacks of pattern blocks.

"How many green triangles are on the graph?"

"Which color pattern block do we have the most of?"

"Which color pattern block do we have the least of?"

"Is there the same number of any color?"

"Now you will have a chance to make your own graph."

"Do you think your graph will look just like this one?"

"Why not?"

- Slide the pattern blocks back into the basket.

"Carefully take a double handful of pattern blocks."

"Sort and stack your pattern blocks."

- Allow time for your child to do this.

"Which stack is the tallest?"

"Which stack is the shortest?"

"Are any stacks the same height?"

"Graph your pattern blocks."

"How many _____ are on your graph?"

"Which color pattern block do you have the most of?"

"Which color pattern block do you have the least of?"

"Is there the same number of any color?"

"Slide your pattern blocks into the basket."

- Save **Master 1-38**.

CLASS PRACTICE

"Let's review the number facts called the doubles."

"I will hold up one of my fact cards."

"Read each problem and say the answer."

- Hold up the large (vertical) fact cards one at a time in random order.

- Repeat several times.

- Give your child **Fact Sheet A 1.2**.

"What number facts do you see on this paper?"

"Say each problem and answer to yourself."

"Write the answer below the problem."

- Allow time for your child to complete the fact sheet.

"Now you will correct your paper using a crayon."

- Read the problems and the answers slowly.

WRITTEN PRACTICE

- Complete **Worksheet 38A** with your child.
- Complete **Worksheet 38B** with your child later in the day.

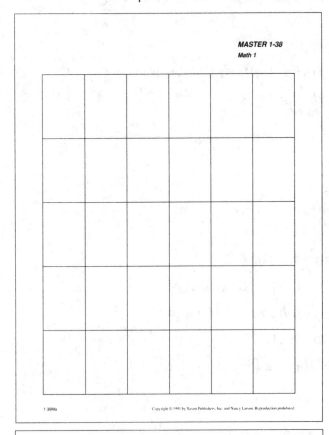

MASTER 1-38
Math 1

1-38Ma

Copyright © 1991 by Saxon Publishers, Inc. and Nancy Larson. Reproduction prohibited.

Name _____ **LESSON 38A**
Math 1

1. Write the number thirty-five.

35 35

2. Renee had 10 pennies. She lost 3 pennies.
Draw a picture and write a number sentence to show the number of pennies she has now.

(P)(P)(P)(P)(P)(P)(P)(X)(X)(X)

Number sentence _____ 10 − 3 = 7

How many pennies does she have now? ___7___ pennies

3. Color the tallest tower red.
Color the second tallest tower yellow.
Color the shortest tower blue.

R   B   Y

4. Write the answers.

3	1	1	2	7	6	8	3
+1	+5	+8	+1	+1	+6	+8	+3
4	6	9	3	8	12	16	6

1-38Wa

Copyright © 1991 by Saxon Publishers, Inc. and Nancy Larson. Reproduction prohibited.

Name _____ **LESSON 38B**
Math 1

1. Write the next 3 numbers as you count backwards.

10, 9, 8, ___, ___, ___

2. Peter had 9 pennies. He gave 6 to Tara.
Draw a picture and write a number sentence to show the number of pennies Peter has now.

(P)(P)(P)(X)(X)(X)(X)(X)(X)

Number sentence _____ 9 − 6 = 3

How many pennies does Peter have now? ___3___ pennies

3. Color the longest train red.
Color the second longest train yellow.
Color the shortest train blue.

B

R

Y

4. Write the answers.

4	1	1	5	1	5	4	9
+1	+9	+1	+1	+6	+5	+4	+9
5	10	2	6	7	10	8	18

1-38Wb

Copyright © 1991 by Saxon Publishers, Inc. and Nancy Larson. Reproduction prohibited.

Lesson 39

writing the number 36
weighing objects using nonstandard units

---

lesson preparation

materials

balance
100 pennies
eraser, crayon, and pencil
8 small objects of different weights
Master 1-39
individual fact cards
Fact Sheet A 1.2

in the morning

• Write the following number pattern on the meeting strip:

| 6, 5, 4, __, __, __ |

Answer: 6, 5, 4, 3, 2, 1

• Put **17 pennies** in the coin cup.

THE MEETING

calendar

• Ask your child to identify the following:

    year

    month

    shapes on the calendar

    today's shape

    shape pattern for the month

• Ask your child to write the date on the calendar.

• Ask your child to do the following:

    identify today's day of the week

    read the days of the week

- Ask your child to write the full date on the meeting strip.

weather graph

- Ask your child to report and graph the weather.
- Ask questions about the graph.

counting

- Count from 1 to 100 using the hundred number chart.
- Count backward from 10 to 1.
- Add another number to the number line.
- Count to check.

number pattern

"Let's read the numbers in our pattern."

"What numbers do you think are missing?"

"Why?"

- Fill in the missing numbers.

"Let's read our number pattern together."

clock

- Remind your child to set the morning/afternoon/evening/night clock.

coin cup

- Ask your child to slide and count the pennies in the coin cup.
- Ask your child to write the money amount on the meeting strip.

right/left

- Ask your child to do several quick physical motions to practice right and left. An activity such as "Simon Says" can be used.

THE LESSON

Writing the Number 36

"The last number we practiced writing was the number 35."

"What number do you think we will learn how to write today?"

- Write the number 36 on the chalkboard.

"What digits do you see in the number 36?"

"How would you tell someone how to write the number 36?"

"Which digit is on the left?"

"Which digit is on the right?"

Weighing Objects Using Nonstandard Units

"Today you will learn how to weigh objects using a balance."

"We will weigh a pencil, an eraser, and a crayon."

• Hold up the pencil, eraser, and crayon.

"Which do you think is the heaviest?"

"Which do you think is the lightest?"

"How can we check?" put them on the balance; the one that goes down is heavier

"Let's try that."

• Weigh two objects at a time until the heaviest object is determined.

• List the objects in order on the chalkboard:

_____   _____   _____

lightest   heaviest

• Remove the objects from the balance.

"What do you notice about the balance when there is nothing on it?" it is level

"When there is nothing on the balance, it is level."

"Now we will use pennies to try to find out how many pennies it will take to balance the (lightest object)."

"I will put the (object) on the left side."

"Now I will put pennies on the right side until the balance is as level as possible."

"Count the pennies as I put them on the right side."

"I will put on one penny at a time."

• Add pennies until the balance is level.

• Record "____ pennies" below the lightest object on the chalkboard.

"Now we will try to find out how many pennies it takes to balance the (middle object)."

"I will put the (object) on the left side."

"Now I will put pennies on the right side until the balance is as level as possible."

"How many pennies do you think it will take to make the balance level?"

• Ask your child to estimate and justify his/her estimate.

> *"Count the pennies as I put them on the right side."*

> *"I will put on one penny at a time."*

- Add pennies until the balance is level.

- Record "_____ pennies" below the middle object on the chalkboard.

> *"Now we will try to find out how many pennies it takes to balance the (heaviest object)."*

> *"I will put the (object) on the left side."*

> *"Now I will put pennies on the right side until the balance is as level as possible."*

> *"How many pennies do you think it will take to make the balance level?"*

- Ask your child to estimate and justify his/her estimate.

> *"Count the pennies as I put them on the right side."*

> *"I will put on one penny at a time."*

- Add pennies until the balance is level.

- Record "_____ pennies" below the heaviest object on the chalkboard.

> *"Which object needed the greatest number of pennies to balance it?"*

> *"Which object needed the fewest number of pennies to balance it?"*

> *"Now you will have a chance to weigh objects using pennies."*

- Allow your child to choose 4 objects to weigh from among 8 selected objects. Use **Master 1-39** to record the results.

CLASS PRACTICE

> *"Use your fact cards to practice the doubles and the adding one facts."*

- Allow time for your child to practice independently.

- Give your child **Fact Sheet A 1.2**.

> *"What number facts do you see on this paper?"*   *doubles*

> *"Say each problem and answer to yourself."*

> *"Write the answer below the problem."*

- Allow time for your child to complete the fact sheet.

> *"Now you will correct your paper using a crayon."*

- Read the problems and the answers slowly.

WRITTEN PRACTICE

- Complete **Worksheet 39A** with your child.
- Complete **Worksheet 39B** with your child later in the day.

Name _____ **MASTER 1-39**
Math 1

answers may vary

I weighed _____.
It weighed _____ pennies.

I weighed _____.
It weighed _____ pennies.

I weighed _____.
It weighed _____ pennies.

I weighed _____.
It weighed _____ pennies.

1-39Ma   Copyright © 1991 by Saxon Publishers, Inc. and Nancy Larson. Reproduction prohibited.

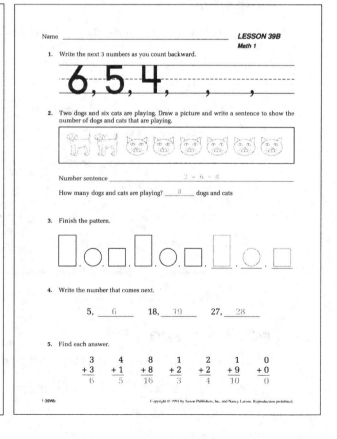

Name _____ **LESSON 39A**
Math 1

1. Write the number thirty-six.

36 36

2. Ted counted 3 cows standing and 2 cows lying down.
   Draw a picture and write a number sentence to show the number of cows Ted saw.

   Number sentence _____ $3 + 2 = 5$
   How many cows did Ted count? ___5___ cows

3. Finish the pattern.

   ○ △ □ ○ △ □ ○ △ □

4. Write the number that comes next.

   7, __8__   15, __16__   25, __26__

5. Find each answer.

4	5	6	1	9	1	1
+4	+1	+6	+7	+9	+8	+0
8	6	12	8	18	9	1

1-39Wa   Copyright © 1991 by Saxon Publishers, Inc. and Nancy Larson. Reproduction prohibited.

Name _____ **LESSON 39B**
Math 1

1. Write the next 3 numbers as you count backward.

   $6, 5, 4,$ ___, ___, ___

2. Two dogs and six cats are playing. Draw a picture and write a sentence to show the number of dogs and cats that are playing.

   Number sentence _____ $2 + 6 = 8$
   How many dogs and cats are playing? ___8___ dogs and cats

3. Finish the pattern.

   □ ○ □ □ ○ □ □ ○ □

4. Write the number that comes next.

   5, __6__   18, __19__   27, __28__

5. Find each answer.

3	4	8	1	2	1	0
+3	+1	+8	+2	+2	+9	+0
6	5	16	3	4	10	0

1-39Wb   Copyright © 1991 by Saxon Publishers, Inc. and Nancy Larson. Reproduction prohibited.

L esson 40

assessment

lesson preparation

materials

Written Assessment #7

Oral Assessment #4

9 yellow and 9 blue linking cubes

in the morning

• Write the following number pattern on the meeting strip:

22, 23, 24, __, __, __

Answer: 22, 23, 24, 25, 26, 27

• Put **20 pennies** in the coin cup.

THE MEETING

calendar

• Ask your child to identify the following:

> year
>
> month
>
> shapes on the calendar
>
> today's shape
>
> shape pattern for the month

• Ask your child to write the date on the calendar.

• Ask your child to do the following:

> identify today's day of the week
>
> read the days of the week

• Ask your child to write the full date on the meeting strip.

weather graph

• Ask your child to report and graph the weather.

• Ask questions about the graph.

counting

- Count from 1 to 100 using the hundred number chart.
- Count backward from 10 to 1.
- Add another number to the number line.
- Count to check.
- Use an orange crayon to color the square for 40.

number pattern

"Let's read the numbers in our pattern."

"What numbers do you think are missing?"

"Why?"

- Fill in the missing numbers.

"Let's read our number pattern together."

clock

- Remind your child to set the morning/afternoon/evening/night clock.

coin cup

- Ask your child to slide and count the pennies in the coin cup.
- Ask your child to write the money amount on the meeting strip.

right/left

- Ask your child to do several quick physical motions to practice right and left. An activity such as "Simon Says" can be used.

ASSESSMENT

- All of the questions on the assessment are based on concepts and skills presented at least five lessons ago. If your child is having difficulty with a specific concept, reteach the concept the following day.

Written Assessment

"Today, I would like to see what you remember from what we have been practicing."

- Give your child **Written Assessment #7**.

"Write your name at the top of the paper."

"I will read the directions for each problem."

- Read the directions for each problem. Allow time for your child to complete each problem before continuing.

• Correct the paper, noting your child's mistakes on the **Individual Recording Form.**

Oral Assessment

• Record your child's responses to the oral interview on the interview sheet.

Teacher _____

Date _____

MATH 1   LESSON 40
Oral Assessment # 4 Recording Form

Materials: 9 yellow linking cubes (unconnected) 9 blue linking cubes (unconnected) Students	•Show the child a group of 8 yellow cubes and a group of 9 blue cubes. *"Which group of cubes has more?"* *"How do you know?"* *"Show me, using the cubes."* •For the next child, use 9 yellow, 8 blue. •Alternate the color of the groups with more.	•Recheck children who had difficulty on previous oral assessments.

1-40La   Copyright © 1991 by Saxon Publishers, Inc. and Nancy Larson. Reproduction prohibited.

Name _____

ASSESSMENT 7
LESSON 40
Math 1

1. Clarence saw seven birds in a tree. Two birds flew away. Draw a picture and write a number sentence to show how many birds are in the tree now.

Number sentence _____ 7 - 2 - 5 _____

How many birds are in the tree now? _____5_____ birds

2. Write the next 3 numbers.

5, 6, 7, ____, ____

3. Circle the one that is different.

4. Continue the pattern.

△ ○ ○ △ ○ ○ △ ○ ○ △ ○

5. Write the answers.

4 + 4 = 8	3 + 3 = 6	8 + 8 = 16
2 + 2 = 4	9 + 9 = 18	5 + 5 = 10
7 + 7 = 14	1 + 1 = 2	6 + 6 = 12

1-40Aa   Copyright © 1991 by Saxon Publishers, Inc. and Nancy Larson. Reproduction prohibited.

Lesson 41

writing the number 37
addition facts—adding zero

---

lesson preparation

materials
9 pennies
addition fact cards — lavender
sixteen 3" × 5" cards
Fact Sheet AA 3.0

the night before
• Use the 3" × 5" cards to make a large set of fact cards for the adding zero facts written
in the following way:

$2 \atop +0$	$0 \atop +2$	$3 \atop +0$	$0 \atop +3$	$4 \atop +0$	$0 \atop +4$	$5 \atop +0$	$0 \atop +5$

$6 \atop +0$	$0 \atop +6$	$7 \atop +0$	$0 \atop +7$	$8 \atop +0$	$0 \atop +8$	$9 \atop +0$	$0 \atop +9$

• Separate the lavender addition fact cards.

in the morning
• Write the following number pattern on the meeting strip:

> 34, 35, 36, ___, ___, ___

Answer: 34, 35, 36, 37, 38, 39

• Put **13 pennies** in the coin cup.

THE MEETING

calendar
• Ask your child to identify the following:

year

month

shapes on the calendar

today's shape

shape pattern for the month

- Ask your child to write the date on the calendar.

- Ask your child to do the following:

    identify today's day of the week

    identify the days of the week

    read the days of the week

    "How many days of the week are there?"

    "Let's count them."

- Ask your child to write the full date on the meeting strip.

weather graph

- Ask your child to report and graph the weather.

- Ask questions about the graph.

counting

- Count from 1 to 100 using the hundred number chart.

- Count backward from 10 to 1.

- Add another number to the number line.

- Count to check.

number pattern

- Ask your child to identify and fill in the missing numbers.

    "Let's read our number pattern together."

clock

- Ask your child to set the morning/afternoon/evening/night clock.

coin cup

- Ask your child to slide and count the pennies in the coin cup.

- Ask your child to write the money amount on the meeting strip.

right/left

- Continue to practice left and right once a week. Practice more often, if necessary.

THE LESSON

Writing the Number 37

"The last number we practiced writing was the number 36."

"What number do you think we will learn how to write today?"

• Write the number 37 on the chalkboard.

"What digits do you see in the number 37?"

"How would you tell someone how to write the number 37?"

"Which digit is on the left?"

"Which digit is on the right?"

Addition Facts — Adding Zero

"What digit do we write to show that we have nothing?"

• Ask your child to write the number 0 on the chalkboard.

"Now I will tell you a some, some more story."

"I have zero pennies in one hand and five pennies in my other hand."

• Show one hand empty, the other with five pennies. Put your hands together and shake the coins.

"How many coins are in my hands now?"

"How will we write a number sentence to show what happened in this story?"

• Write the following on the chalkboard:

$$0 + 5 = 5$$

• Repeat with four pennies and zero pennies, then zero pennies and seven pennies.

• Write the following on the chalkboard:

0	1	2	3	4	5	6	7	8	9
+0	+0	+0	+0	+0	+0	+0	+0	+0	+0

0	0	0	0	0	0	0	0	0	0
+0	+1	+2	+3	+4	+5	+6	+7	+8	+9

"Choose one of these problems."

"How could we use the pennies to show this?"

• Repeat with several more problems.

"Let's fill in all of the other answers."

"Let's read the problems and say the answers together."

- Quickly fill in the answers as you and your child read the problems together.

  "What happens when we add zero to a number?"

  "Will this always happen?"

  "Why?"

  "Today I will give you another set of fact cards."

- Give your child the lavender addition fact cards.

  "Write the answer on the back of each card."

- When your child finishes, give the following directions:

  "Put your cards in a pile."

  "Now read each problem to yourself."

  "See if you can remember the answer."

  "Turn over the card to check the answer."

  "Practice saying the answers to yourself."

- Allow time for your child to practice using the fact cards independently.

  "Let's try to match the cards with the same answers."

  "Put together the cards that have the same answers."

- Allow time for your child to do this.

  "Did you find two cards with the same answer?"

  "What cards are they?"

  "Let's look at these cards."

  "What is the same about these cards?"

  "What is different about these cards?"

  "Did you find two other cards with the same answer?"

  "What cards are they?"

  "Let's look at these cards."

  "What is the same about these cards?"

  "What is different about these cards?"

- Repeat until your child sees the pattern.

  "We will call these our adding zero number facts."

  "Why do you think we call them that?"

  "How can we remember these answers?"

  "When we are adding zero, the answer is the same number."

  "We will add these cards to our other fact cards."

CLASS PRACTICE

- • Give your child **Fact Sheet AA 3.0.**

  "What number facts do you see?"

  "What strategy will you use to find the answers?"

- • Allow time for your child to complete the fact sheet.

- • Correct the fact sheet with your child.

WRITTEN PRACTICE

- • Complete **Worksheet 41A** with your child.

- • Complete **Worksheet 41B** with your child later in the day.

Name _____ **LESSON 41A**
                                Math 1
Date _____

Day of the Week _____

1. Write the number thirty-seven.

   37 37

2. Jessica had a bag of nine marbles. She dropped the bag and a marble rolled out. Draw a picture and write a number sentence to show how many marbles are in the bag now.

   Number sentence _____ 9 - 1 = 8 _____

   How many marbles are in the bag now? ___8___ marbles

3. Color the tallest tower red.
   Color the second tallest tower yellow.
   Color the shortest tower blue.
   Color the second shortest tower green.
   Color the third shortest tower orange.

4. Write the answers.

4	6	5	1	0	8	7	9
+1	+6	+0	+5	+3	+8	+1	+0
5	12	5	6	3	16	8	9

1-41Wa   Copyright © 1991 by Saxon Publishers, Inc. and Nancy Larson. Reproduction prohibited.

Name _____ **LESSON 41B**
                                Math 1

1. Write a number that is between 7 and 10 when you count by 1's.

   7   [8 or 9]   10

2. Frank collected 5 spiders. One spider escaped. Draw a picture and write a number sentence to show how many spiders he has now.

   Number sentence _____ 5 - 1 = 4 _____

   How many spiders does Frank have now? ___4___ spiders

3. Color the longest train red.
   Color the second longest train yellow.
   Color the third longest train orange.
   Color the shortest train blue.
   Color the second shortest train green.

   red
   orange
   blue
   yellow
   green

4. Write the answers.

7	7	4	1	0	4	2	8
+1	+7	+0	+3	+2	+4	+1	+0
8	14	4	4	2	8	3	8

1-41Wb   Copyright © 1991 by Saxon Publishers, Inc. and Nancy Larson. Reproduction prohibited.

Lesson 42

writing the number 38
covering a design in different ways

---

lesson preparation

materials
pattern blocks

Master 1-42

crayons

large fact cards (adding one facts)

Fact Sheet AA 2.0

in the morning
• Write the following number pattern on the meeting strip:

> 8, 7, 6, ___, ___, ___

Answer: *8, 7, 6, 5, 4, 3*

• Put **15 pennies** in the coin cup.

THE MEETING

calendar

• Ask your child to identify the following:

  year

  month

  shapes on the calendar

  today's shape

  shape pattern for the month

• Ask your child to write the date on the calendar.

• Ask your child to do the following:

  identify today's day of the week

  identify the days of the week

  read the days of the week

"How many days of the week are there?"

"Let's count them."

• Ask your child to write the full date on the meeting strip.

weather graph

• Ask your child to report and graph the weather.

• Ask questions about the graph.

counting

• Count from 1 to 100 using the hundred number chart.

• Count backward from 10 to 1.

• Add another number to the number line.

• Count to check.

number pattern

• Ask your child to identify and fill in the missing numbers.

"Let's read our number pattern together."

clock

• Ask your child to set the morning/afternoon/evening/night clock.

coin cup

• Ask your child to slide and count the pennies in the coin cup.

• Ask your child to write the money amount on the meeting strip.

right/left

• Continue to practice left and right once a week. Practice more often, if necessary.

THE LESSON

Writing the Number 38

"The last number we practiced writing was the number 37."

"What number do you think we will learn how to write today?"

• Write the number 38 on the chalkboard.

"What digits do you see in the number 38?"

"How would you tell someone how to write the number 38?"

"Which digit is on the left?"

"Which digit is on the right?"

Covering a Design in Different Ways

"Today you will learn how to use pattern blocks to cover a design in different ways."

- Give your child **Master 1-42**. Put a basket of pattern blocks on the table.

  "Point to the design in the top left-hand corner of your paper."

  "Cover this design using pattern blocks."

- Allow time for your child to cover the design.

  "I would like you to save a picture of how you covered the design."

  "You will do that by tracing the pieces you used and coloring them in."

  "Put the hand you don't write with on the pattern block pieces."

  "Carefully take away one piece."

  "Use your pencil to trace along the edge of the remaining pieces."

  "Now take away another piece."

  "Trace along the edge of the remaining pieces."

  "Continue until all the pieces are gone."

- Allow time for your child to do this.

  "Now color each piece to match the shape."

- Allow time for your child to do this.

  "Point to the design in the top right-hand corner of your paper."

  "Cover this design in a different way using pattern blocks."

  "Trace and color the pieces."

- Allow time for your child to do this.

  "Find two more different ways to cover the design."

  "Trace and color the pieces."

CLASS PRACTICE

"Let's review the adding one facts."

- Use the large (adding one) fact cards.
- Hold up one fact card at a time as your child says the problem and the answer.
- Repeat several times.
- Give your child **Fact Sheet AA 2.0**.

  "What number facts do you see?"

  "What strategy will you use to find the answers?"

- Allow time for your child to complete the fact sheet.
- Correct the fact sheet with your child.

WRITTEN PRACTICE

- Complete **Worksheet 42A** with your child.

- Complete **Worksheet 42B** with your child later in the day.

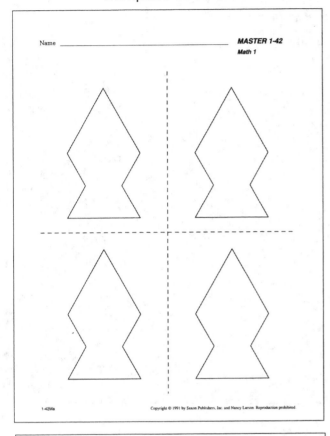

Name _____   *MASTER 1-42*
Math 1

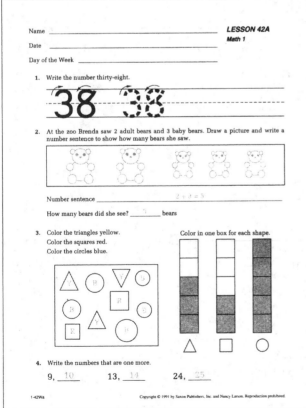

Name _____   *LESSON 42A*
Math 1

Date _____

Day of the Week _____

1. Write the number thirty-eight.

    38 *38*

2. At the zoo Brenda saw 2 adult bears and 3 baby bears. Draw a picture and write a number sentence to show how many bears she saw.

    Number sentence _____

    How many bears did she see? _____ bears

3. Color the triangles yellow.
    Color the squares red.
    Color the circles blue.

    Color in one box for each shape.

4. Write the numbers that are one more.

    9, _10_   13, _14_   24, _25_

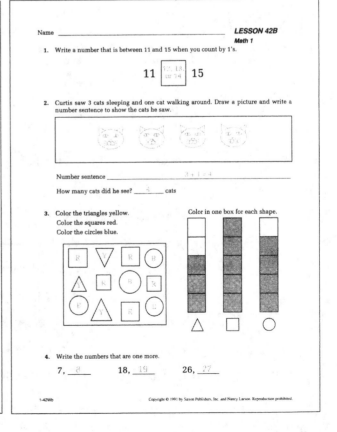

Name _____   *LESSON 42B*
Math 1

1. Write a number that is between 11 and 15 when you count by 1's.

    11 [12, 13, or 14] 15

2. Curtis saw 3 cats sleeping and one cat walking around. Draw a picture and write a number sentence to show the cats he saw.

    Number sentence _____ 3 + 1 = 4 _____

    How many cats did he see? _____ cats

3. Color the triangles yellow.
    Color the squares red.
    Color the circles blue.

    Color in one box for each shape.

4. Write the numbers that are one more.

    7, _8_   18, _19_   26, _27_

Lesson 43

writing the number 39
counting by 10's to 100

---

lesson preparation

materials

hundred number chart

tower of 10 linking cubes

Meeting Book

Fact Sheet A 3.0

in the morning

- Write the following number pattern on the meeting strip:

> 26, 27, 28, __, __, __

Answer: 26, 27, 28, 29, 30, 31

- Put **18 pennies** in the coin cup.

THE MEETING

calendar

- Ask your child to identify the following:

    year

    month

    shapes on the calendar

    today's shape

    shape pattern for the month

- Ask your child to write the date on the calendar.

- Ask your child to do the following:

    identify today's day of the week

    identify the days of the week

    read the days of the week

    "How many days of the week are there?"

> *"Let's count them."*
- Ask your child to write the full date on the meeting strip.

weather graph
- Ask your child to report and graph the weather.
- Ask questions about the graph.

counting
- Count from 1 to 100 using the hundred number chart.
- Count backward from 10 to 1.
- Add another number to the number line.
- Count to check.

number pattern
- Ask your child to identify and fill in the missing numbers.

> *"Let's read our number pattern together."*

clock
- Ask your child to set the morning/afternoon/evening/night clock.

coin cup
- Ask your child to slide and count the pennies in the coin cup.
- Ask your child to write the money amount on the meeting strip.

right/left
- Continue to practice left and right once a week. Practice more often, if necessary.

THE LESSON

Writing the Number 39

> *"The last number we practiced writing was the number 38."*
>
> *"What number do you think we will learn how to write today?"*

- Write the number 39 on the chalkboard.

> *"What digits do you see in the number 39?"*
>
> *"How would you tell someone how to write the number 39?"*
>
> *"Which digit is on the left?"*
>
> *"Which digit is on the right?"*

Counting by 10's to 100

> *"Today you will learn how to count by 10's to 100."*

- Give your child a hundred number chart and a tower of ten linking cubes.

  > *"Each morning we count to 100 together."*

  > *"Let's do that now using the hundred number chart."*

  > *"Point to each number as we count."*

  > *"Each time you come to the end of a row on the hundred number chart, put a linking cube on the number."*

- Count to 100 together.

  > *"What numbers do you think are beneath the cubes?"*

  > *"Let's see if you are right."*

  > *"Start at the top and take one cube off at a time."*

  > *"We will read the numbers underneath."*

- Count by 10's as your child removes each cube.

  > *"When we say these numbers, we are counting by 10's."*

  > *"Let's count by 10's again."*

  > *"Put the linking cubes on top of the numbers as we say them."*

- Count by 10's as your child covers the numbers.

  > *"Now we will count by 10's as you take off the cubes."*

- Count by 10's as your child removes the cubes.

  > *"How many cubes did you use when we counted by 10's to 100?"*

  > *"Do you think you can count by 10's to 100 by yourself?"*

- Ask your child to count. Assist your child, if necessary.

  > *"Let's do that again."*

  > *"Count slowly enough so that I can hear the numbers easily and I will write them on a counting strip in your Meeting Book."*

- Open the Meeting Book to page 48. Write the numbers on the first counting strip as your child counts by 10's. Start at the bottom of the strip and work up (similar to the numbering on a thermometer or graph).

  > *"Now let's count backward from 100 by 10's."*

- Point to the numbers on the counting strip as your child counts.

CLASS PRACTICE

- Give your child **Fact Sheet A 3.0**.

  > *"What number facts do you see?"*

"What strategy will you use to find the answers?"

- Allow time for your child to complete the fact sheet.
- Correct the fact sheet with your child.

WRITTEN PRACTICE

- Complete **Worksheet 43A** with your child.
- Complete **Worksheet 43B** with your child later in the day.

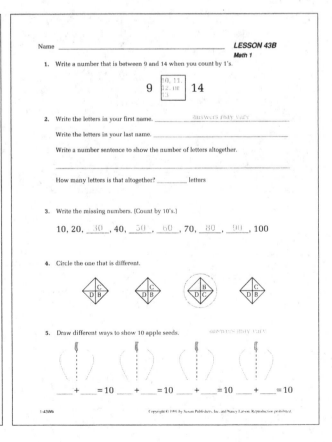

L esson 44

writing the number 40
subtraction facts—subtracting one

---

lesson preparation

materials

2 towers of 10 linking cubes

0–20 number cards (from Master 1-32)

subtraction fact cards (peach)

ten 3" × 5" cards

Fact Sheet S 2.0

the night before

• Use the 3" × 5" cards to make a large set of fact cards for the subtracting one facts written in the following way:

1	2	3	4	5	6	7	8	9	10
− 1	− 1	− 1	− 1	− 1	− 1	− 1	− 1	− 1	− 1

• Separate the peach subtraction fact cards.

in the morning

• Write the following number pattern on the meeting strip:

> 15, 14, 13, __, __, __

Answer: 15, 14, 13, 12, 11, 10

• Put **22 pennies** in the coin cup.

THE MEETING

calendar

• Ask your child to identify the following:

year

month

shapes on the calendar

today's shape

shape pattern for the month

- Ask your child to write the date on the calendar.
- Ask your child to do the following:

    identify today's day of the week

    identify the days of the week

    read the days of the week

    "How many days of the week are there?"

    "Let's count them."

- Ask your child to write the full date on the meeting strip.

weather graph

- Ask your child to report and graph the weather.
- Ask questions about the graph.

counting

- Count from 1 to 100 using the hundred number chart.
- Count backward from 20 to 1.

    "Let's use our counting strip to help us count by 10's to 100."

- Point to each number on the counting strip as your child counts.
- Add another number to the number line.
- Count to check.

number pattern

- Ask your child to identify and fill in the missing numbers.

    "Let's read our number pattern together."

clock

- Ask your child to set the morning/afternoon/evening/night clock.

coin cup

- Ask your child to slide and count the pennies in the coin cup.
- Ask your child to write the money amount on the meeting strip.

right/left

- Continue to practice left and right once a week. Practice more often, if necessary.

THE LESSON

Writing the Number 40

"The last number we practiced writing was the number 39."

"What number do you think we will learn how to write today?"

• Write the number 40 on the chalkboard.

"What digits do you see in the number 40?"

"How would you tell someone how to write the number 40?"

"Which digit is on the left?"

"Which digit is on the right?"

Subtraction Facts — Subtracting One

"Today you will learn how to subtract one from a number."

• Give your child the envelope of number cards 0–20 and two towers of ten linking cubes.

"Put your number cards in order from smallest to largest."

• Allow time for your child to order the number cards.

"Make a train of eight linking cubes."

"Point to the number card that matches this number of cubes."

"Take one car off the train."

"Point to the number card that matches the number of cubes in the train now."

"How much is eight minus one?"

"Make a train of five linking cubes."

"Point to the number card that matches this number of cubes."

"Take away one cube."

"Point to the number card that matches the number of cubes in the train now."

"How much is five take away one?"

• Repeat with 7, 12, 16, and 3 cubes. Alternate use of the terms *minus*, *take away*, and *subtract*.

"What happened when you took away one cube from the train?"

"How did you know what number card to point to?"

"Now you will practice subtracting one without using the cubes."

"Point to the number card for nine."

"Now point to the number card for one less than nine."

• Repeat with 4, 11, 15, and 18.

"Put your number cards in your envelope."

- Write the following on the chalkboard:

1	2	3	4	5	6	7	8	9	10
-1	-1	-1	-1	-1	-1	-1	-1	-1	-1

"These are the subtracting one number facts."

- Point to 4.

$$-1$$

- Cover "– 1" with your hand.

- Point to the top number.

"Make a tower with this number of cubes."

- Point to "– 1."

"What does this tell us to do?"   subtract or take away 1 cube

"Take away one cube from the tower."

"How many linking cubes do you have in your tower now?"

- Record the answer on the chalkboard.

- Repeat with several more examples.

"What are the answers for these other examples?"

"How do you know?"

"Subtracting one is just like counting backward."

- Give your child the peach subtraction fact cards.

"Write the answer on the back of each card."

- When your child finishes, give the following directions:

"Put your cards in a pile."

"Now read each problem to yourself."

"See if you can remember the answer."

"Turn over the card to check the answer."

"Practice saying the answers to yourself."

- Allow time for your child to practice using the fact cards independently.

"We will call these our subtracting one number facts."

"Why do you think we will call them that?"

"How can we remember these answers?"

"Subtracting one is just like counting backward."

CLASS PRACTICE

- Give your child **Fact Sheet S 2.0.**

    "What number facts do you see?"

    "What strategy will you use to find the answers?"

- Allow time for your child to complete the fact sheet.

- Correct the fact sheet together.

WRITTEN PRACTICE

- Complete **Worksheet 44A** with your child.

- Complete **Worksheet 44B** with your child later in the day.

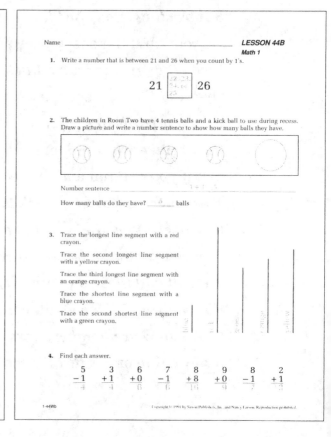

esson 45

writing the number 41
counting dimes

---

lesson preparation

materials

Written Assessment #8

cup of 10 dimes

piece of paper

plastic bag with 80 pennies

plastic bag with 8 dimes

large fact cards (adding one facts)

Fact Sheet AA 2.0

in the morning

• Write the following number pattern on the meeting strip:

> 10, 20, 30, ___, ___, ___

> *Answer: 10, 20, 30, 40, 50, 60*

• Put **19 pennies** in the coin cup.

THE MEETING

calendar

- • Ask your child to identify the following:

    year

    month

    shapes on the calendar

    today's shape

    shape pattern for the month

- • Ask your child to write the date on the calendar.

- • Ask your child to do the following:

    identify today's day of the week

    identify the days of the week

---

read the days of the week

"How many days of the week are there?"

"Let's count them."

- Ask your child to write the full date on the meeting strip.

weather graph

- Ask your child to report and graph the weather.
- Ask questions about the graph.

counting

- Count from 1 to 100 using the hundred number chart.
- Count backward from 20 to 1.

"Let's use our counting strip to help us count by 10's to 100."

- Point to each number on the counting strip as your child counts.
- Add another number to the number line.
- Count to check.

number pattern

- Ask your child to identify and fill in the missing numbers.

"Let's read our number pattern together."

clock

- Ask your child to set the morning/afternoon/evening/night clock.

coin cup

- Ask your child to slide and count the pennies in the coin cup.
- Ask your child to write the money amount on the meeting strip.

right/left

- Continue to practice left and right once a week. Practice more often, if necessary.

ASSESSMENT

Written Assessment

"Today, I would like to see what you remember from what we have been practicing."

- Give your child **Written Assessment #8**.

"Write your name at the top of the paper."

"I will read the directions for each problem."

• Read the directions for each problem. Allow time for your child to complete each problem before continuing.

• Correct the paper, noting your child's mistakes on the **Individual Recording Form**. Review the errors with your child.

THE LESSON

Writing the Number 41

"The last number we practiced writing was the number 40."

"What number do you think we will learn how to write today?"

• Write the number 41 on the chalkboard.

"What digits do you see in the number 41?"

"How would you tell someone how to write the number 41?"

"Which digit is on the left?"

"Which digit is on the right?"

Counting Dimes

• Show your child the bag of 80 pennies.

"What coins do I have in this bag?"   **pennies**

"How much money do you think is in this bag?"

• Ask your child to estimate.

"Let's count the pennies together."

"As we count the pennies, I will put them in stacks of ten."

• Count the pennies with your child. Stack the pennies in piles of ten.

"How much money do we have?"   **80¢**

"How many pennies are in each stack?"   **10**

"Let's count by 10's to see if this is 80¢."

• Point to each stack as your child counts by 10's.

"Today you will learn how to show 80¢ using a different coin."

• Give your child a cup of 10 dimes and a piece of paper.

"Take one coin out of the cup."

"What is this coin called?"   **dime**

"Look at both sides of the dime."

"Are the sides the same?"

"What do you see?"

"One side is called the heads side."

"Which side do you think that is?"

"The back of the coin is called the tails."

"We can remember the names of the sides of a coin by thinking of a dog."

"The head is on one end of a dog and the tail is on the other end."

"Today you will learn how to count dimes."

• Emphasize the next statement.

"A dime is the same as using ten pennies."

"When we count dimes, we count by 10's."

"Put the dimes on your paper."

"Let's count by 10's as we slide the dimes."

"When we have ten dimes we say one dollar."

• Count with your child as he/she slides and counts the dimes.

"Put three dimes on your paper."

"How much money is this?"

"Let's count to check."

• Repeat with 7 dimes, 6 dimes, and 9 dimes.

"How will we show 80¢ using dimes?"

"How many dimes will we use?"

"Let's count the money to check."

• Count the dimes with your child.

"Now let's pretend that we are going to the store and we want to buy something that costs 20¢."

• Write "20¢" on the chalkboard.

"What could we pretend that we are buying for 20¢?"

"Show 20¢ using your dimes."

"How many dimes did you use?"

"Let's count the money to check."

• Repeat with 70¢, 40¢, and 50¢.

"Let's count the dimes as you put them back in the cup."

• Hold up the bag of 80 pennies.

• Hold up the bag of 8 dimes.

"Both of these bags have 80¢."

"If we go to the store to buy something, which is easier to carry? Dimes or pennies?"

- Allow time for your child to discuss the advantages of using dimes rather than pennies.

CLASS PRACTICE

"Let's review the adding one facts."

- Hold up one adding one fact card at a time as your child says the problem and the answer.

- Repeat several times.

- Give your child **Fact Sheet AA 2.0.**

- Allow time for your child to complete the fact sheet.

- Correct the fact sheet with your child.

WRITTEN PRACTICE

- Complete **Worksheet 45A** with your child.

- Complete **Worksheet 45B** with your child later in the day.

Name _____ **ASSESSMENT 8**
LESSON 45
Date _____ **Math 1**

1. Five children were playing a game. Three more children came to play with them. Draw a picture and write a number sentence to show how many children are playing now.

Number sentence _____ 5 + 3 = 8 _____

How many children are playing now? ____8____ children

2. Color the triangles yellow.
How many triangles
did you color? ____4____

Color the squares red.
How many squares
did you color? ____2____

Color the circles blue.
How many circles
did you color? ____4____

3. Write the answers.

$4 + 1 = \underline{5}$ $7 + 1 = \underline{8}$ $9 + 9 = \underline{18}$

$6 + 1 = \underline{7}$ $3 + 3 = \underline{6}$ $5 + 1 = \underline{6}$

$4 + 4 = \underline{8}$ $2 + 1 = \underline{3}$ $7 + 7 = \underline{14}$

1-45Aa

Name _____ **LESSON 45A**
Math 1
Date _____

Day of the Week _____

1. Write the number forty-one.

2. Circle the number in the box that is between 7 and 12 when you count by 1's.

7 ____ 12   ⟨11⟩ 4 13

3. Miss Hart blew up 10 balloons for the party. Two balloons popped. Draw a picture and write a number sentence to show how many balloons she has now.

Number sentence _____ 10 – 2 = 8 _____

How many balloons does she have now? ____8____ balloons

4. How many dimes do you see? ____5____

Count by 10's to find out how much money this is. ____50¢____

5. Write the answers.

$4 + 1 = \underline{5}$ $6 - 1 = \underline{5}$ $7 + 7 = \underline{14}$ $9 - 1 = \underline{8}$ $5 + 0 = \underline{5}$

1-45Wa

Name _____ **LESSON 45B**
Math 1

1. Write a number that is between 17 and 22 when you count by 1's.

17 [18, 19, 20, 21] 22

2. Circle the number in the box that is between 11 and 16 when you count by 1's.

11 ____ 16 | 17 10 ⟨12⟩ |

3. Regina blew up 5 balloons for the party. Three balloons popped. Draw a picture and write a number sentence to show how many balloons she has now.

Number sentence _____ 5 – 3 = 2 _____

How many balloons does she have now? ____2____ balloons

4. How many dimes do you see? ____3____

Count by 10's to find out how much money this is. ____30¢____

5. Write the answers.

$8 - 1 = \underline{7}$ $1 + 5 = \underline{6}$ $9 + 9 = \underline{18}$ $7 - 1 = \underline{6}$ $0 + 4 = \underline{4}$

1-45Wb

Lesson 46

writing the number 42
ordering containers by volume
identifying one-cup liquid measure

---

lesson preparation

materials

1-cup liquid measuring cup (preferably plastic)

5 empty containers

basin, funnel, and newspaper

water (approximately 3 gallons)

food coloring (optional)

masking tape

marker

linking cubes (10 each of red, green, blue, yellow, and black)

large fact cards (subtracting one facts)

Fact Sheet S 2.0

the night before

- Use five empty plastic containers. The containers should be of clearly different sizes. If possible, include liter, quart, half gallon, and pint or half pint containers. Soft drink, milk, shampoo, ketchup, syrup, or salad dressing bottles can be used. Prior to the lesson, use a piece of tape and a marker to label the five containers A, B, C, D, and E.

- Highlight the 1-cup line on the measuring cup with tape or a marker.

in the morning

- Food coloring in the water makes the water level in the containers easier to see. Use a basin or place old newspapers on the floor or table to catch spills. A funnel can also be used to make pouring easier.

- Write the following number pattern on the meeting strip:

> 16, 17, 18, __, __, __

Answer: 16, 17, 18, 19, 20, 21

- Put **5 dimes** in the coin cup.

THE MEETING

calendar

- Ask your child to identify the following:

    year

    month

    shapes on the calendar

    today's shape

    shape pattern for the month

- Ask your child to write the date on the calendar.

- Ask your child to do the following:

    identify today's day of the week

    identify the days of the week

    read the days of the week

    "How many days of the week are there?"

    "Let's count them."

    "What are the weekdays?"

- Ask your child to write the full date on the meeting strip.

weather graph

- Ask your child to report and graph the weather.

- Ask questions about the graph.

counting

- Count from 1 to 100 using the hundred number chart.

- Count backward from 20 to 1.

    "Let's use our counting strip to help us count by 10's to 100."

- Point to each number on the counting strip as your child counts.

- Add another number to the number line.

- Count to check.

number pattern

- Ask your child to identify and fill in the missing numbers.

- Read the number pattern together.

clock

- Ask your child to set the morning/afternoon/evening/night clock.

coin cup

> *"What coin do we have in the coin cup today?"*
>
> *"What do we count by when we count dimes?"*

- Ask your child to slide and count the dimes in the coin cup.
- Ask your child to write the money amount on the meeting strip.

right/left

- Continue to practice left and right once a week. Practice more often, if necessary.

THE LESSON

Writing the Number 42

> *"The last number we practiced writing was the number 41."*
>
> *"What number do you think we will learn how to write today?"*

- Write the number 42 on the chalkboard.

> *"What digits do you see in the number 42?"*
>
> *"How would you tell someone how to write the number 42?"*
>
> *"Which digit is on the left?"*
>
> *"Which digit is on the right?"*

Ordering Containers by Volume
Identifying One-Cup Liquid Measure

- Display the five containers so that your child can see them easily.

> *"Today you will learn how to order containers by volume."*
>
> *"I have five containers."*
>
> *"Look at them carefully."*
>
> *"We are going to fill each container with water."*
>
> *"The smallest container is the one that will hold the least amount of water."*
>
> *"Which container do you think is the smallest?"*
>
> *"Why?"*

- Encourage your child to discuss why he/she thinks a certain container will hold the least.
- Put that container on the far left.

> *"Which container do you think is the smallest now?"*

- Put that container next to the one judged to have the least volume.

- Repeat with the other containers.

- Hold up a one-cup measuring cup.

  "We will use a measuring cup to find how many cups of water each container will hold."

  "Each time we fill this cup, we have one cup of water."

- Point to the highlighted one-cup line on the measuring cup.

  "We will fill the cup to this line for exactly one cup of water."

- Hold up the one-cup measuring cup and the container judged by your child to be the smallest.

  "Let's estimate how many cups of water this container will hold."

  "How many cups of water do you think it will take to fill this container?"

- Record on the chalkboard:

Container	Estimate	Actual
A		
B		
C		
D		
E		

- Record your child's estimate on the chalkboard chart.

  "Let's try it to see."

  "You will keep track of how many cups of water we use."

- Give your child 10 red, 10 blue, 10 green, 10 yellow, and 10 black linking cubes.

  "Every time I pour a cup of water into this container, you will take one (color) linking cube."

  "The tower of (color) linking cubes will show how many cups of water we used to fill this container."

  "Count with me as I pour each cup of water into this container."

- Pour the water into the measuring cup and from the measuring cup into the first container. Estimate to the nearest cup. For example, if a little more than four cups of water was used, write "4 cups + a little." If four and a half cups were used, write "4 cups + a half cup." If a little less than five cups was used, write "5 cups – a little."

  "How many cups of water did we use to fill this container?"

- Record the amount on the chalkboard chart. Stand the tower of linking cubes next to the container.

- Point to the next container in the row.

"Do you think this container will hold more or less water?"

"How many cups of water do you think this container will hold?"

- Record the estimate on the chalkboard.

"Every time I pour a cup of water into the container, you will take one (color) linking cube."

"The tower of (color) linking cubes will show how many cups of water we used to fill this container."

"Count with me as I pour each cup of water into this container."

"How many cups of water did we use to fill this container?"

- Record the amount on the chalkboard chart. Stand the tower of linking cubes next to the container.

- Repeat with the remaining containers, using a different color linking cube for each.

"Which container has the smallest volume?"

"How do you know?"

"Which container has the greatest volume?"

"How do you know?"

"Did we put the containers in order from smallest to largest?"

- Adjust the order of the containers, if necessary.

"Let's look at our towers."

- Stand the towers next to each other.

"What do you notice?" *the towers go up like steps*

- Optional: Put the containers, the plastic measuring cup, and the basin in an area near a sink. Additional plastic containers can be added for your child to fill and compare. Allow time for your child to estimate, fill, and count the number of cups of water needed to fill each container.

CLASS PRACTICE

"Let's review the subtracting one facts."

- Hold up one subtracting one fact card at a time as your child says the problem and the answer.

- Repeat several times.

- Give your child **Fact Sheet S 2.0.**

- Allow time for your child to complete the fact sheet.

- Correct the fact sheet with your child.

WRITTEN PRACTICE

• Complete **Worksheet 46A** with your child.

• Complete **Worksheet 46B** with your child later in the day.

Name _____   **LESSON 46A**
                                 Math 1
Date _____

Day of the Week _____

1. Write the number forty-two.

   42 42

2. Jason used 3 cups of water to fill one bottle. He used 2 cups of water to fill another bottle. Draw a picture and write a number sentence to show how many cups of water he used.

   Number sentence _____3 + 2 = 5_____

   How many cups of water did he use? ____5____ cups

3. Circle the one that is different.

4. How many dimes do you see? ____6____

   How much money is this? ____60¢____

5. Write the letter G in the fourth square.
   Write the letter O in the second square.
   Write the letter L in the first square.
   Write the letter N in the third square.

   | L | O | N | G |

1-46Wa

Name _____   **LESSON 46B**
                                 Math 1

1. Circle the number in the box that is between 5 and 8 when you count by 1's.

   5 [ ] 8   [9 2 (7)]

2. Frank used 5 cups of water to fill one bottle. He used 3 cups of water to fill another bottle. Draw a picture and write a number sentence to show how many cups of water he used.

   Number sentence _____5 + 3 = 8_____

   How many cups of water did he use? ____8____ cups

3. Circle the one that is different.

4. How many dimes do you see? ____4____

   How much money is this? ____40¢____

5. Write the letter H in the second square.
   Write the letter O in the middle square.
   Write the letter T in the last square.
   Write the letter R in the fourth square.
   Write the letter S in the first square.

   | S | H | O | R | T |

1-46Wb

Lesson 47

writing the number 43
counting by 2's

---

lesson preparation

materials

5 dolls, stuffed animals, or action figures

individual fact cards

Fact Sheet A 1.2

in the morning

• Write the following number pattern on the meeting strip:

> 41, 42, 43, ___, ___, ___

Answer: 41, 42, 43, 44, 45, 46

• Put **8 dimes** in the coin cup.

THE MEETING

calendar

- Ask your child to identify the following:

    year

    month

    shapes on the calendar

    today's shape

    shape pattern for the month

- Ask your child to write the date on the calendar.

- Ask your child to do the following:

    identify today's day of the week

    identify the days of the week

    read the days of the week

"How many days of the week are there?"

"Let's count them."

"What are the weekdays?"

- Ask your child to write the full date on the meeting strip.

weather graph

- Ask your child to report and graph the weather.
- Ask questions about the graph.

counting

- Count from 1 to 100 using the hundred number chart.
- Count backward from 20 to 1.

"Let's use our counting strip to help us count by 10's to 100."

- Point to each number on the counting strip as your child counts.
- Add another number to the number line.
- Count to check.

number pattern

- Ask your child to identify and fill in the missing numbers.
- Read the number pattern together.

clock

- Ask your child to set the morning/afternoon/evening/night clock.

coin cup

"What coin do we have in the coin cup today?

"What do we count by when we count dimes?"

- Ask your child to slide and count the dimes in the coin cup.
- Ask your child to write the money amount on the meeting strip.

right/left

- Continue to practice left and right once a week. Practice more often, if necessary.

THE LESSON

Writing the Number 43

"The last number we practiced writing was the number 42."

"What number do you think we will learn how to write today?"

- Write the number 43 on the chalkboard.

"What digits do you see in the number 43?"

"How would you tell someone how to write the number 43?"

"Which digit is on the left?"

"Which digit is on the right?"

Counting by 2's

"Today you will learn how to count by 2's."

"We did a great job estimating and filling our containers with water yesterday."

"I think we should give ourselves a pat on the back."

"There is a saying that people use when they want to congratulate someone."

"We can say it for ourselves."

"It goes like this: 2, 4, 6, 8 . . . who do we appreciate? (family name, family name), hooray!"

"Let's say it together."

- Repeat together.

"When we say that, we are counting by 2's."

"Let's say it again."

- Repeat together.

"What do we have on our bodies that we have two of?" **arms, hands, legs, feet, eyes, ears, etc.**

- Place 5 dolls, stuffed animals, or action figures in a row.

"What do these _____ have two of?"

"How many eyes does each _____ have?"

"Let's count by 2's to find out how many eyes they have altogether."

"Two, 4, 6, 8, 10."

"How many eyes in all?" **10**

"Five _____ have ten eyes."

"Wasn't that a quick way to count?"

- Remove 1 doll, stuffed animal, or action figure.

"How many ears does each _____ have?"

"Let's count by 2's to find out how many ears they have altogether."

"Two, 4, 6, 8."

"How many ears in all?"

"Four _____ have eight ears."

> *"Now we will slap our legs with our hands as we count by 2's to ten."*
>
> *"Let's slap and count together."*
>
> *"Two, 4, 6, 8, 10."*

CLASS PRACTICE

> *"Today you will use your individual fact cards to practice the addition number facts."*

- Allow time for your child to practice his/her number facts independently.

- Give your child **Fact Sheet A 1.2.**

> *"What number facts do you see?"*

- Allow time for your child to complete the fact sheet.

- Correct the fact sheet with your child.

WRITTEN PRACTICE

- Complete **Worksheet 47A** with your child.

- Complete **Worksheet 47B** with your child later in the day.

Name _____ LESSON 47A
Date _____ Math 1
Day of the Week _____

1. Write the number forty-three.

$$43 \quad 43$$

2. Cory and 4 of his friends hung their coats near the back door. Draw a picture and write a number sentence to show how many coats they hung by the door.

Number sentence _____ 1 + 4 = 5

How many coats are hung near the door? ____5____ coats

3. How many squares are in each train? ____6____

Color. How many are left?

5 ▨▨▨▨▨☐ 1

3 ▨▨▨☐☐☐ 3

4. Finish the pattern.

☐ △ △ ☐ △ △ ☐ △ △

5. Find each answer.

4	0	6	1	9	4	8	4
−1	+3	+6	+5	+0	+4	−1	+1
3	3	12	6	9	8	7	5

Name _____ LESSON 47B
Math 1

1. Circle the number in the box that is between 6 and 12 when you count by 1's.

6 ☐ 12   5 (9) 13

2. David and two of his friends took off their hats when they came into the house. They put their hats on a table by the door. Draw a picture and write a number sentence to show how many hats are on the table.

Number sentence _____ 1 + 2 = 3

How many hats are on the table near the door? ____3____ hats

3. How many squares are in each train? ____8____

Color. How many are left?

1 ▨☐☐☐☐☐☐☐ 7

4 ▨▨▨▨☐☐☐☐ 4

4. Finish the pattern.

☐ ○ ○ ☐ ○ ○ ☐ ○ ○

5. Find each answer.

7	5	0	1	7	3	0	8
−1	+5	+5	+6	+7	−1	+9	+8
6	10	5	7	11	2	9	16

---

esson 48

writing the number 44
telling time to the hour

---

lesson preparation

materials

demonstration clock

individual clocks

small bell

individual fact cards

Fact Sheet A 2.0

in the morning

• Write the following number pattern on the meeting strip:

> 40, 50, 60, ___, ___, ___

Answer: 40, 50, 60, 70, 80, 90

• Put **9 dimes** in the coin cup.

THE MEETING

calendar

- • Ask your child to identify the following:

    year

    month

    shapes on the calendar

    today's shape

    shape pattern for the month

- • Ask your child to write the date on the calendar.

- • Ask your child to do the following:

    identify today's day of the week

    identify the days of the week

    read the days of the week

    "How many days of the week are there?"

"Let's count them."

"What are the weekdays?"

• Ask your child to write the full date on the meeting strip.

weather graph

• Ask your child to report and graph the weather.

• Ask questions about the graph.

counting

• Count from 1 to 100 using the hundred number chart.

• Count backward from 20 to 1.

"Let's use our counting strip to help us count by 10's to 100."

• Point to each number on the counting strip as your child counts.

• Add another number to the number line.

• Count to check.

number pattern

• Ask your child to identify and fill in the missing numbers.

• Read the number pattern together.

clock

• Ask your child to set the morning/afternoon/evening/night clock.

coin cup

"What coin do we have in the coin cup today?

"What do we count by when we count dimes?"

• Ask your child to slide and count the dimes in the coin cup.

• Ask your child to write the money amount on the meeting strip.

right/left

• Continue to practice left and right once a week. Practice more often, if necessary.

THE LESSON

Writing the Number 44

"The last number we practiced writing was the number 43."

"What number do you think we will learn how to write today?"

• Write the number 44 on the chalkboard.

"What digits do you see in the number 44?"

"How would you tell someone how to write the number 44?"

"Which digit is on the left?"

"Which digit is on the right?"

Telling Time to the Hour

"Each day we have been talking about morning, afternoon, evening, and night."

"Today you will learn how to tell time to the hour."

"We begin our day with The Meeting."

"If we wanted to invite someone to visit us to see our math meeting, we could tell them to visit us in the morning."

"But they would want to know exactly when to come to visit."

"We would need to tell them clock time."

"We use a clock to tell us when it is time to get up in the morning, when it is time to eat lunch, and when it is time to go to bed."

• Show your child a conventional clock.

"Where are some other clocks in our house?"

"Every clock in our house shows the same time."

"Our clock shows the same time as the clocks at _____ 's house."

"It shows the same time as the clocks that many people wear."

"Clocks that we wear are called watches."

• Use a demonstration clock.

"Let's look at the clock face."

"What do you see?"

"What numbers do you see?"

"What number is at the top? . . . at the bottom?"

• Point to the hands on the clock.

"These are called the hands on the clock."

"All clocks have at least two hands."

"Are both of the hands on this clock the same?"

"How are they different?"   *one is long and one is short*

"The short hand is also called the hour hand."

"It tells us what hour it is."

• Show 2:00 on the demonstration clock.

"When the long hand points to the twelve, a new hour is beginning."

"The short hand points to the hour."

"We read this time as two o'clock because the hour hand is pointing to the two."

- Show 7:00 on the demonstration clock.

"A new hour has begun."

"What time is it?"   seven o'clock

"What number does the long hand point to?"   **12**

"What number does the short hand point to?"   **7**

- Repeat with 10:00 and 4:00.

- Give your child an individual clock.

- Show 3:00 on the demonstration clock.

"Make your clock look like mine."

- Allow time for your child to do this.

"Is the long hand on your clock pointing to the twelve?"

"Is the hour hand on your clock pointing to the three?"

"What time is it?"   three o'clock

- Repeat with 9:00.

"Show five o'clock on your clock."

- Allow time for your child to do this.

"Where is the long hand pointing?"

"Where is the hour hand pointing?"

"Beginning today, you will have a special job."

- Hold up a small bell.

"Each time a new hour begins, you will ring this bell."

"You will say, 'It is _____ o'clock and all is well.' "

"Then you will show that time on your small clock."

"Let's practice that."

"We will pretend that my clock is a real clock."

- Set your clock to show two o'clock. Ask your child to ring the bell, announce the time, and set his/her individual clock.

CLASS PRACTICE

"Today you will use your individual fact cards to practice the addition number facts."

- Allow time for your child to practice his/her number facts independently.
- Give your child **Fact Sheet A 2.0.**

  "What number facts do you see?"

  "What strategy will you use to find the answer?"

- Allow time for your child to complete the fact sheet.
- Correct the fact sheet with your child.

WRITTEN PRACTICE

- Complete **Worksheet 48A** with your child.
- Complete **Worksheet 48B** with your child later in the day.

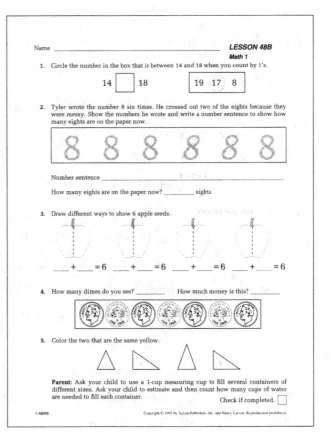

esson 49

writing the number 45
identifying even numbers to 20

---

lesson preparation

materials

16 pennies

Meeting Book

large fact cards

Fact Sheet A 3.0

in the morning

• Write the following number pattern on the meeting strip:

> 2, 4, 6, ___, ___, ___

Answer: 2, 4, 6, 8, 10, 12

• Put **7 dimes** in the coin cup.

THE MEETING

calendar

• Ask your child to identify the following:

year

month

shapes on the calendar

today's shape

shape pattern for the month

• Ask your child to write the date on the calendar.

• Ask your child to do the following:

identify today's day of the week

identify the days of the week

read the days of the week

"How many days of the week are there?"

"Let's count them."

"What are the weekdays?"

• Ask your child to write the full date on the meeting strip.

weather graph

• Ask your child to report and graph the weather.

• Ask questions about the graph.

counting

• Count from 1 to 100 using the hundred number chart.

• Count backward from 20 to 1.

"Let's use our counting strip to help us count by 10's to 100."

• Point to each number on the counting strip as your child counts.

• Add another number to the number line.

• Count to check.

number pattern

• Ask your child to identify and fill in the missing numbers.

• Read the number pattern together.

clock

• Ask your child to set the morning/afternoon/evening/night clock.

• Throughout the day, your child announces the time on the hour and sets the demonstration clock.

coin cup

"What coin do we have in the coin cup today?

"What do we count by when we count dimes?"

• Ask your child to slide and count the dimes in the coin cup.

• Ask your child to write the money amount on the meeting strip.

right/left

• Continue to practice left and right once a week. Practice more often, if necessary.

THE LESSON

Writing the Number 45

"The last number we practiced writing was the number 44."

"What number do you think we will learn how to write today?"

• Write the number 45 on the chalkboard.

"What digits do you see in the number 45?"

"How would you tell someone how to write the number 45?"

"Which digit is on the left?"

"Which digit is on the right?"

Identifying Even Numbers to 20

• Write "0, 2, 4, 6, ___" on the chalkboard.

"What will be the next number?" **8**

"Let's read the numbers together." **0, 2, 4, 6, 8**

"Today you will learn a special name for these numbers."

"What did we do to get from 0 to 2?" **we skipped a number**

"What number is missing?" **1**

• Record the following on the chalkboard:

<pre>
          1
    0   2   4   6   8
</pre>

"What did we do to get from 2 to 4?" **we skipped a number**

"What number is missing?" **3**

• Record the following on the chalkboard:

<pre>
       1   3
    0   2   4   6   8
</pre>

"What did we do to get from 4 to 6?" **we skipped a number**

"What number is missing?" **5**

• Record the following on the chalkboard:

<pre>
       1   3   5
    0   2   4   6   8
</pre>

"What did we do to get from 6 to 8?" **we skipped a number**

"What number is missing?" **7**

• Record the following on the chalkboard:

<pre>
       1   3   5   7
    0   2   4   6   8
</pre>

"What do you think the number next to the eight will be if we skip a number?"

• Record "10" on the chalkboard:

<pre>
       1   3   5   7
    0   2   4   6   8   10
</pre>

"What number is missing?"

- Repeat to 20.

- Circle 0, 2, 4, 6, 8, 10, 12, 14, 16, 18, and 20.

"All of these numbers are called even numbers."

"Remember when we counted by 2's and said 'Two, 4, 6, 8, who do we appreciate? (family name, family name), hooray!'?"

"Those are the even numbers."

"We can change our cheer to 'Two, 4, 6, 8, even numbers are really great!'."

"When we say even numbers, we are counting by 2's."

"Let's count by 2's to 20 together."

"We will count slowly enough so that I can write the numbers we say on a counting strip in your Meeting Book."

- Open the Meeting Book to page 48.

- Write the numbers on the second counting strip as your child counts by 2's. Start at the bottom and work up. Begin with zero.

"Let's count backward from 20 by 2's."

- Point as you count with your child.

- Give your child 15 pennies.

"Count these pennies."

- Allow time for your child to do this.

"Do you have an odd or even number of pennies?"

"Remember that the numbers we circled are the even numbers."

"Put your pennies in piles of two."

- Allow time for your child to do this.

"What happened?"

- Give your child another penny.

"How many pennies do you have now?"   **16**

"Is that an even number?"

"Put your pennies in piles of two."

- Allow time for your child to do this.

"What happened?"

"Count your pennies by 2's."

"Now you will need only ten pennies."

"Give me your extra pennies."

"Put your pennies in piles of two."

> *"How many piles of pennies do you have?"* **5**
>
> *"Let's count by 2's to count the pennies."*

CLASS PRACTICE

> *"Let's review all of the addition number facts."*

- Hold up one fact card at a time as your child says the problem and the answer.

- Repeat several times.

- Give your child **Fact Sheet A 3.0.**

  "What number facts do you see?"

  "What strategy will you use to find the answers?"

- Allow time for your child to complete the fact sheet.

- Correct the fact sheet with your child.

WRITTEN PRACTICE

- Complete **Worksheet 49A** with your child.

- Complete **Worksheet 49B** with your child later in the day.

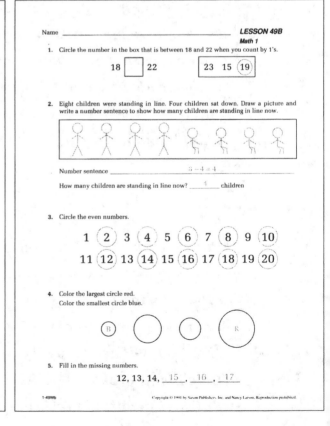

Lesson 50

assessment

lesson preparation

materials
Written Assessment #9
Oral Assessment #5

in the morning
• Write the following number pattern on the meeting strip:

> 36, 37, 38, ___, ___, ___

Answer: 36, 37, 38, 39, 40, 41

• Put **4 dimes** in the coin cup.

THE MEETING

calendar

• Ask your child to identify the following:

> year
>
> month
>
> shapes on the calendar
>
> today's shape
>
> shape pattern for the month

• Ask your child to write the date on the calendar.

• Ask your child to do the following:

> identify today's day of the week
>
> identify the days of the week
>
> read the days of the week

"How many days of the week are there?"

"Let's count them."

"What are the weekdays?"

• Ask your child to write the full date on the meeting strip.

weather graph

- Ask your child to report and graph the weather.
- Ask questions about the graph.

counting

- Count from 1 to 100 using the hundred number chart.
- Count backward from 20 to 1.

   "Let's use our counting strip to help us count by 10's to 100."

- Point to each number on the counting strip as your child counts.

   "Let's use our counting strip to help us count by 2's to 20."

- Point to each number on the counting strip as your child counts.
- Add another number to the number line.
- Count to check.
- Use an orange crayon to color the square for 50.

number pattern

- Ask your child to identify and fill in the missing numbers.
- Read the number pattern together.

clock

- Ask your child to set the morning/afternoon/evening/night clock.
- Throughout the day, your child announces the time on the hour and sets the demonstration clock.

coin cup

   "What coin do we have in the coin cup today?

   "What do we count by when we count dimes?"

- Ask your child to slide and count the dimes in the coin cup.
- Ask your child to write the money amount on the meeting strip.

right/left

- Continue to practice left and right once a week. Practice more often, if necessary.

ASSESSMENT

- All of the questions on the assessment are based on concepts and skills presented at least five lessons ago. If your child is having difficulty with a specific concept, reteach the concept the following day.

Written Assessment

> *"Today I would like to see what you remember from what we have been practicing."*

- Give your child **Written Assessment #9.**

> *"Write your name at the top of the paper."*

> *"I will read the directions for each problem."*

- Read the directions for each problem. Allow time for your child to complete each problem before continuing.

- Correct the paper, noting your child's mistakes on the **Individual Recording Form.** Review the errors with your child.

Oral Assessment

- Record your child's responses to the oral interview on the interview sheet.

Teacher _____

Date _____

MATH 1   LESSON 50
Oral Assessment # 5 Recording Form

Students	*"Make up a some, some more story."	*"Make up a some, some went away story."

1-50La

Copyright © 1991 by Saxon Publishers, Inc. and Nancy Larson. Reproduction prohibited.

Name _____

Date _____

ASSESSMENT 9
LESSON 50
Math 1

1. Six dogs were playing. Two dogs went home. Draw a picture and write a number sentence to show how many dogs are playing now.

Number sentence _____ $6 - 2 = 4$

How many dogs are playing now? ___4___ dogs

2. Color the longest train red.
   Color the second longest train yellow.
   Color the shortest train blue.

   red

   blue

   yellow

3. Write the numbers that are one more.

   5, _6_   16, _17_   24, _25_

4. Write the answers.

$$\frac{\begin{array}{r}5\\+0\end{array}}{5} \quad \frac{\begin{array}{r}7\\+1\end{array}}{8} \quad \frac{\begin{array}{r}8\\+8\end{array}}{16} \quad \frac{\begin{array}{r}6\\+0\end{array}}{6} \quad \frac{\begin{array}{r}3\\+1\end{array}}{4} \quad \frac{\begin{array}{r}2\\+0\end{array}}{2} \quad \frac{\begin{array}{r}5\\+5\end{array}}{10} \quad \frac{\begin{array}{r}9\\+0\end{array}}{9}$$

1-50Aa

Copyright © 1991 by Saxon Publishers, Inc. and Nancy Larson. Reproduction prohibited.

Lesson 51

writing the number 46
identifying and locating numbers on the hundred number chart

---

lesson preparation

materials

hundred number chart

4 linking cubes (red, yellow, green, blue)

large fact cards (adding one facts)

Fact Sheet A 2.0

the night before

• Cover 36, 51, and 17 on the hundred chart with a red, yellow, and blue linking cube.

in the morning

• Write the following number pattern on the meeting strip:

> 8, 10, 12, ___, ___, ___

Answer: 8, 10, 12, 14, 16, 18

• Put **6 dimes** in the coin cup.

THE MEETING

calendar

• Ask your child to identify the following:

    year

    month

    shapes on the calendar

    today's shape

    shape pattern for the month

• Ask your child to write the date on the calendar.

• Ask your child to do the following:

    identify today's day of the week

    identify the days of the week

"What day of the week was it yesterday?"

"What day of the week will it be tomorrow?"

- Ask your child to identify the following:

    number of days in a week

    weekdays

- Ask your child to write the full date on the meeting strip.

weather graph

- Ask your child to report and graph the weather.

- Ask questions about the graph.

counting

- Count from 1 to 100 using the hundred number chart.

- Count backward from 30 to 1.

- Count by 10's to 100.

    "Let's use our counting strip to help us count by 2's to 20."

- Point to each number on the counting strip as your child counts.

- Add another number to the number line.

    "We will count the numbers on our number line in a new way."

    "We will count by 10's as far as we can and then count by 1's."

- Point and count in the following way: 10, 20, 30, 40, 50, 51.

    "How many 10's did we count?"

- Point to the 5 in 51.

    "And how many more did we count?"

- Point to the 1 in 51.

    "What number is (5) tens and (1) more?"

number pattern

- Ask your child to identify and fill in the missing numbers.

- Read the number pattern together.

clock

- Ask your child to set the morning/afternoon/evening/night clock.

- Throughout the day, your child announces the time on the hour and sets the demonstration clock.

coin cup

- Ask your child to slide and count the dimes in the coin cup.

- Ask your child to record the amount of money in the coin cup on the meeting strip.

right/left

- Continue to practice left and right once a week. Practice more often, if necessary.

THE LESSON

Writing the Number 46

"The last number we practiced writing was the number 45."

"What number do you think we will learn how to write today?"

- Write the number 46 on the chalkboard.

"What digits do you see in the number 46?"

"How would you tell someone how to write the number 46?"

"Which digit is on the left?"

"Which digit is on the right?"

Identifying and Locating Numbers on the Hundred Number Chart

"Today you will learn how to identify and locate numbers on a hundred number chart."

"Close your eyes."

- Cover 17, 36, 51, and 83 on the hundred number chart using different colored linking cubes.

"Open your eyes."

"I have covered four numbers on the hundred number chart."

"Try to guess one of my covered numbers."

- Ask your child to name a color and identify the number beneath.

"How did you know that ____ is under the _____ cube?"

"Let's check to see."

- Remove the cube.
- Repeat with the other three cubes.

"Now I will close my eyes."

"Use the linking cubes to cover 4 numbers."

"After you do this, I will try to guess the numbers you covered."

- Take turns covering and identifying the covered number two or three times.

"Now I will say a number."

"Point to the number on your chart."

"Thirty-seven."

"How can we find thirty-seven quickly?"

- Repeat with 52, 21, 40, 16, 9, and 33.

"Let's play a game."

"I will give you a clue and you will try to find my secret number."

"Point to my secret number on your hundred number chart."

"The number before 72."

"The number after 17."

"The number between 37 and 39."

"One more than 23."

"One less than 45."

"The number before 30."

"The number after 60."

"The number between 72 and 74."

"One more than 86."

"One less than 40."

- Repeat with additional numbers, if necessary.

- Write the following on the chalkboard:

$$56 \ \square \ 73$$

"What is a number between 56 and 73?"

"What is another number between 56 and 73?"

- Encourage your child to name as many numbers as possible.

CLASS PRACTICE

"Let's review the adding one facts."

- Hold up one large fact card at a time as your child says the problem and the answer.

- Repeat several times.

- Give your child **Fact Sheet A 2.0.**

"What number facts do you see?"

"What strategy will you use to find the answers?"

- Allow time for your child to complete the fact sheet.

• Correct the fact sheet with your child.

WRITTEN PRACTICE

• Complete **Worksheet 51A** with your child.
• Complete **Worksheet 51B** with your child later in the day.

Name _____ **LESSON 51A**
    Math 1
Date _____

Day of the Week _____

1. Write the number forty-six.

    46 46

2. Weston had 3 dimes. His sister gave him 2 more dimes. Draw a picture and write a number sentence to show how many dimes he has now.

    (D) (D) (D)   (D) (D)

    Number sentence _____ 3 + 2 = 5 _____
    How many dimes does he have now? ___5___ dimes

3. Write the numbers that are one less.

    ___7___, 8   ___14___, 15   ___22___, 23   ___56___, 57

4. Use the graph to answer the questions.

    | Sunny | ☀ ☀ ☀ ☀ | | |
    | Cloudy | ☁ ☁ ☁ ☁ ☁ ☁ |
    | Snowy | ❄ ❄ ❄ | | |

    How many sunny days were there?
    ___4___
    How many cloudy and snowy days were there altogether?
    ___9___

5. Find each answer.

    $\begin{array}{r}3\\+1\\\hline4\end{array}$ $\begin{array}{r}4\\+0\\\hline4\end{array}$ $\begin{array}{r}5\\-1\\\hline4\end{array}$ $\begin{array}{r}6\\+6\\\hline12\end{array}$ $\begin{array}{r}8\\-1\\\hline7\end{array}$ $\begin{array}{r}1\\+7\\\hline8\end{array}$

Name _____ **LESSON 51B**
    Math 1

1. Circle the number that is one more than 31.

    39   58   (32)   20

2. Peter had 4 dimes. His brother gave him 4 more dimes. Draw a picture and write a number sentence to show how many dimes he has now.

    (D) (D)   (D) (D)
     (D) (D)   (D) (D)

    Number sentence _____ 4 + 4 = 8 _____
    How many dimes does he have now? ___8___ dimes

3. Write the numbers that are one less.

    ___5___, 6   ___16___, 17   ___24___, 25   ___63___, 64

4. Use the graph to answer the questions.

    | Sunny | ☀ ☀ ☀ | | |
    | Cloudy | ☁ ☁ ☁ ☁ ☁ |
    | Snowy | ❄ ❄ ❄ ❄ | |

    How many sunny days were there?
    ___3___
    How many cloudy and snowy days were there altogether?
    ___9___

5. Find each answer.

    $\begin{array}{r}7\\+1\\\hline8\end{array}$ $\begin{array}{r}6\\+0\\\hline6\end{array}$ $\begin{array}{r}8\\-1\\\hline7\end{array}$ $\begin{array}{r}7\\+7\\\hline14\end{array}$ $\begin{array}{r}3\\-1\\\hline2\end{array}$ $\begin{array}{r}1\\+5\\\hline6\end{array}$

---

esson 52

writing the number 47
counting dimes and pennies

---

lesson preparation

materials

hundred number chart

1 cup of 23 pennies and 1 cup of 10 dimes

large fact cards

Fact Sheet A 2.2

in the morning

• Write the following number pattern on the meeting strip:

> 100, 90, 80, __, __, __

> *Answer: 100, 90, 80, 70, 60, 50*

• Put **7 dimes** in the coin cup.

THE MEETING

calendar

• Ask your child to identify the following:

> year

> month

> shapes on the calendar

> today's shape

> shape pattern for the month

• Ask your child to write the date on the calendar.

• Ask your child to do the following:

> identify today's day of the week

> identify the days of the week

"What day of the week was it yesterday?"

"What day of the week will it be tomorrow?"

• Ask your child to identify the following:

    number of days in a week

    weekdays

• Ask your child to write the full date on the meeting strip.

weather graph

• Ask your child to report and graph the weather.

• Ask questions about the graph.

counting

• Count from 1 to 100 using the hundred number chart.

• Count backward from 30 to 1.

• Count by 10's to 100.

"Let's use our counting strip to help us count by 2's to 20."

• Point to each number on the counting strip as your child counts.

• Add another number to the number line.

"We will count the numbers on our number line in a new way."

"We will count by 10's as far as we can and then count by 1's."

• Point and count in the following way: 10, 20, 30, 40, 50, 51, 52.

"How many 10's did we count?"

• Point to the 5 in 52.

"And how many more did we count?"

• Point to the 2 in 52.

"What number is (5) tens and (2) more?"

number pattern

• Ask your child to identify and fill in the missing numbers.

• Read the number pattern together.

clock

• Ask your child to set the morning/afternoon/evening/night clock.

• Throughout the day, your child announces the time on the hour and sets the demonstration clock.

coin cup

• Ask your child to slide and count the dimes in the coin cup.

• Ask your child to record the amount of money in the coin cup on the meeting strip.

right/left

- Continue to practice left and right once a week. Practice more often, if necessary.

THE LESSON

Writing the Number 47

"The last number we practiced writing was the number 46."

"What number do you think we will learn how to write today?"

- Write the number 47 on the chalkboard.

"What digits do you see in the number 47?"

"How would you tell someone how to write the number 47?"

"Which digit is on the left?"

"Which digit is on the right?"

Counting Dimes and Pennies

- Give your child a cup of 23 pennies and a hundred number chart.

"Use the pennies to cover the numbers on the hundred number chart."

"Start with the number one."

"Cover the numbers in order."

"Count the number of pennies to yourself as you cover the numbers."

- When your child is finished, continue.

"How many pennies do you have?"

"Lift up the last penny."

"What number is underneath?"

"Pennies take a long time to count."

"There is another coin we can use to make it easier."

- Give your child a cup of ten dimes.

"What are these coins called?" **dimes**

"We can use one dime instead of ten pennies."

"Begin with 1."

"Count ten pennies."

"Take them off the chart."

"Put a dime on the 10."

"Start on the second row."

"Count ten more pennies."

"Take them off the chart."

"Put a dime on the 20."

"Do you have ten more pennies on your chart?" **no**

"You don't have enough pennies to trade for a dime."

"Now we will count by 10's to count the dimes."

"Then we will count our extra pennies."

"Let's count our money together." **10, 20, 21, 22, 23**

"Put your dimes and pennies back in the cups."

"Let's practice counting dimes and pennies."

"Put 3 dimes and 5 pennies on the table."

"We will count the dimes first and then the pennies."

"When we count dimes, what do we count by?" **10's**

"Let's count the dimes together." **10, 20, 30**

"When we count pennies, what do we count by?" **1's**

"We will count by 1's beginning at 30." **30, 31, 32, 33, 34, 35**

"How much money is 3 dimes and 5 pennies?" **35¢**

- Write "3 dimes and 5 pennies = 35¢" on the chalkboard.

- Repeat with 4 dimes, 3 pennies; 7 dimes, 2 pennies; and 9 dimes, 6 pennies.

- Write "54¢" on the chalkboard.

  "Show 54¢ using dimes and pennies."

  "How many dimes did you use?" **5**

  "How many pennies did you use?" **4**

- Record "54¢ = 5 dimes and 4 pennies" on the chalkboard.

- Repeat with 81¢, 17¢, and 65¢.

  "Put the dimes and pennies in the cups."

CLASS PRACTICE

"Let's review all the number facts."

- Hold up one large fact card at a time as your child says the problem and the answer.

- Repeat several times.

- Give your child **Fact Sheet A 2.2.**

"What number facts do you see?"

"What strategies will you use to find the answers?"

- Allow time for your child to complete the fact sheet.
- Correct the fact sheet with your child.

WRITTEN PRACTICE

- Complete **Worksheet 52A** with your child.
- Complete **Worksheet 52B** with your child later in the day.

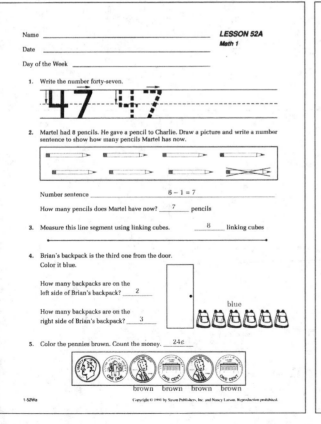

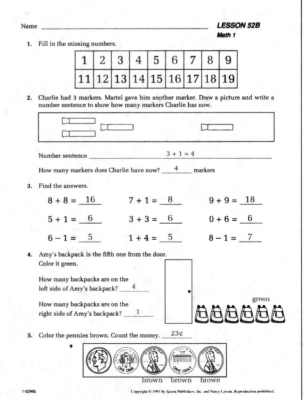

Lesson 53

writing the number 48
counting by 10's and 2's

---

lesson preparation

materials

large bag of unshelled peanuts

10 cups or bowls

Master 1-53

brown crayon

1 sheet of newspaper

large fact cards (subtracting one facts)

Fact Sheet S 2.0

in the morning

• Write the following number pattern on the meeting strip:

> 42, 43, 44, ___, ___, ___

Answer: 42, 43, 44, 45, 46, 47

• Put **1 dime** and **8 pennies** in the coin cup.

THE MEETING

calendar

• Ask your child to identify the following:

  year

  month

  shapes on the calendar

  today's shape

  shape pattern for the month

• Ask your child to write the date on the calendar.

• Ask your child to do the following:

  identify today's day of the week

  identify the days of the week

"What day of the week was it yesterday?"

"What day of the week will it be tomorrow?"

- Ask your child to identify the following:

    number of days in a week

    weekdays

- Ask your child to write the full date on the meeting strip.

weather graph

- Ask your child to report and graph the weather.

- Ask questions about the graph.

counting

- Count from 1 to 100 using the hundred number chart.

- Count backward from 30 to 1.

- Count by 10's to 100.

    "Let's use our counting strip to help us count by 2's to 20."

- Point to each number on the counting strip as your child counts.

- Add another number to the number line.

- Point and count in the following way: 10, 20, 30, 40, 50, 51, 52, 53.

    "How many 10's did we count?"

- Point to the 5 in 53.

    "And how many more did we count?"

- Point to the 3 in 53.

    "What number is (5) tens and (3) more?"

number pattern

- Ask your child to identify and fill in the missing numbers.

- Read the number pattern together.

clock

- Ask your child to set the morning/afternoon/evening/night clock.

- Throughout the day, your child announces the time on the hour and sets the demonstration clock.

coin cup

- Ask your child to slide and count the dimes in the coin cup.

- Ask your child to record the amount of money in the coin cup on the meeting strip.

right/left

- Continue to practice left and right once a week. Practice more often, if necessary.

THE LESSON

Writing the Number 48

"The last number we practiced writing was the number 47."

"What number do you think we will learn how to write today?"

- Write the number 48 on the chalkboard.

"What digits do you see in the number 48?"

"How would you tell someone how to write the number 48?"

"Which digit is on the left?"

"Which digit is on the right?"

Counting by 10's and 2's

- Put a piece of newspaper on the table.

- Hold up a peanut.

"What is this?"

- Give your child the peanut.

"Look at this peanut very carefully without touching it."

"What do you notice about the peanut?"

- Write your child's observations on a piece of paper.

- Title the paper *All About Peanuts.*

"Touch the peanut carefully."

"What do you feel?"

- Write your child's observations on a piece of paper.

"Carefully shake the peanut next to your ear."

"What do you hear?"

- Write your child's observations on a piece of paper.

"Put the peanut near your nose."

"What do you smell?"

- Write your child's observations on a piece of paper.

"What do you think is inside the peanut shell?"

"I will show you how to open a peanut."

- Demonstrate using another peanut.

   "Now open your peanut."

   "What is inside?"

   "We call these nuts."

   "Look at the nuts."

   "What do you see?"

   "How do they feel?"

- Write your child's observations on a piece of paper.

   "You may eat the nuts."

   "How do they taste?"

- Write your child's observations on a piece of paper.

   "What different parts of your body did you use to find out about the peanut?"   *eyes, fingers, ears, nose, mouth*

- At the bottom of the paper write "I used my eyes, fingers, ears, nose, and mouth to find out about peanuts."

- Give your child the bag of peanuts and 10 cups (bowls).

   "Put ten peanuts in each cup (bowl)."

- Allow time for your child to do this.

   "Let's count by 10's to see how many peanuts are in the cups altogether."

   "Why will we count by 10's?"   *each cup has 10 peanuts*

- Point to each cup as your child counts by 10's.

- Give your child **Master 1-53,** a brown crayon, and one of the cups of peanuts.

   "Put one peanut in each box on this paper."

   "How many peanuts do you have on your paper?"   **10**

   "Now you will draw a picture of the nuts inside each peanut, just like we drew a picture of the seeds inside our apples."

   "Use a brown crayon to draw a picture of the nuts in each peanut."

- Demonstrate on the chalkboard how to draw the nuts.

   "Sometimes the nut splits in half."

- Demonstrate.

   "If this happens, put the two halves together and draw only one nut."

   "You will draw only the pictures of the peanuts with exactly two nuts in the shell."

   "If you find a peanut that has one or three nuts, you can eat them."

   "When you have drawn a picture of the nuts, put them in the cup."

"Tomorrow we will use these nuts to make a special treat."

- Allow time for your child to open and draw the nuts.

"Count by 2's to find the number of nuts in your peanuts."

- Save the nuts to use in Lesson 54.

CLASS PRACTICE

"Let's review the subtracting one facts."

- Hold up one large fact card at a time as your child says the problem and the answer.

- Repeat several times.

- Give your child **Fact Sheet S 2.0**.

"What number facts do you see?"

"What strategy will you use to find the answers?"

- Allow time for your child to complete the fact sheet.

- Correct the fact sheet with your child.

WRITTEN PRACTICE

- Complete **Worksheet 53A** with your child.

- Complete **Worksheet 53B** with your child later in the day.

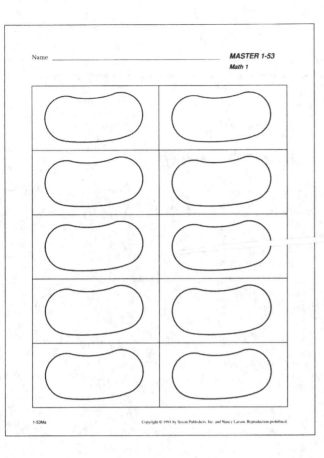

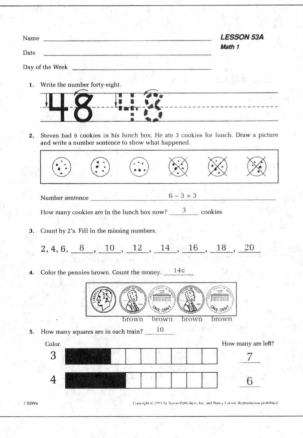

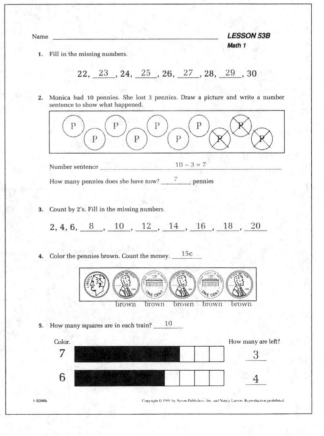

esson 54

writing the number 49
following a recipe
identifying one half and one fourth

---

lesson preparation

materials

chart paper and marker

1 cup shelled peanuts

blender or food processor

vegetable oil

measuring cup and teaspoon

cutting board and knife

1 cracker that can be divided in half

1 celery stalk

napkins

individual fact cards

Fact Sheet A 2.2

the night before

• Write the following recipe on the chalkboard or on paper:

Peanut Butter
1 cup peanuts
1 teaspoon oil
Mix in a blender or food processor until smooth.

in the morning

• Write the following number pattern on the meeting strip:

6, 8, 10, __, __, __

Answer: 6, 8, 10, 12, 14, 16

• Put **2 dimes** and **3 pennies** in the coin cup.

THE MEETING

calendar

- Ask your child to identify the following:

    year

    month

    shapes on the calendar

    today's shape

    shape pattern for the month

- Ask your child to write the date on the calendar.

- Ask your child to do the following:

    identify today's day of the week

    identify the days of the week

    "What day of the week was it yesterday?"

    "What day of the week will it be tomorrow?"

- Ask your child to identify the following:

    number of days in a week

    weekdays

- Ask your child to write the full date on the meeting strip.

weather graph

- Ask your child to report and graph the weather.

- Ask questions about the graph.

counting

- Count from 1 to 100 using the hundred number chart.

- Count backward from 30 to 1.

- Count by 10's to 100.

    "Let's use our counting strip to help us count by 2's to 20."

- Point to each number on the counting strip as your child counts.

- Add another number to the number line.

- Point and count in the following way: 10, 20, 30, 40, 50, 51, 52, 53, 54.

    "How many 10's did we count?"

- Point to the 5 in 54.

    "And how many more did we count?"

- Point to the 4 in 54.

"What number is (5) tens and (4) more?"

number pattern

- Ask your child to identify and fill in the missing numbers.
- Read the number pattern together.

clock

- Ask your child to set the morning/afternoon/evening/night clock.
- Throughout the day, your child announces the time on the hour and sets the demonstration clock.

coin cup

- Ask your child to slide and count the dimes in the coin cup.
- Ask your child to record the amount of money in the coin cup on the meeting strip.

right/left

- Continue to practice left and right once a week. Practice more often, if necessary.

THE LESSON

Writing the Number 49

"The last number we practiced writing was the number 48."

"What number do you think we will learn how to write today?"

- Write the number 49 on the chalkboard.

"What digits do you see in the number 49?"

"How would you tell someone how to write the number 49?"

"Which digit is on the left?"

"Which digit is on the right?"

Following a Recipe
Identifying One Half and One Fourth

"Today you will learn how to follow a recipe."

"You will also learn how to identify one half and one fourth."

- Point to the recipe.

"This is a recipe."

"It tells us how to make something."

"What do you think we are going to make today?"

"Let's read our recipe together."

• Read the recipe with your child.

"What does our recipe tell us to do?"

"Let's measure one cup of peanuts into the blender."

• Ask your child to measure the peanuts.

"How much oil does our recipe tell us to use?"

"A teaspoon is about the same size as the spoon we use to eat cereal or ice cream."

"When we follow a recipe, we usually use a measuring spoon that is the official size of a teaspoon."

"Sometimes a teaspoon has the letters 'tsp.' written on it."

"Why do you think they use these letters?"

• Underline the letters *t*, *s*, and *p* in teaspoon.

"We will add one teaspoon of oil for each cup of peanuts."

• Ask your child to measure the oil.

• Mix the peanut butter. If the mixture is too thick, stop to scrape the blades and add more oil. Set the mixture aside.

"We will eat our peanut butter on celery and crackers."

• Show your child the celery stalk and cracker.

"We will share this cracker and celery stalk."

• Hold up the cracker.

"How will we divide this cracker so that each of us will have a fair share?"   *in half*

• Divide the cracker in half.

• Draw a cracker on the chalkboard.

"Show me how to divide this chalkboard cracker in half."

• Ask your child to draw a line to divide the cracker in half.

"Let's divide the celery so that we have 4 pieces of the same size."

"Watch how I divide the celery so that we have 4 equal pieces."

"First I will divide the celery stalk in half."

• Cut the celery crosswise.

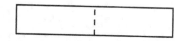

"How many pieces do we have now?"

"Now I will divide each half in half again."

- Cut the celery pieces in half again.

"How many pieces do we have now?" **4**

"When we have four pieces exactly the same size, each piece is called one fourth."

- Draw a piece of celery on the chalkboard.

"Show me how to divide this piece of celery into fourths."

- Ask your child to draw the lines to divide the celery into fourths.

"Let's count the pieces to check."

"Now you and I will eat half of a cracker with peanut butter."

"We will also each eat one fourth of a celery stalk with peanut butter."

"We can eat another fourth later."

- Give your child a cracker with peanut butter and a piece of celery with peanut butter.

"Which do you like better?"

CLASS PRACTICE

"Today you will use your individual fact cards to practice the addition number facts."

- Allow time for your child to practice his/her number facts independently.
- Give your child **Fact Sheet A 2.2.**

"What number facts do you see?"

"What strategy will you use to find the answers?"

- Allow time for your child to complete the fact sheet.
- Correct the fact sheet with your child.

WRITTEN PRACTICE

- Complete **Worksheet 54A** with your child.
- Complete **Worksheet 54B** with your child later in the day.

LESSON 54A
Math 1

Name _____

Date _____

Day of the Week _____

1. Write the number forty-nine.

49 49

2. Eight icicles were hanging from the roof. Four fell off. Draw a picture and write a number sentence to show what happened.

Number sentence _____ $8 - 4 = 4$

How many icicles are hanging from the roof now? __4__ icicles

3. Write the numbers that are one less and one more.

__12__ , 13, __14__   __24__ , 25, __26__

__8__ , 9, __10__   __29__ , 30, __31__

4. Color the penny brown. Count the money. __61¢__

brown

5. Mrs. Murray divided this cracker in half.
Draw a line to divide the cracker in half.

She put peanut butter on one of the halves.
Use a brown crayon to show the peanut butter.
She put jelly on the other half.
Use a purple crayon to show the jelly.

brown | purple

1-54Wa

LESSON 54B
Math 1

Name _____

1. Fill in the missing numbers.

| 41 | 42 | 43 | 44 | 45 | 46 | 47 | 48 | 49 | 50 |

2. Six birds were eating at a bird feeder. Three birds flew away. Draw a picture and write a number sentence to show what happened.

Number sentence _____ $6 - 3 = 3$

How many birds are at the feeder now? __3__ birds

3. Write the numbers that are one less and one more.

__16__ , 17, __18__   __33__ , 34, __35__

__5__ , 6, __7__   __19__ , 20, __21__

4. Color the pennies brown. Count the money. __43¢__

brown brown brown

5. Ms. Mulligan divided this cracker in half.
Draw a line to divide the cracker in half.

She put peanut butter on one of the halves.
Use a brown crayon to show the peanut butter.
She put jelly on the other half.
Use a purple crayon to show the jelly.

brown | purple

1-54Wb

Lesson 55

writing the number 50
identifying odd and even numbers

---

lesson preparation

materials

Written Assessment #10

Meeting Book

large fact cards

Fact Sheet A 3.2

in the morning

• Write the following number pattern on the meeting strip:

> 19, 18, 17, ___, ___, ___

Answer: 19, 18, 17, 16, 15, 14

• Put **6 dimes** and **1 penny** in the coin cup.

THE MEETING

calendar

• Ask your child to identify the following:

    year

    month

    shapes on the calendar

    today's shape

    shape pattern for the month

• Ask your child to write the date on the calendar.

• Ask your child to do the following:

    identify today's day of the week

    identify the days of the week

"What day of the week was it yesterday?"

"What day of the week will it be tomorrow?"

- Ask your child to identify the following:

  number of days in a week

  weekdays

- Ask your child to write the full date on the meeting strip.

weather graph

- Ask your child to report and graph the weather.

- Ask questions about the graph.

counting

- Count from 1 to 100 using the hundred number chart.

- Count backward from 30 to 1.

- Count by 10's to 100.

  "Let's use our counting strip to help us count by 2's to 20."

- Point to each number on the counting strip as your child counts.

- Add another number to the number line.

- Point and count in the following way: 10, 20, 30, 40, 50, 51, 52, 53, 54, 55.

  "How many 10's did we count?"

- Point to the 5 in the tens' place.

  "And how many more did we count?"

- Point to the 5 in the ones' place.

  "What number is (5) tens and (5) more?"

number pattern

- Ask your child to identify and fill in the missing numbers.

- Read the number pattern together.

clock

- Ask your child to set the morning/afternoon/evening/night clock.

- Throughout the day, your child announces the time on the hour and sets the demonstration clock.

coin cup

- Ask your child to slide and count the dimes in the coin cup.

- Ask your child to record the amount of money in the coin cup on the meeting strip.

right/left

- Continue to practice left and right once a week. Practice more often, if necessary.

ASSESSMENT

Written Assessment

"Today, I would like to see what you remember from what we have been practicing."

- Give your child **Written Assessment #10**.

"Write your name at the top of the paper."

"I will read the directions for each problem."

- Read the directions for each problem. Allow time for your child to complete each problem before continuing.

- Correct the paper, noting your child's mistakes on the **Individual Recording Form**. Review the errors with your child.

THE LESSON

Writing the Number 50

"The last number we practiced writing was the number 49."

"What number do you think we will learn how to write today?"

- Write the number 50 on the chalkboard.

"What digits do you see in the number 50?"

"How would you tell someone how to write the number 50?"

"Which digit is on the left?"

"Which digit is on the right?"

Identifying Odd and Even Numbers

"Today you will learn to identify and count by odd and even numbers."

"Count by 2's to 20."

"I will write the numbers on the chalkboard as you say them."

- As you write the even numbers on the chalkboard, leave space for the odd numbers.

"Let's continue the pattern of our even numbers."

"What number will be next?"   **22**

"What number will be next?"   **24**

"Can we keep going?"

- Fill in several more numbers.

"Now let's count backward by 2's from 20."

"What about zero?"

"Why will zero be an even number?"   **because it fits the pattern**

"What is the pattern for the even numbers?"   **add 2 (skip 1)**

"When we say the even numbers, it is just like adding two."

"What is 6 plus 2?"   **8**

"What is 4 plus 2?"   **6**

"What is 12 plus 2?"   **14**

"Adding one to a number was just like counting, and adding two to a number is like counting by 2's."

"We have some numbers between the even numbers that are missing."

"What are these numbers?"

- Record them on the chalkboard in the following manner:

"These numbers also have a special name."

"Do you know what they are called?"   **odd numbers**

"They are called odd numbers."

"Let's read the odd numbers together."

"What is the pattern for the odd numbers?"   **add 2 to an odd number**

"What is 5 plus 2?"   **7**

"What is 7 plus 2?"   **9**

"What is 11 plus 2?"   **13**

"What is 15 plus 2?"   **17**

"Let's say the odd numbers together."

"Count slowly so that I can write the odd numbers on a counting strip in the Meeting Book."

- Open the Meeting Book to page 48.

- Write the numbers on the third counting strip as your child counts. Start at the bottom and work up.

CLASS PRACTICE

"Let's review all the number facts."

- Hold up one large fact card at a time as your child says the problem and answer.

- Repeat several times.

- Give your child **Fact Sheet A 3.2.**

  "What number facts do you see?"

  "What strategies will you use to find the answers?"

- Allow time for your child to complete the fact sheet.

- Correct the fact sheet with your child.

WRITTEN PRACTICE

- Complete **Worksheet 55A** with your child.
- Complete **Worksheet 55B** with your child later in the day.

Name _____   **ASSESSMENT 10**

Date _____   **LESSON 55**

                                           Math 1

1. Billy counted nine date tags on the calendar. He put one more date tag on the calendar. Draw a picture and write a number sentence to show how many date tags are on the calendar now.

   Number sentence _____ $9 + 1 = 10$ _____

   How many date tags did he count? ___10___ date tags

2. How many dimes do you see? ___7___

   How much money is this? ___70¢___

3. Find the answers.

   $$\begin{array}{cccccccc} 6 & 5 & 8 & 7 & 0 & 7 & 1 & 4 \\ +0 & -1 & +1 & +7 & +4 & -1 & +3 & -1 \\ \hline 6 & 4 & 9 & 14 & 4 & 6 & 4 & 3 \end{array}$$

4. Use linking cubes to measure this line segment. ___8___ cubes

5. Count by 10's. Fill in the missing numbers.

   10, 20, 30, __40__ , __50__ , __60__ , __70__ , __80__ , __90__ , __100__

Name _____   **LESSON 55A**

                                           Math 1

Date _____

Day of the Week _____

1. Write the number fifty.

   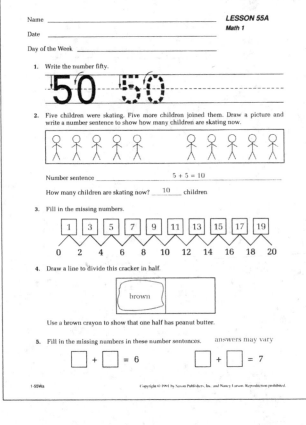

2. Five children were skating. Five more children joined them. Draw a picture and write a number sentence to show how many children are skating now.

   Number sentence _____ $5 + 5 = 10$ _____

   How many children are skating now? ___10___ children

3. Fill in the missing numbers.

1	3	5	7	9	11	13	15	17	19

   0   2   4   6   8   10   12   14   16   18   20

4. Draw a line to divide this cracker in half.

   brown

   Use a brown crayon to show that one half has peanut butter.

5. Fill in the missing numbers in these number sentences.   answers may vary

   ☐ + ☐ = 6   ☐ + ☐ = 7

Name _____   **LESSON 55B**

                                           Math 1

1. Fill in the missing numbers.

41	42	43	44	45	46	47	48	49	50

2. Eight children were skating. Three children were cold and went home. Draw a picture and write a number sentence to show how many children are skating now.

   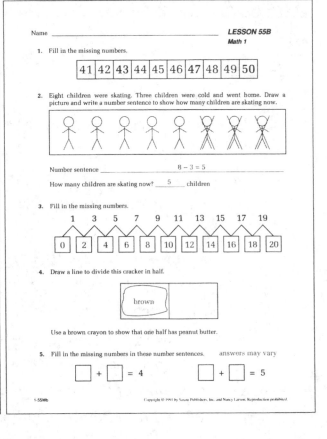

   Number sentence _____ $8 - 3 = 5$ _____

   How many children are skating now? ___5___ children

3. Fill in the missing numbers.

   1   3   5   7   9   11   13   15   17   19

0	2	4	6	8	10	12	14	16	18	20

4. Draw a line to divide this cracker in half.

   brown

   Use a brown crayon to show that one half has peanut butter.

5. Fill in the missing numbers in these number sentences.   answers may vary

   ☐ + ☐ = 4   ☐ + ☐ = 5

esson 56

writing the number 51
numbering a clock face
drawing time to the hour on a clock

---

lesson preparation

materials

2 demonstration clocks

Master 1-56

large fact cards

Fact Sheet A 3.2

in the morning

- Write the following number pattern on the meeting strip:

> 1, 3, 5, __, __, __

Answer: 1, 3, 5, 7, 9, 11

- Put **5 dimes** and **9 pennies** in the coin cup.

THE MEETING

calendar

- Ask your child to identify the following:

    year

    month

    shapes on the calendar

    today's shape

    shape pattern for the month

- Ask your child to write the date on the calendar.

- Ask your child to do the following:

    identify today's day of the week

    identify the days of the week

"What day of the week was it yesterday?"

"What day of the week will it be tomorrow?"

- Ask your child to identify the following:

    number of days in a week

    weekdays

- Ask your child to write the full date on the meeting strip.

weather graph

- Ask your child to report and graph the weather.

- Ask questions about the graph.

counting

- Count from 1 to 100 using the hundred number chart.

- Count backward from 30 to 1.

- Count by 10's to 100.

- Count backward from 100 by 10's.

- Count by 2's to 20.

    "Let's use our counting strips to help us say the odd numbers."

- Point to each number on the counting strip as you count together.

- Add another number to the number line.

    "Let's count the numbers on our number line."

    "We will count by 10's as far as we can and then count by 1's."

    "How many 10's did we count?"

    "And how many more did we count?"

    "What number is _____ tens and _____ more?"

number pattern

- Ask your child to identify and fill in the missing numbers.

- Read the number pattern together.

clock

- Ask your child to set the morning/afternoon/evening/night clock.

- Throughout the day, your child announces the time on the hour and sets the demonstration clock.

coin cup

- Ask your child to slide and count the dimes in the coin cup.

- Ask your child to record the amount of money in the coin cup on the meeting strip.

right/left

- Continue to practice left and right once a week. Practice more often, if necessary.

THE LESSON

Writing the Number 51

"The last number we practiced writing was the number 50."

"What number do you think we will learn how to write today?"

- Write the number 51 on the chalkboard.

"What digits do you see in the number 51?"

"How would you tell someone how to write the number 51?"

"Which digit is on the left?"

"Which digit is on the right?"

Numbering a Clock Face
Drawing Time to the Hour on a Clock

"Today you will learn how to draw the time on a clock."

"You will also learn how to number a clock face."

- Set a demonstration clock to show 3:00.

"What time does this clock show?"

- Give your child a clock.

"Make your clock show the same time."

"Which hand tells you the hour?"

"This is called the hour hand."

"Which hand is longer?"

"Which hand is shorter?"

"Show 7:00 on your clock."

- Allow time for your child to do this.

"Show 2:00 on your clock."

- Give your child **Master 1-56**.

"Point to the clock in the top left-hand corner of the paper."

"We will number this clock face so that it looks just like our clock."

"What number is at the top of the clock?"

"What number is at the bottom of the clock?"

"What number is to the right of the twelve?"

- Continue numbering the rest of the clock face.

- Number one more clock with your child.

"Number the last two clock faces the same way."

- Watch and assist your child as he/she numbers the other two clocks independently.

- Write "5:00" on the chalkboard.

"This is the way five o'clock looks on a digital clock."

"Why do you think it is called a digital clock?"   *the time is shown using digits*

"Write this digital time in the box in the upper left-hand corner of your paper."

"Set your individual clock to show 5:00."

"Draw the hands on the clock in the upper left-hand corner of your paper."

"Where does the long hand point?"

"This hand goes through the twelve."

"Where does the hour hand point?"

"This hand just touches the number five."

- Repeat with 10:00, 1:00, and 6:00.

CLASS PRACTICE

"Let's review all the number facts."

- Hold up one large fact card at a time as your child says the problem and answer.

- Repeat several times.

- Give your child **Fact Sheet A 3.2.**

"What number facts do you see?"

"What strategies will you use to find the answers?"

- Allow time for your child to complete the fact sheet.

- Correct the fact sheet with your child.

WRITTEN PRACTICE

- Complete **Worksheet 56A** with your child.

- Complete **Worksheet 56B** with your child later in the day.

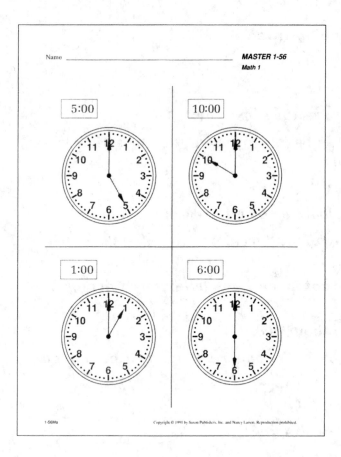

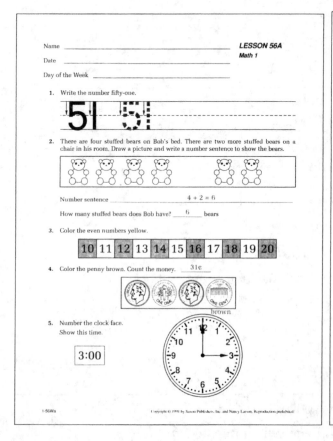

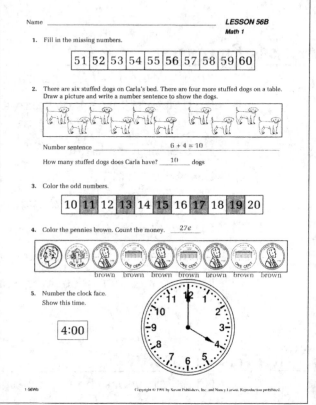

Lesson 57

writing the number 52
adding two to an even number

---

lesson preparation

materials

1 tower of 10 linking cubes

yellow crayon

Master 1-57

individual fact cards

Fact Sheet A 3.2

in the morning

• Write the following number pattern on the meeting strip:

> 10, 12, 14, ___, ___, ___

Answer: 10, 12, 14, 16, 18, 20

• Put **7 dimes** and **4 pennies** in the coin cup.

THE MEETING

calendar

• Ask your child to identify the following:

> year
>
> month
>
> shapes on the calendar
>
> today's shape
>
> shape pattern for the month

• Ask your child to write the date on the calendar.

• Ask your child to do the following:

> identify today's day of the week
>
> identify the days of the week

"What day of the week was it yesterday?"

"What day of the week will it be tomorrow?"

- Ask your child to identify the following:

  number of days in a week

  weekdays

- Ask your child to write the full date on the meeting strip.

weather graph

- Ask your child to report and graph the weather.

- Ask questions about the graph.

counting

- Count from 1 to 100 using the hundred number chart.

- Count backward from 30 to 1.

- Count by 10's to 100.

- Count backward from 100 by 10's.

- Count by 2's to 20.

- Say the odd numbers to 19.

- Add another number to the number line.

  "Let's count the numbers on our number line."

  "We will count by 10's as far as we can and then count by 1's."

  "How many 10's did we count?"

  "And how many more did we count?"

  "What number is _____ tens and _____ more?"

number pattern

- Ask your child to identify and fill in the missing numbers.

- Read the number pattern together.

clock

- Ask your child to set the morning/afternoon/evening/night clock.

- Throughout the day, your child announces the time on the hour and sets the demonstration clock.

  "Beginning today, you will write the digital time for each new hour in this box on the chalkboard."

- Draw a box for the digital time on the chalkboard.

coin cup

- Ask your child to slide and count the dimes in the coin cup.

- Ask your child to record the amount of money in the coin cup on the meeting strip.

right/left

• Continue to practice left and right once a week. Practice more often, if necessary.

THE LESSON

Writing the Number 52

"The last number we practiced writing was the number 51."

"What number do you think we will learn how to write today?"

• Write the number 52 on the chalkboard.

"What digits do you see in the number 52?"

"How would you tell someone how to write the number 52?"

"Which digit is on the left?"

"Which digit is on the right?"

Adding Two to an Even Number

"Today you will learn how to add two to an even number."

"Tell me the even numbers."

• Write the following on the chalkboard:

    0   2   4   6   8   10   12   14   16   18   20

"Let's add two to each number."

• Erase the numbers 10–20.

• Write the following on the chalkboard:

$$\begin{array}{ccccc} 0 & 2 & 4 & 6 & 8 \\ +2 & +2 & +2 & +2 & +2 \end{array}$$

"We will use linking cubes to help us find the answers for these problems."

• Give your child a tower of ten linking cubes.

"Unsnap your cubes."

"What is zero plus two?"

"Show that with your cubes."

"How many cubes is that?"

"Add two cubes to your train of two."

"How many cubes do you have now?"

"Add two cubes to your train of four."

"How many cubes do you have now?"

- Record the answers beneath each problem as your child uses the cubes to find the answers.

- Repeat with 6 + 2 and 8 + 2.

"What happened when we added two to an even number?"

"Let's read these problems together."

- Point to each problem as you read the problems with your child.

"Now I will say an adding two problem."

"Let's see how fast you can say the answer."

- Do not erase the answers on the chalkboard. Allow your child to refer to them as you say the problems in random order. (Use the following facts only: 0 + 2, 2 + 0, 2 + 2, 4 + 2, 2 + 4, 6 + 2, 2 + 6, 8 + 2, 2 + 8.)

- Give your child **Master 1-57** and a yellow crayon.

"Today we will use only the top half of this paper."

"We will show all the even numbers on the hundred number chart."

"Point to the hundred number chart at the top of the paper."

"Point to the smallest even number on this hundred number chart."

"What number is it?"

"Color the square with the number 2 using a yellow crayon."

"Point to the number that is two more than two."

"Two more than two is four."

"Color this square yellow."

- Continue until you reach 20.

"What is the pattern on the hundred number chart when we add two to an even number?"

"Keep adding two and coloring the boxes on the hundred number chart."

- When your child finishes, continue.

"Let's read the yellow numbers together."

"Do you see a pattern on the hundred number chart?"

"What is it?"

- Save **Master 1-57** for use in Lesson 58.

294

CLASS PRACTICE

"Today you will use your individual fact cards to practice the addition number facts."

- Allow time for your child to practice his/her number facts independently.
- Give your child **Fact Sheet A 3.2.**

  "What number facts do you see?"

  "What strategies will you use to find the answers?"

- Allow time for your child to complete the fact sheet.
- Correct the fact sheet with your child.

WRITTEN PRACTICE

- Complete **Worksheet 57A** with your child.
- Complete **Worksheet 57B** with your child later in the day.

Name _____ **MASTER 1-57**
Math 1

Even
Numbers

1	2	3	4	5	6	7	8	9	10
11	12	13	14	15	16	17	18	19	20
21	22	23	24	25	26	27	28	29	30
31	32	33	34	35	36	37	38	39	40
41	42	43	44	45	46	47	48	49	50
51	52	53	54	55	56	57	58	59	60
61	62	63	64	65	66	67	68	69	70
71	72	73	74	75	76	77	78	79	80
81	82	83	84	85	86	87	88	89	90
91	92	93	94	95	96	97	98	99	100

Odd
Numbers

1	2	3	4	5	6	7	8	9	10
11	12	13	14	15	16	17	18	19	20
21	22	23	24	25	26	27	28	29	30
31	32	33	34	35	36	37	38	39	40
41	42	43	44	45	46	47	48	49	50
51	52	53	54	55	56	57	58	59	60
61	62	63	64	65	66	67	68	69	70
71	72	73	74	75	76	77	78	79	80
81	82	83	84	85	86	87	88	89	90
91	92	93	94	95	96	97	98	99	100

1-57Ma

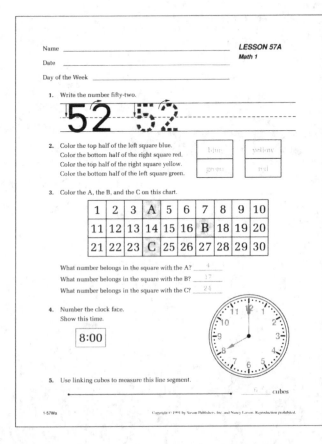

Name _____ **LESSON 57A**
Math 1

Date _____

Day of the Week _____

1. Write the number fifty-two.

   52 52

2. Color the top half of the left square blue.
   Color the bottom half of the right square red.
   Color the top half of the right square yellow.
   Color the bottom half of the left square green.

blue	yellow
green	red

3. Color the A, the B, and the C on this chart.

1	2	3	A	5	6	7	8	9	10
11	12	13	14	15	16	B	18	19	20
21	22	23	C	25	26	27	28	29	30

   What number belongs in the square with the A? ___4___
   What number belongs in the square with the B? ___17___
   What number belongs in the square with the C? ___24___

4. Number the clock face.
   Show this time.

   8:00

5. Use linking cubes to measure this line segment.

   •———————————— ___6___ cubes

1-57Wa

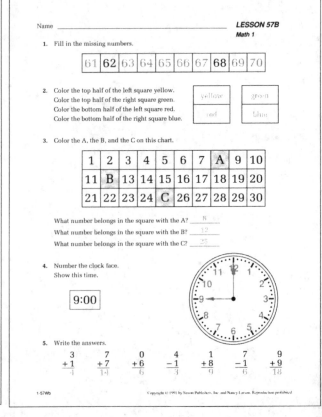

Name _____ **LESSON 57B**
Math 1

1. Fill in the missing numbers.

61	62	63	64	65	66	67	68	69	70

2. Color the top half of the left square yellow.
   Color the top half of the right square green.
   Color the bottom half of the left square red.
   Color the bottom half of the right square blue.

yellow	green
red	blue

3. Color the A, the B, and the C on this chart.

1	2	3	4	5	6	7	A	9	10
11	B	13	14	15	16	17	18	19	20
21	22	23	24	C	26	27	28	29	30

   What number belongs in the square with the A? ___8___
   What number belongs in the square with the B? ___12___
   What number belongs in the square with the C? ___25___

4. Number the clock face.
   Show this time.

   9:00

5. Write the answers.

$\begin{array}{r}3\\+1\\\hline 4\end{array}$	$\begin{array}{r}7\\+7\\\hline 14\end{array}$	$\begin{array}{r}0\\+6\\\hline 6\end{array}$	$\begin{array}{r}4\\-1\\\hline 3\end{array}$	$\begin{array}{r}1\\+8\\\hline 9\end{array}$	$\begin{array}{r}7\\-1\\\hline 6\end{array}$	$\begin{array}{r}9\\+9\\\hline 18\end{array}$

1-57Wb

esson 58

writing the number 53
adding two to an odd number

---

lesson preparation

materials

1 tower of 10 linking cubes

Master 1-57 (from Lesson 57)

orange crayon

addition fact cards — green

Fact Sheet AA 4.0

the night before

• Separate the green addition fact cards.

in the morning

• Write the following number pattern on the meeting strip:

> 26, 27, 28, __, __, __

Answer: 26, 27, 28, 29, 30, 31

• Put **8 dimes** and **2 pennies** in the coin cup.

THE MEETING

calendar

   • Ask your child to identify the following:

   year

   month

   shapes on the calendar

   today's shape

   shape pattern for the month

   • Ask your child to write the date on the calendar.

   • Ask your child to do the following:

   identify today's day of the week

   identify the days of the week

"What day of the week was it yesterday?"

"What day of the week will it be tomorrow?"

- Ask your child to identify the following:

    number of days in a week

    weekdays

- Ask your child to write the full date on the meeting strip.

weather graph

- Ask your child to report and graph the weather.

- Ask questions about the graph.

counting

- Count from 1 to 100 using the hundred number chart.

- Count backward from 30 to 1.

- Count by 10's to 100.

- Count backward from 100 by 10's.

- Count by 2's to 20.

- Say the odd numbers to 19.

- Add another number to the number line.

    "Let's count the numbers on our number line."

    "We will count by 10's as far as we can and then count by 1's."

    "How many 10's did we count?"

    "And how many more did we count?"

    "What number is _____ tens and _____ more?"

number pattern

- Ask your child to identify and fill in the missing numbers.

- Read the number pattern together.

clock

- Ask your child to set the morning/afternoon/evening/night clock.

- Throughout the day, your child announces the time on the hour, sets the demonstration clock, and writes the digital time for each new hour on the chalkboard.

coin cup

- Ask your child to slide and count the dimes in the coin cup.

- Ask your child to record the amount of money in the coin cup on the meeting strip.

right/left

- Continue to practice left and right once a week. Practice more often, if necessary.

THE LESSON

Writing the Number 53

"The last number we practiced writing was the number 52."

"What number do you think we will learn how to write today?"

- Write the number 53 on the chalkboard.

"What digits do you see in the number 53?"

"How would you tell someone how to write the number 53?"

"Which digit is on the left?"

"Which digit is on the right?"

Adding Two to an Odd Number

"Yesterday we practiced adding two to an even number."

"How did we do that?"

"Today you will learn how to add two to an odd number."

"Tell me the odd numbers."

- Write the following on the chalkboard:

  1   3   5   7   9   11   13   15   17   19

"Let's add two to each number."

- Erase the numbers 11–19.

- Write the following on the chalkboard:

$$\begin{array}{ccccc} 1 & 3 & 5 & 7 & 9 \\ +2 & +2 & +2 & +2 & +2 \end{array}$$

"We will use linking cubes to help us find the answers for these problems."

- Give your child a tower of ten cubes.

"Unsnap your cubes."

"What is one plus two?"

"Show that with your cubes."

"How many cubes is that?"

"Add two cubes to the train of three."

"How many cubes do you have now?"

"Add two cubes to the train of five."

"How many cubes do you have now?"

- Record the answers beneath each problem as your child uses the cubes to find the answers.

- Repeat with 7 + 2.

"Do we have enough cubes to find the answer for nine plus two?"

"How do you know?"

"What happened when we added two to an odd number?"   the answer was odd

"Let's read these problems together."

- Point to each problem as you read the problems with your child.

"Now I will say an adding two problem."

"Let's see how fast you can say the answer."

- Do not erase the answers on the chalkboard. Allow children to refer to them as you say the problems in random order. (Use the following facts only: 1 + 2, 2 + 1, 3 + 2, 2 + 3, 5 + 2, 2 + 5, 7 + 2, 2 + 7, 9 + 2, 2 + 9.)

- Give your child an orange crayon and **Master 1-57** (hundred number chart) from Lesson 57.

"Today we will use only the bottom half of this paper."

"We will show all the odd numbers on the hundred number chart."

"Point to the hundred number chart at the bottom of the page."

"Point to the smallest odd number on the hundred number chart."

"What number did you find?"   1

"Color the square with the number one using an orange crayon."

"Point to the number that is two more than one."

"Two more than one is three."

"Color this square orange."

- Continue until you reach 19.

"What is the pattern on the hundred number chart when we add two to an odd number?"

"Keep adding two and coloring in the boxes on your hundred number chart."

- When your child finishes, continue.

"Let's read the orange numbers together."

"What do you notice about the patterns on these hundred number charts?"

"Now I will give you your own set of fact cards for the adding two facts."

- Give your child the green addition fact cards.

"Use your hundred number chart or your linking cubes to help you find each answer."

"Write the answer on the back of each card."

- When your child finishes, give the following directions:

"Put your cards in a pile."

"Now read each problem to yourself."

"See if you remember the answer."

"Turn over the card to check the answer."

"Practice saying the answers to yourself."

- Allow time for your child to use the fact cards independently.

"We will call these our adding two facts."

"How can we remember these answers?"   *if we begin with an even number, we will get the next even number; if we begin with an odd number, we will get the next odd number*

CLASS PRACTICE

- Give your child **Fact Sheet AA 4.0.**

"What number facts do you see?"

"What strategy will you use to find the answers?"

- Allow time for your child to complete the fact sheet.
- Correct the fact sheet with your child.

WRITTEN PRACTICE

- Complete **Worksheet 58A** with your child.
- Complete **Worksheet 58B** with your child later in the day.

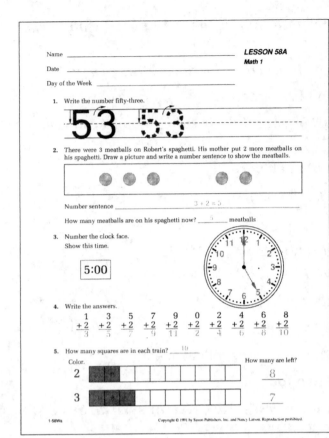

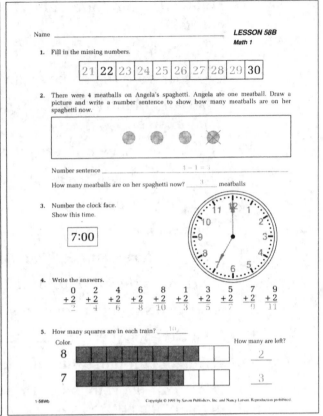

LESSON 58A
Math 1

Name _____

Date _____

Day of the Week _____

1. Write the number fifty-three.

53 53

2. There were 3 meatballs on Robert's spaghetti. His mother put 2 more meatballs on his spaghetti. Draw a picture and write a number sentence to show the meatballs.

Number sentence _____ 3 + 2 = 5 _____

How many meatballs are on his spaghetti now? ___5___ meatballs

3. Number the clock face.
   Show this time.

   5:00

4. Write the answers.

   1   3   5   7   9   0   2   4   6   8
   +2   +2   +2   +2   +2   +2   +2   +2   +2   +2
   3   5   7   9   11   2   4   6   8   10

5. How many squares are in each train? ___10___

   Color.   How many are left?

   2   8

   3   7

1-58Wa

LESSON 58B
Math 1

Name _____

1. Fill in the missing numbers.

   | 21 | 22 | 23 | 24 | 25 | 26 | 27 | 28 | 29 | 30 |

2. There were 4 meatballs on Angela's spaghetti. Angela ate one meatball. Draw a picture and write a number sentence to show how many meatballs are on her spaghetti now.

Number sentence _____ 4 − 1 = 3 _____

How many meatballs are on her spaghetti now? ___3___ meatballs

3. Number the clock face.
   Show this time.

   7:00

4. Write the answers.

   0   2   4   6   8   1   3   5   7   9
   +2   +2   +2   +2   +2   +2   +2   +2   +2   +2
   2   4   6   8   10   3   5   7   9   11

5. How many squares are in each train? ___10___

   Color.   How many are left?

   8   2

   7   3

1-58Wb

Lesson **59**

writing the number 54
covering a design with pattern blocks
sorting, counting, and recording the pattern blocks used to cover a design

---

lesson preparation

materials

fourteen 3" × 5" cards

pattern blocks

Masters 1-59A and 1-59B

Fact Sheet AA 4.0

the night before

• Use the 3" × 5" cards to make a large set of fact cards for the adding two facts. Write them in the following way:

3 + 2	2 + 3	4 + 2	2 + 4	5 + 2	2 + 5	6 + 2

2 + 6	7 + 2	2 + 7	8 + 2	2 + 8	9 + 2	2 + 9

in the morning

• Write the following number pattern on the meeting strip:

50, 60, 70, __, __, __

Answer: 50, 60, 70, 80, 90, 100

• Put **9 dimes** and **8 pennies** in the coin cup.

THE MEETING

calendar

- Ask your child to identify the following:

  year

  month

  shapes on the calendar

  today's shape

  shape pattern for the month

- Ask your child to write the date on the calendar.

- Ask your child to do the following:

  identify today's day of the week

  identify the days of the week

  "What day of the week was it yesterday?"

  "What day of the week will it be tomorrow?"

- Ask your child to identify the following:

  number of days in a week

  weekdays

- Ask your child to write the full date on the meeting strip.

weather graph

- Ask your child to report and graph the weather.

- Ask questions about the graph.

counting

- Count from 1 to 100 using the hundred number chart.

- Count backward from 30 to 1.

- Count by 10's to 100.

- Count backward from 100 by 10's.

- Count by 2's to 20.

- Say the odd numbers to 19.

- Add another number to the number line.

  "Let's count the numbers on our number line."

  "We will count by 10's as far as we can and then count by 1's."

  "How many 10's did we count?"

  "And how many more did we count?"

"What number is _____ tens and _____ more?"

number pattern

- Ask your child to identify and fill in the missing numbers.

- Read the number pattern together.

clock

- Ask your child to set the morning/afternoon/evening/night clock.

- Throughout the day, your child announces the time on the hour, sets the demonstration clock, and writes the digital time for each new hour on the chalkboard.

coin cup

- Ask your child to slide and count the dimes in the coin cup.

- Ask your child to record the amount of money in the coin cup on the meeting strip.

right/left

- Continue to practice left and right once a week. Practice more often, if necessary.

THE LESSON

Writing the Number 54

"The last number we practiced writing was the number 53."

"What number do you think we will learn how to write today?"

- Write the number 54 on the chalkboard.

"What digits do you see in the number 54?"

"How would you tell someone how to write the number 54?"

"Which digit is on the left?"

"Which digit is on the right?"

Covering a Design with Pattern Blocks
Sorting, Counting, and Recording the Pattern Blocks Used to Cover a Design

- Draw a model of the chart (**Master 1-59B**) on the chalkboard.

"Today you will learn how to cover a design using pattern blocks and fill in a chart to show the number of pieces you used."

- Hold up **Master 1-59A**.

"What shape is this?"

"You will try to cover this triangle in four different ways."

"You will make a chart to show all the different ways you covered the design."

"Let me show you how you will do this."

- Cover the design with pattern blocks.

"First I covered the design with pattern blocks."

- Demonstrate as you say the following:

"Now I will put the extra pattern blocks back in the container."

"Next, I will take the pattern blocks off the design, sort them, and count how many I used."

"I will count one color at a time."

- Point to the **Master 1-59B** chart on the chalkboard.

"On my chart I will write how many blocks of each color I used."

- Demonstrate with each color.

"I will count how many pattern blocks I used altogether and write that number at the bottom next to the word 'total.' "

"Now I will cover the large triangle again, using different blocks."

"What will I do after I finish covering the triangle?"

- Demonstrate the steps as your child describes them.

"Now it is your turn to cover the triangle."

- Give your child **Masters 1-59A** and **1-59B** and the container of pattern blocks.

"Find four different ways to cover the large triangle."

"Record the pattern blocks you used, just like I did."

CLASS PRACTICE

"Let's review the adding two facts."

- Hold up one large fact card at a time as your child says the problem and the answer.

- Repeat several times.

- Give your child **Fact Sheet AA 4.0.**

"What number facts do you see?"

"What strategy will you use to find the answers?"

- Allow time for your child to complete the fact sheet.

- Correct the fact sheet together.

WRITTEN PRACTICE

- • Complete **Worksheet 59A** with your child.

- • Complete **Worksheet 59B** with your child later in the day.

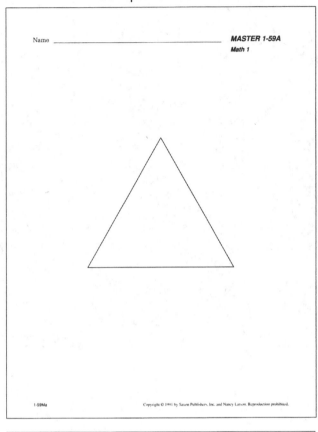

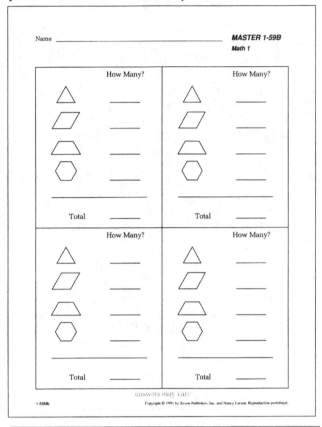

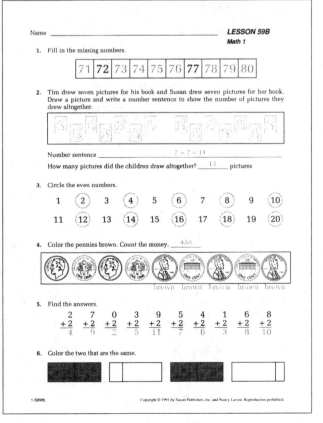

Lesson 60

assessment

---

lesson preparation

materials
Written Assessment #11
Oral Assessment #6
individual clock

in the morning
• Write the following number pattern on the meeting strip:

> 45, 46, 47, ___, ___, ___

Answer: 45, 46, 47, 48, 49, 50

• Put **3 dimes** and **7 pennies** in the coin cup.

THE MEETING

calendar

• Ask your child to identify the following:

> year
>
> month
>
> shapes on the calendar
>
> today's shape
>
> shape pattern for the month

• Ask your child to write the date on the calendar.

• Ask your child to do the following:

> identify today's day of the week
>
> identify the days of the week

> ***"What day of the week was it yesterday?"***

> ***"What day of the week will it be tomorrow?"***

• Ask your child to identify the following:

> number of days in a week
>
> weekdays

- Ask your child to write the full date on the meeting strip.

weather graph

- Ask your child to report and graph the weather.
- Ask questions about the graph.

counting

- Count from 1 to 100 using the hundred number chart.
- Count backward from 30 to 1.
- Count by 10's to 100.
- Count backward from 100 by 10's.
- Count by 2's to 20.
- Say the odd numbers to 19.
- Add another number to the number line.
- Use an orange crayon to color the square for 60.

   "Let's count the numbers on our number line."

   "We will count by 10's as far as we can and then count by 1's."

   "How many 10's did we count?"

   "And how many more did we count?"

   "What number is _____ tens and _____ more?"

number pattern

- Ask your child to identify and fill in the missing numbers.
- Read the number pattern together.

clock

- Ask your child to set the morning/afternoon/evening/night clock.
- Throughout the day, your child announces the time on the hour, sets the demonstration clock, and writes the digital time for each new hour on the chalkboard.

coin cup

- Ask your child to slide and count the dimes in the coin cup.
- Ask your child to record the amount of money in the coin cup on the meeting strip.

right/left

- Continue to practice left and right once a week. Practice more often, if necessary.

ASSESSMENT

- All of the questions on the assessment are based on concepts and skills presented at least five lessons ago. If your child is having difficulty with a specific concept, reteach the concept the following day.

Written Assessment

"Today, I would like to see what you remember from what we have been practicing."

- Give your child **Written Assessment #11**.

"Write your name at the top of the paper."

"I will read the directions for each problem."

- Read the directions for each problem. Allow time for your child to complete that problem before continuing.

- Correct the paper, noting your child's mistakes on the **Individual Recording Form**. Review the errors with your child.

Oral Assessment

- Record your child's responses to the oral interview on the interview sheet.

Teacher _____

Date _____

Materials:
Individual clock

MATH 1   LESSON 60
Oral Assessment # 6 Recording Form

Students	A. •Show three o'clock on the clock. *"What time is it?"*	B. •Give the child the individual clock. *"Show eight o'clock."*

1-60La

Name _____

Date _____

ASSESSMENT 11
LESSON 60
Math 1

1. Bonnie had 7 dimes. She gave 2 dimes to her brother. Draw the dimes and write a number sentence to show how many dimes she has now.

   (D) (D) (D) (D) (D) (Ⓓ) (Ⓓ)

   Number sentence _____ $7 - 2 = 5$ _____

   How many dimes does she have now? ___5___ dimes

2. Count by 2's. Fill in the missing numbers.

   2, 4, 6, __8__, __10__, __12__, __14__, __16__, __18__, __20__

3. Write the numbers that are one less.

   __6__ , 7   __17__ , 18   __22__ , 23

4. Use the graph to answer the questions.

Sunny	☀ ☀ ☀ ☀ ☀			
Cloudy	☁ ☁ ☁			
Snowy	❄ ❄			

   How many sunny days were there?
   ___6___

   How many cloudy and snowy days were there altogether?
   ___5___

5. How many squares are in each train? ___10___

   Color.   How many are left?

   4 ▣▣▣▣ □□□□□□   ___6___

   7 ▣▣▣▣▣▣▣ □□□   ___3___

1-60Aa

Lesson 61

writing the number 55
comparing length
measuring length using nonstandard units

---

lesson preparation

materials

5 pencils of differing lengths (include 1 new pencil)

linking cubes in towers of 10

4 objects to be measured, 6" – 15"

Master 1-61

large fact cards (adding two facts)

Fact Sheet AA 4.0

in the morning

• Write the following number pattern on the meeting strip:

7, 9, 11, ___, ___, ___

Answer: 7, 9, 11, 13, 15, 17

• Put **4 dimes** and **6 pennies** in the coin cup.

THE MEETING

calendar

• Ask your child to identify the following:

year

month

shapes on the calendar

today's shape

shape pattern for the month

• Ask your child to write the date on the calendar.

• Ask your child to do the following:

identify today's day of the week

identify the days of the week

"What day of the week was it yesterday?"

"What day of the week will it be tomorrow?"

- Ask your child to identify the following:

    number of days in a week

    weekdays

- Ask your child to write the full date on the meeting strip.

weather graph

- Ask your child to report and graph the weather.

- Ask questions about the graph.

counting

- Count from 46 to 75 using the hundred number chart.

- Count backward from 30 to 1.

- Count by 10's to 100.

- Count backward from 100 by 10's.

- Count by 2's to 20.

- Say the odd numbers to 19.

- Add another number to the number line.

    "Let's count the numbers on our number line."

    "We will count by 10's as far as we can and then count by 1's."

    "How many 10's did we count?"

    "And how many more did we count?"

    "What number is _____ tens and _____ more?"

number pattern

- Ask your child to identify and fill in the missing numbers.

- Read the number pattern together.

clock

- Ask your child to set the morning/afternoon/evening/night clock.

- Throughout the day, your child announces the time on the hour, sets the demonstration clock, and writes the digital time for each new hour on the chalkboard.

coin cup

- Ask your child to slide and count the dimes in the coin cup.

- Ask your child to record the amount of money in the coin cup on the meeting strip.

right/left

- Continue to practice left and right once a week. Practice more often, if necessary.

THE LESSON

Writing the Number 55

"The last number we practiced writing was the number 54."

"What number do you think we will learn how to write today?"

- Write the number 55 on the chalkboard.

"What digits do you see in the number 55?"

"How would you tell someone how to write the number 55?"

"Which digit is on the left?"

"Which digit is on the right?"

Comparing Length
Measuring Length Using Nonstandard Units

"Today you will learn how to measure the length of objects using linking cubes."

"You will also learn how to order objects from shortest to longest."

- Show your child five pencils of varying lengths. Include one new pencil.

"Put these pencils in order from shortest to longest."

- Allow time for your child to do this.

"Which pencil is the longest?"

"Which pencil is the shortest?"

- Hold up the new pencil. Hold one linking cube next to the pencil.

"How many cubes do you think I will need to use to make a train that is just as long as this pencil?"

"Let's measure the pencil using the linking cubes."

- Snap together the cubes one at a time as your child counts. Show your child how the end of the tower and the end of the pencil almost match.

"The pencil is about _____ linking cubes long."

- Show your child four objects of different lengths (6–15 inches). Choose objects whose length is the most obvious dimension (e.g., a marker, a ruler, or a crayon).

"Now you will use trains of linking cubes to measure these objects."

- Hold up the shortest object.

"Use the linking cubes to measure the length of (this object)."

- Allow time for your child to measure the object by snapping the linking cubes together.

"How many linking cubes long is the _____?"

- Record on the chalkboard:

Object | Length
_____ | _____ linking cubes

- Hold up the object just measured and another object.

"The (first object) was _____ linking cubes long."

"How long do you think this (other object) will be?"

- Ask your child to measure the object by snapping the linking cubes together.

"How many linking cubes long is the _____?"

- Record on the chalkboard chart.

- Repeat with the last two objects.

"Now you will choose four objects to measure using linking cubes."

"What are some things you could measure?"

- Give your child **Master 1-61**.

"Draw a picture of what you are going to measure in each box on this paper."

"When you finish, measure each object with linking cubes and write the length below the picture."

- Give your child linking cubes in towers of 10.

- Check your child's measurements.

CLASS PRACTICE

- Practice the adding two facts using the large fact cards.

- Give your child **Fact Sheet AA 4.0**.

"What number facts do you see?"

"What strategy will you use to find the answer?"

- Allow time for your child to complete the fact sheet.

- Correct the fact sheet together.

WRITTEN PRACTICE

- Complete **Worksheet 61A** with your child.

- Complete **Worksheet 61B** with your child later in the day.

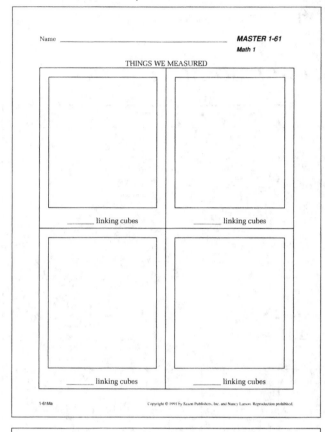

Name _____ **MASTER 1-61**
Math 1

THINGS WE MEASURED

_____ linking cubes   _____ linking cubes

_____ linking cubes   _____ linking cubes

1-61Ma   Copyright © 1991 by Saxon Publishers, Inc. and Nancy Larson. Reproduction prohibited.

Name _____ **LESSON 61A**
Date _____ Math 1
Day of the Week _____

1. Write the number fifty-five two more times. How many digits are on the line? __8__

    55 55

2. The children chose 6 books for Mrs. Stewart to read. She read 2 books. Draw a picture and write a number sentence to show how many more books Mrs. Stewart has left to read.

    Number Sentence _____ 6 − 2 = 4

    How many books does Mrs. Stewart have left to read? __4__ books

3. Color the pennies brown. Count the money. __43¢__

    blue   red   brown brown brown

4. Circle the fifth coin in Problem 3 using a red crayon.
    Circle the second coin in Problem 3 using a blue crayon.

5. Use linking cubes to measure this line segment. __7__ cubes

6. Write 6 different examples that have a sum of 6. answers may vary

    ☐+☐ ☐+☐ ☐+☐ ☐+☐ ☐+☐ ☐+☐
      6   6   6   6   6   6

1-61Wa   Copyright © 1991 by Saxon Publishers, Inc. and Nancy Larson. Reproduction prohibited.

Name _____ **LESSON 61B**
Math 1

1. Fill in the missing numbers.

    1, 3, 5, __7__ , __9__ , __11__ , __13__ , __15__
    __12__ , __13__ , __14__ , 15, 16, 17, __18__ , __19__ , __20__

2. The children chose 8 books for Mr. Conklin to read. He read 7 books. Draw a picture and write a number sentence to show how many more books Mr. Conklin has left to read.

    Number sentence _____ 8 − 7 = 1

    How many books does Mr. Conklin have left to read? __1__ books

3. Color the pennies brown. Count the money. __34¢__   orange

    green brown brown brown brown

4. Circle the third coin in Problem 3 using a green crayon.
    Circle the seventh coin in Problem 3 using an orange crayon.

5. Number the clock face.
    Show the time.

    6:00

    answers may vary

6. Write 6 different examples that have a sum of 8.

    ☐+☐ ☐+☐ ☐+☐ ☐+☐ ☐+☐ ☐+☐
      8   8   8   8   8   8

1-61Wb   Copyright © 1991 by Saxon Publishers, Inc. and Nancy Larson. Reproduction prohibited.

Lesson 62

writing the number 56
subtracting zero
subtracting a number from itself

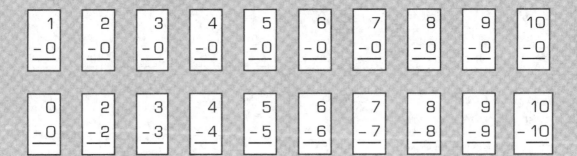

THE MEETING

calendar

- Ask your child to identify the following:

    year

    month

    shapes on the calendar

    today's shape

    shape pattern for the month

- Ask your child to write the date on the calendar.

- Ask your child to do the following:

    identify today's day of the week

    identify the days of the week

  "What day of the week was it yesterday?"

  "What day of the week will it be tomorrow?"

- Ask your child to identify the following:

    number of days in a week

    weekdays

- Ask your child to write the full date on the meeting strip.

weather graph

- Ask your child to report and graph the weather.

- Ask questions about the graph.

counting

- Count from 27 to 64 using the hundred number chart.

- Count backward from 30 to 1.

- Count by 10's to 100.

- Count backward from 100 by 10's.

- Count by 2's to 20.

- Say the odd numbers to 19.

- Add another number to the number line.

  "Let's count the numbers on our number line."

  "We will count by 10's as far as we can and then count by 1's."

  "How many 10's did we count?"

  "And how many more did we count?"

  "What number is _____ tens and _____ more?"

number pattern

- Ask your child to identify and fill in the missing numbers.

- Read the number pattern together.

clock

- Ask your child to set the morning/afternoon/evening/night clock.

- Throughout the day, your child announces the time on the hour, sets the demonstration clock, and writes the digital time for each new hour on the chalkboard.

coin cup

- Ask your child to slide and count the dimes in the coin cup.

- Ask your child to record the amount of money in the coin cup on the meeting strip.

right/left

- Continue to practice left and right once a week. Practice more often, if necessary.

THE LESSON

Writing the Number 56

"The last number we practiced writing was the number 55."

"What number do you think we will learn how to write today?"

- Write the number 56 on the chalkboard.

"What digits do you see in the number 56?"

"How would you tell someone how to write the number 56?"

"Which digit is on the left?"

"Which digit is on the right?"

Subtracting Zero
Subtracting a Number From Itself

"Today you will learn how to subtract zero from a number and how to subtract a number from itself."

- Give your child a cup of 10 pennies.

- Write "4 – 4 = _____" on the chalkboard.

"Let's use the pennies to find the answer for this problem."

"What does the problem tell us to do first?"   *put 4 pennies on the table*

"What does the problem tell us to do next?" **take away 4 pennies**

"How many pennies do you have now?" **0**

• Record "4 – 4 = 0" on the chalkboard.

"Let's try another problem."

• Repeat with the following:

$$8 - 8 = \underline{\quad} \qquad 6 - 6 = \underline{\quad} \qquad 5 - 5 = \underline{\quad}$$

"We can write these problems a different way."

• Write the following on the chalkboard:

$$\begin{array}{cccccccccc} 0 & 1 & 2 & 3 & 4 & 5 & 6 & 7 & 8 & 9 \\ -0 & -1 & -2 & -3 & -4 & -5 & -6 & -7 & -8 & -9 \end{array}$$

"Let's act out these problems using pennies."

• Point to:
$$\begin{array}{c} 5 \\ -5 \end{array}$$

"The top number tells us how many pennies we have."

"How many pennies do we have?" **5**

"Put five pennies on the table."

"What does the minus sign tell us to do?" **take some away**

"How many will we take away?" **5**

"Put five pennies back in the cup."

"How many pennies do you have on the table now?" **0**

• Repeat with three more problems.

"Now let's try some problems without using pennies."

"Put your pennies in the cup."

"Let's read each problem together."

"What is the answer?"

• Write each answer below the problem.

"Do you see a pattern?"

"We call these the subtracting a number from itself facts."

• Write the following on the chalkboard:

$$\begin{array}{cccccccccc} 0 & 1 & 2 & 3 & 4 & 5 & 6 & 7 & 8 & 9 \\ -0 & -0 & -0 & -0 & -0 & -0 & -0 & -0 & -0 & -0 \end{array}$$

"Let's act out these problems using pennies."

• Point to:
$$\begin{array}{c} 3 \\ -0 \end{array}$$

"The top number tells us how many pennies we have."

"How many pennies do we have?"   **3**

"Put three pennies on the table."

"What does the minus sign tell us to do?"   **take some away**

"How many will we take away?"   **0**

"Put zero pennies back in the cup."

"How many pennies do you have on the table now?"   **3**

- Repeat with three more problems.

"Now let's try some problems without using pennies."

"Put your pennies in the cup."

"Let's read each problem together."

"What is the answer?"

- Write each answer below the problem.

"Do you see a pattern?"

"We call these the subtracting zero facts."

"How can we remember these answers?"

- Give your child the lavender subtraction fact cards (subtracting zero and subtracting a number from itself).

"Write the answer on the back of each card."

"Put these with your other fact cards."

CLASS PRACTICE

- Practice the subtracting zero and the subtracting a number from itself facts using the large fact cards.
- Give your child **Fact Sheet S 3.2**.

"What number facts do you see?"

- Allow time for your child to complete the fact sheet.
- Correct the fact sheet together.

WRITTEN PRACTICE

- Complete **Worksheet 62A** with your child.
- Complete **Worksheet 62B** with your child later in the day.

LESSON 62A
Math 1

Name _____

Date _____

Day of the Week _____

1. Write the number fifty-six three more times. How many digits are on the line? __10__

56 56 _____

2. Clara has a box of eight crayons. Jennifer has the same number of crayons in her box. Draw a picture and write a number sentence to show how many crayons the girls have.

Number Sentence _____ 8 + 8 = 16 _____

How many crayons do the girls have? __16__ crayons

3. Measure this line segment using pennies.

•————————————→ __6__ pennies.

4. Write the numbers that are one less and one more.

__15__, 16, __17__   __8__, 9, __10__   __29__, 30, __31__

5. Count by 10's. Fill in the missing numbers.

10, 20, 30, __40__, __50__, __60__, __70__, __80__, __90__, __100__

6. Write the answers.

6	4	3	2	5	9	7	8	7
−0	−1	−3	−0	−5	−1	−0	−8	−1
6	3	0	2	0	8	7	0	6

1-62Wa

LESSON 62B
Math 1

Name _____

1. Color the penny brown. Count the money. __7¢__

brown

2. Mrs. Blake bought 6 oranges. Mrs. Shaw bought the same number of oranges. Draw a picture and write a number sentence to show how many oranges they bought.

Number sentence _____ 6 + 6 = 12 _____

How many oranges did they buy? __12__ oranges

3. Measure this line segment using pennies.

•————————————→ __4__ pennies

4. Write the numbers that are one less and one more.

__11__, 12, __13__   __18__, 19, __20__   __22__, 23, __24__

5. Count backward by 10's. Fill in the missing numbers.

100, 90, 80, __70__, __60__, __50__, __40__, __30__, __20__, __10__

6. Write the answers.

5	9	2	3	6	4	8	6
−0	−9	−1	−3	−0	−1	−0	−1
5	0	1	0	6	3	8	5

1-62Wb

Lesson 63

writing the number 57
writing the numbers 0–10 using words

---

lesson preparation

materials

piece of paper

large fact cards (adding two facts)

Fact Sheet A 4.0

in the morning

• Write the following on the meeting strip:

> 40, 50, 60, __, __, __

Answer: 40, 50, 60, 70, 80, 90

• Put **1 dime** and **8 pennies** in the coin cup.

THE MEETING

calendar

• Ask your child to identify the following:

    year

    month

    shapes on the calendar

    today's shape

    shape pattern for the month

• Ask your child to write the date on the calendar.

• Ask your child to do the following:

    identify today's day of the week

    identify the days of the week

"What day of the week was it yesterday?"

"What day of the week will it be tomorrow?"

• Ask your child to identify the following:

    number of days in a week

weekdays
- Ask your child to write the full date on the meeting strip.

weather graph
- Ask your child to report and graph the weather.
- Ask questions about the graph.

counting
- Count from 72 to 98 using the hundred number chart.
- Count backward from 30 to 1.
- Count by 10's to 100.
- Count backward from 100 by 10's.
- Count by 2's to 20.
- Say the odd numbers to 19.
- Add another number to the number line.

"Let's count the numbers on our number line."

"We will count by 10's as far as we can and then count by 1's."

"How many 10's did we count?"

"And how many more did we count?"

"What number is _____ tens and _____ more?"

number pattern
- Ask your child to identify and fill in the missing numbers.
- Read the number pattern together.

clock
- Ask your child to set the morning/afternoon/evening/night clock.
- Throughout the day, your child announces the time on the hour, sets the demonstration clock, and writes the digital time for each new hour on the chalkboard.

coin cup
- Ask your child to slide and count the dimes in the coin cup.
- Ask your child to record the amount of money in the coin cup on the meeting strip.

right/left
- Continue to practice left and right once a week. Practice more often, if necessary.

THE LESSON

Writing the Number 57

> *"The last number we practiced writing was the number 56."*

> *"What number do you think we will learn how to write today?"*

- Write the number 57 on the chalkboard.

> *"What digits do you see in the number 57?"*

> *"How would you tell someone how to write the number 57?"*

> *"Which digit is on the left?"*

> *"Which digit is on the right?"*

Writing the Numbers 0–10 Using Words

> *"Today you will learn how to write the numbers from zero to ten using words."*

- Write the following on the chalkboard:

0	6
1	7
2	8
3	9
4	10
5	

> *"These symbols are the quick way to write the numbers from zero to ten."*

> *"Let's spell each of these words together."*

- Spell each number word with your child.

> *"Now we will play a game."*

> *"I will write a secret number word on this paper."*

- Use "five" for the first example. Record the word on scrap paper. Leave the spelling for all the words visible to your child.

- Write ___ ___ ___ ___ on the chalkboard.

> *"The blank lines tell you how many letters are in my word."*

> *"How many letters are in my secret number word?"* **4**

> *"You will try to guess my secret number word by guessing what letters will fill the blanks."*

> *"You can guess the letters in any order."*

> *"When you guess a correct letter, I will fill in the blank."*

> *"If the letter is incorrect, I will write it on the side."*

• Play the game several times.

"Now you will have a chance to choose words for me to guess."

• Take turns choosing and guessing words.

CLASS PRACTICE

"Today we will practice the adding two facts."

"What strategy will you use to find the answers?"

• Practice the adding two facts using the large fact cards.

• Give your child **Fact Sheet A 4.0**.

• Allow time for your child to complete the fact sheet.

• Correct the fact sheet together.

WRITTEN PRACTICE

• Complete **Worksheet 63A** with your child.

• Complete **Worksheet 63B** with your child later in the day.

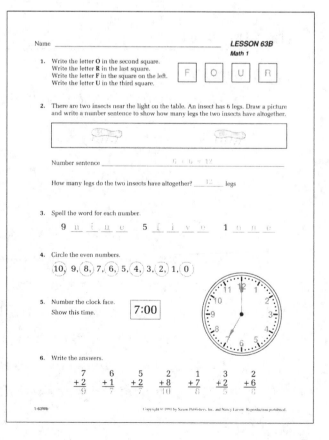

esson 64

writing the number 58
identifying pairs

---

lesson preparation

materials

4 cups of pennies (7, 12, 15, 18 pennies)

4 pieces of paper

large fact cards (subtracting zero and subtracting a number from itself)

Fact Sheet S 3.2

in the morning

• Write the following number pattern on the meeting strip:

11, 13, 15, ___, ___, ___

Answer: 11, 13, 15, 17, 19, 21

• Put **6 dimes** and **3 pennies** in the coin cup.

THE MEETING

calendar

• Ask your child to identify the following:

year

month

shapes on the calendar

today's shape

shape pattern for the month

• Ask your child to write the date on the calendar.

• Ask your child to do the following:

identify today's day of the week

identify the days of the week

"What day of the week was it yesterday?"

"What day of the week will it be tomorrow?"

- Ask your child to identify the following:

    number of days in a week

    weekdays

- Ask your child to write the full date on the meeting strip.

weather graph

- Ask your child to report and graph the weather.

- Ask questions about the graph.

counting

- Count from 33 to 71 using the hundred number chart.

- Count backward from 30 to 1.

- Count by 10's to 100.

- Count backward from 100 by 10's.

- Count by 2's to 20.

- Say the odd numbers to 19.

- Add another number to the number line.

    "Let's count the numbers on our number line."

    "We will count by 10's as far as we can and then count by 1's."

    "How many 10's did we count?"

    "And how many more did we count?"

    "What number is _____ tens and _____ more?"

number pattern

- Ask your child to identify and fill in the missing numbers.

- Read the number pattern together.

clock

- Ask your child to set the morning/afternoon/evening/night clock.

- Throughout the day, your child announces the time on the hour, sets the demonstration clock, and writes the digital time for each new hour on the chalkboard.

coin cup

- Ask your child to slide and count the dimes in the coin cup.

- Ask your child to record the amount of money in the coin cup on the meeting strip.

right/left

- Continue to practice left and right once a week. Practice more often, if necessary.

THE LESSON

Writing the Number 58

"The last number we practiced writing was the number 57."

"What number do you think we will learn how to write today?"

- Write the number 58 on the chalkboard.

"What digits do you see in the number 58?"

"How would you tell someone how to write the number 58?"

"Which digit is on the left?"

"Which digit is on the right?"

Identifying Pairs

"Today you will learn about pairs."

"If I wanted to describe what you are wearing on your feet, I would say that you are wearing a pair of shoes."

"How many shoes are you wearing?"

"How many things do you think are in a pair?"

"What else comes in pairs?"   *socks, mittens, gloves, earrings*

"In order to have a pair, we must have two items or things that we use together."

"We usually don't wear only one shoe or one sock or one glove."

"We usually wear a pair."

- Put 5–10 pairs of shoes in a row on the floor.

"Let's count how many pairs of shoes we have."

- Point to each pair of shoes as you count with your child: 1 pair, 2 pairs, 3 pairs, etc.

- Record "_____ pairs of shoes" on the chalkboard.

"Now let's count to find how many shoes that is."

"How can we do this?"   *count each shoe or count by 2's*

"Let's count by 2's to find the number of shoes in _____ pairs."

- Record "_____ shoes" on the chalkboard.

"Today you will practice making pairs using pennies."

"I will give you a cup with some pennies."

"You will put the pennies in pairs."

"How many pennies are in a pair?"

- Give your child a cup of 12 pennies and a piece of paper.

"Put the pennies in pairs."

- Allow time for your child to do this.

"How many pairs do you have?"

"Are there any pennies left over?"

"Let's count by 2's to find how much money this is."

- Ask your child to point to each pair of pennies as you count by 2's together.

- Leave the pennies in pairs on the paper. Move the paper aside.

- Give your child a cup of 15 pennies and another piece of paper.

"Put the pennies in pairs."

- Allow time for your child to do this.

"How many pairs do you have?"

"Are there any pennies left over?"

"Let's count by 2's to find how much money this is."

- Count the pennies with your child.

- Leave the pennies in pairs on the paper. Move the paper aside.

- Repeat, using cups of 18 and 7 pennies.

"Which papers have an even number of pennies?"

"How do you know?"

"An even number of pennies can always be put in pairs."

"Which papers have an odd number of pennies?"

"How do you know?"

"When we have an odd number of pennies, one penny will not have a partner."

CLASS PRACTICE

- Use the large fact cards to practice the subtracting zero and subtracting a number from itself facts.

- Give your child **Fact Sheet S 3.2**.

- Allow time for your child to complete the fact sheet.

- Correct the fact sheet together.

WRITTEN PRACTICE

- •Complete **Worksheet 64A** with your child.
- •Complete **Worksheet 64B** with your child later in the day.

Name _____ **LESSON 64A**
Math 1

Date _____

Day of the Week _____

1. Write the number fifty-eight three more times. How many digits are on the line? 10

   58 58

2. Sandra's mother bought her 3 pairs of socks. Draw the socks.

   How many socks is that? ___6___ socks

3. Spell the word for each number.

   0 _z e r o_   4 _f o u r_   2 _t w o_

4. Measure this line segment using pennies.

   _____8_____ pennies

5. Finish the pattern.

   □,△,○,○,□,△,○,○,□,△,○,○

6. Write the answers.

   $\frac{7}{-0}$ $\frac{5}{+1}$ $\frac{9}{-1}$ $\frac{4}{-4}$ $\frac{0}{+5}$ $\frac{3}{-1}$ $\frac{9}{+1}$ $\frac{2}{-0}$ $\frac{2}{+5}$
   7   6   8   0   5   2   10   2   7

1-64Wa   Copyright © 1991 by Saxon Publishers, Inc. and Nancy Larson. Reproduction prohibited.

Name _____ **LESSON 64B**
Math 1

1. Circle the one that is different.

2. Duane's mother bought him 5 pairs of socks. Draw the socks.

   How many socks is that? ___10___ socks

3. Spell the word for each number.

   2 _t w o_   0 _z e r o_   4 _f o u r_

4. Measure this line segment using pennies. ___5___ pennies

5. Finish the pattern.

   △,○,□,□,△,○,□,□,△,○,□,□

6. Find the answers.

   $\frac{4}{-0}$ $\frac{3}{+1}$ $\frac{8}{-1}$ $\frac{7}{+2}$ $\frac{6}{-6}$ $\frac{0}{+9}$ $\frac{2}{-1}$ $\frac{2}{+8}$ $\frac{4}{-4}$
   4   4   7   9   0   9   1   10   0

1-64Wb   Copyright © 1991 by Saxon Publishers, Inc. and Nancy Larson. Reproduction prohibited.

L esson 65

writing the number 59
identifying the season—winter

---

lesson preparation

materials

Written Assessment #12

Meeting Book

crayons

large fact cards (adding two facts)

Fact Sheet A 4.0

in the morning

• Write the following number pattern on the meeting strip:

> 14, 16, 18, __, __, __

Answer: 14, 16, 18, 20, 22, 24

• Put **7 dimes** and **2 pennies** in the coin cup.

THE MEETING

calendar

  • Ask your child to identify the following:

    year

    month

    shapes on the calendar

    today's shape

    shape pattern for the month

  • Ask your child to write the date on the calendar.

  • Ask your child to do the following:

    identify today's day of the week

    identify the days of the week

  "What day of the week was it yesterday?"

"What day of the week will it be tomorrow?"

- Ask your child to identify the following:

    number of days in a week

    weekdays

- Ask your child to write the full date on the meeting strip.

weather graph

- Ask your child to report and graph the weather.
- Ask questions about the graph.

counting

- Count from 49 to 82 using the hundred number chart.
- Count backward from 30 to 1.
- Count by 10's to 100.
- Count backward from 100 by 10's.
- Count by 2's to 20.
- Say the odd numbers to 19.
- Add another number to the number line.

    "Let's count the numbers on our number line."

    "We will count by 10's as far as we can and then count by 1's."

    "How many 10's did we count?"

    "And how many more did we count?"

    "What number is _____ tens and _____ more?"

number pattern

- Ask your child to identify and fill in the missing numbers.
- Read the number pattern together.

clock

- Ask your child to set the morning/afternoon/evening/night clock.
- Throughout the day, your child announces the time on the hour, sets the demonstration clock, and writes the digital time for each new hour on the chalkboard.

coin cup

- Ask your child to slide and count the dimes in the coin cup.
- Ask your child to record the amount of money in the coin cup on the meeting strip.

right/left

- Continue to practice left and right once a week. Practice more often, if necessary.

ASSESSMENT

Written Assessment

"Today, I would like to see what you remember from what we have been practicing."

- Give your child **Written Assessment #12**.

"Write your name at the top of the paper."

"I will read the directions for each problem."

- Read the directions for each problem. Allow time for your child to complete that problem before continuing.

- Correct the paper, noting your child's mistakes on the **Individual Recording Form**. Review the errors with your child.

THE LESSON

Writing the Number 59

"The last number we practiced writing was the number 58."

"What number do you think we will learn how to write today?"

- Write the number 59 on the chalkboard.

"What digits do you see in the number 59?"

"How would you tell someone how to write the number 59?"

"Which digit is on the left?"

"Which digit is on the right?"

Identifying the Season — Winter

"Today you will learn about a new season."

"On December _____, a new season begins." (Note: The actual date varies from year to year.)

"What season is it now?"   winter

"How is winter different from fall?"   temperature, amount of daylight, plants and trees are different, clothing worn, etc.

"What do you do differently in the winter?"

"Today we will look at the tree (or plant) we chose in the fall."

"What did it look like then?"

"We will go outside to look at it again today."

- Open the Meeting Book to page 18.

"You will draw a picture of the tree (plant) in the Meeting Book."

"You will also write about how the tree (plant) looks in winter."

- Go outside to observe the tree (plant).

"What does the tree look like now?"

"How is this different from when we saw it in the fall?"

"What does it feel like outside in winter?"

"How is this different from when we were outside in the fall?"

"Draw a picture and write about how the tree looks in winter."

- Encourage your child to write about the tree (plant) using approximate spelling. Do not correct your child's writing; rather let this be documentation of how your child's writing develops during the year.

- Optional: Take a picture of your child next to the tree (plant).

CLASS PRACTICE

"Today you will practice the adding two facts."

"What strategy will you use to find the answers?"

- Use the large fact cards to practice the adding two facts.
- Give your child **Fact Sheet A 4.0.**
- Correct the fact sheet together.
- Play the Number Word Guessing Game several times.

WRITTEN PRACTICE

- Complete **Worksheet 65A** with your child.
- Complete **Worksheet 65B** with your child later in the day.

Name _____ **ASSESSMENT 12**
LESSON 65
Date _____ Math 1

1. Write the letters in your first name. _____ answers may vary _____

   Write the letters in your last name. _____

   Write a number sentence to show the number of letters altogether. _____

   How many letters is that altogether? _____ letters

2. Color the pennies brown. Count the money. ___62¢___

   Brown   Brown

3. Fill in the missing numbers.

   | 31 | **32** | 33 | 34 | 35 | 36 | 37 | 38 | **39** | 40 |

4. Write the odd numbers.

   1, 3, 5, __7__, __9__, __11__, __13__, __15__, __17__, __19__

5. Find the answers.

   $\begin{array}{r} 5 \\ +0 \\ \hline 5 \end{array}$ $\begin{array}{r} 7 \\ +7 \\ \hline 14 \end{array}$ $\begin{array}{r} 3 \\ +1 \\ \hline 4 \end{array}$ $\begin{array}{r} 6 \\ +2 \\ \hline 8 \end{array}$ $\begin{array}{r} 1 \\ +8 \\ \hline 9 \end{array}$ $\begin{array}{r} 2 \\ +5 \\ \hline 7 \end{array}$ $\begin{array}{r} 4 \\ -1 \\ \hline 3 \end{array}$ $\begin{array}{r} 9 \\ -1 \\ \hline 8 \end{array}$

6. Show this time on the clockface.

   4:00

1-65Aa   Copyright © 1991 by Saxon Publishers, Inc. and Nancy Larson. Reproduction prohibited.

Name _____ **LESSON 65A**
Math 1
Date _____

Day of the Week _____

1. Write the number fifty-nine two more times. How many digits are on the line? __8__

   59 **59**

2. There are four small boxes and one large box in Peter's room. Draw a picture and write a number sentence to show how many boxes there are.

   □ □ □ □   ▭

   Number Sentence _____ 4 + 1 = 5 _____

   How many boxes are there in Peter's room? __5__ boxes

3. Choose 4 even numbers.
   Add 2 to each number.
   Find the answers.
   answers may vary

   $\begin{array}{r} \square \\ +2 \\ \hline \square \end{array}$ $\begin{array}{r} \square \\ +2 \\ \hline \square \end{array}$ $\begin{array}{r} \square \\ +2 \\ \hline \square \end{array}$ $\begin{array}{r} \square \\ +2 \\ \hline \square \end{array}$

4. Spell the word for each number.

   7 __s e v e n__   10 __t e n__   6 __s i x__

5. How many socks are in the box? __12__ socks

   Circle the pairs.

   How many pairs of socks are there? __6__ pairs

1-65Wa   Copyright © 1991 by Saxon Publishers, Inc. and Nancy Larson. Reproduction prohibited.

Name _____ **LESSON 65B**
Math 1

1. Color the longest train yellow.
   Color the second longest train red.
   Color the shortest train green.
   Color the second shortest train blue.

   R
   Y
   G
   B

2. There are three small boxes and two large boxes in Susan's room. Draw a picture and write a number sentence to show how many boxes there are.

   □ □ □   ▭ ▭

   Number Sentence _____ 3 + 2 = 5 _____

   How many boxes are there in Susan's room? __5__ boxes

3. Choose 4 odd numbers.
   Add 2 to each number.
   Find the answers.
   answers may vary

   $\begin{array}{r} \square \\ +2 \\ \hline \square \end{array}$ $\begin{array}{r} \square \\ +2 \\ \hline \square \end{array}$ $\begin{array}{r} \square \\ +2 \\ \hline \square \end{array}$ $\begin{array}{r} \square \\ +2 \\ \hline \square \end{array}$

4. Spell the word for each number.

   6 __s i x__   7 __s e v e n__   10 __t e n__

5. How many shoes are in the box? __8__ shoes

   Circle the pairs.

   How many pairs of shoes are there? __4__ pairs

1-65Wb   Copyright © 1991 by Saxon Publishers, Inc. and Nancy Larson. Reproduction prohibited.

Lesson 66

writing the number 60
writing money amounts using the cent symbol
paying for items using dimes and pennies

---

lesson preparation

materials

cup of 10 pennies

cup of 10 dimes

piece of paper

6 empty food cans or boxes

6 paper tags

tape

individual fact cards

Fact Sheet A 4.0

the night before

• Six empty food cans and/or boxes are needed for this lesson. For pricing and stacking, it is easier if the bottom of a can is removed rather than the top.

in the morning

• Write the following number pattern on the meeting strip:

> 53, 52, 51, __, __, __

Answer: 53, 52, 51, 50, 49, 48

• Put **7 dimes** and **2 pennies** in the coin cup.

THE MEETING

calendar

• Ask your child to identify the following:

year

month

shapes on the calendar

today's shape

shape pattern for the month

- Ask your child to write the date on the calendar.
- Ask your child to do the following:

  identify today's day of the week

  identify the days of the week

  "What day of the week was it yesterday?"

  "What day of the week will it be tomorrow?"

- Ask your child to identify the following:

  number of days in a week

  weekdays

- Ask your child to write the full date on the meeting strip.

weather graph

- Ask your child to report and graph the weather.
- Ask questions about the graph.

counting

- Count from 64 to 92 using the hundred number chart.
- Count backward from 30 to 1.
- Count by 10's to 100.
- Count backward from 100 by 10's.
- Count by 2's to 20.
- Say the odd numbers to 19.
- Add another number to the number line.

  "Let's count the numbers on our number line."

  "We will count by 10's as far as we can and then count by 1's."

  "How many 10's did we count?"

  "And how many more did we count?"

  "What number is _____ tens and _____ more?"

number pattern

- Ask your child to identify and fill in the missing numbers.
- Read the number pattern together.

clock

- Ask your child to set the morning/afternoon/evening/night clock.

- Throughout the day, your child announces the time on the hour, sets the demonstration clock, and writes the digital time for each new hour on the chalkboard.

coin cup

- Ask your child to slide and count the dimes in the coin cup.

- Ask your child to record the amount of money in the coin cup on the meeting strip.

right/left

- Continue to practice left and right once a week. Practice more often, if necessary.

THE LESSON

Writing the Number 60

"The last number we practiced writing was the number 59."

"What number do you think we will learn how to write today?"

- Write the number 60 on the chalkboard.

"What digits do you see in the number 60?"

"How many dimes will we use to make 60¢?"

- Use dimes to demonstrate.

"How many groups of 10 are in 60?"

"Let's count by 10's to check."

Writing Money Amounts Using the Cent Symbol
Paying for Items Using Dimes and Pennies

"Today you will learn how to write money amounts."

"You also will learn how to pay for items using dimes and pennies."

"Each (week) we go food (grocery) shopping."

"Where do we go?"

"What kinds of things do they sell in the food (grocery) store?"

"How do you know where to find things in the store?"

"We are going to set up a pretend grocery store."

"What kinds of things do you think we could sell in our store?"

- Show your child the six items for the store.

"Today I have six items for our store."

"What do I have?"

"We will put price tags on our items just like they do in the store."

"All of the things in our store will cost less than sixty cents."

"_____ will cost 35 cents."

- Write "35¢" on the chalkboard.

- Give your child a price tag.

"Write 35 cents on this price tag."

- Tape the tag to the item.

"How many dimes and pennies will we use to buy this?"

- Repeat with the next five items using the following prices: 12¢, 51¢, 23¢, 4¢, and 40¢.

"What costs the most in our store?"

"What costs the least?"

"Today we are going to pretend that you are buying things in our store."

- Give your child a cup of 10 dimes, a cup of 10 pennies, and a piece of paper.

- Hold up an item.

"How much does this cost?"

"Show me that with your money."

"How many dimes did you use?"

"How many pennies did you use?"

"Which digit in the number _____ tells us the number of dimes?"

"Which digit in the number _____ tells us the number of pennies?"

"Let's count the money to check."

"Put the coins back in your cups."

- Repeat with several items.

"Now you will buy two things with your money."

- Hold up the 51¢ item.

"Show me what coins you will use to pay for this."

"How many dimes did you use?" **5**

"How many pennies did you use?" **1**

"How much money is that?" **51¢**

"Let's count to check."

"Do not put the coins back in the cups."

"You will use some more coins to buy the next item."

- Hold up the 35¢ item.

"Show me what coins you will use to pay for this."

"How many dimes did you use?" **3**

"How many pennies did you use?" **5**

"How much money is that?" **35¢**

"Let's count to check."

"Now put all of the dimes together on the left side of your paper."

"How many dimes do you have?" **8**

"Now put all of the pennies together on the right side of your paper."

"How many pennies do you have?" **6**

"How much money do you have now?" **86¢**

"Let's count to check."

"Put the coins back in the cups."

"Let's pretend that you are buying some more things."

• Hold up the 12¢ item.

"Show me what coins you will use to pay for this."

"How many dimes did you use?" **1**

"How many pennies did you use?" **2**

"How much money is that?" **12¢**

"Let's count to check."

"Do not put the coins back in the cups."

"You will use some more coins to buy the next item."

• Hold up the 23¢ item.

"Show me the coins you will use to pay for this."

"How many dimes did you use?" **2**

"How many pennies did you use?" **3**

"Let's count to check."

"Now put all the dimes together on the left side of your paper."

"How many dimes do you have?" **3**

"Now put all the pennies together on the right side of your paper."

"How many pennies do you have?" **5**

"How much money do you have now?" **35¢**

"Let's count to check."

"Put the coins back in the cups."

"Let's pretend that you are buying some more things."

- Repeat with 35¢ and 4¢, and 51¢ and 40¢.

  "We will need more items for our store."

  "In our pretend store we will only use empty boxes and cans."

  "We will save clean empty cans and boxes for our store."

- You will need 25–30 items for Lesson 73. In Lesson 73 your child will be setting up a store. Your child will be sorting and arranging the items and "buying" them using dimes and pennies. Your child will begin adding two-digit numbers, with and without regrouping, as he/she records his/her purchases on "receipts."

- Optional: A field trip to a local grocery store can be planned at this time. At the store your child can interview people who work in the store and draw maps of the layout of the store.

CLASS PRACTICE

"Today you will use your individual fact cards to practice the adding two facts."

"Use your green fact cards to practice."

- Allow time for your child to practice his/her number facts independently.

- Give your child **Fact Sheet A 4.0**.

  "What number facts do you see?"

  "What strategy will you use to find the answers?"

- Correct the fact sheet with your child.

- Play the Number Word Guessing Game several times.

WRITTEN PRACTICE

- Complete **Worksheet 66A** with your child.

- Complete **Worksheet 66B** with your child later in the day.

Name _____ **LESSON 66A**
Date _____ Math 1
Day of the Week _____

1. Write the number sixty 2 more times. How many digits are on the line? ____8____

   60 60

2. Write a number word that has 4 letters. ___ ___ ___ ___
   Write a number word that has 3 letters. ___ ___ ___   answers may vary
   How many letters is that altogether? ___7___ letters

3. How many dimes and pennies will you need to buy the pencil?
   37¢   ___3___ dimes   ___7___ pennies

4. Draw a line to divide this cracker in half.
   Use a brown crayon to show that one half has peanut butter on it.
   brown

5. Carol's lunch box is the sixth one from the window.
   Color it red.
   How many lunch boxes are on the right side of Carol's lunch box? ___5___ boxes
   How many lunch boxes are on the left side of Carol's lunch box? ___1___ boxes

6. Spell the word for each number.
   8 _e__i__g__h__t_   3 _t__h__r__e__e_

7. Find the answers.
   8 − 1 = _7_   5 − 5 = _0_   2 − 0 = _2_

1-66Wa

Name _____ **LESSON 66B**
Math 1

1. Circle the number in the box that is between 15 and 23 when you count by 1's.
   15 [ ] 23   (17) 14 24

2. Write a number word that has 3 letters. ___ ___ ___
   Write a different number word that has 3 letters. ___ ___ ___   answers may vary
   How many letters is that altogether? ___6___ letters

3. How many dimes and pennies will you need to buy the marker?
   24¢   ___2___ dimes   ___4___ pennies

4. Draw a line to divide this cracker in half.
   Use a brown crayon to show that one half has peanut butter on it.

5. Mike's lunch box is the third one from the window.
   Color it red.
   How many lunch boxes are on the right side of Mike's lunch box? ___3___ boxes
   How many lunch boxes are on the left side of Mike's lunch box? ___4___ boxes

6. Spell the word for each number.
   3 _t__h__r__e__e_   8 _e__i__g__h__t_

7. Find the answers.
   7 − 7 = _0_   6 − 0 = _6_   4 − 1 = _3_

1-66Wb

esson 67

writing the number 61
dividing a square into halves

---

lesson preparation

materials

sharp knife and cutting board

two slices of bread (trim to square)

two 6" paper squares

scissors

large fact cards (subtraction facts)

Fact Sheet S 3.2

in the morning

• Write the following on the meeting strip:

> 77, 78, 79, ___, ___, ___

> *Answer: 77, 78, 79, 80, 81, 82*

• Put **4 dimes** and **5 pennies** in the coin cup.

THE MEETING

calendar

- • Ask your child to identify the following:

  year

  month

  shapes on the calendar

  today's shape

  shape pattern for the month

- • Ask your child to write the date on the calendar.

- • Ask your child to do the following:

  identify today's day of the week

  identify the days of the week

  "What day of the week was it yesterday?"

"What day of the week will it be tomorrow?"

- Ask your child to identify the following:

  number of days in a week

  weekdays

- Ask your child to write the full date on the meeting strip.

weather graph

- Ask your child to report and graph the weather.
- Ask questions about the graph.

counting

- Count from 74 to 99 using the hundred number chart.
- Count backward from 30 to 1.
- Count by 10's to 100.
- Count backward from 100 by 10's.
- Count by 2's to 20.
- Say the odd numbers to 19.
- Add another number to the number line.

  "Let's count the numbers on our number line."

  "We will count by 10's as far as we can and then count by 1's."

  "How many 10's did we count?"

  "And how many more did we count?"

  "What number is _____ tens and _____ more?"

number pattern

- Ask your child to identify and fill in the missing numbers.
- Read the number pattern together.

clock

- Ask your child to set the morning/afternoon/evening/night clock.
- Throughout the day, your child announces the time on the hour, sets the demonstration clock, and writes the digital time for each new hour on the chalkboard.

coin cup

- Ask your child to slide and count the dimes in the coin cup.
- Ask your child to record the amount of money in the coin cup on the meeting strip.

right/left

- Continue to practice left and right once a week. Practice more often, if necessary.

THE LESSON

Writing the Number 61

"The last number we practiced writing was the number 60."

"What number do you think we will learn how to write today?"

- Write the number 61 on the chalkboard.

"What digits do you see in the number 61?"

"How many dimes and pennies will we use to make 61¢?"

- Use dimes and pennies to demonstrate.

"How many groups of 10 are in 61?"

"How many extra 1's do we have?"

"Let's count by 10's and 1's to check."

Dividing a Square into Halves

"Today you will learn how to divide a square in half in different ways."

"We divided apples and crackers in half."

"How did we do this?"

- Draw a picture of an apple on the chalkboard.

"Let's pretend that this is an apple."

"Show me how to cut this pretend apple in half."

- Ask your child to draw a line to show where to cut the apple.

"When we cut an apple in half, how many pieces do we have?"

- Repeat, using a picture of a cracker.

- Hold up one slice of bread.

"I have a whole piece of bread."

"I would like to share my piece of bread with you."

"How much of my whole piece should I give you?"   half

- Draw a square to represent the piece of bread on the chalkboard.

"This is a picture of the piece of bread."

"Show me how to cut this piece of bread in half."

- Ask your child to draw a line to show where to cut the bread. Your child will probably draw the line in the following way:

"When we cut a whole piece of bread in half, how many pieces do we have?" **2**

"Are they the same?"

"Now I will cut the real piece of bread in half so the pieces will look like those on the chalkboard."

- Cut the bread.

"How can I check to make sure that you and I will each have an equal share of the bread?" **match the pieces**

- Show your child that the pieces match.

"What shape is each piece?" **rectangle**

"How many equal pieces did we get from one whole slice?" **2**

"We call each fractional piece one half."

"How many halves are in one whole?" **2**

"I have another piece of bread."

"This time I will cut the piece of bread in half a different way."

- Cut the bread in half like this:

"How can I check to make sure that I cut the piece of bread in half?" **match the halves**

"When something is cut in half, the two pieces will be the same size."

- Draw another square on the chalkboard.

"Draw a line to show how I cut the piece of bread in half this time."

- Ask your child to draw a line to show where the bread was cut.

"What shape is each piece?" **triangle**

- Hold up a 6" paper square.

"We will pretend that this is a slice of bread."

"Let's fold it to show how I cut one of the pieces of bread in half."

"How will we do that?"

- Ask your child to fold the paper.

"How do you know that each piece is one half?" there are two equal pieces

- Hold up another 6" paper square.

"We will pretend that this is the other slice of bread."

"Let's fold it to show the other way I cut a piece of bread in half."

- Ask your child to fold the paper.

"How do you know that each piece is one half?" there are two equal pieces

- Give your child a pair of scissors.

"Cut each of the pieces of bread in half along the fold."

"Mix up the pieces."

"Now put the pieces of pretend bread back together to make two whole slices."

CLASS PRACTICE

- Use the large fact cards to practice the subtracting zero and the subtracting a number from itself facts.
- Give your child **Fact Sheet S 3.2**.
- Correct the fact sheet with your child.
- Play the Number Word Guessing Game several times.

WRITTEN PRACTICE

- Complete **Worksheet 67A** with your child.
- Complete **Worksheet 67B** with your child later in the day.

LESSON 67A
Math 1

Name _____

Date _____

Day of the Week _____

1. Write the number sixty-one 3 more times. How many digits are on the line? ___ 10

/61 61

2. Phillip has pet birds. He has 3 birds in one bird cage and 4 birds in another bird cage. Draw a picture and write a number sentence to show how many birds he has.

Number sentence _____ 3 + 4 = 7

How many pet birds does Phillip have? ___ 7 ___ birds

3. Count by 10's. Fill in the missing numbers.

10, _20_ , _30_ , _40_ , _50_ , _60_ , _70_ , _80_ , _90_ , _100_

4. Color the pennies brown. Count the money. ___ 35¢

brown brown brown brown brown

5. What time is shown on the clock?

8:00

6. Draw lines to show how to divide the squares in half two different ways.

1-67Wa

Copyright © 1991 by Saxon Publishers, Inc. and Nancy Larson. Reproduction prohibited.

LESSON 67B
Math 1

Name _____

1. Show a parent how to divide a piece of bread in half two different ways. Draw lines to show how you did this.

Color one half of each slice brown to show the peanut butter.

2. Sarah gave her dog Spot three dog biscuits. She gave her dog Stripe four dog biscuits. Draw a picture and write a number sentence to show how many dog biscuits Sarah gave her dogs.

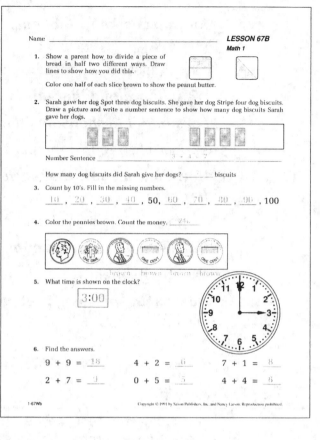

Number Sentence _____ 3 + 4 = 7

How many dog biscuits did Sarah give her dogs? _____ biscuits

3. Count by 10's. Fill in the missing numbers.

_10_ , _20_ , _30_ , _40_ , 50, _60_ , _70_ , _80_ , _90_ , 100

4. Color the pennies brown. Count the money. ___ 24¢

brown brown brown brown

5. What time is shown on the clock?

3:00

6. Find the answers.

9 + 9 = _18_   4 + 2 = _6_   7 + 1 = _8_

2 + 7 = _9_   0 + 5 = _5_   4 + 4 = _8_

1-67Wb

Copyright © 1991 by Saxon Publishers, Inc. and Nancy Larson. Reproduction prohibited.

Lesson 68

writing the number 62
subtracting half of a number

---

lesson preparation

materials

ten 3" × 5" cards

cup of 20 pennies

subtraction fact cards — tan

Fact Sheet S 1.2

the night before

• Use the 3" × 5" cards to make a large set of fact cards for the subtracting half of a number facts. Write them in the following way:

2	4	6	8	10	12	14	16	18	20
− 1	− 2	− 3	− 4	− 5	− 6	− 7	− 8	− 9	− 10

• Separate the tan subtraction fact cards.

in the morning

• Write the following number pattern on the meeting strip:

> 100, 90, 80, ___, ___, ___

> *Answer: 100, 90, 80, 70, 60, 50*

• Put **8 dimes** and **9 pennies** in the coin cup.

THE MEETING

calendar

• Ask your child to identify the following:

    year

    month

    shapes on the calendar

    today's shape

    shape pattern for the month

- Ask your child to write the date on the calendar.
- Ask your child to do the following:

    identify today's day of the week

    identify the days of the week

    "What day of the week was it yesterday?"

    "What day of the week will it be tomorrow?"

- Ask your child to identify the following:

    number of days in a week

    weekdays

- Ask your child to write the full date on the meeting strip.

weather graph

- Ask your child to report and graph the weather.
- Ask questions about the graph.

counting

- Count from 24 to 67 using the hundred number chart.
- Count backward from 30 to 1.
- Count by 10's to 100.
- Count backward from 100 by 10's.
- Count by 2's to 20.
- Say the odd numbers to 19.
- Add another number to the number line.

    "Let's count the numbers on our number line."

    "We will count by 10's as far as we can and then count by 1's."

    "How many 10's did we count?"

    "And how many more did we count?"

    "What number is _____ tens and _____ more?"

number pattern

- Ask your child to identify and fill in the missing numbers.
- Read the number pattern together.

clock

- Ask your child to set the morning/afternoon/evening/night clock.
- Throughout the day, your child announces the time on the hour, sets the demonstration clock, and writes the digital time for each new hour on the chalkboard.

coin cup

- Ask your child to slide and count the dimes in the coin cup.
- Ask your child to record the amount of money in the coin cup on the meeting strip.

right/left

- Continue to practice left and right once a week. Practice more often, if necessary.

THE LESSON

Writing the Number 62

"The last number we practiced writing was the number 61."

"What number do you think we will learn how to write today?"

- Write the number 62 on the chalkboard.

"What digits do you see in the number 62?"

"How many dimes and pennies will we use to make 62¢?"

- Use dimes and pennies to demonstrate.

"How many groups of 10 are in 62?"

"How many extra 1's do we have?"

"Let's count by 10's and 1's to check."

Subtracting Half of a Number

"Today you will learn how to subtract half of a number."

- Give your child a cup of 20 pennies.
- Write the following on the chalkboard:

$$\begin{array}{r} 10 \\ -\ 5 \\ \hline \end{array}$$

"Let's use the pennies to find the answer for this problem."

"What does the problem tell us to do first?"   **put 10 pennies on the table**

"What does the problem tell us to do next?"   **take away 5 pennies**

"Show that using the pennies."

"How many pennies do you have on the table?"   **5**

- Record the following on the chalkboard:

$$\begin{array}{r} 10 \\ -\ 5 \\ \hline 5 \end{array}$$

"Let's try another problem."

- Repeat with the following:

14	12	8
$-\ 7$	$-\ 6$	$-\ 4$

"What do you notice about each of these problems?" **they are the same as doubles going the other way**

"Make up another problem like this, so the answer is the same as the number we take away."

- Write your child's problem on the chalkboard.

"Let's use the pennies to check the answer."

- Continue until all doubles combinations are listed.

"What do these problems look like?" **the doubles**

"Do you see a pattern?"

"How can you remember these answers?"

"We will call these problems the subtracting half of a double facts."

- Give your child the tan subtraction fact cards.

"Put these with your other fact cards."

CLASS PRACTICE

- Use the large fact cards to practice the subtracting half of a double facts.
- Give your child **Fact Sheet S 1.2**.

"What number facts do you see?"

"What strategy can you use to find the answers?"

- Correct the fact sheet with your child.

WRITTEN PRACTICE

- Complete **Worksheet 68A** with your child.
- Complete **Worksheet 68B** with your child later in the day.

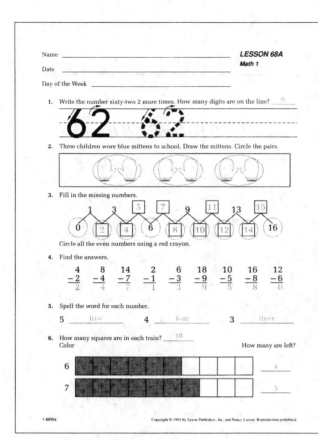

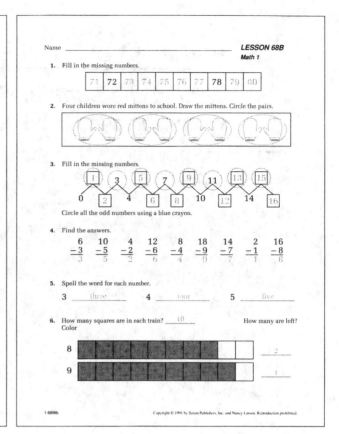

esson 69

writing the number 63
graphing pieces used to cover a design

---

lesson preparation

materials
Masters 1-69A and 1-69B

pattern blocks

crayons

large fact cards (addition facts)

Fact Sheet A 4.2

in the morning
• Write the following number pattern on the meeting strip:

> 20, 22, 24, ___, ___, ___

Answer: 20, 22, 24, 26, 28, 30

• Put **3 dimes** and **7 pennies** in the coin cup.

THE MEETING

calendar

• Ask your child to identify the following:

  year

  month

  shapes on the calendar

  today's shape

  shape pattern for the month

• Ask your child to write the date on the calendar.

• Ask your child to do the following:

  identify today's day of the week

  identify the days of the week

"What day of the week was it yesterday?"

"What day of the week will it be tomorrow?"

- Ask your child to identify the following:

  number of days in a week

  weekdays

- Ask your child to write the full date on the meeting strip.

weather graph

- Ask your child to report and graph the weather.
- Ask questions about the graph.

counting

- Count from 39 to 69 using the hundred number chart.
- Count backward from 30 to 1.
- Count by 10's to 100.
- Count backward from 100 by 10's.
- Count by 2's to 20.
- Say the odd numbers to 19.
- Add another number to the number line.

  "Let's count the numbers on our number line."

  "We will count by 10's as far as we can and then count by 1's."

  "How many 10's did we count?"

  "And how many more did we count?"

  "What number is _____ tens and _____ more?"

number pattern

- Ask your child to identify and fill in the missing numbers.
- Read the number pattern together.

clock

- Ask your child to set the morning/afternoon/evening/night clock.
- Throughout the day, your child announces the time on the hour, sets the demonstration clock, and writes the digital time for each new hour on the chalkboard.

coin cup

- Ask your child to slide and count the dimes in the coin cup.
- Ask your child to record the amount of money in the coin cup on the meeting strip.

right/left

- Continue to practice left and right once a week. Practice more often, if necessary.

THE LESSON

Writing the Number 63

"The last number we practiced writing was the number 62."

"What number do you think we will learn how to write today?"

- Write the number 63 on the chalkboard.

"What digits do you see in the number 63?"

"How many dimes and pennies will we use to make 63¢?"

- Use dimes and pennies to demonstrate.

"How many groups of 10 are in 63?"

"How many extra 1's do we have?"

"Let's count by 10's and 1's to check."

Graphing Pieces Used to Cover a Design

"Today you will learn how to make a graph to show the pattern block pieces you use to cover a design."

- Give your child **Master 1-69A**.

"Use the pattern blocks to cover this design."

- Allow time for your child to do this.

"Put away all the extra pattern blocks."

- Remove the extra pattern blocks from your child's area.

"Now sort the pattern block pieces you used."

- Allow time for your child to do this.

"How did you sort your pieces?"   *by color/shape*

"Now you will make a graph of the pattern blocks you used to cover your design."

- Give your child **Master 1-69B**.

"You will use a crayon to match each color pattern block."

"How many yellow pattern blocks did you use?"

"On the graph, find the column with the picture of the hexagon."

"Use a yellow crayon to color one box for each yellow hexagon you used in your design."

"How many boxes will you color?"

- Allow time for your child to color.
- Repeat with each color pattern block.

"What color pattern block did you use the most of?"

"What color pattern block did you use the fewest of?"

CLASS PRACTICE

- Use the large fact cards to practice all the addition facts.
- Give your child **Fact Sheet A 4.2**.

"What number facts do you see?"

"What strategies will you use to find the answers?"

- Correct the fact sheet with your child.

WRITTEN PRACTICE

- Complete **Worksheet 69A** with your child.
- Complete **Worksheet 69B** with your child later in the day.

Name _____ **MASTER 1-69A**
                                    Math 1

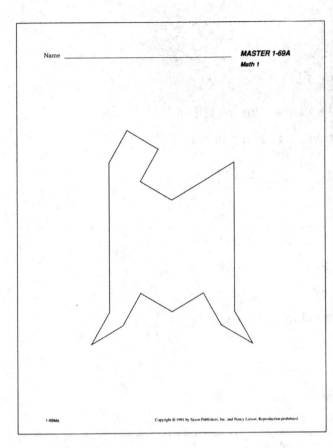

1-69Ma   Copyright © 1991 by Saxon Publishers, Inc. and Nancy Larson. Reproduction prohibited.

Name _____ **MASTER 1-69B**
                                    Math 1

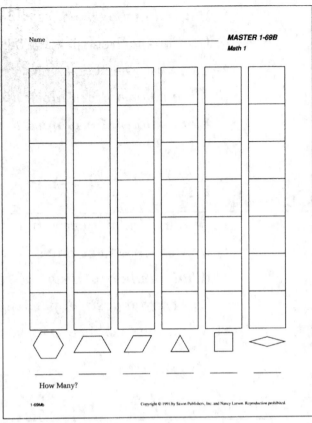

How Many?

1-69Mb   Copyright © 1991 by Saxon Publishers, Inc. and Nancy Larson. Reproduction prohibited.

Name _____ **LESSON 69A**
                                    Math 1
Date _____

Day of the Week _____

1. Write the number sixty-three 3 more times. How many digits are on the line? ___10___

    63 63

2. Tamara had nine dimes. She gave three dimes to Michelle. Draw the dimes and write a number sentence to show how many dimes she has now.

    Ⓓ Ⓓ Ⓓ Ⓓ Ⓓ Ⓓ Ⓧ Ⓧ Ⓧ

    Number sentence _____ 9 − 3 = 6 _____

    How many dimes does she have now? __6__ dimes

    Count by 10's to find out how much money this is. __60¢__

3. Draw lines to divide the squares in half two different ways.

4. Number the clock face.
    Show this time.
    5:00

5. Write the answers.

    7   4   8   6   0   2   9   1   7
   +2   +1   +8   +2   +5   +2   +2   +7   +1
   --- --- --- --- --- --- --- --- ---
    9   5   16   8   5   7   11   8   8

1-69Wa   Copyright © 1991 by Saxon Publishers, Inc. and Nancy Larson. Reproduction prohibited.

Name _____ **LESSON 69B**
                                    Math 1

1. Write a number that is between 35 and 43 when you count by 1's.

    35 [   ] 43   answers may vary

2. Melissa had eight dimes. She gave three dimes to Jason. Draw the dimes and write a number sentence to show how many dimes she has now.

    Ⓓ Ⓓ Ⓓ Ⓓ Ⓓ Ⓧ Ⓧ Ⓧ

    Number sentence _____ 8 − 3 = 5 _____

    How many dimes does she have now? __5__ dimes

    Count by 10's to find out how much money this is. __50¢__

3. Draw a line to divide the rectangle in half.

4. Number the clock face.
    Show this time.
    10:00

5. Write the answers.

    8   0   9   5   1   0   2   8
   +2   +5   +1   +2   +6   +3   +4   +8
   --- --- --- --- --- --- --- ---
   10   5   10   7   7   3   6   16

1-69Wb   Copyright © 1991 by Saxon Publishers, Inc. and Nancy Larson. Reproduction prohibited.

esson 70

assessment

lesson preparation

materials
Written Assessment #13
Oral Assessment #7
cup of 10 pennies
9 dimes and 9 pennies

in the morning
• Write the following number pattern on the meeting strip:

53, 52, 51, ___, ___, ___

Answer: 53, 52, 51, 50, 49, 48

• Put **7 dimes** and **2 pennies** in the coin cup.

THE MEETING

calendar

• Ask your child to identify the following:

    year

    month

    shapes on the calendar

    today's shape

    shape pattern for the month

• Ask your child to write the date on the calendar.

• Ask your child to do the following:

    identify today's day of the week

    identify the days of the week

  "What day of the week was it yesterday?"

  "What day of the week will it be tomorrow?"

• Ask your child to identify the following:

    number of days in a week

weekdays

- Ask your child to write the full date on the meeting strip.

weather graph

- Ask your child to report and graph the weather.

- Ask questions about the graph.

counting

- Count from 52 to 83 using the hundred number chart.

- Count backward from 30 to 1.

- Count by 10's to 100.

- Count backward from 100 by 10's.

- Count by 2's to 20.

- Say the odd numbers to 19.

- Add another number to the number line.

- Use an orange crayon to color the square for 70.

  "Let's count the numbers on our number line."

  "We will count by 10's as far as we can and then count by 1's."

  "How many 10's did we count?"

  "And how many more did we count?"

  "What number is _____ tens and _____ more?"

number pattern

- Ask your child to identify and fill in the missing numbers.

- Read the number pattern together.

clock

- Ask your child to set the morning/afternoon/evening/night clock.

- Throughout the day, your child announces the time on the hour, sets the demonstration clock, and writes the digital time for each new hour on the chalkboard.

coin cup

- Ask your child to slide and count the dimes in the coin cup.

- Ask your child to record the amount of money in the coin cup on the meeting strip.

right/left

- Continue to practice left and right once a week. Practice more often, if necessary.

ASSESSMENT

- All of the questions on the assessment are based on concepts and skills presented at least five lessons ago. If your child is having difficulty with a specific concept, reteach the concept the following day.

Written Assessment

- Give your child **Written Assessment #13.**

- Read the directions for each problem. Allow time for your child to complete each problem before continuing.

- Correct the paper, noting your child's mistakes on the **Individual Recording Form.** Review the errors with your child.

Oral Assessment

- Record your child's responses to the oral interview on the interview sheet.

Teacher _____

Date _____

MATH 1   LESSON 70

Oral Assessment # 7 Recording Form

Materials: 9 dimes 9 pennies			•If the child does not successfully count the money, ask the following questions: *"How many dimes do you have?"* *"How much money is that?"* *"How many pennies do you have?"* *"How much money is that?"* *"How much money is this altogether?"*
Students	*"What are the days of the week?"*	•Give the child 6 dimes and 3 pennies. (Vary amounts for different children.) *"How much money is this?"*	

1-70La   Copyright © 1991 by Saxon Publishers, Inc. and Nancy Larson. Reproduction prohibited.

Name _____

Date _____

ASSESSMENT 13
LESSON 70
Math 1

1. Tim has 3 pairs of socks. Draw the socks. Circle the pairs.

   How many socks did you draw? ___6___ socks

2. Write the numbers that are one less and one more.

   ___7___, 8, ___9___   ___15___, 16, ___17___   ___28___, 29, ___30___

3. Measure this line segment using pennies. ___7___ pennies

4. Continue the pattern.

   △,○,▭,△,○,▭, _△_ , _○_ , _▭_ , _△_

5. Color the fourth poster from the door red.

   How many posters are to the right of the red poster? ___2___

   How many posters are to the left of the red poster? ___3___

   Color the second poster from the door yellow.

6. Find the answers.

   $5 + 2 =$ ___7___ $6 - 0 =$ ___6___ $1 + 6 =$ ___7___

   $4 - 1 =$ ___3___ $9 + 2 =$ ___11___ $8 + 8 =$ ___16___

1-70Aa   Copyright © 1991 by Saxon Publishers, Inc. and Nancy Larson. Reproduction prohibited.

L esson 71

writing the number 64
tallying
counting by 5's

---

lesson preparation ————————————————————————

materials

20–30 toys in a box

paper

20 pennies and container

large fact cards (subtracting half of a double facts)

Fact Sheet S 1.2

in the morning

• Write the following number pattern on the meeting strip:

> 21, 31, 41, __, __, __

Answer: 21, 31, 41, 51, 61, 71

• Put **9 dimes** and **4 pennies** in the coin cup.

THE MEETING ——————————————————————————————

calendar

• Ask your child to identify the following:

year

month

shapes on the calendar

today's shape

shape pattern for the month

• Ask your child to write the date on the calendar.

• Ask your child to do the following:

identify today's day of the week

identify the days of the week

"What day of the week was it yesterday?"

"What day of the week will it be tomorrow?"

• Ask your child to identify the following:

    number of days in a week

    weekdays

• Ask your child to write the full date on the meeting strip.

weather graph

• Ask your child to report and graph the weather.

• Ask questions about the graph.

counting

• Count from 21 to 65 using the hundred number chart.

• Count by 10's to 100.

• Count backward from 100 by 10's.

• Count by 2's to 20.

• Say the odd numbers to 19.

• Add another number to the number line.

"We will count the numbers on the number line by 10's as far as we can and then count by 1's."

• Point to the multiples of 10 as you count together.

"How many 10's did we count?"

• Point to the digit in the tens' place.

"And how many more did we count?"

• Point to the digit in the ones' place.

"What number is _____ tens and _____ more?"

number pattern

• Ask your child to identify and fill in the missing numbers.

• Read the number pattern together.

clock

• Ask your child to set the morning/afternoon/evening/night clock.

• Throughout the day, your child announces the time on the hour, sets the demonstration clock, and writes the digital time for each new hour on the chalkboard.

coin cup

• Ask your child to slide and count the dimes in the coin cup.

- Ask your child to record the amount of money in the coin cup on the meeting strip.

right/left

- Continue to practice left and right once a week. Practice more often, if necessary.

THE LESSON

Writing the Number 64

"The last number we practiced writing was the number 63."

"What number do you think we will learn how to write today?"

- Write the number 64 on the chalkboard.

"What digits do you see in the number 64?"

"How many dimes and pennies will we use to make 64¢?"

- Use dimes and pennies to demonstrate.

"How many groups of 10 are in 64?"

"How many extra 1's do we have?"

"Let's count by 10's and 1's to check."

Tallying
Counting by 5's

"Today you will learn how to tally and how to count by 5's."

"Tallying is the way people keep track of things they are counting."

"When we tally, we make marks like this."

- Write the following on the chalkboard: ЖЖ

- Show your child the box of toys.

"Let's tally the number of toys in this box."

"As you take a toy from the box, I will draw a tally mark on the chalkboard."

"Watch how I make tally marks."

- Record in the following way on the chalkboard:

toys
ЖЖ
ЖЖ
ЖЖ
II

"When I draw tally marks, I draw four marks down and then one across."

"How many tally marks are in each bundle?"   5

"Let's count the tally marks."

- Count the individual tally marks. Write "5, 10, 15, . . ." after each group of tally marks.

"When we count groups of tally marks, we count by 5's."

"Let's count by 5's to 50."

- Count by 5's to 50 with your child.

"Let's count by 5's to 50 again as I write the numbers on a counting strip in the Meeting Book."

- Record the numbers on the fourth counting strip on page 48 in the Meeting Book. (Begin at the bottom with zero.)

"We can pretend that our fingers are tally marks."

"How many fingers do you have on one hand?"

"Most people have five fingers on each hand."

"We can hold them like this to show groups of 5's, just like groups of tally marks."

- Demonstrate.

"Let's count how many fingers we have altogether."

- Hold up your hands as you count by 5's together.

"Let's count by 5's to find the number of toes we have altogether."

- Count by 5's to 20.

"Now you will have a chance to practice making tally marks."

- Give your child a piece of paper.

"I have some pennies."

"As I drop them in a cup, make a tally mark for each penny you hear."

"When will you draw the mark across to close the bundle?"   *for the fifth penny*

- Use 8 pennies and a cup or container so that your child can hear the sound of the falling coins easily.

- Repeat, using 11, 14, 9, and 20 pennies.

"Make tally marks to show seven."

"Make tally marks to show twelve."

• Practice making tally marks for several more numbers, if necessary.

CLASS PRACTICE

• Use the large fact cards to practice the subtracting half of a double facts.

• Give your child **Fact Sheet S 1.2.**

"What number facts do you see?"

"What strategy can you use to find the answers?"

• Correct the fact sheet with your child.

WRITTEN PRACTICE

• Complete **Worksheet 71A** with your child.

• Complete **Worksheet 71B** with your child later in the day.

Name _____   **LESSON 71A**
Date _____   Math 1
Day of the Week _____

1. Write the number sixty-four three more times. How many digits are on the line? _10_

    6̶4̶ 6̶4̶

2. Ian put 5 stars on the paper. Roseann put 2 more stars on the paper. Draw a picture and write a number sentence to show how many stars are on the paper now.

    ☆ ☆ ☆ ☆ ☆   ☆ ☆

    Number sentence ____5 + 2 = 7____

    How many stars are on the paper now? _7_ stars

3. Use tally marks to show how many fingers you have.

    卌 卌

4. Color the right half of the top rectangle yellow.

    Color the left half of the bottom rectangle red.

    Color the left half of the top rectangle blue.

    Color the right half of the bottom rectangle green.

    | Blue | Yellow |
    | Red | Green |

5. Count by 5's. Fill in the missing numbers.

    5, 10, 15, _20_ , _25_ , _30_ , _35_ , _40_ , _45_ , _50_

6. Write the answers.

    1 + 5 = _6_   6 + 0 = _6_   8 + 8 = _16_

    7 + 2 = _9_   9 + 1 = _10_   2 + 5 = _7_

1-71Wa   Copyright © 1991 by Saxon Publishers, Inc. and Nancy Larson. Reproduction prohibited.

Name _____   **LESSON 71B**
                                          Math 1

1. Color the L, M, and N on this chart.

    | ▆ | 42 | 43 | 44 | 45 | 46 | 47 | 48 | 49 | 50 |
    | 51 | 52 | 53 | 54 | 55 | ▆ | 57 | 58 | 59 | 60 |
    | 61 | 62 | 63 | 64 | 65 | 66 | 67 | 68 | 69 | ▆ |

    What number belongs in the square with the L? _56_   M? _70_   N? _41_

2. Miss Latham had 6 magnets on her refrigerator. Michael gave her 2 more magnets for her refrigerator. Draw a picture and write a number sentence to show how many magnets are on the refrigerator now.

    ☐ ☐ ☐ ☐ ☐ ☐   ☐ ☐

    Number sentence ____6 + 2 = 8____

    How many magnets are on the refrigerator now? _8_ magnets

3. Use tally marks to show the number of toes you have.

    卌 卌

4. Color the right half of the bottom rectangle red.

    Color the left half of the top rectangle yellow.

    Color the right half of the top rectangle blue.

    Color the left half of the bottom rectangle green.

    | Yellow | Blue |
    | Green | Red |

5. Count by 5's. Fill in the missing numbers.

    _5_ , 10, _15_ , 20, _25_ , 30, _35_ , 40, _45_ , 50

6. Write the answers.

    4 + 4 = _8_   2 + 3 = _5_   7 + 7 = _14_

    7 + 1 = _8_   4 + 0 = _4_   6 + 2 = _8_

1-71Wb   Copyright © 1991 by Saxon Publishers, Inc. and Nancy Larson. Reproduction prohibited.

---

esson 72

writing the number 65
using a ruler to draw a line segment

---

lesson preparation

materials

Master 1-72

ruler

crayons

large fact cards (adding two facts)

Fact Sheet A 4.0

in the morning

• Write the following number pattern on the meeting strip:

> 5, 10, 15, __, __, __

> *Answer: 5, 10, 15, 20, 25, 30*

• Put **13 pennies** in the coin cup.

THE MEETING

calendar

> • Ask your child to identify the following:
>
> > year
> >
> > month
> >
> > shapes on the calendar
> >
> > today's shape
> >
> > shape pattern for the month
>
> • Ask your child to write the date on the calendar.
>
> • Ask your child to do the following:
>
> > identify today's day of the week
> >
> > identify the days of the week
>
> **"What day of the week was it yesterday?"**
>
> **"What day of the week will it be tomorrow?"**

- Ask your child to identify the following:

  number of days in a week

  weekdays

- Ask your child to write the full date on the meeting strip.

weather graph

- Ask your child to report and graph the weather.

- Ask questions about the graph.

counting

"Let's count by 5's to 50."

- Count from 21 to 57 using the hundred number chart.

- Count by 10's to 100.

- Count backward from 100 by 10's.

- Count by 2's to 20.

- Say the odd numbers to 19.

- Add another number to the number line.

"We will count the numbers on the number line by 10's as far as we can and then count by 1's."

- Point to the multiples of 10 as you count together.

"How many 10's did we count?"

- Point to the digit in the tens' place.

"And how many more did we count?"

- Point to the digit in the ones' place.

"What number is _____ tens and _____ more?"

number pattern

- Ask your child to identify and fill in the missing numbers.

- Read the number pattern together.

clock

- Ask your child to set the morning/afternoon/evening/night clock.

- Throughout the day, your child announces the time on the hour, sets the demonstration clock, and writes the digital time for each new hour on the chalkboard.

coin cup

"Today there are only pennies in the coin cup."

"Stack the pennies in groups of five and make tally marks to show the number of pennies in the coin cup."

- Allow time for your child to stack the pennies in piles of five and to draw the tally marks on the back of the meeting strip.

"Let's count the tally marks together."

- Point to each group of tally marks as you count by 5's and 1's with your child.

"Write this amount of money in the box on the meeting strip."

right/left

- Continue to practice left and right once a week. Practice more often, if necessary.

THE LESSON

Writing the Number 65

"The last number we practiced writing was the number 64."

"What number do you think we will learn how to write today?"

- Write the number 65 on the chalkboard.

"What digits do you see in the number 65?"

"How many dimes and pennies will we use to make 65¢?"

- Use dimes and pennies to demonstrate.

"How many groups of 10 are in 65?"

"How many extra 1's do we have?"

"Let's count by 10's and 1's to check."

Using a Ruler to Draw a Line Segment

"Each day you begin your practice paper by writing your name."

"You write your name on a line segment."

"Today you will learn how to draw line segments."

"A line segment is a straight line with two endpoints."

"We draw line segments when we connect the dots in a dot-to-dot puzzle."

"What kinds of things do you think we could use to help us draw line segments?"

"Why do you think we will use a ruler instead of other things with straight edges?"

"A ruler is easy to use because it is easy to hold, it is sturdy, and it has a smooth, straight edge."

"It is important to handle a ruler carefully so the edge stays smooth."

"How will you handle a ruler in a safe and careful way?"

- Allow time for your child to suggest appropriate ways to handle a ruler.

"I am going to draw a line segment on the chalkboard."

"I will hold the ruler with the hand that I don't write with."

"Watch how I spread my fingers to keep the ruler from slipping."

- Demonstrate on the chalkboard.

"When I draw a line segment, I trace along the edge of the ruler as I hold the ruler steady with my other hand."

- Draw the line segment.

"Watch what will happen if I don't hold my ruler still."

- Demonstrate what happens when the ruler slips.

- Put two points on the chalkboard about 10 inches apart.

"These are endpoints."

"I will draw a line segment between these endpoints."

"I will put my ruler just below the endpoints."

"I will hold the ruler with the hand that I don't write with."

"Watch how I spread my fingers to keep the ruler from slipping."

- Demonstrate on the chalkboard.

"When I draw a line segment, I trace along the edge of the ruler as I hold the ruler steady with my other hand."

- Draw the line segment.

"Now you will have a chance to practice drawing line segments using a ruler."

- Give your child **Master 1-72** and a ruler.

"Draw a line segment at the top of the paper."

"Write your name on the line segment."

- Allow time for your child to do this.

"Draw another line segment just below the first line segment."

"Write the date on the second line segment."

- Allow time for your child to do this.

"Now draw a line segment across the paper."

- Allow time for your child to draw the line segment.

"Now draw a line segment halfway across the paper."

- Allow time for your child to draw the line segment.

"There are some endpoints on your paper."

"You will connect the endpoints to make a picture."

"This is just like a dot-to-dot puzzle."

"One line segment is drawn for you."

"First you will draw a line segment from endpoint A to endpoint B."

"How will you do that?"

- Allow time for your child to draw the line segment.

"The name of this line segment is line segment AB."

"Now you will draw a line segment from endpoint B to endpoint C."

"How will you do that?"

- Allow time for your child to draw the line segment.

"The name of this line segment is line segment BC."

- Repeat with line segments CD and DE.

"What did you make?"   a star

"How many small triangles do you see in this star?"   5

"Color the triangles yellow."

"How many sides does the shape in the middle have?"   5

"This shape is called a pentagon."

"Color the pentagon blue."

CLASS PRACTICE

"Let's review the adding two number facts."

"What strategy will you use to find the answers?"

- Use the large fact cards to practice the adding two facts.
- Give your child **Fact Sheet A 4.0**.
- Correct the fact sheet with your child.

WRITTEN PRACTICE

- Complete **Worksheet 72A** with your child.
- Complete **Worksheet 72B** with your child later in the day.

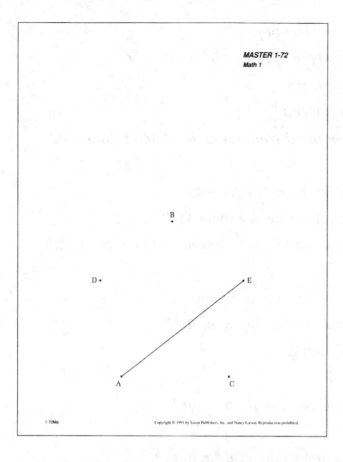

MASTER 1-72
Math 1

B
•

D •   • E

A   • C

Name _____   **LESSON 72A**
Date _____   Math 1
Day of the Week _____

1. Write the number sixty-five two more times. How many digits are on the line? __8__

65 65

2. Mrs. Trotter cut 3 slices of bread in half. Draw a picture of the pieces of bread. How many children can have a piece of bread?

__6__ children

3. Count the tally marks.
__27__ tally marks

4. Color the pennies brown. Count the money. __16¢__

5. Circle the number that is between 27 and 35.

27 [ ] 35   36 24 (31)

6. Write the answers.

5 + 2 = __7__   0 + 3 = __3__   4 + 1 = __5__

1 + 6 = __7__   2 + 7 = __9__   7 + 7 = __14__

Name _____   **LESSON 72B**
Math 1

1. Fill in the missing numbers.

5, 10, 15, __20__ , __25__ , __30__ , __35__ , __40__ , __45__

24, 25, 26, __27__ , __28__ , __29__ , __30__ , __31__ , __32__

2. Mrs. Wescott cut 4 apples in half. Draw a picture of the pieces of apple. How many children can have a piece of apple?

__8__ children

3. Count the tally marks.
__24__ tally marks

4. Color the pennies brown. Count the money. __24¢__

5. Circle the number that is between 43 and 52.

43 [ ] 52   42 (48) 53

6. Write the answers.

8 + 2 = __10__   6 + 0 = __6__   8 + 1 = __9__

1 + 5 = __6__   2 + 5 = __7__   9 + 9 = __18__

Lesson 73

writing the number 66
sorting common items

---

lesson preparation

materials

paper (12–16 pieces)

marker

25–30 empty food cans or boxes

large fact cards (addition facts)

Fact Sheet A 4.2

in the morning

• Write the following number pattern on the meeting strip:

> 37, 47, 57, __, __, __

Answer: 37, 47, 57, 67, 77, 87

• Put **16 pennies** in the coin cup.

THE MEETING

calendar

- Ask your child to identify the following:

    year

    month

    shapes on the calendar

    today's shape

    shape pattern for the month

- Ask your child to write the date on the calendar.

- Ask your child to do the following:

    identify today's day of the week

    identify the days of the week

"What day of the week was it yesterday?"

"What day of the week will it be tomorrow?"

- Ask your child to identify the following:

    number of days in a week

    weekdays

- Ask your child to write the full date on the meeting strip.

weather graph

- Ask your child to report and graph the weather.
- Ask questions about the graph.

counting

"Let's count by 5's to 50."

- Count from 23 to 60 using the hundred number chart.
- Count by 10's to 100.
- Count backward from 100 by 10's.
- Count by 2's to 20.
- Say the odd numbers to 19.
- Add another number to the number line.

"We will count the numbers on the number line by 10's as far as we can and then count by 1's."

- Point to the multiples of 10 as you count together.

"How many 10's did we count?"

- Point to the digit in the tens' place.

"And how many more did we count?"

- Point to the digit in the ones' place.

"What number is _____ tens and _____ more?"

number pattern

- Ask your child to identify and fill in the missing numbers.
- Read the number pattern together.

clock

- Ask your child to set the morning/afternoon/evening/night clock.
- Throughout the day, your child announces the time on the hour, sets the demonstration clock, and writes the digital time for each new hour on the chalkboard.

coin cup

"Today there are only pennies in the coin cup."

"Stack the pennies in groups of five and make tally marks to show the number of pennies in the coin cup."

- Allow time for your child to stack the pennies in piles of five and to draw the tally marks on the back of the meeting strip.

"Let's count the tally marks together."

- Point to each group of tally marks as you count by 5's and 1's with your child.

"Write this amount of money in the box on the meeting strip."

right/left

- Continue to practice left and right once a week. Practice more often, if necessary.

THE LESSON

Writing the Number 66

"The last number we practiced writing was the number 65."

"What number do you think we will learn how to write today?"

- Write the number 66 on the chalkboard.

"What digits do you see in the number 66?"

"How many dimes and pennies will we use to make 66¢?"

- Use dimes and pennies to demonstrate.

"How many groups of 10 are in 66?"

"How many extra 1's do we have?"

"Let's count by 10's and 1's to check."

Sorting Common Items

"A few days ago you used dimes and pennies to buy groceries."

"Today we will make a store so that you can practice buying items."

"You will learn how to sort items for our store."

- Show your child the empty boxes and cans.

"Let's arrange our groceries like they do in the grocery (food) store."

"How do you think we will do that?"

- Ask your child for sorting strategies.

"What are some of the different sections in the grocery (food) store?"

- Write the section names on individual pieces of paper. The section names might include cereal, frozen food, pet food, soup, fruits and vegetables, dairy products, soft drinks, etc.

"What types of items will we find in each section?"

- Allow time for your child to discuss the types of items found in each section of the store.

"Let's work together to sort our boxes and cans."

- Hold up one can or box.

"What is this?"

"In what section of our store should we put this?"

- Place the item on the appropriate piece of paper.

- Repeat until all the items are sorted.

"Which sections of our store need more items?"

- Save empty boxes and cans for these sections.

"Our store needs a name."

"What could we call our store?"

- Suggest that your child choose a name that is not the name of a local store.

"Later today you can make a sign to show our store's name."

"We will need to arrange the items neatly on the shelves like they do in the grocery store."

"How could we do that?"

- Allow time for your child to organize the store.

"Tomorrow we will buy items from our store."

CLASS PRACTICE

- Use the large fact cards to practice the addition facts.

- Give your child **Fact Sheet A 4.2**.

"What number facts do you see?"

"What strategies will you use to find the answers?"

- Correct the fact sheet with your child.

WRITTEN PRACTICE

- Complete **Worksheet 73A** with your child.

- Complete **Worksheet 73B** with your child later in the day.

Name _____ ***LESSON 73A***
(Draw a line segment for your name.)   Math 1

Date _____

Day of the Week _____

1. Write the number sixty-six three more times. How many digits are on the line? __10__

2. Mrs. Parker has 4 large pink flowers and 2 small yellow flowers in a vase on her desk. Draw a picture and write a number sentence to show how many flowers are in the vase.

Number sentence _____ 4 + 2 = 6 _____

How many flowers are in the vase? __6__ flowers

3. Number the clock face.
Show five o'clock on the clocks.

5:00

4. How many dimes and pennies will you need to buy the juice?

 29¢   __2__ dimes   __9__ pennies

5. Write the answers.

4	4	6	6	8	16
− 0	+ 0	− 1	+ 1	+ 8	− 8
4	4	5	7	16	8

1-73Wa

Name _____ ***LESSON 73B***
                                         Math 1

1. Write the numbers that are one less than each number.

__5__ , 6   __19__ , 20   __36__ , 37

2. Mrs. Pinkerton had five rulers. She gave Mrs. Howell two rulers. Draw a picture and write a number sentence to show how many rulers Mrs. Pinkerton has now.

Number sentence _____ 5 − 2 = 3 _____

How many rulers does Mrs. Pinkerton have now? __3__ rulers

3. Number the clock face.
Show nine o'clock on the clocks.

9:00

4. How many dimes and pennies will you need to buy the milk?

 35¢   __3__ dimes   __5__ pennies

5. Write the answers.

9	9	7	7	5	10
− 0	+ 0	− 1	+ 1	+ 5	− 5
9	9	6	8	10	5

1-73Wb

Lesson 74

writing the number 67
adding two-digit numbers using dimes and
pennies (without regrouping)

---

lesson preparation

materials

price tags for the store items

sorted store items from Lesson 73

sales receipt from a grocery store

Master 1-74

piece of paper

cup of 10 dimes and cup of 10 pennies

large fact cards (subtraction facts)

Fact Sheet S 3.4

the night before

• Put price tags on the items in the store using only the following amounts: 1¢–4¢, 10¢–
14¢, 20¢–24¢, 30¢–34¢, and 40¢–44¢.

in the morning

• Write the following number pattern on the meeting strip:

> 76, 77, 78, ___, ___, ___

Answer: 76, 77, 78, 79, 80, 81

• Put **24 pennies** in the coin cup.

THE MEETING

calendar

• Ask your child to identify the following:

year

month

shapes on the calendar

today's shape

shape pattern for the month

- Ask your child to write the date on the calendar.
- Ask your child to do the following:

    identify today's day of the week

    identify the days of the week

    "What day of the week was it yesterday?"

    "What day of the week will it be tomorrow?"

- Ask your child to identify the following:

    number of days in a week

    weekdays

- Ask your child to write the full date on the meeting strip.

weather graph

- Ask your child to report and graph the weather.
- Ask questions about the graph.

counting

"Let's count by 5's to 50."

- Count from 46 to 76 using the hundred number chart.
- Count by 10's to 100.
- Count backward from 100 by 10's.
- Count by 2's to 20.
- Say the odd numbers to 19.
- Add another number to the number line.

    "We will count the numbers on the number line by 10's as far as we can and then count by 1's."

- Point to the multiples of 10 as you count together.

    "How many 10's did we count?"

- Point to the digit in the tens' place.

    "And how many more did we count?"

- Point to the digit in the ones' place.

    "What number is _____ tens and _____ more?"

number pattern

- Ask your child to identify and fill in the missing numbers.
- Read the number pattern together.

clock

- Ask your child to set the morning/afternoon/evening/night clock.
- Throughout the day, your child announces the time on the hour, sets the demonstration clock, and writes the digital time for each new hour on the chalkboard.

coin cup

"Stack the pennies from the coin cup in groups of five and make tally marks to show the number of pennies."

- Allow time for your child to do this.
- Point to each group of tally marks as you count by 5's and 1's with your child.
- Ask your child to record the amount of money on the meeting strip.

right/left

- Continue to practice left and right once a week. Practice more often, if necessary.

THE LESSON

Writing the Number 67

"The last number we practiced writing was the number 66."

"What number do you think we will learn how to write today?"

- Write the number 67 on the chalkboard.

"What digits do you see in the number 67?"

"How many dimes and pennies will we use to make 67¢?"

- Use dimes and pennies to demonstrate.

"How many groups of 10 are in 67?"

"How many extra 1's do we have?"

"Let's count by 10's and 1's to check."

Adding Two-Digit Numbers Using Dimes and Pennies (Without Regrouping)

"Today you will learn how to add two-digit numbers using dimes and pennies."

"Yesterday we made a store."

"How did we do that?"

- Allow time for your child to describe the store.

"Today we will pretend that we are buying items at our store."

"When we buy things at a grocery (food) store, how does the cashier know how much money we need to pay?"

• Allow time for your child to discuss this.

"The cashier uses a machine called a cash register to find out how much money we owe."

"The cash register prints the name and the cost of each thing we are buying and adds the amounts."

• Show your child a grocery (food) store sales receipt.

"This piece of paper is called a sales receipt."

• Give your child **Master 1-74**.

"We will pretend that these are sales receipts like the ones the cashier gives us at a grocery store."

"We don't have a cash register to print the name of the item and the cost, so we will have to do that ourselves."

• Draw a large copy of a receipt on the chalkboard. Use it to demonstrate the following:

"A store writes its name at the top of its receipt."

"Write our store name at the top of your first receipt."

• Allow time for your child to write the name of the store.

"Now we will pretend that we are going shopping."

"What two things should we buy?"

• Ask your child to choose 2 items.

• Hold up the first item.

"What is this?"

"Write this name on the first line of your receipt."

"You can spell the name as it sounds or copy the name from the container."

"What is the cost of this item?"

"Write this on your receipt next to the name of the item."

• Repeat with the second item.

"Now you will use your dimes and pennies to find out how much these two items will cost altogether."

• Give your child a piece of paper, a cup of 10 dimes, and a cup of 10 pennies.

"How many dimes and pennies will you need for the first item?"

"Put these coins on your paper."

"How many dimes and pennies will you need for the second item?"

"Put these coins on your paper."

"Now put all the dimes together and all the pennies together."

"How many dimes do you have?"

"How many pennies do you have?"

"How much money is this altogether?"

"What is the total cost of the _____ and the _____?"

"Write this amount next to the word 'total.' "

"Put the coins back in the cups."

- Repeat with 2 more items.

- Allow time for your child to fill in the other 2 receipts independently.

"When you finish, return your items to the correct section and put them on the shelves neatly."

CLASS PRACTICE

- Use the large fact cards to practice the subtraction facts.

- Give your child **Fact Sheet S 3.4**.

"What number facts do you see?"

"What strategies will you use to find the answers?"

- Correct the fact sheet with your child.

WRITTEN PRACTICE

- Complete **Worksheet 74A** with your child.

- Complete **Worksheet 74B** with your child later in the day.

Name _____ **MASTER 1-74**
Math 1

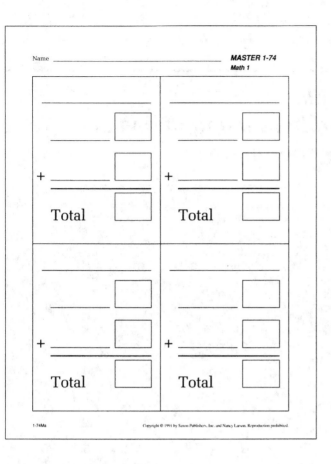

+ _____ ☐

Total ☐

+ _____ ☐

Total ☐

+ _____ ☐

Total ☐

+ _____ ☐

Total ☐

1-74Ma   Copyright © 1991 by Saxon Publishers, Inc. and Nancy Larson. Reproduction prohibited.

Name ●_____● **LESSON 74A**
(Draw a line segment for your name.)   Math 1

Date _____

Day of the Week _____

1. Write the number sixty-seven two more times. How many digits are on the line? __8__

6̶7̶ 6̶7̶

2. There were nine envelopes in the writing center. Ann used one envelope to send a letter to her mother. Draw a picture and write a number sentence to show the number of envelopes in the writing center now.

✉✉✉✉✉✉✉✉✉̶

Number sentence _____9 − 1 = 8_____

How many envelopes are in the writing center now? __8__ envelopes

3. Virginia made a pattern using the △ green and □ orange pattern blocks. Show a pattern Virginia could have made.

answers may vary

4. Write five different examples with a sum of 7.

☐   ☐   ☐   ☐   ☐
+☐   +☐   +☐   +☐   +☐
7   7   7   7   7

5. Use a crayon to circle all the even numbers in Problem 4.

1-74Wa   Copyright © 1991 by Saxon Publishers, Inc. and Nancy Larson. Reproduction prohibited.

Name _____ **LESSON 74B**
Math 1

1. Circle the one that is different.

2. Uncle Eddie had 6 tennis balls. He lost one tennis ball when he hit it over the fence. Draw a picture and write a number sentence to show the number of tennis balls he has now.

⊛⊛⊛⊛⊛⊗̶

Number sentence _____6 − 1 = 5_____

How many tennis balls does Uncle Eddie have now? __5__ tennis balls

3. Jackie made a different pattern using the △ green and □ orange pattern blocks. Show a pattern Jackie could have made.

answers may vary

4. Write five different examples with a sum of 5.

☐   ☐   ☐   ☐   ☐
+☐   +☐   +☐   +☐   +☐
5   5   5   5   5

5. Use a crayon to circle all the even numbers in Problem 4.

1-74Wb   Copyright © 1991 by Saxon Publishers, Inc. and Nancy Larson. Reproduction prohibited.

---

esson 75

writing the number 68
adding two-digit numbers using dimes and pennies (without regrouping)

---

lesson preparation

materials

Written Assessment #14

sorted store items

Master 1-75

cup of 10 dimes and cup of 10 pennies

large fact cards (addition facts)

Fact Sheet A 4.2

in the morning

• Write the following number pattern on the meeting strip:

> 25, 30, 35, ___, ___, ___

Answer: *25, 30, 35, 40, 45, 50*

• Put **28 pennies** in the coin cup.

THE MEETING

calendar

- • Ask your child to identify the following:

    year

    month

    shapes on the calendar

    today's shape

    shape pattern for the month

- • Ask your child to write the date on the calendar.

- • Ask your child to do the following:

    identify today's day of the week

    identify the days of the week

"What day of the week was it yesterday?"

"What day of the week will it be tomorrow?"

- Ask your child to identify the following:

     number of days in a week

     weekdays

- Ask your child to write the full date on the meeting strip.

weather graph

- Ask your child to report and graph the weather.

- Ask questions about the graph.

counting

"Let's count by 5's to 50."

- Count from 29 to 65 using the hundred number chart.

- Count by 10's to 100.

- Count backward from 100 by 10's.

- Count by 2's to 20.

- Say the odd numbers to 19.

- Add another number to the number line.

"We will count the numbers on the number line by 10's as far as we can and then count by 1's."

- Point to the multiples of 10 as you count together.

"How many 10's did we count?"

- Point to the digit in the tens' place.

"And how many more did we count?"

- Point to the digit in the ones' place.

"What number is _____ tens and _____ more?"

number pattern

- Ask your child to identify and fill in the missing numbers.

- Read the number pattern together.

clock

- Ask your child to set the morning/afternoon/evening/night clock.

- Throughout the day, your child announces the time on the hour, sets the demonstration clock, and writes the digital time for each new hour on the chalkboard.

coin cup

> *"Stack the pennies from the coin cup in groups of five and make tally marks to show the number of pennies."*

- Allow time for your child to do this.

- Point to each group of tally marks as you count by 5's and 1's with your child.

- Ask your child to record the amount of money on the meeting strip.

right/left

- Continue to practice left and right once a week. Practice more often, if necessary.

ASSESSMENT

Written Assessment

- Give your child **Written Assessment #14**.

- Read the directions for each problem. Allow time for your child to complete each problem before continuing.

- Correct the paper, noting your child's mistakes on the **Individual Recording Form**. Review the errors with your child.

THE LESSON

Writing the Number 68

> *"The last number we practiced writing was the number 67."*

> *"What number do you think we will learn how to write today?"*

- Write the number 68 on the chalkboard.

> *"What digits do you see in the number 68?"*

> *"How many dimes and pennies will we use to make 68¢?"*

- Use dimes and pennies to demonstrate.

> *"How many groups of 10 are in 68?"*

> *"How many extra 1's do we have?"*

> *"Let's count by 10's and 1's to check."*

Adding Two-Digit Numbers Using Dimes and Pennies (Without Regrouping)

> *"Today you will continue to learn how to add two-digit numbers using dimes and pennies."*

"We will buy items at our store."

"We will take turns being the cashier and the customer."

"The customer will choose two items in the store to buy and bring them to the cashier."

"The cashier will write the name of the store, the names of the items, and the prices on the receipt."

"The customer will use dimes and pennies to pay for the items."

"They will work together to count the money the customer spent altogether."

"The cashier will write the total amount of money on the receipt next to the word 'total.' "

"Let's try that."

"You will be the cashier."

- Draw a receipt on the chalkboard.

- Choose 2 items from the classroom store.

"I will buy these two items."

"What will you write on the receipt?"   name of the store, names of the items, prices

- Allow time for your child to do this.

"Let's predict how many dimes and pennies I will need to buy these items."

"How many pennies do you think I will give you altogether?"

"How do you know?"

"How many dimes do you think I will give you altogether?"

"How do you know?"

"Now I will use dimes and pennies to show the cost of each item."

- Put the money for each item in front of the item.

"Now I will put all the pennies together and all the dimes together."

- Put the pennies together and the dimes together.

"Now we will count to see how many pennies I used altogether."

- Count the pennies with your child.

"Was your prediction correct?"

"Now we will count to see how many dimes I used altogether."

- Count the dimes with your child.

"Was your prediction correct?"

"We have _____ dimes and _____ pennies."

"How much money is this altogether?"

- Record the total amount on the chalkboard receipt.

  "Now we will trade jobs."

  "I will be the cashier and you will be the customer."

  "I will return my two items while you select the two items you want to buy."

  "I will fill in the receipt."

  "How will I do that?"

- Ask your child to describe what to write on the chalkboard receipt.

- Fill in the name of the store, the names of the items, and the prices on the receipt.

  "Let's try to predict how many pennies and dimes you will give me."

  "How many pennies do you think you will give me altogether?"

  "How do you know?"

  "How many dimes do you think you will give me altogether?"

  "How do you know?"

  "Now you will show each of these amounts using dimes and pennies."

- Ask your child to put the money for each item in front of the item.

  "Now you will put all the dimes together and all the pennies together."

  "How many pennies did you use?"

  "Let's count them together."

  "Was your prediction correct?"

  "How many dimes did you use?"

  "Let's count them together."

  "Was your prediction correct?"

  "We have _____ dimes and _____ pennies."

  "How much money is this altogether?"

  "How will I write this on the receipt?"

- Record the total amount on the chalkboard receipt.

  "Now we will put the items neatly back on the shelves."

  "Let's practice buying some more items from our store."

  "We will take turns being the cashier and the customer."

- Use **Master 1-75**.

- Make additional copies of **Master 1-75**, if desired.

CLASS PRACTICE

- Use the large fact cards to practice the addition facts.
- Give your child **Fact Sheet A 4.2**.

  "What number facts do you see?"

  "What strategies will you use to find the answers?"

- Correct the fact sheet with your child.

WRITTEN PRACTICE

- Complete **Worksheet 75A** with your child.
- Complete **Worksheet 75B** with your child later in the day.

Name _____ **ASSESSMENT 14**
LESSON 75
Date _____ Math 1

1. Peggy counted six blue price tags and two yellow price tags. Draw the tags and write a number sentence to show the number of tags she counted.

   [price tags grid]

   Number sentence _____ 6 + 2 = 8 _____

   How many tags did Peggy count? _____ tags

2. What day of the week is it today? _____

3. Write a number word that has **3** letters. _____

   Write a number word that has **4** letters. _____

4. Write the answers.

   $$\begin{array}{cccccc} 5 & 7 & 9 & 5 & 8 & 6 & 8 \\ -0 & -7 & +1 & +2 & -8 & -0 & +2 \\ \hline 5 & 0 & 10 & 7 & 0 & 6 & 10 \end{array}$$

5. Finish the pattern.

   45, 46, 47, _48_ , _49_ , _50_ , _51_ , _52_ , _53_ , _54_

6. Number the clock face.

   Show two o'clock on the clocks.

   2:00   [clock face]

1-75Aa   Copyright © 1991 by Saxon Publishers, Inc. and Nancy Larson. Reproduction prohibited.

Name _____ **MASTER 1-75**
Math 1

_____		_____	
+ _____	[ ]	+ _____	[ ]
Total	[ ]	Total	[ ]
_____		_____	
+ _____	[ ]	+ _____	[ ]
Total	[ ]	Total	[ ]

1-75Ma   Copyright © 1991 by Saxon Publishers, Inc. and Nancy Larson. Reproduction prohibited.

Name • _____ • **LESSON 75A**
(Draw a line segment for your name.)   Math 1

Date _____

Day of the Week _____

1. Write the number sixty-eight two more times. How many digits are on the line? _____

   68 68

2. Donald used 5 green pattern blocks and 3 blue pattern blocks to make a design. He took off 1 green pattern block. Draw a picture and write a number sentence to show how many green pattern blocks are in his design now.

   [pattern blocks]

   Number sentence _____ 5 − 1 = 4 _____

   How many green pattern blocks are in his design now? _____ green pattern blocks

3. Draw tally marks to show the number of children in your class.

   [box]

4. Choose **4 even** numbers.
   Write them in the circles.
   Add **1** to each number.
   Find the answers.
   Are the answers
   even or odd numbers? _____

   ○ + 1   ○ + 1   ○ + 1   ○ + 1
   □   □   □   □

5. How many dimes and pennies will you need to buy the ruler?

   [ruler] 27¢   _____ dimes   _____ pennies

6. Write the answers.

   6 − 0 = _6_   4 − 1 = _3_   14 − 7 = _7_

   5 − 5 = _0_   6 − 3 = _3_   8 − 1 = _7_

1-75Wa   Copyright © 1991 by Saxon Publishers, Inc. and Nancy Larson. Reproduction prohibited.

Name _____ **LESSON 75B**
Math 1

1. Fill in the missing numbers.

   | 61 | 62 | 63 | 64 | 65 | 66 | **67** | 68 | 69 | 70 |
   | 71 | 72 | 73 | **74** | 75 | 76 | 77 | 78 | 79 | 80 |

2. Elise used 6 green pattern blocks and 2 orange pattern blocks to make a design. She took off 1 green pattern block. Draw a picture and write a number sentence to show how many green pattern blocks are in the design now.

   [pattern blocks]

   Number sentence _____ 6 − 1 = 5 _____

   How many green pattern blocks are in her design now? _____ green pattern blocks

3. Draw tally marks to show the number of people who live in your house.

   [box]

   How many tally marks did you draw? _____

4. Choose **4 odd** numbers.
   Write them in the circles.
   Add **1** to each number.
   Find the answers.
   Are the answers
   even or odd numbers? _____

   ○ + 1   ○ + 1   ○ + 1   ○ + 1
   □   □   □   □

5. How many dimes and pennies will you need to buy the notebook?

   [notebook] 63¢   _____ dimes   _____ pennies

6. Write the answers.

   9 − 9 = _0_   8 − 4 = _4_   18 − 9 = _9_

   5 − 1 = _4_   2 − 0 = _2_   7 − 1 = _6_

1-75Wb   Copyright © 1991 by Saxon Publishers, Inc. and Nancy Larson. Reproduction prohibited.

Lesson 76

writing the number 69
addition facts—showing doubles plus one facts

lesson preparation

materials

Master 1-76

2 towers of 10 linking cubes (different colors)

large fact cards (addition facts)

Fact Sheet A 4.2

in the morning

• Write the following number pattern on the meeting strip:

| 17, 15, 13, ___, ___, ___ |

Answer: 17, 15, 13, 11, 9, 7

• Put **21 pennies** in the coin cup.

THE MEETING

calendar

• Ask your child to identify the following:

> year
>
> month
>
> shapes on the calendar
>
> today's shape
>
> shape pattern for the month

• Ask your child to write the date on the calendar.

• Ask your child to do the following:

> identify today's day of the week
>
> identify the days of the week

"What day of the week was it yesterday?"

"What day of the week will it be tomorrow?"

- Ask your child to identify the following:

    number of days in a week

    weekdays

- Ask your child to write the full date on the meeting strip.

weather graph

- Ask your child to report and graph the weather.

- Ask questions about the graph.

counting

"Let's count by 5's to 50."

- Count from 45 to 75 using the hundred number chart.

- Count by 10's to 100.

- Count backward from 100 by 10's.

- Count by 2's to 20.

- Say the odd numbers to 19.

- Add another number to the number line.

"We will count the numbers on the number line by 10's as far as we can and then count by 1's."

- Point to the multiples of 10 as you count together.

"How many 10's did we count?"

- Point to the digit in the tens' place.

"And how many more did we count?"

- Point to the digit in the ones' place.

"What number is _____ tens and _____ more?"

number pattern

- Ask your child to identify and fill in the missing numbers.

- Read the number pattern together.

clock

- Ask your child to set the morning/afternoon/evening/night clock.

- Throughout the day, your child announces the time on the hour, sets the demonstration clock, and writes the digital time for each new hour on the chalkboard.

coin cup

"Stack the pennies from the coin cup in groups of five and make tally marks to show the number of pennies."

- Allow time for your child to do this.

- Point to each group of tally marks as you count by 5's and 1's with your child.

- Ask your child to record the amount of money on the meeting strip.

right/left

- Continue to practice left and right once a week. Practice more often, if necessary.

THE LESSON

Writing the Number 69

"The last number we practiced writing was the number 68."

"What number do you think we will learn how to write today?"

- Write the number 69 on the chalkboard.

"What digits do you see in the number 69?"

"How many dimes and pennies will we use to make 69¢?"

- Use dimes and pennies to demonstrate.

"How many groups of 10 are in 69?"

"How many extra 1's do we have?"

"Let's count by 10's and 1's to check."

Addition Facts—Showing Doubles Plus One Facts

- Give your child two towers of 10 linking cubes. Use a different color for each tower.

"Today you will learn how to show addition facts called the doubles plus one facts."

"What are the doubles facts?"

- List them on the chalkboard.

"How do you know that these are the doubles?"   the numbers being added are the same

"Make a tower of three linking cubes using only one color."

"Make another tower of three linking cubes using the other color."

"Put the towers next to each other."

"What do you notice?"   they are the same height

"How many cubes is this altogether?"   6

"We can write this as 'three plus three equals six.' "

- Write "3 + 3 = 6" on the chalkboard.

"What do we call this example?" a doubles fact

"Now add a cube to the tower on the right."

"Put the towers next to each other."

"What do you notice?" the one on the right has one more cube

"How did we change our double?" added one

"We had six and now we have one more."

"How many cubes do we have altogether?" 7

"What number sentence can we write for the towers?"

"We can write this as 'three plus four equals seven.' "

- Write "3 + 4 = 7" on the chalkboard below 3 + 3 = 6.

"Take off the extra cube."

"Now add a cube to the tower on the left."

"Put the towers next to each other."

"What do you notice?" the one on the left has one more cube

"How did we change our double?" we added one

"We had six and now we have one more."

"How many cubes do we have altogether?" 7

"What number sentence can we write for the towers?"

"We can write this as 'four plus three equals seven.' "

- Write "4 + 3 = 7" on the chalkboard below 3 + 4 = 7.

"Make a tower of five linking cubes using only one color."

"Make another tower of five linking cubes using the other color."

"Put the towers next to each other."

"What do you notice?" they are the same height

"How many cubes is this altogether?" 10

"We can write this as 'five plus five equals ten.' "

- Write "5 + 5 = 10" on the chalkboard.

"What do we call this example?" a doubles fact

"Now add a cube to the tower on the right."

"Put the towers next to each other."

"What do you notice?" the one on the right has one more cube

"How did we change our double?" added one

"We had ten and now we have one more."

"How many cubes do we have altogether?" 11

"What number sentence can we write for the towers?"

"We can write this as 'five plus six equals eleven.' "

- Write "5 + 6 = 11" on the chalkboard below 5 + 5 = 10.

"Take off the extra cube."

"Now add a cube to the tower on the left."

"Put the towers next to each other."

"What do you notice?"   the one on the left has one more cube

"How did we change our double?"   added one

"We had ten and now we have one more."

"How many cubes do we have altogether?"   11

"What number sentence can we write for the towers?"

"We can write this as 'six plus five equals eleven.' "

- Write "6 + 5 = 11" on the chalkboard below 5 + 6 = 11.
- Repeat with 2 + 2, 4 + 4, 7 + 7, 6 + 6, and 8 + 8.
- Give your child **Master 1-76**.

"Write your name at the top of the paper."

"Fold your paper in half along the dotted line."

- Demonstrate how to fold the paper.

"Put your paper on the table so that you can see your name."

"What kind of problems are these?"   doubles

"Write the answers on your paper as quickly as you can."

- When your child finishes, continue.

"Let's read the problems and the answers together."

- Read the problems and the answers with your child.

"Now turn to the other half of your paper."

"Look at the first row."

"Read the problems in the first row."

"How are they the same?"

"How are they different?"

- Repeat with the second, third, and fourth rows.

"The first problem in each row is a doubles fact."

"The second problem in each row is a doubles plus one fact."

"The answer for each doubles plus one fact is one more than the doubles fact before it."

"Let's read the problems together as you write the answers."

Class Practice

- Use the large fact cards to practice the addition facts.
- Give your child **Fact Sheet A 4.2**.

  "What number facts do you see?"

  "What strategies will you use to find the answers?"

- Correct the fact sheet with your child.

Written Practice

- Complete **Worksheet 76A** with your child.
- Complete **Worksheet 76B** with your child later in the day.

Name _____

MASTER 1-76
Math 1

4 + 4	4 + 4	4 + 5
7 + 7	7 + 7	7 + 8
5 + 5	5 + 5	5 + 6
3 + 3	3 + 3	3 + 4
6 + 6	6 + 6	6 + 7
8 + 8	8 + 8	8 + 9
2 + 2	2 + 2	2 + 3

1-76Ma   Copyright © 1991 by Saxon Publishers, Inc. and Nancy Larson. Reproduction prohibited.

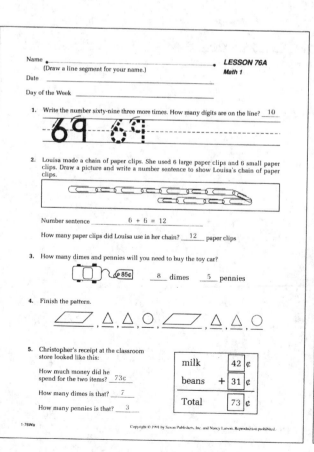

Name •_____• **LESSON 76A**
  (Draw a line segment for your name.)   Math 1

Date _____

Day of the Week _____

1. Write the number sixty-nine three more times. How many digits are on the line? __10__

2. Louisa made a chain of paper clips. She used 6 large paper clips and 6 small paper clips. Draw a picture and write a number sentence to show Louisa's chain of paper clips.

    Number sentence ____6 + 6 = 12____

    How many paper clips did Louisa use in her chain? __12__ paper clips

3. How many dimes and pennies will you need to buy the toy car?

    85¢   __8__ dimes   __5__ pennies

4. Finish the pattern.

5. Christopher's receipt at the classroom store looked like this:

    How much money did he spend for the two items? __73¢__

    How many dimes is that? __7__

    How many pennies is that? __3__

milk	42	¢
beans +	31	¢
Total	73	¢

1-76Wa   Copyright © 1991 by Saxon Publishers, Inc. and Nancy Larson. Reproduction prohibited.

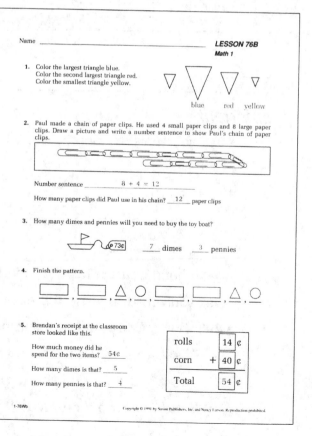

Name _____   **LESSON 76B**
                 Math 1

1. Color the largest triangle blue.
    Color the second largest triangle red.
    Color the smallest triangle yellow.

    blue   red   yellow

2. Paul made a chain of paper clips. He used 4 small paper clips and 8 large paper clips. Draw a picture and write a number sentence to show Paul's chain of paper clips.

    Number sentence ____8 + 4 = 12____

    How many paper clips did Paul use in his chain? __12__ paper clips

3. How many dimes and pennies will you need to buy the toy boat?

    73¢   __7__ dimes   __3__ pennies

4. Finish the pattern.

5. Brendan's receipt at the classroom store looked like this.

    How much money did he spend for the two items? __54¢__

    How many dimes is that? __5__

    How many pennies is that? __4__

rolls	14	¢
corn +	40	¢
Total	54	¢

1-76Wb   Copyright © 1991 by Saxon Publishers, Inc. and Nancy Larson. Reproduction prohibited.

Lesson 77

writing the number 70
addition facts—identifying the doubles plus one facts

---

lesson preparation

materials

2 towers of 10 linking cubes

Meeting Book

Master 1-77

large fact cards (subtraction facts)

Fact Sheet S 3.4

in the morning

• Write the following number pattern on the meeting strip:

> 40, 35, 30, __, __, __

> *Answer: 40, 35, 30, 25, 20, 15*

• Put **35 pennies** in the coin cup.

THE MEETING

calendar

• Ask your child to identify the following:

  year

  month

  shapes on the calendar

  today's shape

  shape pattern for the month

• Ask your child to write the date on the calendar.

• Ask your child to do the following:

  identify today's day of the week

  identify the days of the week

"What day of the week was it yesterday?"

"What day of the week will it be tomorrow?"

• Ask your child to identify the following:

  number of days in a week

  weekdays

• Ask your child to write the full date on the meeting strip.

weather graph

• Ask your child to report and graph the weather.

• Ask questions about the graph.

counting

"Let's count by 5's to 50."

• Count from 69 to 98 using the hundred number chart.

• Count by 10's to 100.

• Count backward from 100 by 10's.

• Count by 2's to 20.

• Say the odd numbers to 19.

• Add another number to the number line.

"We will count the numbers on the number line by 10's as far as we can and then count by 1's."

• Point to the multiples of 10 as you count together.

"How many 10's did we count?"

• Point to the digit in the tens' place.

"And how many more did we count?"

• Point to the digit in the ones' place.

"What number is _____ tens and _____ more?"

number pattern

• Ask your child to identify and fill in the missing numbers.

• Read the number pattern together.

clock

• Ask your child to set the morning/afternoon/evening/night clock.

• Throughout the day, your child announces the time on the hour, sets the demonstration clock, and writes the digital time for each new hour on the chalkboard.

coin cup

> *"Stack the pennies from the coin cup in groups of five and make tally marks to show the number of pennies."*

- Allow time for your child to do this.

- Point to each group of tally marks as you count by 5's and 1's with your child.

- Ask your child to record the amount of money on the meeting strip.

right/left

- Continue to practice left and right once a week. Practice more often, if necessary.

THE LESSON

Writing the Number 70

> *"The last number we practiced writing was the number 69."*

> *"What number do you think we will learn how to write today?"*

- Write the number 70 on the chalkboard.

> *"What digits do you see in the number 70?"*

> *"How many dimes and pennies will we use to make 70¢?"*

- Use dimes and pennies to demonstrate.

> *"How many groups of 10 are in 70?"*

> *"How many extra 1's do we have?"*

> *"Let's count by 10's to check."*

Addition Facts—Identifying the Doubles Plus One Facts

> *"Today you will learn how to identify addition facts called the doubles plus one facts."*

> *"What did we do with our linking cubes yesterday?"*   made towers

> *"What kind of towers did we make?"*   towers that were the same height

- Make two towers of 4 linking cubes each. Hold up one tower.

> *"How many linking cubes are in this tower?"*   4

- Hold up the other tower.

> *"How many linking cubes are in this tower?"*   4

> *"What number sentence will we write for these towers?"*   4 + 4 = 8

- Write "4 + 4 = 8" on the chalkboard.

> *"What did we do with our towers next?"*   added one cube to one tower

- Add a cube to the tower on the right.

  "What number sentence will we write for these towers now?" $4 + 5 = 9$

- Write "4 + 5 = 9" on the chalkboard.

  "We call this a doubles plus one fact because it started as a double and we added one more."

  "Open the Meeting Book to pages 46–47."

  "Look at 4 and 5 on the number line."

  "What do you notice?"   they are next to each other on the number line

  "What other numbers are next to each other on the number line?"

- List the combinations on the chalkboard. Limit the numbers to numbers less than 10.

1 + 2	2 + 3	3 + 4
4 + 5	5 + 6	6 + 7
7 + 8	8 + 9	

  "These numbers are next to each other when we count by 1's."

  "When people add numbers that are next to each other when they count by 1's, they have a strategy for adding them."

  "They use the doubles to help them."

  "They look for the smaller number and they double it."

  "Let's try this together."

- Point to the 6 + 7 combination.

  "We will double the smaller number."

  "Which number will we double?" 6

- Circle the 6.

  "If six and six is twelve, then six plus seven is how many?" 13

  "Why?"   because 7 is one more than 6

- Record the answer next to the problem.

  "Let's try another pair of numbers."

- Point to the 3 + 4 combination.

  "We will double the smaller number."

  "Which number will we double?" 3

- Circle the 3.

  "If three and three is six, then three plus four is how many?"   7

  "Why?"   because 4 is one more than 3

- Record the answer next to the problem.

- Repeat with each combination.

"How will we know if a number fact is a doubles plus one fact?"
the numbers are next to each other when we count by 1's

- Write the following number facts on the chalkboard:

2 + 8 =	5 + 6 =	7 + 3 =	5	4	6	7
8 + 9 =	1 + 4 =	4 + 3 =	+4	+7	+9	+8

"Let's circle a number fact that is a doubles plus one fact."

"What number fact can we circle?"   *one of the following: 5 + 6,*
8 + 9, 4 + 3,   5   7
                  +4, +8

"How do you know?"   *the numbers are next to each other when we*
count by 1's

- Repeat until all the doubles plus one facts are circled.

"Now you will have a chance to identify doubles plus one facts."

- Give your child **Master 1-77**.

"Now you will be a doubles plus one detective."

- Show your child how to hold his/her fingers like a magnifying glass as he/she looks for the doubles plus one facts.

"Circle all the doubles plus one facts."

- When your child finishes, continue.

"What facts did you circle in the first row?"

- Repeat with each row.

- Save the paper for use in Lesson 78.

CLASS PRACTICE

- Use the large fact cards to practice the subtraction facts.

- Give your child **Fact Sheet S 3.4**.

"What number facts do you see?"

"What strategies will you use to find the answers?"

- Correct the fact sheet with your child.

WRITTEN PRACTICE

- Complete **Worksheet 77A** with your child.

- Complete **Worksheet 77B** with your child later in the day.

Name _____ **MASTER 1-77**
Math 1

Circle the doubles plus one facts.

5 + 6 = _____   2 + 7 = _____   3 + 4 = _____

1 + 9 = _____   8 + 7 = _____   2 + 3 = _____

6 + 0 = _____   9 + 8 = _____   5 + 4 = _____

$$\begin{array}{r} 3 \\ + 4 \\ \hline \end{array} \qquad \begin{array}{r} 7 \\ + 8 \\ \hline \end{array} \qquad \begin{array}{r} 2 \\ + 6 \\ \hline \end{array} \qquad \begin{array}{r} 1 \\ + 7 \\ \hline \end{array} \qquad \begin{array}{r} 2 \\ + 5 \\ \hline \end{array}$$

$$\begin{array}{r} 9 \\ + 7 \\ \hline \end{array} \qquad \begin{array}{r} 6 \\ + 5 \\ \hline \end{array} \qquad \begin{array}{r} 4 \\ + 8 \\ \hline \end{array} \qquad \begin{array}{r} 9 \\ + 8 \\ \hline \end{array} \qquad \begin{array}{r} 7 \\ + 5 \\ \hline \end{array}$$

1-77Ma

Name _____ **LESSON 77A**
(Draw a line segment for your name.)   **Math 1**
Date _____

Day of the Week _____

1. Write the number seventy 3 more times. How many digits are on the line? __10__

   7̷0 70

2. Write a number word that has **4** letters. ___ ___ ___ ___

   Write a number word that has **5** letters. ___ ___ ___ ___ ___

   Write a number sentence to show how
   many letters you wrote altogether. ____4 + 5 = 9____

   How many letters are in the two number words altogether? __9__ letters

3. Color the bottom half of
   the right-hand circle blue.   Red   Yellow

   Color the top half of
   the middle circle yellow.   Blue

   Color the top half of the left-hand circle red.

4. Show four o'clock on the clocks. **4:00** (clock)

5. Measure this line segment using pennies.

   ____4____ pennies

6. Warren's receipt at the classroom
   store looked like this.

soap	40	¢
tuna +	24	¢
Total	64	¢

   How much money did he
   spend for the two items? __64¢__

   How many dimes is that? __6__

   How many pennies is that? __4__

1-77Wa

Name _____ **LESSON 77B**
Math 1

1. Circle the number that is between 24 and 32.

   24 [ ] 32   16 34 23 (27)

2. Write a number word that has **3** letters. ___ ___ ___

   Write a number word that has **4** letters. ___ ___ ___ ___

   Write a number sentence to show how
   many letters you wrote altogether. ____3 + 4 = 7____

   How many letters are in the two number words altogether? __7__ letters

3. Color the top half of
   the middle circle green.   Green

   Color the bottom half of
   the right-hand circle red.   Blue   Red

   Color the bottom half of
   the left-hand circle blue.

4. Show seven o'clock on the clocks. **7:00** (clock)

5. Measure this line segment using pennies.

   ____2____ pennies

6. Simon's receipt at the classroom
   store looked like this.

juice	32	¢
noodles +	20	¢
Total	52	¢

   How much money did he
   spend for the two items? __52¢__

   How many dimes is that? __5__

   How many pennies is that? __2__

1-77Wb

Lesson 78

writing the number 71
addition facts—doubles plus one facts

---

lesson preparation

materials

sixteen 3" × 5" cards

Master 1-77 (from Lesson 77)

large fact cards (various, see below)

Fact Sheet S 3.4

the night before

• Use the 3" × 5" cards to make a large set of fact cards for the doubles plus one facts. Write them in the following way:

1	2	3	4	5	6	7	8
+ 2	+ 3	+ 4	+ 5	+ 6	+ 7	+ 8	+ 9

2	3	4	5	6	7	8	9
+ 1	+ 2	+ 3	+ 4	+ 5	+ 6	+ 7	+ 8

• The following large fact cards will be used during the lesson:

7	5	7	6	0	8	5	3	6
+ 2	+ 4	+ 7	+ 1	+ 3	+ 9	+ 5	+ 4	+ 5

in the morning

• Write the following number pattern on the meeting strip:

20, 22, 24, ___, ___, ___

Answer: 20, 22, 24, 26, 28, 30

• Put **31 pennies** in the coin cup.

THE MEETING

calendar

- Ask your child to identify the following:

    year

    month

    shapes on the calendar

    today's shape

    shape pattern for the month

- Ask your child to write the date on the calendar.

- Ask your child to do the following:

    identify today's day of the week

    identify the days of the week

"What day of the week was it yesterday?"

"What day of the week will it be tomorrow?"

- Ask your child to identify the following:

    number of days in a week

    weekdays

- Ask your child to write the full date on the meeting strip.

weather graph

- Ask your child to report and graph the weather.

- Ask questions about the graph.

counting

"Let's count by 5's to 50."

- Count from 47 to 74 using the hundred number chart.

- Count backward from 30 to 1.

- Count by 10's to 100.

- Count backward from 100 by 10's.

- Count by 2's to 20.

- Say the odd numbers to 19.

- Add another number to the number line.

"Let's count the numbers on our number line."

"We will count by 10's as far as we can and then count by 1's."

"How many 10's did we count?"

"And how many more did we count?"

"What number is _____ tens and _____ more?"

number pattern

- Ask your child to identify and fill in the missing numbers.
- Read the number pattern together.

clock

- Ask your child to set the morning/afternoon/evening/night clock.
- Throughout the day, your child announces the time on the hour, sets the demonstration clock, and writes the digital time for each new hour on the chalkboard.

coin cup

"Stack the pennies from the coin cup in groups of five and make tally marks to show the number of pennies."

- Allow time for your child to do this.
- Point to each group of tally marks as you count by 5's and 1's with your child.
- Ask your child to record the amount of money on the meeting strip.

right/left

- Continue to practice left and right once a week. Practice more often, if necessary.

THE LESSON

Writing the Number 71

"The last number we practiced writing was the number 70."

"What number do you think we will learn how to write today?"

- Write the number 71 on the chalkboard.

"What digits do you see in the number 71?"

"How many dimes and pennies will we use to make 71¢?"

- Use dimes and pennies to demonstrate.

"How many groups of 10 are in 71?"

"How many extra 1's do we have?"

"Let's count by 10's and 1's to check."

Addition Facts—Doubles Plus One Facts

- Give your child **Master 1-77.**

"What do we call the problems that you circled on your paper?" doubles plus one facts

"Today you will learn how to find the answers for the doubles plus one facts."

"What do you notice about the numbers in the circled problems?" one number is one more than the other

"Point to the first problem."

"Which is the smaller number?" 5

"Circle this number."

"We will double the smaller number."

"If 5 + 5 = 10, then 5 + 6 is what?" 11

"Point to the next doubles plus one problem."

"Which is the smaller number?" 3

"Circle this number."

"We will double the smaller number."

"If 3 + 3 = 6, then 3 + 4 is what?" 7

- Repeat with all the doubles plus one problems on **Master 1-77**.

- Place the following large fact cards on the table:

7	5	7	6	0	8	5	3	6
$+2$	$+4$	$+7$	$+1$	$+3$	$+9$	$+5$	$+4$	$+5$

"What types of facts do you see?" (doubles, + 1, + 0, + 2, doubles + 1 facts)

"Which of these facts is an adding zero fact?" 0 + 3

- Repeat with adding one, adding two, and doubles facts.

"What do we call the problems we have left?" doubles plus one facts

"How can we find the answers?" double the smaller number and add one

"Let's try that with each of the cards."

- Hold up one double plus one fact card.

"What is the smaller number?"

"Double that number."

"Now add one."

"What is the answer?"

- Repeat with each of the doubles plus one fact cards.

"Can you think of another doubles plus one fact?"

• Write the fact on the chalkboard.

"How do we know that this is a doubles plus one fact?"

"How will we find the answer?" double the smaller number and add one

"What number will we double?"

"What is the answer?"

CLASS PRACTICE

• Use the large fact cards to practice the subtraction facts.

• Give your child **Fact Sheet S 3.4.**

"What number facts do you see?"

"What strategies will you use to find the answers?"

• Correct the fact sheet with your child.

WRITTEN PRACTICE

• Complete **Worksheet 78A** with your child.

• Complete **Worksheet 78B** with your child later in the day.

Name _____ **LESSON 78A**
(Draw a line segment for your name.)   **Math 1**

Date _____

Day of the Week _____

1. Write the number seventy-one four more times. How many digits are on the line? ____

   71 71

2. Doreen had 6 dimes. She gave Harvey a dime. Draw a picture and write a number sentence to show the dimes Doreen has now.

   Number sentence _____

   How many dimes does Doreen have now? ____ dimes

   How much money is that? _____

3. Write four number words that have four letters.

4. Choose **4 odd** numbers. Write them in the circles. Add 2. Find the answers.

   ○ + 2   ○ + 2   ○ + 2   ○ + 2
   □   □   □   □

   Are the answers even or odd numbers? ____

5. Show eleven o'clock on the clocks.

6. Write the answers.

   6 − 6 = ____   4 − 1 = ____

   5 − 0 = ____   16 − 8 = ____

1-78Wa   Copyright © 1991 by Saxon Publishers, Inc. and Nancy Larson. Reproduction prohibited.

Name _____ **LESSON 78B**
                          Math 1

1. Write a number that is between 19 and 25.

   19 □ 25

2. Melissa had 8 dimes. She gave Lena 2 dimes. Draw a picture and write a number sentence to show the dimes Melissa has now.

   Number sentence _____

   How many dimes does Melissa have now? ____ dimes

   How much money is this? _____

3. Write four number words that have three letters.

4. Choose **4 even** numbers. Write them in the circles. Add 2. Find the answers.

   ○ + 2   ○ + 2   ○ + 2   ○ + 2
   □   □   □   □

   Are the answers even or odd numbers? ____

5. Show ten o'clock on the clocks.

6. Write the answers.

   8 − 8 = ____   9 − 0 = ____

   14 − 7 = ____   9 − 1 = ____

1-78Wb   Copyright © 1991 by Saxon Publishers, Inc. and Nancy Larson. Reproduction prohibited.

Lesson 79

writing the number 72
addition facts — doubles plus one facts

---

lesson preparation

materials

addition fact cards — pink

Fact Sheet AA 5.1

the night before

• Separate the pink addition fact cards.

in the morning

• Write the following number pattern on the meeting strip:

> 44, 43, 42, ___, ___, ___

Answer: 44, 43, 42, 41, 40, 39

• Put **19 pennies** in the coin cup.

THE MEETING

calendar

• Ask your child to identify the following:

  year

  month

  shapes on the calendar

  today's shape

  shape pattern for the month

• Ask your child to write the date on the calendar.

• Ask your child to do the following:

  identify today's day of the week

  identify the days of the week

"What day of the week was it yesterday?"

"What day of the week will it be tomorrow?"

• Ask your child to identify the following:

> number of days in a week

> weekdays

• Ask your child to write the full date on the meeting strip.

weather graph

• Ask your child to report and graph the weather.

• Ask questions about the graph.

counting

"Let's count by 5's to 50."

• Count from 28 to 53 using the hundred number chart.

• Count backward from 30 to 1.

• Count by 10's to 100.

• Count backward from 100 by 10's.

• Count by 2's to 20.

• Say the odd numbers to 19.

• Add another number to the number line.

"Let's count the numbers on our number line."

"We will count by 10's as far as we can and then count by 1's."

"How many 10's did we count?"

"And how many more did we count?"

"What number is _____ tens and _____ more?"

number pattern

• Ask your child to identify and fill in the missing numbers.

• Read the number pattern together.

clock

• Ask your child to set the morning/afternoon/evening/night clock.

• Throughout the day, your child announces the time on the hour, sets the demonstration clock, and writes the digital time for each new hour on the chalkboard.

coin cup

"Stack the pennies from the coin cup in groups of five and make tally marks to show the number of pennies."

• Allow time for your child to do this.

• Point to each group of tally marks as you count by 5's and 1's with your child.

• Ask your child to record the amount of money on the meeting strip.

right/left

• Continue to practice left and right once a week. Practice more often, if necessary.

THE LESSON

Writing the Number 72

"The last number we practiced writing was the number 71."

"What number do you think we will learn how to write today?"

• Write the number 72 on the chalkboard.

"What digits do you see in the number 72?"

"How many dimes and pennies will we use to make 72¢?"

• Use dimes and pennies to demonstrate.

"How many groups of 10 are in 72?"

"How many extra 1's do we have?"

"Let's count by 10's and 1's to check."

Addition Facts—Doubles Plus One Facts

"Today you will learn the answers for the doubles plus one facts."

• Write the following problem on the chalkboard: 6
                                                                                 + 7

"What do you notice about the numbers in this problem?"   they are next to each other when we count by 1's

"What do we call this problem?"   doubles plus one facts

"How will we find this answer?"   double the six and add one

• Circle the 6 in the problem.

"We will double the smaller number and add one."

"What is the answer?"

• Repeat with the following problem: 5
                                                                    + 4

• Give your child the pink fact cards.

"How will we find the answer for each of these problems?"   double the smaller number and add one

"Write the answer on the back of each card."

• If necessary, give your child two towers of 10 linking cubes with which to check his/her answers.

"Now let's try to match the fact cards that have the same answer."

"Put the cards that have the same answer together."

- Allow time for your child to do this.

"Did you find two cards with the same answer?"

"What cards are they?"

"Let's look at these cards."

"What is the same about them?"   the same numbers are added

"What is different about them?"   position of the numbers

"Each of these facts uses the same numbers, but the numbers switched places."

"We will call these switcharound facts."

"Did you find two other cards with the same answer?"

"What cards are they?"

"Let's look at these cards."

"What is the same about them?"

"What is different about them?"

"Each of these facts uses the same numbers, but the numbers switched places."

"We will call these switcharound facts."

- Repeat with all the cards.

"Put your cards in a pile."

"Now read each problem to yourself."

"See if you can remember the answer."

"Turn over the card to check the answer."

"Practice saying the answers to yourself."

- Allow time for your child to practice using the fact cards independently.

CLASS PRACTICE

- Give your child **Fact Sheet AA 5.1.**

- Correct the fact sheet with your child.

WRITTEN PRACTICE

- Complete **Worksheet 79A** with your child.

- Complete **Worksheet 79B** with your child later in the day.

LESSON 79A
Math 1

Name _____
(Draw a line segment for your name.)

Date _____

Day of the Week _____

1. Write the number seventy-two 2 more times. How many digits are on the line? __8__

72 72

2. Mrs. Carrano has 5 pairs of earrings. Draw the earrings.

OO OO OO OO OO

How many earrings does she have? __10__ earrings

3. Divide the squares in half two different ways.

Color one half of the left square red.

Color one half of the right square blue.

Red

Blue

4. Draw tally marks to show the number of date tags on the calendar.

How many tally marks did you make? _____ tally marks

5. Write the answers.

$$\begin{array}{cc} & Blue \\ \begin{array}{r}2\\+3\\\hline 5\end{array} & \begin{array}{r}7\\+6\\\hline 13\end{array} & \boxed{\begin{array}{r}5\\+6\\\hline 11\end{array}} & \begin{array}{r}3\\+4\\\hline 7\end{array} & \begin{array}{r}8\\+7\\\hline 15\end{array} & \begin{array}{r}Red\\9\\+8\\\hline 17\end{array} & \begin{array}{r}4\\+5\\\hline 9\end{array}\end{array}$$

Circle the sixth example using a red crayon.

Circle the third example using a blue crayon.

1-79Wa

LESSON 79B
Math 1

Name _____

1. Fill in the missing numbers.

1, 3, 5, __7__ , __9__ , __11__ , __13__ , __15__ , __17__

66, 67, 68, __69__ , __70__ , __71__ , __72__ , __73__ , __74__

2. Curtis has 4 pairs of shoes. Draw the shoes.

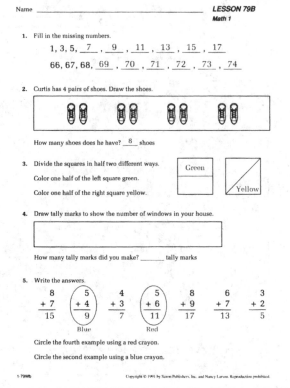

How many shoes does he have? __8__ shoes

3. Divide the squares in half two different ways.

Color one half of the left square green.

Color one half of the right square yellow.

Green

Yellow

4. Draw tally marks to show the number of windows in your house.

How many tally marks did you make? _____ tally marks

5. Write the answers.

$$\begin{array}{r}8\\+7\\\hline 15\end{array} \quad \boxed{\begin{array}{r}5\\+4\\\hline 9\end{array}} \quad \begin{array}{r}4\\+3\\\hline 7\end{array} \quad \boxed{\begin{array}{r}5\\+6\\\hline 11\end{array}} \quad \begin{array}{r}8\\+9\\\hline 17\end{array} \quad \begin{array}{r}6\\+7\\\hline 13\end{array} \quad \begin{array}{r}3\\+2\\\hline 5\end{array}$$

Blue   Red

Circle the fourth example using a red crayon.

Circle the second example using a blue crayon.

1-79Wb

esson 80

assessment

THE MEETING

calendar

• Ask your child to identify the following:

   year

   month

   shapes on the calendar

   today's shape

   shape pattern for the month

• Ask your child to write the date on the calendar.

• Ask your child to do the following:

   identify today's day of the week

   identify the days of the week

"What day of the week was it yesterday?"

"What day of the week will it be tomorrow?"

• Ask your child to identify the following:

   number of days in a week

   weekdays

• Ask your child to write the full date on the meeting strip.

weather graph

- Ask your child to report and graph the weather.
- Ask questions about the graph.

counting

"Let's count by 5's to 50."

- Count from 18 to 43 using the hundred number chart.
- Count backward from 30 to 1.
- Count by 10's to 100.
- Count backward from 100 by 10's.
- Count by 2's to 20.
- Say the odd numbers to 19.
- Add another number to the number line.
- Use an orange crayon to color the square for 80.

"Let's count the numbers on our number line."

"We will count by 10's as far as we can and then count by 1's."

"How many 10's did we count?"

"And how many more did we count?"

"What number is _____ tens and _____ more?"

number pattern

- Ask your child to identify and fill in the missing numbers.
- Read the number pattern together.

clock

- Ask your child to set the morning/afternoon/evening/night clock.
- Throughout the day, your child announces the time on the hour, sets the demonstration clock, and writes the digital time for each new hour on the chalkboard.

coin cup

"Stack the pennies from the coin cup in groups of five and make tally marks to show the number of pennies."

- Allow time for your child to do this.
- Point to each group of tally marks as you count by 5's and 1's with your child.
- Ask your child to record the amount of money on the meeting strip.

right/left

- Continue to practice left and right once a week. Practice more often, if necessary.

ASSESSMENT

- All of the questions on the assessment are based on concepts and skills presented at least five lessons ago. If your child is having difficulty with a specific concept, reteach the concept the following day.

Written Assessment

- Give your child **Written Assessment #15.**

- Read the directions for each problem. Allow time for your child to complete each problem before continuing to the next.

- Correct the paper, noting your child's mistakes on the **Individual Recording Form.** Review the errors with your child.

Oral Assessment

- Record your child's responses to the oral interview on the interview sheet.

Name _____ **ASSESSMENT 15**
LESSON 80
Date _____ Math 1

1. Joan made 5 tally marks. Then she made 3 more tally marks. Draw the tally marks and write a number sentence to show how many tally marks she made altogether.

| $\bcancel{||||}$ ||| |

Number sentence _____ $5 + 3 = 8$ _____

How many tally marks did she make altogether? ___8___ tally marks

2. Circle the number that is between 34 and 43.

34 ☐ 43   33 ⟨38⟩ 44

3. Color the bottom half of the left circle red.

Color the top half of the right circle green.

Color the bottom half of the right circle blue.

Color the top half of the left circle yellow.

Yellow   Green
Red   Blue

4. How many dimes and pennies will you need to buy the book?

☐ 85¢   ___8___ dimes   ___5___ pennies

5. Count by 5's. Fill in the missing numbers.

5, 10, 15, _20_ , _25_ , _30_ , _35_ , _40_ , _45_ , _50_

6. Write **3 even** numbers in the circles.
Add **1.**
Write the answers.

○   ○   ○
+ 1   + 1   + 1
☐   ☐   ☐

Are the answers
odd or even numbers? _odd_

1-80Aa   Copyright © 1991 by Saxon Publishers, Inc. and Nancy Larson. Reproduction prohibited.

Teacher _____ **MATH 1   LESSON 80**
Date _____   Oral Assessment # 8 Recording Form

Materials:
calendar on
bulletin board

Students	•Point to a date tag on the calendar "What is this date?" "What day of the week is it?"	"Point to the tag for _[date]_ ."	"What will the date be tomorrow?"

1-80La   Copyright © 1991 by Saxon Publishers, Inc. and Nancy Larson. Reproduction prohibited.

416

L esson 81

writing the number 73
identifying how many more

---

lesson preparation

materials

2 towers of 10 linking cubes (use a different color for each tower)

large fact cards (doubles plus one facts)

Fact Sheet AA 5.1

in the morning

- Write the following number pattern on the meeting strip:

> 73, 72, 71, __, __, __

> *Answer: 73, 72, 71, 70, 69, 68*

- Put **35 pennies** in the coin cup.

THE MEETING

calendar

- Ask your child to identify the following:

  year

  month

  shapes on the calendar

  today's shape

  shape pattern for the month

- Ask your child to write the date on the calendar.

- Ask your child to do the following:

  identify today's day of the week, yesterday's day of the week, and tomorrow's day of the week

  read the days of the week

  identify the weekdays

  identify the number of days in a week

- Ask your child to write the full date on the meeting strip.

weather graph

- Ask your child to report and graph the weather.
- Ask questions about the graph.

counting

- Count from 30 to 62 using the hundred number chart.
- Count by 5's to 50.
- Count by 10's to 100.
- Count backward from 100 by 10's.
- Count by 2's to 20.
- Count backward from 20 by 2's.
- Say the odd numbers to 19.
- Say the odd numbers backward from 19.
- Add another number to the number line.

  "We will count numbers on the number line by 10's as far as we can and then count by 1's."

- Point to the multiples of 10 as you count together.

  "How many 10's did we count?"

- Point to the digit in the tens' place.

  "And how many more did we count?"

- Point to the digit in the ones' place.

  "What number is _____ tens and _____ more?"

number pattern

- Ask your child to identify and fill in the missing numbers.
- Read the number pattern together.

clock

- Ask your child to set the morning/afternoon/evening/night clock.
- Throughout the day, your child announces the time on the hour, sets the demonstration clock to show the time, and writes the digital time on the chalkboard.

coin cup

- Ask your child to stack the pennies in groups of 5 and make tally marks to show the number of pennies.
- Point to each group of tally marks as you count by 5's with your child.
- Ask your child to record the amount of money on the meeting strip.

right/left

- Continue to practice left and right once a week. Practice more often, if necessary.

THE LESSON

Writing the Number 73

"The last number we practiced writing was the number 72."

"What number do you think we will learn how to write today?"

- Write the number 73 on the chalkboard.

"What digits do you see in the number 73?"

"How many dimes and pennies will we use to make 73¢?"

- Use dimes and pennies to demonstrate.

"How many groups of 10 are in 73?"

"How many extra 1's do we have?"

"Let's count by 10's and 1's to check."

Identifying How Many More

"Today you will learn how to identify how many more things are in one group than in another."

- Give your child 2 towers of 10 linking cubes. Each tower should be a different color.

"Make a tower of three linking cubes using one color and a tower of seven linking cubes using the other color."

- Allow time for your child to make the towers.

"Hold up the tower that has more cubes."

"Stand the towers next to each other."

"How many linking cubes don't have a partner?"   4

"How many extra linking cubes are in the taller tower?"   4

"We say that this tower has four more than the other."

- Repeat with towers of 5 and 9, 7 and 6, and 3 and 8.
- Repeat with towers of 1 and 4, 6 and 8, and 5 and 10, if desired.

"Snap your cubes into towers of ten."

CLASS PRACTICE

> *"Let's practice the doubles plus one number facts."*
>
> *"What strategy will you use to find the answers?"*

- Use the large fact cards to practice the doubles plus one facts.
- Give your child **Fact Sheet AA 5.1**.
- Correct the fact sheet with your child.

WRITTEN PRACTICE

- Complete **Worksheet 81A** with your child.
- Complete **Worksheet 81B** with your child later in the day.

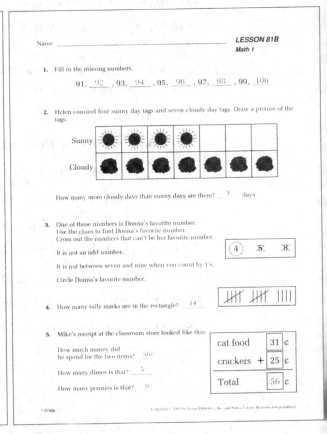

Lesson 82

writing the number 74
identifying how many more on a graph

---

lesson preparation

materials

graphing grid (see below)

fifteen 3" square tags for the graph

crayons

10 linking cubes

glue stick

large fact cards (doubles plus one facts)

Fact Sheet A 5.1

the night before

• Prepare the following graphing grid prior to the lesson. Chart paper, poster board, or a window shade can be used for the graphing grid.

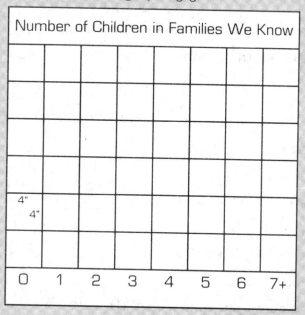

in the morning

• Write the following number pattern on the meeting strip:

> 20, 25, 30, ___, ___, ___

Answer: 20, 25, 30, 35, 40, 45

• Put **28 pennies** in the coin cup.

THE MEETING

calendar

- Ask your child to identify the following:

    year

    month

    shapes on the calendar

    today's shape

    shape pattern for the month

- Ask your child to write the date on the calendar.

- Ask your child to do the following:

    identify today's day of the week, yesterday's day of the week, and tomorrow's day of the week

    read the days of the week

    identify the weekdays

    identify the number of days in a week

- Ask your child to write the full date on the meeting strip.

weather graph

- Ask your child to report and graph the weather.

- Ask questions about the graph.

counting

- Count from 21 to 57 using the hundred number chart.

- Count by 5's to 50.

- Count by 10's to 100.

- Count backward from 100 by 10's.

- Count by 2's to 20.

- Count backward from 20 by 2's.

- Say the odd numbers to 19.

- Say the odd numbers backward from 19.

- Add another number to the number line.

    "We will count numbers on the number line by 10's as far as we can and then count by 1's."

- Point to the multiples of 10 as you count together.

    "How many 10's did we count?"

- Point to the digit in the tens' place.

"And how many more did we count?"

• Point to the digit in the ones' place.

"What number is _____ tens and _____ more?"

number pattern

• Ask your child to identify and fill in the missing numbers.

• Read the number pattern together.

clock

• Ask your child to set the morning/afternoon/evening/night clock.

• Throughout the day, your child announces the time on the hour, sets the demonstration clock to show the time, and writes the digital time on the chalkboard.

coin cup

• Ask your child to stack the pennies in groups of 5 and make tally marks to show the number of pennies.

• Point to each group of tally marks as you count by 5's and 1's with your child.

• Ask your child to record the amount of money on the meeting strip.

right/left

• Continue to practice left and right once a week. Practice more often, if necessary.

THE LESSON

Writing the Number 74

"The last number we practiced writing was the number 73."

"What number do you think we will learn how to write today?"

• Write the number 74 on the chalkboard.

"What digits do you see in the number 74?"

"How many dimes and pennies will we use to make 74¢?"

• Use dimes and pennies to demonstrate.

"How many groups of 10 are in 74?"

"How many extra 1's do we have?"

"Let's count by 10's and 1's to check."

Identifying How Many More on a Graph

"Today you will learn how to identify how many more tags are in one column on a graph than in another column."

"Let's make a graph to show the number of children in our family and other families we know."

- Give your child a 3" × 3" paper tag.

  "Draw your face and write your name on this tag."

  "Now draw a face for each of your brothers and sisters."

- If your child has an extended family, accept his/her choice of the children to include as brothers and sisters.

- Allow time for your child to draw the faces.

  "Let's think of some other families that we know."

  "How about the (name of family)?"

  "How many children are in that family?"

- Write the family name on another tag and quickly draw a face to show each child.

- Repeat with 8–13 more families.

- Show your child the graphing grid.

  "The title of our graph is 'Number of Children in Families We Know.'"

  "How do you think we will graph our tags?"

  "Let's see how many families have four children."

  "Find all the tags with four faces on them."

  "Where will we put these tags on our graph?" in the column above the 4

- Glue the tags to the graph.

  "Let's see how many families have two children."

  "Find all the tags with two faces on them."

  "Where will we put these tags on our graph?" in the column above the 2

- Glue the tags to the graph.

- Repeat with 5, 0, 1, 6, 3, and 7 or more children.

  "What do you notice about our graph?"

- Allow time for your child to offer as many observations as possible. Record them on the chalkboard, if desired.

- Ask the following questions if the information was not offered by your child:

  "Let's use our graph to find out how many families have five children . . . three children . . . one child . . . seven or more children . . . two children . . . six children . . . four children . . . zero children."

"Now let's look only at the columns of families with two children and three children."

- Cover the other columns, if possible.

"Which column has more?"

- Give your child a tower of 10 linking cubes.

"Make a tower of linking cubes to show how many families have two children."

"How many linking cubes will you use?"

- Allow time for your child to make the tower.

"Make another tower to show how many families have three children."

"How many linking cubes will you use?"

- Allow time for your child to do this.

"Hold the towers next to each other."

"Do your towers look like the columns on the graph?"

"Some cubes don't have partners."

"How many extra cubes are in the taller tower?"

"We say that this tower has _____ more than the other."

"How many more families have _____ children than _____ children?"

"We can use the graph to find out how many more are in one column than in another by counting the tags that don't have partners."

- Show this on the graph.
- Repeat with families with 4 children and 5 children, and then 1 child and 0 children.

"Make up a 'more than' question about our graph."

"Let's answer the question using the graph."

- Point to the columns being compared.

"Let's see how many tags don't have partners."

- Allow time for your child to ask several questions.

CLASS PRACTICE

"Let's practice the doubles plus one number facts."

"What strategy will you use to find the answers?"

- Use the large fact cards to practice the doubles plus one facts.
- Give your child **Fact Sheet A 5.1.**
- Correct the fact sheet with your child.

WRITTEN PRACTICE

- • Complete **Worksheet 82A** with your child.
- • Complete **Worksheet 82B** with your child later in the day.

Name _____ **LESSON 82A**
(Draw a line segment for your name.) **Math 1**

Date _____

Day of the Week _____

1. Write the number seventy-four 4 more times. How many digits are on the line? _12_

74 74

2. Four children said that blue
   is their favorite color.   blue
   Two children said that red is
   their favorite color.
   Five children said that   red
   yellow is their favorite color.
   Color the graph to show the
   children's favorite colors.   yellow

   Which color did the
   greatest number of children like? _yellow_
   Which color did the
   fewest number of children like? _red_
   How many more
   children like yellow than like red? _3_

3. Divide each circle in half.
   Color one half of the left circle green.

4. Write four different examples that have a sum of 4.

   □ + □ = 4   □ + □ = 4   □ + □ = 4   □ + □ = 4

5. Jed's receipt at the classroom store looked like this:

yogurt	13	¢
raisins +	34	¢
Total	47	¢

   How much money did
   he spend for the two items? _47¢_
   How many dimes is that? _4_
   How many pennies is that? _7_

1-82Wa   Copyright © 1991 by Saxon Publishers, Inc. and Nancy Larson. Reproduction prohibited.

Name _____ **LESSON 82B**
Math 1

1. Fill in the mising numbers.

   10, 20, 30, _40_ , _50_ , _60_ , _70_ , _80_ , _90_ , _100_

2. Three children said that
   orange is their favorite color.   orange
   Six children said that green
   is their favorite color.
   Four children said that   green
   purple is their favorite color.
   Color the graph to show the
   children's favorite colors.   purple

   Which color did the
   greatest number of children like? _green_
   Which color did the
   fewest number of children like? _orange_
   How many more
   children like green than like purple? _2_

3. Divide each circle in half.
   Color one half of the right circle red.

4. Write four different examples that have a sum of 5.

   □ + □ = 5   □ + □ = 5   □ + □ = 5   □ + □ = 5

5. Carol's receipt at the classroom store looked like this:

beans	25	¢
eggs +	24	¢
Total	49	¢

   How much money did
   she spend for the two items? _49¢_
   How many dimes is that? _4_
   How many pennies is that? _9_

1-82Wb   Copyright © 1991 by Saxon Publishers, Inc. and Nancy Larson. Reproduction prohibited.

Lesson 83

writing the number 75
making congruent shapes

THE MEETING

calendar

• Ask your child to identify the following:

> year
>
> month
>
> shapes on the calendar
>
> today's shape
>
> shape pattern for the month

• Ask your child to write the date on the calendar.

• Ask your child to do the following:

> identify today's day of the week, yesterday's day of the week, and tomorrow's day of the week
>
> read the days of the week
>
> identify the weekdays
>
> identify the number of days in a week

• Ask your child to write the full date on the meeting strip.

weather graph

• Ask your child to report and graph the weather.

• Ask questions about the graph.

counting

• Count from 13 to 36 using the hundred number chart.

• Count by 5's to 50.

• Count by 10's to 100.

• Count backward from 100 by 10's.

• Count by 2's to 20.

• Count backward from 20 by 2's.

• Say the odd numbers to 19.

• Say the odd numbers backward from 19.

• Add another number to the number line.

"We will count numbers on the number line by 10's as far as we can and then count by 1's."

• Point to the multiples of 10 as you count together.

"How many 10's did we count?"

• Point to the digit in the tens' place.

"And how many more did we count?"

• Point to the digit in the ones' place.

"What number is _____ tens and _____ more?"

number pattern

• Ask your child to identify and fill in the missing numbers.

• Read the number pattern together.

clock

• Ask your child to set the morning/afternoon/evening/night clock.

• Throughout the day, your child announces the time on the hour, sets the demonstration clock to show the time, and writes the digital time on the chalkboard.

coin cup

• Ask your child to stack the pennies in groups of 5 and make tally marks to show the number of pennies.

• Point to each group of tally marks as you count by 5's and 1's with your child.

• Ask your child to record the amount of money on the meeting strip.

right/left

• Continue to practice left and right once a week. Practice more often, if necessary.

THE LESSON

Writing the Number 75

"The last number we practiced writing was the number 74."

"What number do you think we will learn how to write today?"

• Write the number 75 on the chalkboard.

"What digits do you see in the number 75?"

"How many dimes and pennies will we use to make 75¢?"

• Use dimes and pennies to demonstrate.

"How many groups of 10 are in 75?"

"How many extra 1's do we have?"

"Let's count by 10's and 1's to check."

Making Congruent Shapes

"Today you will learn how to make congruent shapes."

"We will use a geoboard and geobands to do this."

• Give your child a geoboard and 4 geobands.

"We will use one geoband for each side of a shape."

"How many geobands will we need to use to make a triangle?"   3

"How many sides does a triangle have?"   3

"Make a triangle on your geoboard using one geoband for each side."

"I'll make a triangle on my geoboard also."

• When you both finish, continue.

"Are our triangles the same?"

"What's different about them?"

• Make the following triangle on your geoboard. Use 3 geobands.

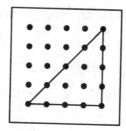

- Show your child your geoboard.

  "Copy my triangle on your geoboard."

- Ask your child to put his/her geoboard next to yours.

  "Are our triangles the same?"

  "How do you know?"

  "We call these congruent triangles."

  "When two things are exactly the same shape and size, we say that they are congruent."

- Make the following square on your geoboard. Use 4 geobands.

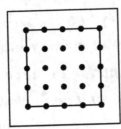

- Show your child the geoboard.

  "What shape did I make?" square

  "I made a square using four geobands."

  "Copy my square on your geoboard."

- Ask your child to put his/her geoboard next to yours.

  "Are our squares the same?"

  "How do you know?" they are the same shape and size

  "We call these congruent squares."

- Make the following rectangle on your geoboard. Use 4 geobands.

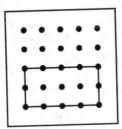

- Show your child the geoboard.

  "What shape did I make?" rectangle

  "I made a rectangle using four geobands."

  "Copy my rectangle on your geoboard."

- Ask your child to put his/her geoboard next to yours.

  "Are the rectangles the same?"

  "How do you know?" they are the same shape and size

"We call these congruent rectangles."

"Now make a shape for me to copy."

- Copy your child's shape.

"Let's check to make sure that our shapes are congruent."

"Now we will take turns making and copying shapes."

CLASS PRACTICE

"Let's practice the doubles plus one number facts."

"What strategy will you use to find the answers?"

- Use the large fact cards to practice the doubles plus one facts.
- Give your child **Fact Sheet A 5.1**.
- Correct the fact sheet with your child.

WRITTEN PRACTICE

- Complete **Worksheet 83A** with your child.
- Complete **Worksheet 83B** with your child later in the day.

Name _____   **LESSON 83A**
(Draw a line segment for your name.)   **Math 1**

Date _____

Day of the Week _____

1. Write the number seventy-five three more times. How many digits are on the line? __10__

75 75 _____

2. Eight children used a red crayon and ten children used a green crayon. Show on the graph how many children used each color.

red ▮▮▮▮▮▮▮▮

green ▮▮▮▮▮▮▮▮▮▮

How many more children used green than red? __2__ children

3. Color the congruent triangles red. (Congruent triangles are the same size and shape.)

4. Draw tally marks to show 25.

| |||| |||| |||| |||| |||| |

5. There are 8 sneakers in the closet.

Draw the sneakers.

Circle the pairs.

How many pairs of sneakers are there? __4__

6. Write the answers.

8	6	3	8	9	3	12	5	14
+ 7	+ 5	+ 4	+ 9	− 9	− 1	− 6	− 0	− 7
15	11	7	17	0	2	6	5	7

1-83Wa

Name _____   **LESSON 83B**
   Math 1

1. Fill in the missing numbers.

41	42	43	44	45	46	47	48	49	50
51	52	53	54	55	56	57	58	59	60

2. Ten children used blue crayons and six children used yellow crayons. Show on the graph how many children used each color.

blue ▮▮▮▮▮▮▮▮▮▮

yellow ▮▮▮▮▮▮

How many more children used blue than used yellow? __4__ children

3. Color the congruent rectangles blue. (Congruent rectangles are the same size and shape.)

Blue   Blue

4. Draw tally marks to show 20.

| |||| |||| |||| |||| |

5. There are 10 boots inside the door.

Draw the boots.

Circle the pairs.

How many pairs of boots are there? __5__

6. Write the answers.

2	8	4	6	6	8	7	18	2
+ 3	+ 7	+ 5	+ 5	− 1	− 4	− 7	− 9	− 0
5	15	9	11	5	4	0	9	2

1-83Wb

Lesson 84

writing the number 76
counting large collections
grouping by 10's and 1's

---

lesson preparation

materials

3 bags with 60–100 objects each

Masters 1-84A and 1-84B

large fact cards (doubles plus one facts)

Fact Sheet A 5.1

the night before

• Fill 3 small plastic bags with 60 to 100 objects each. Suggestions for objects to fill the bags include the following: elbow macaroni, small stones, beans, paper clips, screws, buttons, pennies, small rubber bands, and crayons.

in the morning

• Write the following number pattern on the meeting strip:

> 63, 62, 61, ___, ___, ___

Answer: *63, 62, 61, 60, 59, 58*

• Put **21 pennies** in the coin cup.

THE MEETING

calendar

• Ask your child to identify the following:

year

month

shapes on the calendar

today's shape

shape pattern for the month

• Ask your child to write the date on the calendar.

- Ask your child to do the following:

    identify today's day of the week, yesterday's day of the week, and tomorrow's day of the week

    read the days of the week

    identify the weekdays

    identify the number of days in a week

- Ask your child to write the full date on the meeting strip.

weather graph

- Ask your child to report and graph the weather.

- Ask questions about the graph.

counting

- Count from 19 to 52 using the hundred number chart.

- Count by 5's to 50.

- Count by 10's to 100.

- Count backward from 100 by 10's.

- Count by 2's to 20.

- Count backward from 20 by 2's.

- Say the odd numbers to 19.

- Say the odd numbers backward from 19.

- Add another number to the number line.

    "We will count numbers on the number line by 10's as far as we can and then count by 1's."

- Point to the multiples of 10 as you count together.

    "How many 10's did we count?"

- Point to the digit in the tens' place.

    "And how many more did we count?"

- Point to the digit in the ones' place.

    "What number is _____ tens and _____ more?"

number pattern

- Ask your child to identify and fill in the missing numbers.

- Read the number pattern together.

clock

- Ask your child to set the morning/afternoon/evening/night clock.

- Throughout the day, your child announces the time on the hour, sets the demonstration clock to show the time, and writes the digital time on the chalkboard.

coin cup

- Ask your child to stack the pennies in groups of 5 and make tally marks to show the number of pennies.

- Point to each group of tally marks as you count by 5's and 1's with your child.

- Ask your child to record the amount of money on the meeting strip.

right/left

- Continue to practice left and right once a week. Practice more often, if necessary.

THE LESSON

Writing the Number 76

"The last number we practiced writing was the number 75."

"What number do you think we will learn how to write today?"

- Write the number 76 on the chalkboard.

"What digits do you see in the number 76?"

"How many dimes and pennies will we use to make 76¢?"

- Use dimes and pennies to demonstrate.

"How many groups of 10 are in 76?"

"How many extra 1's do we have?"

"Let's count by 10's and 1's to check."

Counting Large Collections
Grouping by 10's and 1's

"Today you will learn how to count a large collection of objects."

- Show your child a bag of (objects).

"How many _____ do you think are in this bag?"

- Do not comment on the reasonableness of your child's estimate.

"Let's count the _____ together."

"How could we do that?"

"We could count these _____ by 1's."

"When we count by 1's, we have to be careful that we don't lose our place, that we don't mix in the ones we've already counted, or that we don't forget to count some."

"There is another way to count a large number of objects."

"Many people count a large number of objects by putting them in groups of ten."

"Then they count by 10's to find the total number of objects."

"Let's find the number of _____ in this bag by putting the _____ in groups of ten."

- Put **Masters 1-84A** and **1-84B** on the table.

"I will count out ten _____ and put them in a circle on this paper."

- Count 10 objects and put them in a circle on the paper.

"Now I will count out ten more _____ and put them in another circle on the paper."

- Count 10 objects and put them in another circle on the paper.

"I will put ten _____ in each of the circles until I don't have ten more _____ left."

- Continue until all possible groups of 10 objects in the bag are used.

"I will put the extras in the square labeled 'extras.'"

"Let's count by 10's to see how many _____ were in the bag."

- Point to each group of 10 objects as you count by 10's together.

"Now we will count the extra _____ by 1's."

- Point to each extra object as you count on by 1's together.

"Now you will have a bag of (objects) to count." .

- Give your child **Master 1-84A**, **Master 1-84B**, and a bag of (objects).

"Carefully open your bag and take out a handful of (objects)."

"How many will you put in each circle?"   10

"Put ten (objects) in the first circle."

"Do you have enough to put ten in another circle?"   yes

"Keep putting ten in each circle."

"If you don't have enough for another ten, put the extras in the square."

- When your child finishes, continue.

"Let's count your (objects) together."

- Point to each group as your child counts by 10's and then counts the extra ones.

"Carefully put the (objects) back in the bag."

- Repeat with another bag of objects.
- Save **Masters 1-84A** and **1-84B**.

CLASS PRACTICE

"Let's practice the doubles plus one number facts."

"What strategy will you use to find the answers?"

- Use the large fact cards to practice the doubles plus one facts.
- Give your child **Fact Sheet A 5.1**.
- Correct the fact sheet with your child.

WRITTEN PRACTICE

- Complete **Worksheet 84A** with your child.
- Complete **Worksheet 84B** with your child later in the day.

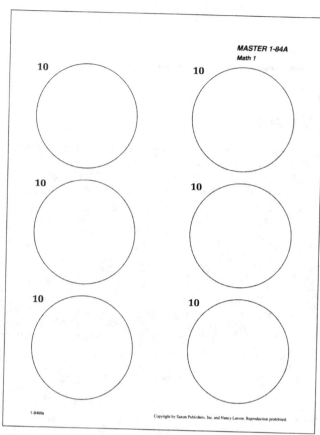

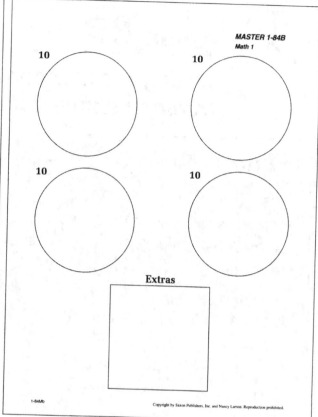

Name _____
(Draw a line segment for your name.)

LESSON 84A
Math 1

Date _____

Day of the Week _____

1. Write the number seventy-six two more times. How many digits are on the line? __8__

76 76

2. Write your first name. Put one letter in each square.

Write your last name. Put one letter in each square.

Which has more letters, your first or last name? **first   last   same**

How many more letters does it have? _____ letters

3. Color the congruent shapes green.

□ Green ○ △ △ ◇ Green

4. Write the answers.

4	4	3	3	3	6	6
+4	+5	+0	+1	+2	+6	+7
8	9	3	4	5	12	13

5. Theresa's receipt at the classroom store looked like this:

How much money did
she spend for the two items? __59¢__

How many dimes is that? __5__

How many pennies is that? __9__

cake mix	18	¢
juice +	41	¢
Total	59	¢

Name _____

LESSON 84B
Math 1

1. Circle the number that is between 24 and 26.

23   24   (25)   26   27   28

2. Write the first name of someone who lives with you. Put one letter in each square.

Write that person's last name. Put one letter in each square.

Which has more letters, their first or last name? **first   last   same**

How many more letters does it have? _____ letters

3. Color the congruent shapes green.

Green □ ○ △ △ Green

4. Write the answers.

3	3	8	8	8	5	5
+3	+4	+0	+1	+2	+5	+6
6	7	8	9	10	10	11

5. Ted's receipt at the classroom store looked like this:

How much money did
he spend for the two items? __82¢__

How many dimes is that? __8__

How many pennies is that? __2__

crackers	22	¢
napkins +	60	¢
Total	82	¢

esson 85

writing the number 77
trading pennies for dimes

---

lesson preparation

materials

Written Assessment #16

plastic bag of 25 pennies

plastic bag of 42 pennies

cup of 40 pennies

cup of 4 dimes

Master 1-84B

large fact cards (addition facts)

Fact Sheet A 5.2

in the morning

• Write the following number pattern on the meeting strip:

> 29, 39, 49, ___, ___, ___

Answer: 29, 39, 49, 59, 69, 79

• Put **36 pennies** in the coin cup.

THE MEETING

calendar

• Ask your child to identify the following:

>   year

>   month

>   shapes on the calendar

>   today's shape

>   shape pattern for the month

• Ask your child to write the date on the calendar.

• Ask your child to do the following:

>   identify today's day of the week, yesterday's day of the week, and tomorrow's day of the week

read the days of the week

identify the weekdays

identify the number of days in a week

- Ask your child to write the full date on the meeting strip.

weather graph

- Ask your child to report and graph the weather.
- Ask questions about the graph.

counting

- Count by 5's to 50.
- Count by 10's to 100.
- Count backward from 100 by 10's.
- Count by 2's to 20.
- Count backward from 20 by 2's.
- Say the odd numbers to 19.
- Say the odd numbers backward from 19.
- Add another number to the number line.

   "We will count numbers on the number line by 10's as far as we can and then count by 1's."

- Point to the multiples of 10 as you count together.

   "How many 10's did we count?"

- Point to the digit in the tens' place.

   "And how many more did we count?"

- Point to the digit in the ones' place.

   "What number is _____ tens and _____ more?"

number pattern

- Ask your child to identify and fill in the missing numbers.
- Read the number pattern together.

clock

- Ask your child to set the morning/afternoon/evening/night clock.
- Throughout the day, your child announces the time on the hour, sets the demonstration clock to show the time, and writes the digital time on the chalkboard.

coin cup

- Ask your child to stack the pennies in groups of 5 and make tally marks to show the number of pennies.

- Point to each group of tally marks as you count by 5's and 1's with your child.

- Ask your child to record the amount of money on the meeting strip.

right/left

- Continue to practice left and right once a week. Practice more often, if necessary.

ASSESSMENT

Written Assessment

- Give your child **Written Assessment #16**.

- Read the directions for each problem. Allow time for your child to complete each problem before continuing to the next.

- Correct the paper, noting your child's mistakes on the **Individual Recording Form**. Review the errors with your child.

THE LESSON

Writing the Number 77

"The last number we practiced writing was the number 76."

"What number do you think we will learn how to write today?"

- Write the number 77 on the chalkboard.

"What digits do you see in the number 77?"

"How many dimes and pennies will we use to make 77¢?"

- Use dimes and pennies to demonstrate.

"How many groups of 10 are in 77?"

"How many extra 1's do we have?"

"Let's count by 10's and 1's to check."

Trading Pennies for Dimes

"Today you will learn how to trade pennies for dimes."

- Show your child a plastic bag of 25 pennies.

"How many pennies do you think are in this bag?"

- Ask your child to estimate the number of pennies.

  "Let's count them together."

  "I will put the pennies in groups of ten as we count."

- Put the pennies in groups of 10 on **Master 1-84B** as you count the pennies with your child.

  "Let's count by 10's and 1's to find out how much money this is."

- Point to each group of 10 pennies as you count by 10's with your child. Point to each extra penny as you count on by 1's.

  "How much money do we have?" 25¢

  "We have two groups of ten pennies and five extra pennies."

  "Let's trade each group of ten pennies for a dime."

  "How many dimes will we need?" 2

- Trade each group of 10 pennies for a dime. Put a dime in each circle to replace the 10 pennies.

  "Let's count the money together."

- Point to each dime and penny as you count the money with your child.

  "How much money do we have?" 25¢

- Show your child the plastic bag of 42 pennies.

  "How many pennies do you think are in this bag?"

- Ask your child to estimate the number of pennies.

  "Let's count them together."

  "I will put the pennies in groups of ten as we count."

- Put the pennies in groups of ten on **Master 1-84B** as you count the pennies with your child.

  "Let's count by 10's and 1's to find out how much money this is."

- Point to each group of 10 pennies as you count by 10's with your child. Point to each extra penny as you count on by 1's.

  "How much money do we have?" 42¢

  "We have four groups of ten pennies and two extra pennies."

  "Let's trade each group of ten pennies for a dime."

  "How many dimes will we need?" 4

- Trade each group of 10 pennies for a dime. Put a dime in each circle to replace the 10 pennies.

  "Let's count the money together."

- Point to each dime and penny as you count the money with your child.

  "How much money do we have?" 42¢

"Now you will have a chance to practice trading pennies for dimes."

- Give your child a cup of 40 pennies and **Master 1-84B.**

  "Put the pennies in groups of ten on this paper."

- Allow time for your child to do this.

  "How many groups of ten pennies do you have on your paper?"　4

  "You have four groups of ten pennies and no extra pennies."

  "Let's count by 10's to find out how much money this is."

  "Point to each group of ten pennies as we count by 10's."

- Count by 10's with your child.

  "How much money do you have?"　40¢

  "Let's trade each group of ten pennies for a dime."

  "How many dimes will you need?"　4

- Give your child a cup of 4 dimes.

  "Trade each group of ten pennies for a dime."

- Allow time for your child to do this.

  "Point to each dime as we count the money together."

- Count by 10's with your child.

  "How much money do we have now?"　40¢

  "Put the dimes in the dime cup."

- Take 3 pennies from your child's cup.

  "Now put the pennies in groups of ten on your paper."

- Allow time for your child to do this.

  "How many groups of ten pennies do you have on your paper?"　3

  "How many extra pennies do you have?"　7

  "You have three groups of ten pennies and seven extra pennies."

  "Trade each group of ten pennies for a dime."

- Allow time for your child to do this.

  "Let's count the money together."

  "Point to each dime as we count by 10's."

- Count by 10's with your child.

  "Now point to each penny as we count by 1's."

- Count on by 1's with your child.

  "How much money do we have?"　37¢

  "Put the pennies in the penny cup and the dimes in the dime cup."

"Each morning you will put the pennies from the coin cup in groups of ten and trade them for dimes, just as we did today."

- Save **Masters 1-84A** and **1-84B**.

CLASS PRACTICE

- Use the large fact cards to practice the addition facts with your child.
- Give your child **Fact Sheet A 5.2**.

  "What number facts do you see?"

  "What strategies will you use to find the answers?"

- Correct the fact sheet with your child.

WRITTEN PRACTICE

- Complete **Worksheet 85A** with your child.
- Complete **Worksheet 85B** with your child later in the day.

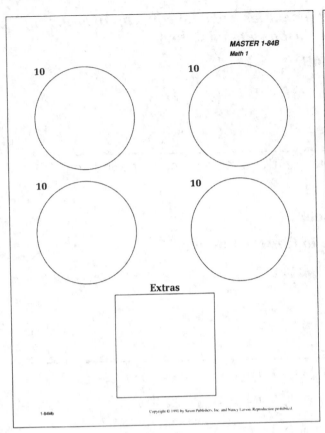

MASTER 1-84B
Math 1

10

10

10

10

Extras

1-84Mb

Copyright © 1991 by Saxon Publishers, Inc. and Nancy Larson. Reproduction prohibited.

Name _____

Date _____

Day of the Week _____

ASSESSMENT 16
LESSON 85
Math 1

1. There were eight crackers on a plate. Phil ate four crackers. Draw a picture and write a number sentence to show what happened.

Number sentence _____ 8 − 4 = 4 _____

How many crackers are on the plate now? ___4___ crackers

2. Count the tally marks. How many tally marks are there? ___16___ tally marks

    卌 卌 卌 丨

3. Color the X, Y, and Z on this chart.

31	32	33	34	35	36	37	38	39	Y
Z	42	43	44	45	46	47	48	49	50
51	52	53	54	55	56	57	X	59	60

What number belongs in the square with the X? ___58___

What number belongs in the square with the Y? ___40___

What number belongs in the square with the Z? ___41___

4. Divide the squares in half two different ways. Color one half of each square red.

   Red   Red

5. Write five different examples that have a sum of 6.

   + ⬚   + ⬚   + ⬚   + ⬚   + ⬚
   ——   ——   ——   ——   ——
    6   6   6   6   6

1-85Aa

Copyright © 1991 by Saxon Publishers, Inc. and Nancy Larson. Reproduction prohibited.

Name •_____•
(Draw a line segment for your name.)

Date _____

Day of the Week _____

LESSON 85A
Math 1

1. Write the number seventy-seven 4 more times. How many digits are on the line? ___12___

   77 77

2. Four children chose chocolate milk.
   Three children chose white milk.
   Draw a picture of the glasses of milk on the graph.

   | chocolate | | | | |
   | white | | | | |

   How many more children chose chocolate milk than chose white milk? ___1___ child

3. Annette put her beads on the string to make a pattern. Color the beads to show a pattern.

   ○─○─○─○─○─○─○─○─○─○

   What pattern did she make? _____

4. I have 14 pennies. Draw the pennies. Circle a group of 10 pennies.

   P P P P P P P
   P P P P P P P

   If I trade 10 pennies for a dime, how many dimes and extra pennies will I have? ___1___ dime ___4___ pennies

5. Circle the doubles plus one addition examples. Write all the answers.

    6   2   0   7   3   6   2
   + 5   + 7   + 8   + 8   + 4   + 1   + 5
   ——   ——   ——   ——   ——   ——   ——
    11   9   8   15   7   7   7

1-85Wa

Copyright © 1991 by Saxon Publishers, Inc. and Nancy Larson. Reproduction prohibited.

Name _____

LESSON 85B
Math 1

1. Write the numbers that are one less and one more than each number.

   _15_ , 16, _17_   _26_ , 27, _28_   _48_ , 49, _50_

2. Two children chose grape juice.
   Four children chose orange juice.
   Draw a picture of the glasses of juice on the graph.

   | grape | | | | |
   | orange | | | | |

   How many more children chose orange juice than chose grape juice? ___2___ children

3. Vinny put his beads on the string to make a pattern. He made a different pattern than Annette did. Color the beads to show a pattern.

   ○─○─○─○─○─○─○─○─○─○

   What pattern did he make? _____

4. I have 17 pennies. Draw the pennies. Circle a group of 10 pennies.

   P P P P P P P P
   P P P P P P P

   If I trade 10 pennies for a dime, how many dimes and extra pennies will I have? ___1___ dime ___7___ pennies

5. Circle the doubles plus one addition examples. Write all the answers.

    9   4   1   2   6   2   9
   + 2   + 5   + 7   + 0   + 7   + 6   + 8
   ——   ——   ——   ——   ——   ——   ——
    11   9   8   2   13   8   17

1-85Wb

Copyright © 1991 by Saxon Publishers, Inc. and Nancy Larson. Reproduction prohibited.

Lesson 86

writing the number 78
adding two-digit numbers using dimes and pennies (with regrouping)

lesson preparation

materials

new price tags for the store items

sorted store items

Master 1-86

cup of 10 dimes and cup of 20 pennies

large fact cards (addition facts)

Fact Sheet A 5.2

the night before

• Put new price tags on half of the items in the classroom store using the following prices: 5¢–9¢, 15¢–19¢, 25¢–29¢, 35¢–39¢, and 45¢–49¢.

in the morning

• Write the following number pattern on the meeting strip:

> 23, 25, 27, ___, ___, ___

Answer: 23, 25, 27, 29, 31, 33

• Put **23 pennies** in the coin cup.

THE MEETING

calendar

• Ask your child to identify the following:

year

month

shapes on the calendar

today's shape

shape pattern for the month

• Ask your child to write the date on the calendar.

- Ask your child to do the following:

  identify today's day of the week, yesterday's day of the week, and tomorrow's day of the week

  read the days of the week

  identify the weekdays

  identify the number of days in a week

- Ask your child to write the full date on the meeting strip.

weather graph

- Ask your child to report and graph the weather.

- Ask questions about the graph.

counting

- Count by 5's to 50.

- Count by 10's to 100.

- Count backward from 100 by 10's.

- Count by 2's to 20.

- Count backward from 20 by 2's.

- Say the odd numbers to 19.

- Say the odd numbers backward from 19.

- Add another number to the number line.

  "We will count numbers on the number line by 10's as far as we can and then count by 1's."

- Point to the multiples of 10 as you count together.

  "How many 10's did we count?"

- Point to the digit in the tens' place.

  "And how many more did we count?"

- Point to the digit in the ones' place.

  "What number is _____ tens and _____ more?"

number pattern

- Ask your child to identify and fill in the missing numbers.

- Read the number pattern together.

clock

- Ask your child to set the morning/afternoon/evening/night clock.

• Throughout the day, your child announces the time on the hour, sets the demonstration clock to show the time, and writes the digital time on the chalkboard.

coin cup

"Beginning today you will do something new with the pennies in the coin cup."

"You will trade them for dimes."

• Give your child **Master 1-84B**.

"Put the pennies in groups of ten on this paper."

"Put the extras in the space labeled 'extras.' "

• Allow time for your child to do this.

"Now trade each group of ten pennies for a dime."

"How many dimes will you need?"

"Let's check by trading each group of ten pennies for a dime."

• Ask your child to trade each group of 10 pennies for a dime.

"How many dimes do you have?"

"How many extra pennies do you have?"

"How much money is this?"

• Ask your child to record the amount of money on the meeting strip.

right/left

• Continue to practice left and right once a week. Practice more often, if necessary.

THE LESSON

Writing the Number 78

"The last number we practiced writing was the number 77."

"What number do you think we will learn how to write today?"

• Write the number 78 on the chalkboard.

"What digits do you see in the number 78?"

"How many dimes and pennies will we use to make 78¢?"

• Use dimes and pennies to demonstrate.

"How many groups of 10 are in 78?"

"How many extra 1's do we have?"

"Let's count by 10's and 1's to check."

Adding Two-Digit Numbers Using Dimes and Pennies (With Regrouping)

"Today you will learn how to add two-digit numbers using dimes and pennies."

"I put new price tags on some of the items in our store."

"Today you will practice buying some of these items."

- Give your child **Master 1-86**.

"What will you write on your receipts?"   name of the store, names of the items, prices of the items, total cost of the items

"Write the name of our store at the top of each receipt."

- Allow time for your child to do this.

- Display 10 of the items with new price tags.

"Choose two of these items to buy."

- Hold up the first item.

"What is this?"

"Write this name on the first line."

"Spell the name as it sounds or copy the name from the container."

"What is the cost of this item?"

"Write this on your receipt next to the name of the item."

- Repeat with the second item.

"Now you will use dimes and pennies to find out how much these two items will cost altogether."

- Give your child a cup of 10 dimes and a cup of 20 pennies.

"How many dimes and pennies will you need for the first item?"

"Put these coins on the table."

- Allow time for your child to do this.

"How many dimes and pennies will you need for the second item?"

"Put these coins on the table."

- Allow time for your child to do this.

"Now put the dimes together and the pennies together."

"How many pennies do you have?"

"How many dimes do you have?"

"Let's count the money."

"We will begin with the dimes."

- Count the money with your child.

"Do you have enough pennies to trade for a dime?"

"Put ten of the pennies in a group."

- Allow time for your child to do this.

"Now put these ten pennies in the penny cup and take a dime out of the dime cup."

"You traded ten pennies for one dime."

"How many dimes do you have now?"

"How many pennies do you have now?"

"How much money is this altogether?"

"Let's count to check."

"What is the total cost of the _____ and the _____?"

"Write this amount next to the word 'total.' "

"Put the coins back in the cups."

- Repeat with the next 3 receipts.

"Whenever we have more than ten pennies, we will trade ten pennies for a dime."

- Provide extra copies of **Master 1-86** and cups of dimes and pennies for your child to use during free time.

CLASS PRACTICE

- Use the large fact cards to practice the addition facts with your child.
- Give your child **Fact Sheet A 5.2**.

"What number facts do you see?"

"What strategies will you use to find the answers?"

- Correct the fact sheet with your child.

WRITTEN PRACTICE

- Complete **Worksheet 86A** with your child.
- Complete **Worksheet 86B** with your child later in the day.

MASTER 1-86
Math 1

Name _____

```
  _____        _____
        [ ]                 [ ]

        [ ]                 [ ]
+ _____      + _____

  Total  [ ]          Total  [ ]


  _____        _____
        [ ]                 [ ]

        [ ]                 [ ]
+ _____      + _____

  Total  [ ]          Total  [ ]
```

1-86Ma   Copyright © 1991 by Saxon Publishers, Inc. and Nancy Larson. Reproduction prohibited.

LESSON 86A
Math 1

Name _____
(Draw a line segment for your name.)

Date _____

Day of the Week _____

1. Write the number seventy-eight three more times. How many digits are on the line? __10__

   78 78 _____

2. Mrs. Dietsch counted six red shoes and eight blue shoes in the closet. Draw a picture and write a number sentence to show the shoes in the closet.

   red 000000   blue 00000000

   Number sentence _____ 6 + 8 = 14 _____

   How many shoes are in the closet? __14__ shoes

3. William's receipt at the classroom store looked like this:

   How much money did
   he spend for the two items? __58¢__

   How many dimes is that? __5__

   How many pennies is that? __8__

pickles	27	¢
pie +	31	¢
Total	58	¢

4. Sara put her pennies in groups of 10.

   How many pennies does she have? __32__ pennies

   Sara traded the groups of pennies for dimes.

   How many dimes did she get? __3__ dimes

   o = penny

5. Write the answers.

   7 − 1 = __6__   16 − 8 = __8__   2 − 0 = __2__

1-86Wa   Copyright © 1991 by Saxon Publishers, Inc. and Nancy Larson. Reproduction prohibited.

LESSON 86B
Math 1

Name _____

1. Circle the one that is different.

   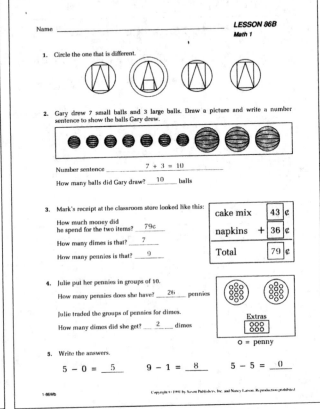

2. Gary drew 7 small balls and 3 large balls. Draw a picture and write a number sentence to show the balls Gary drew.

   Number sentence _____ 7 + 3 = 10 _____

   How many balls did Gary draw? __10__ balls

3. Mark's receipt at the classroom store looked like this:

   How much money did
   he spend for the two items? __79¢__

   How many dimes is that? __7__

   How many pennies is that? __9__

cake mix	43	¢
napkins +	36	¢
Total	79	¢

4. Julie put her pennies in groups of 10.

   How many pennies does she have? __26__ pennies

   Julie traded the groups of pennies for dimes.

   How many dimes did she get? __2__ dimes

   Extras

   o = penny

5. Write the answers.

   5 − 0 = __5__   9 − 1 = __8__   5 − 5 = __0__

1-86Wb   Copyright © 1991 by Saxon Publishers, Inc. and Nancy Larson. Reproduction prohibited.

esson 87

writing the number 79
telling time to the half hour

---

lesson preparation

materials

demonstration clocks

large fact cards (addition facts)

Fact Sheet A 5.2

in the morning

• Write the following number pattern on the meeting strip:

> __, __, __, 5, 4, 3

Answer: 8, 7, 6, 5, 4, 3

• Put **14 pennies** in the coin cup.

THE MEETING

calendar

• Ask your child to identify the following:

year

month

shapes on the calendar

today's shape

shape pattern for the month

• Ask your child to write the date on the calendar.

• Ask your child to do the following:

identify today's day of the week, yesterday's day of the week, and tomorrow's day of the week

read the days of the week

identify the weekdays

identify the number of days in a week

• Ask your child to write the full date on the meeting strip.

---

weather graph

- Ask your child to report and graph the weather.

- Ask questions about the graph.

counting

- Count by 5's to 50.

- Count by 10's to 100.

- Count backward from 100 by 10's.

- Count by 2's to 20.

- Count backward from 20 by 2's.

- Say the odd numbers to 19.

- Say the odd numbers backward from 19.

- Add another number to the number line.

"We will count numbers on the number line by 10's as far as we can and then count by 1's."

- Point to the multiples of 10 as you count together.

"How many 10's did we count?"

- Point to the digit in the tens' place.

"And how many more did we count?"

- Point to the digit in the ones' place.

"What number is _____ tens and _____ more?"

number pattern

- Ask your child to identify and fill in the missing numbers.

- Read the number pattern together.

clock

- Ask your child to set the morning/afternoon/evening/night clock.

- Throughout the day, your child announces the time on the hour, sets the demonstration clock to show the time, and writes the digital time on the chalkboard.

coin cup

- Give your child **Master 1-84B**.

"Put pennies in groups of ten on this paper."

"Put the extras in the space labeled 'extras.' "

- Allow time for your child to do this.

"Trade each group of ten pennies for a dime."

"How many dimes will you need?"

"Let's check by trading each group of ten pennies for a dime."

- Ask your child to trade each group of 10 pennies for a dime.

"How many dimes do you have?"

"How many extra pennies do you have?"

"How much money is this?"

- Ask your child to record the amount of money on the meeting strip.

right/left

- Continue to practice left and right once a week. Practice more often, if necessary.

The Lesson

Writing the Number 79

"The last number we practiced writing was the number 78."

"What number do you think we will learn how to write today?"

- Write the number 79 on the chalkboard.

"What digits do you see in the number 79?"

"How many dimes and pennies will we use to make 79¢?"

- Use dimes and pennies to demonstrate.

"How many groups of 10 are in 79?"

"How many extra 1's do we have?"

"Let's count by 10's and 1's to check."

Telling Time to the Half Hour

"Today you will learn how to tell time to the half hour."

"A few days ago you divided squares of bread in half."

- Draw the following on the chalkboard:

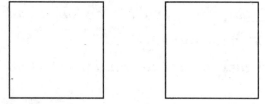

"Let's pretend that these squares are pieces of bread."

"Show one way to divide a square in half."

- Ask your child to draw a line to divide the first square in half.

"Do you know another way to divide a square in half?"

- Ask your child to draw a line to divide the second square in half.

- Draw the following on the chalkboard:

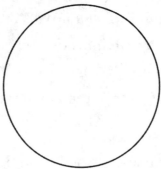

"If we had a round piece of bread, how could we cut it in half?"

- Ask your child to draw a line to divide the circle in half.

"What else do we have in our house that has the shape of a circle?"

"How would we cut it in half?"

- Ask your child for several suggestions.

"Let's look at our clock face."

"If we wanted to cut it in half, how could we do it?"

- Draw and number a clock face on the chalkboard.

- If your child does not draw a line from the 12 to the 6, draw another clock face and ask: "Is there another way to cut the clock face in half?"

"When you drew a line to divide this clock face in half, what numbers did the line touch?" **12 and 6**

- Give your child a demonstration clock.

"Show seven o'clock on this clock."

- Ask your child to show seven o'clock on the demonstration clock.

- Point to the hour hand.

"What do we call this?" **hour hand**

- Point to the minute hand.

"What do we call this?" **long hand**

"There is another name for the long hand."

"It is called the minute hand."

"Where does the minute hand point when it is seven o'clock?" **at the 12**

"I will move the minute hand slowly around the clock."

"Say stop when you think it has gone halfway around the clock face."

- Slowly move the minute hand until your child says stop at half past seven.

"The clock shows half past seven."

"That means that a half hour has gone by."

"Where is the minute hand pointing when it is half past seven?"   at the 6

"Is the hour hand still pointing to the seven?"   no

"Is it pointing to the eight yet?"   no

"Where is the hour hand pointing when it is half past seven?"   halfway between the 7 and the 8

"When the long hand takes half of its long trip around the clock, the short hand takes half of its short trip from one number to the next."

"Show two o'clock on this clock."

• Allow your child time to do this.

"I will move the minute hand slowly around the clock."

"Say stop when you think it has gone halfway around the clock face."

• Slowly move the minute hand until your child says stop at half past two.

"What time is it now?"   half past two

"Where is the minute hand pointing when it is half past two?"   at the 6

"Is the hour hand still pointing to the two?"   no

"Is it pointing to the three yet?"   no

"Where is the hour hand pointing when it is half past two?"   halfway between the 2 and the 3

• Repeat with 9:00, 12:00, and 6:00.

"Show ten o'clock on the clock."

"Now show half past ten."

"Where does the minute hand point?"   at the 6

"Will the hour hand point to the ten?"   no

"Will the hour hand point to the eleven?"   no

"Where does the hour hand point?"   halfway between the 10 and 11

• Repeat with 4:00, 8:00, and 1:00.

CLASS PRACTICE

• Use the large fact cards to practice the addition facts with your child.

• Give your child **Fact Sheet A 5.2**.

"What number facts do you see?"

"What strategies will you use to find the answers?"

• Correct the fact sheet with your child.

WRITTEN PRACTICE

• Complete **Worksheet 87A** with your child.

• Complete **Worksheet 87B** with your child later in the day.

Name ●_____
(Draw a line segment for your name.)

LESSON 87A
Math 1

Date _____

Day of the Week _____

1. Write the number seventy-nine three more times. How many digits did you write? __6__

79 79

2. Art put his crayons in groups of 10.

   How many crayons does he have? __30__ crayons

   Extras

3. Show half past four on the clock.

4. This is Susan's receipt. Use dimes and pennies to find the total amount Susan spent.

soup	38	¢
cake +	21	¢
Total	59	¢

5. Fill in the missing numbers.

   5, 10, 15, __20__, __25__, __30__, __35__, __40__, __45__, __50__

6. How many dimes and pennies will you need to buy the apple?

   26¢   __2__ dimes   __6__ pennies

1-87Wa   Copyright © 1991 by Saxon Publishers, Inc. and Nancy Larson. Reproduction prohibited.

Name _____

LESSON 87B
Math 1

1. Circle the number that is between 46 and 53.

   46 [ ] 53   41 57 45 (52) 44

2. Amy put her colored pencils in groups of 10. How many colored pencils does she have?

   __13__ colored pencils

   Extras

3. Show half past two on the clock.

4. Marsha's receipt at the classroom store looked like this:

   How much money did she spend for the two items? __48¢__

   How many dimes is that? __4__

   How many pennies is that? __8__

cereal	32	¢
cheese +	16	¢
Total	48	¢

5. Fill in the missing numbers.

   50, 45, 40, __35__, __30__, __25__, __20__, __15__, __10__, __5__

6. How many dimes and pennies will you need to buy the orange?

   31¢   __3__ dimes   __1__ penny

1-87Wb   Copyright © 1991 by Saxon Publishers, Inc. and Nancy Larson. Reproduction prohibited.

---

esson 88

writing the number 80
dividing a square into fourths
coloring halves and fourths

lesson preparation

materials

four 6" white paper squares

crayons

Master 1-88

optional: 1 slice of bread, peanut butter, napkins, knife

large fact cards (addition facts)

Fact Sheet A 5.2

in the morning

• Write the following number pattern on the meeting strip:

> ——, ——, ——, 8, 9, 10

Answer: 5, 6, 7, 8, 9, 10

• Put **22 pennies** in the coin cup.

THE MEETING

calendar

• Ask your child to identify the following:

> year
>
> month
>
> shapes on the calendar
>
> today's shape
>
> shape pattern for the month

• Ask your child to write the date on the calendar.

• Ask your child to do the following:

> identify today's day of the week, yesterday's day of the week, and tomorrow's day of the week

read the days of the week

identify the weekdays

identify the number of days in a week

- Ask your child to write the full date on the meeting strip.

weather graph

- Ask your child to report and graph the weather.

- Ask questions about the graph.

counting

- Count by 5's to 50.

- Count by 10's to 100.

- Count backward from 100 by 10's.

- Count by 2's to 20.

- Count backward from 20 by 2's.

- Say the odd numbers to 19.

- Say the odd numbers backward from 19.

- Add another number to the number line.

"We will count numbers on the number line by 10's as far as we can and then count by 1's."

- Point to the multiples of 10 as you count together.

"How many 10's did we count?"

- Point to the digit in the tens' place.

"And how many more did we count?"

- Point to the digit in the ones' place.

"What number is _____ tens and _____ more?"

number pattern

- Ask your child to identify and fill in the missing numbers.

- Read the number pattern together.

clock

- Ask your child to set the morning/afternoon/evening/night clock.

"Beginning today you will also announce the time on the half hour."

- Throughout the day, your child announces the time on the hour and the half hour, sets the demonstration clock to show the time, and writes the digital time on the chalkboard.

coin cup

- Give your child **Master 1-84B**.

  "Put pennies in groups of ten on this paper."

  "Put the extras in the space labeled 'extras.' "

- Allow time for your child to do this.

  "Trade each group of ten pennies for a dime."

  "How many dimes will you need?"

  "Let's check by trading each group of ten pennies for a dime."

- Ask your child to trade each group of 10 pennies for a dime.

  "How many dimes do you have?"

  "How many extra pennies do you have?"

  "How much money is this?"

- Ask your child to record the amount of money on the meeting strip.

right/left

- Continue to practice left and right once a week. Practice more often, if necessary.

THE LESSON

Writing the Number 80

  "The last number we practiced writing was the number 79."

  "What number do you think we will learn how to write today?"

- Write the number 80 on the chalkboard.

  "What digits do you see in the number 80?"

  "How many dimes and pennies will we use to make 80¢?"

- Use dimes and pennies to demonstrate.

  "How many groups of 10 are in 80?"

  "How many extra 1's do we have?"

  "Let's count by 10's to check."

Dividing a Square into Fourths
Coloring Halves and Fourths

  "You have already learned how to divide a square in half."

  "Today you will learn how to divide a square into smaller equal parts called fourths."

"You also will learn how to color halves and fourths."

- Draw two squares on the chalkboard.

  "How can we divide a square in half?"

  "Is there another way to divide a square in half?"

- Ask your child to draw lines on the chalkboard square to divide each square in half in a different way.

- Use a 6" square piece of paper.

  "Watch as I fold this piece of paper in half."

  "I am carefully matching the corners and edges of the paper."

  "Now I will use one hand to hold the sides I matched and the other hand to crease the paper."

- Demonstrate.

  "What did I do?"   *folded the paper in half*

  "Now you will have a chance to do this."

- Give your child a 6" construction paper square.

  "Fold your square in half just like I folded mine."

- Allow time for your child to do this.

  "Open up your paper."

  "How many parts do you have?"   *2*

  "Are they the same size?"

  "How can you show that they are the same size?"

  "Close your paper."

  "What do you think will happen if we fold our papers in half again?"

  "How many parts do you think we will have then?"

  "Let's try it."

- Fold your paper as your child folds his/hers.

  "Open the paper."

  "How many parts do you have now?"   *4*

  "Are all the parts the same size?"   *yes*

  "When there are four equal parts, each part is called one fourth."

  "I will trace along the fold lines using a black crayon to show the equal parts."

- Quickly trace the fold lines using a black crayon and color one fourth of the square using a different color crayon.

  "How many fourths are colored?"   *one fourth*

- Color one more fourth.

  "How many fourths are colored now?"   *two fourths*

- Repeat with three and four fourths.

  "Use a black crayon to trace your fold lines."

- Allow time for your child to do this.

  "Now use a different color crayon to color one fourth of your square."

  "How many parts will you color?" 1

- Allow time for your child to do this.

- Use another 6" square.

  "How can I fold this square in half in a different way?"

- Fold the square diagonally.

- Give your child another 6" square.

  "Fold this square in half just like I did."

- Allow time for your child to do this.

  "Open up your paper."

  "How many parts do you have?"

  "Close your paper."

  "What do you think will happen if we fold our papers in half again?"

  "How many parts do you think we will have then?"

  "Let's try it."

  "How will we fold the paper in half?"

- Demonstrate.

  "Fold your paper in half."

  "Open your paper."

  "How many parts do you have now?"

  "What do we call the parts when we have four equal parts?" *fourths*

- Quickly trace the fold lines and use a different color crayon to color one fourth of the square.

  "How many fourths are colored?" *one fourth*

- Color one more fourth.

  "How many fourths are colored now?"

- Repeat with three and four fourths.

  "Use a black crayon to trace your fold lines."

- Allow time for your child to do this.

  "Now use a different color crayon to color one fourth of your square."

  "How many parts will you color?" 1

- Allow time for your child to do this.

- Give your child **Master 1-88.**

"Divide the first square in half."

"Try to make equal parts."

"You divided the square almost in half because you did it without measuring."

"Divide the second square in half in a different way."

"Try to make equal parts."

"Point to the square at the bottom left-hand corner."

"Draw lines to divide this square into fourths."

"Try to make equal parts."

"Make the lines look like one of your paper squares."

"Point to the square at the bottom right-hand corner."

"Draw lines to divide this square into fourths in a different way."

"Try to make equal parts."

"Make the lines look like your other paper square."

"Color one half of each of the top squares."

- Allow time for your child to color.

"Color one fourth of each of the bottom squares."

- Allow time for your child to color.

"Which is more, one half or one fourth?"

- Optional:

"Today we will have a snack of peanut butter and bread."

"I will put peanut butter on half of your piece of bread."

"Circle the square that shows how you would like peanut butter on a piece of bread."

"When I give you your piece of bread and peanut butter, fold the bread in half to make a sandwich."

- Use a loaf of sliced bread with square slices, if possible. Spread the peanut butter on half of the slice according to your child's picture.

"Does the peanut butter on your slice of bread look like your picture?"

CLASS PRACTICE

- Use the large fact cards to practice the addition facts with your child.
- Give your child **Fact Sheet A 5.2.**

"What number facts do you see?"

"What strategies will you use to find the answers?"

- Correct the fact sheet with your child.

WRITTEN PRACTICE

- Complete **Worksheet 88A** with your child.
- Complete **Worksheet 88B** with your child later in the day.

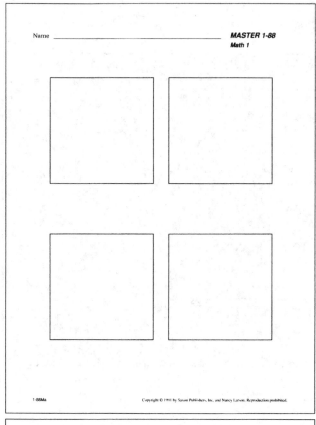

Name _____ **MASTER 1-88**
Math 1

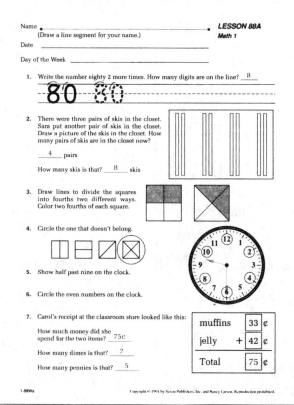

Name _____ **LESSON 88A**
(Draw a line segment for your name.) **Math 1**

Date _____

Day of the Week _____

1. Write the number eighty 2 more times. How many digits are on the line? __8__

2. There were three pairs of skis in the closet. Sara put another pair of skis in the closet. Draw a picture of the skis in the closet. How many pairs of skis are in the closet now?

___4___ pairs

How many skis is that? __8__ skis

3. Draw lines to divide the squares into fourths two different ways. Color two fourths of each square.

4. Circle the one that doesn't belong.

5. Show half past nine on the clock.

6. Circle the even numbers on the clock.

7. Carol's receipt at the classroom store looked like this:

How much money did she spend for the two items? __75¢__

How many dimes is that? __7__

How many pennies is that? __5__

muffins		33	¢
jelly	+	42	¢
Total		75	¢

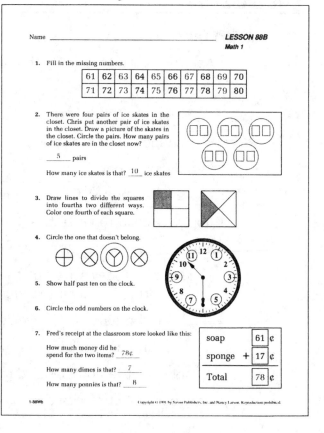

Name _____ **LESSON 88B**
Math 1

1. Fill in the missing numbers.

61	62	63	64	65	66	67	68	69	70
71	72	73	74	75	76	77	78	79	80

2. There were four pairs of ice skates in the closet. Chris put another pair of ice skates in the closet. Draw a picture of the skates in the closet. Circle the pairs. How many pairs of ice skates are in the closet now?

___5___ pairs

How many ice skates is that? __10__ ice skates

3. Draw lines to divide the squares into fourths two different ways. Color one fourth of each square.

4. Circle the one that doesn't belong.

5. Show half past ten on the clock.

6. Circle the odd numbers on the clock.

7. Fred's receipt at the classroom store looked like this:

How much money did he spend for the two items? __78¢__

How many dimes is that? __7__

How many pennies is that? __8__

soap		61	¢
sponge	+	17	¢
Total		78	¢

esson 89

writing the number 81
adding ten to a number

---

lesson preparation

materials

hundred number chart

cup of 10 pennies

Fact Sheet A 5.2

in the morning

- Write the following number pattern on the meeting strip:

> ___, ___, ___, 15, 16, 17

Answer: *12, 13, 14, 15, 16, 17*

- Put **31 pennies** in the coin cup.

THE MEETING

calendar

- Ask your child to identify the following:

    year

    month

    shapes on the calendar

    today's shape

    shape pattern for the month

- Ask your child to write the date on the calendar.

- Ask your child to do the following:

    identify today's day of the week, yesterday's day of the week, and tomorrow's day of the week

    read the days of the week

    identify the weekdays

    identify the number of days in a week

- Ask your child to write the full date on the meeting strip.

weather graph

- Ask your child to report and graph the weather.
- Ask questions about the graph.

counting

- Count by 5's to 50.
- Count by 10's to 100.
- Count backward from 100 by 10's.
- Count by 2's to 20.
- Count backward from 20 by 2's.
- Say the odd numbers to 19.
- Say the odd numbers backward from 19.
- Add another number to the number line.

"We will count numbers on the number line by 10's as far as we can and then count by 1's."

- Point to the multiples of 10 as you count together.

"How many 10's did we count?"

- Point to the digit in the tens' place.

"And how many more did we count?"

- Point to the digit in the ones' place.

"What number is _____ tens and _____ more?"

number pattern

- Ask your child to identify and fill in the missing numbers.
- Read the number pattern together.

clock

- Ask your child to set the morning/afternoon/evening/night clock.
- Throughout the day, your child announces the time on the hour and the half hour, sets the demonstration clock to show the time, and writes the digital time on the chalkboard.

coin cup

- Give your child **Master 1-84B**.

"Put pennies in groups of ten on this paper."

"Put the extras in the space labeled 'extras.' "

- Allow time for your child to do this.

"Trade each group of ten pennies for a dime."

"How many dimes will you need?"

"Let's check by trading each group of ten pennies for a dime."

- Ask your child to trade each group of 10 pennies for a dime.

"How many dimes do you have?"

"How many extra pennies do you have?"

"How much money is this?"

- Ask your child to record the amount of money on the meeting strip.

right/left

- Continue to practice left and right once a week. Practice more often, if necessary.

THE LESSON

Writing the Number 81

"The last number we practiced writing was the number 80."

"What number do you think we will learn how to write today?"

- Write the number 81 on the chalkboard.

"What digits do you see in the number 81?"

"How many dimes and pennies will we use to make 81¢?"

- Use dimes and pennies to demonstrate.

"How many groups of 10 are in 81?"

"How many extra 1's do we have?"

"Let's count by 10's and 1's to check."

Adding Ten to a Number

"Today you will learn how to add ten to a number."

- Give your child a hundred number chart and a cup of 10 pennies.

"Put a penny on the number six."

"Now count ten more and put a penny where you stop."

"What number is your penny covering?"   16

"Six and ten more is sixteen."

"Now count ten more and put a penny where you stop."

"What number is your penny covering?"   26

"Sixteen and ten more is twenty-six."

- Repeat until all the pennies are used.

"What do you notice about the pennies on your chart?"   they are in a line

"What numbers do you think are under the pennies?"

"Let's read the numbers as you take the pennies off one at a time."

"Start with the penny at the top."

- Read the numbers slowly with your child as he/she removes the pennies.

- Point to the numbers on the hundred number chart as you say the following:

"Six and ten more is sixteen, sixteen and ten more is twenty-six, twenty-six and ten more is thirty-six, etc."

"Put a penny on the number nine."

"Now count ten more and put a penny where you stop."

"What number is your penny covering?"   19

"Ten more than nine is nineteen."

"Now count ten more and put a penny where you stop."

"What number is your penny covering?"   29

"Ten more than nineteen is twenty-nine."

- Repeat until all the pennies are used.

"What numbers do you think are under the pennies?"

"Let's read the numbers as we take the pennies off one at a time."

"Start with the penny at the top."

- Read the numbers slowly with your child as he/she removes the pennies.

- Point to the numbers on the hundred number chart as you say the following:

"Nine and ten more is nineteen, nineteen and ten more is twenty-nine, twenty-nine and ten more is thirty-nine, etc."

- Repeat, beginning with 3, if desired.

"Put your pennies in the cup."

"How can we use the hundred number chart to help us add ten to a number without counting?"

"Let's start with seven and keep adding ten."

"Put your finger on the number seven on your hundred number chart."

"What is ten more than seven?"   17

"What is ten more than seventeen?"   27

"What is ten more than twenty-seven?"   37

- Repeat to 97.

"Point to forty-two."

"Point to the number that is ten more than forty-two."

"*What number is ten more than forty-two?*" 52

- Repeat with 86, 15, 31, 73, and 68.

CLASS PRACTICE

"*Use your individual fact cards to practice the addition facts.*"

- Allow time for your child to practice the addition number facts independently.

- Give your child **Fact Sheet A 5.2**.

"*What number facts do you see?*"

"*What strategies will you use to find the answers?*"

- Correct the fact sheet with your child.

WRITTEN PRACTICE

- Complete **Worksheet 89A** with your child.

- Complete **Worksheet 89B** with your child later in the day.

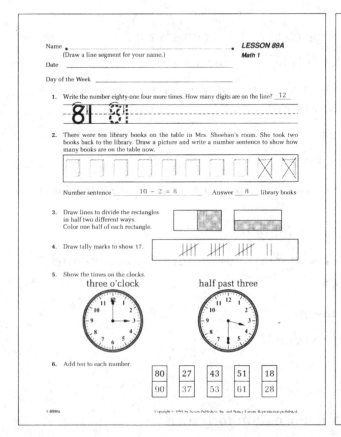

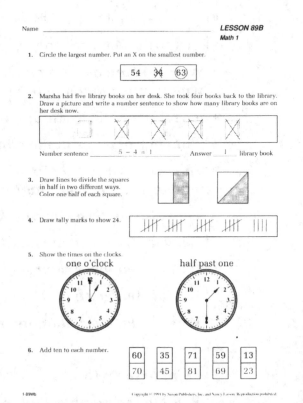

esson 90

assessment

lesson preparation

materials

store items priced at 32¢ and 14¢

10 dimes

20 pennies

Written Assessment #17

Oral Assessment #9

in the morning

• Write the following number pattern on the meeting strip:

> 23, 25, 27, __, __, __

Answer: 23, 25, 27, 29, 31, 33

• Put **23 pennies** in the coin cup.

THE MEETING

calendar

- • Ask your child to identify the following:

    year

    month

    shapes on the calendar

    today's shape

    shape pattern for the month

- • Ask your child to write the date on the calendar.

- • Ask your child to do the following:

    identify today's day of the week, yesterday's day of the week, and tomorrow's day of the week

    read the days of the week

    identify the weekdays

    identify the number of days in a week

- • Ask your child to write the full date on the meeting strip.

weather graph

- Ask your child to report and graph the weather.
- Ask questions about the graph.

counting

- Count by 5's to 50.
- Count by 10's to 100.
- Count backward from 100 by 10's.
- Count by 2's to 20.
- Count backward from 20 by 2's.
- Say the odd numbers to 19.
- Say the odd numbers backward from 19.
- Add another number to the number line.
- Use an orange crayon to color the square for 90.

"We will count numbers on the number line by 10's as far as we can and then count by 1's."

- Point to the multiples of 10 as you count together.

"How many 10's did we count?"

- Point to the digit in the tens' place.

"And how many more did we count?"

- Point to the digit in the ones' place.

"What number is _____ tens and _____ more?"

number pattern

- Ask your child to identify and fill in the missing numbers.
- Read the number pattern together.

clock

- Ask your child to set the morning/afternoon/evening/night clock.
- Throughout the day, your child announces the time on the hour and the half hour, sets the demonstration clock to show the time, and writes the digital time on the chalkboard.

coin cup

- Give your child **Master 1-84B**.

"Put pennies in groups of ten on this paper."

"Put the extras in the space labeled 'extras.'"

- Allow time for your child to do this.

"Trade each group of ten pennies for a dime."

"How many dimes will you need?"

"Let's check by trading each group of ten pennies for a dime."

- Ask your child to trade each group of 10 pennies for a dime.

"How many dimes do you have?"

"How many extra pennies do you have?"

"How much money is this?"

- Ask your child to record the amount of money on the meeting strip.

right/left

- Continue to practice left and right once a week. Practice more often, if necessary.

ASSESSMENT

- All of the questions on the assessment are based on concepts and skills presented at least five lessons ago. If your child is having difficulty with a specific concept, reteach the concept the following day.

Written Assessment

- Give your child **Written Assessment #17**.

- Read the directions for each problem. Allow time for your child to complete each problem before continuing to the next.

- Correct the paper, noting your child's mistakes on the **Individual Recording Form**.

Oral Assessment

- Record your child's responses to the oral interview on the interview sheet.

Name _____
(Draw a line segment for your name.)

Date _____

Day of the Week _____

1. Write a number word that has **4** letters. _____

   Write a number word that has **5** letters. _____

   How many letters is that altogether? ___9___ letters

2. Draw tally marks to show 26.

   | ‖‖‖ ‖‖‖ ‖‖‖ ‖‖‖ ‖‖‖ | |

3. Morgan counted seven sunny day tags and five cloudy day tags. Draw a picture of the tags.

   Sunny ☀ ☀ ☀ ☀ ☀ ☀ ☀ ☐ ☐ ☐

   Cloudy ● ● ● ● ● ☐ ☐ ☐ ☐ ☐

   How many more sunny days than cloudy days were there? ___2___ days

4. Quiana put the pencils in groups of 10. How many pencils does she have?

   ___53___ pencils

5. Eric's receipt at the classroom store looked like this:

   How much money did he spend for the two items? __67¢__

   How many dimes is that? __6__

   How many pennies is that? __7__

cereal	42	¢
juice +	25	¢
Total	67	¢

6. Write the answers.

6	5	0	8	7	2	4	5
+2	+6	+3	+7	+1	+9	+3	+2
8	11	3	15	8	11	7	7

1-90Aa

Teacher _____

Date _____

Materials:
Store items priced at 32¢ and 14¢
10 dimes 20 pennies

Students	"Count by 10's." • Stop the children at 100.	"Count by 5's." • Stop the children at 50.	•Show the child store items priced at 32¢ and 14¢. •Use dimes and pennies to show each amount. "What is the total cost of these two items?"	
			Show each amount using fewest pennies	Count money to find total

1-90La

esson 91

writing the number 82
counting by 10's from a single-digit number

---

lesson preparation

materials

hundred number chart

Master 1-91

large fact cards (subtraction facts)

Fact Sheet S 3.4

in the morning

• Write the following number pattern on the meeting strip:

> 64, 63, 62, __, __, __

Answer: 64, 63, 62, 61, 60, 59

• Put **37 pennies** in the coin cup.

THE MEETING

calendar

- • Ask your child to identify the following:

    year

    month

    shapes on the calendar

    today's shape

    shape pattern for the month

- • Ask your child to write the date on the calendar.

- • Ask your child to do the following:

    identify today's day of the week, yesterday's day of the week, and tomorrow's day of the week

    read the days of the week

    identify the weekdays

    identify the number of days in a week

- • Ask your child to write the full date on the meeting strip.

weather graph

- Ask your child to report and graph the weather.
- Ask questions about the graph.

counting

- Count by 5's to 50.
- Count by 10's to 100.
- Count backward from 100 by 10's.
- Count by 2's to 20.
- Count backward from 20 by 2's.
- Say the odd numbers to 19.
- Say the odd numbers backward from 19.
- Add another number to the number line.

"We will count numbers on the number line by 10's as far as we can and then count by 1's."

- Point to the multiples of 10 as you count together.

"How many 10's did we count?"

- Point to the digit in the tens' place.

"And how many more did we count?"

- Point to the digit in the ones' place.

"What number is _____ tens and _____ more?"

number pattern

- Ask your child to identify and fill in the missing numbers.
- Read the number pattern together.

clock

- Ask your child to set the morning/afternoon/evening/night clock.
- Throughout the day, your child announces the time on the hour and the half hour, sets the demonstration clock to show the time, and writes the digital time on the chalkboard.

coin cup

- Ask your child to put the pennies in groups of 10 and trade groups of 10 pennies for dimes.
- Ask your child to identify the number of dimes and the number of extra pennies and to record the total amount of money on the meeting strip.

right/left

- Continue to practice left and right once a week. Practice more often, if necessary.

THE LESSON

Writing the Number 82

"The last number we practiced writing was the number 81."

"What number do you think we will learn how to write today?"

- Write the number 82 on the chalkboard.

"What digits do you see in the number 82?"

"How many dimes and pennies will we use to make 82¢?"

- Use dimes and pennies to demonstrate.

"How many groups of 10 are in 82?"

"How many extra 1's do we have?"

"Let's count by 10's and 1's to check."

Counting by 10's from a Single-Digit Number

"Each day we have been counting by 10's, beginning with ten."

"Let's do that together."

- Count with your child as you point to the numbers on the hundred number chart.

"Today you will learn how to count by 10's, beginning with a single-digit number."

"This will help us find the answer when we are adding ten to a number."

"When we counted by 10's from ten, which way did I move my finger on the hundred number chart?"   down

"If we begin at four and count by 10's, what numbers do you think we will say?"

"Let's try that."

- Point to each number as your child counts by 10's, beginning with 4.

"Let's count by 10's starting with six."

- Point to each number as your child counts by 10's, beginning with 6.

"Choose a number for us to start with."

- Point to each number as your child counts by 10's, beginning with the chosen number.

"There is a rhyming story (rap) we can say that will help us practice counting by 10's."

- Give your child **Master 1-91**.

"This is how it goes."

"Read the words with me."

- Point to each word as you read the first line.

"I can count by 10's, it's fun, it's fun."

"I can count by 10's and I'll start with one."

- Point to the numbers on the hundred number chart as you count by 10's from 1 to 91.

"One, 11, 21, 31, 41, 51, 61, 71, 81, 91."

- After each verse, say "ugh" 2 or 3 times in rhythm.
- Repeat with the other verses.

"Now you will have a chance to write the numbers for each verse."

"Write the numbers for each verse as we say them."

- Repeat the rhyming story slowly as your child writes the numbers.
- Save **Master 1-91**.

CLASS PRACTICE

- Use the large fact cards to practice the subtraction facts.
- Give your child **Fact Sheet S 3.4**.

"What number facts do you see?"

"What strategies will you use to find the answer?"

- Correct the fact sheet with your child.

WRITTEN PRACTICE

- Complete **Worksheet 91A** with your child.
- Complete **Worksheet 91B** with your child later in the day.

Name _____ **MASTER 1-91**
Math 1

I can count by 10's, it's fun, it's fun. I can count by 10's and I'll start with one.

I can count by 10's, can you, can you? I can count by 10's and I'll start with two.

I can count by 10's, oh gee, oh gee. I can count by 10's and I'll start with three.

I can count by 10's, with numbers galore. I can count by 10's and I'll start with four.

I can count by 10's, like the bees in a hive. I can count by 10's and I'll start with five.

I can count by 10's, without any tricks. I can count by 10's and I'll start with six.

I can count by 10's, going up to heaven. I can count by 10's and I'll start with seven.

I can count by 10's, because in Math I'm great. I can count by 10's and I'll start with eight.

I can count by 10's, yes, I know I'm divine. I can count by 10's and I'll start with nine.

I can count by 10's, dear gentlemen. I can count by 10's and I'll start with ten.

1-91Ma

Name •_____• **LESSON 91A**
(Draw a line segment for your name.) **Math 1**

Date _____

Day of the Week _____

1. Write the number eighty-two three more times. How many digits are on the line? _10_

   82 82

2. Write a story for the number sentence **4 + 1 = 5.**

   _____
   _____

3. Three children chose apples.
   Five children chose oranges.
   Draw a picture of the apples
   and oranges on the graph.

apple	○ ○ ○			
orange	○ ○ ○ ○ ○			

   ○ apple   ○ orange

   How many more children chose oranges than apples? _2_ children

4. Draw lines to divide the squares into fourths in two different ways.

   Color one fourth of each square.

5. Count by 10's from 7. Fill in the numbers you say.

7	17	27	37	47	57	67	77	87	97

6. Write the answers.

   $7 - 1 = \underline{6}$ $7 + 6 = \underline{13}$ $12 - 6 = \underline{6}$

   $6 + 2 = \underline{8}$ $8 - 0 = \underline{8}$ $4 + 5 = \underline{9}$

1-91Wa

Name _____ **LESSON 91B**
Math 1

1. Write a number that is between 49 and 55.

   49 [ ] 55

2. Write a story for the number sentence **1 + 5 = 6.**

   _____
   _____

3. Four children chose peaches.
   Five children chose bananas.
   Draw a picture of the
   peaches and bananas on the
   graph.

peach	○ ○ ○ ○			
banana	)))))			

   ○ peach   ) banana

   How many more children chose bananas than peaches? _1_ child

4. Draw lines to divide the squares into fourths in two different ways.

   Color three fourths of each square.

5. Count by 10's from 8. Fill in the numbers you say.

8	18	28	38	48	58	68	78	88	98

6. Write the answers.

   $9 - 1 = \underline{8}$ $8 + 9 = \underline{17}$ $14 - 7 = \underline{7}$

   $7 + 2 = \underline{9}$ $5 - 0 = \underline{5}$ $6 + 5 = \underline{11}$

1-91Wb

Lesson 92

writing the number 83
adding ten to a number

lesson preparation

materials

10 dimes and 10 pennies
small cup
6" × 9" piece of white construction paper
6" × 9" piece of yellow construction paper
individual fact cards (subtraction)
Fact Sheet S 3.4

the night before

• Tape together a piece of yellow and white construction paper to make a work mat.

yellow	white

in the morning

• Write the following number pattern on the meeting strip:

___, ___, ___, 11, 10, 9

Answer: 14, 13, 12, 11, 10, 9

• Put **27 pennies** in the coin cup.

THE MEETING

calendar

• Ask your child to identify the following:

year

month

shapes on the calendar

today's shape

shape pattern for the month

- Ask your child to write the date on the calendar.
- Ask your child to do the following:

    identify today's day of the week, yesterday's day of the week, and tomorrow's day of the week

    read the days of the week

    identify the weekdays

    identify the number of days in a week

- Ask your child to write the full date on the meeting strip.

weather graph

- Ask your child to report and graph the weather.
- Ask questions about the graph.

counting

- Say the "Counting by 10's Rap" on **Master 1-91** together. Point to the numbers on the hundred number chart as your child counts.
- Count by 5's to 50.
- Count by 10's to 100.
- Count backward from 100 by 10's.
- Count by 2's to 20.
- Count backward from 20 by 2's.
- Say the odd numbers to 19.
- Say the odd numbers backward from 19.
- Add another number to the number line.

    "We will count numbers on the number line by 10's as far as we can and then count by 1's."

- Point to the multiples of 10 as you count together.

    "How many 10's did we count?"

- Point to the digit in the tens' place.

    "And how many more did we count?"

- Point to the digit in the ones' place.

    "What number is _____ tens and _____ more?"

number pattern

- Ask your child to identify and fill in the missing numbers.
- Read the number pattern together.

clock

- Ask your child to set the morning/afternoon/evening/night clock.

- Throughout the day, your child announces the time on the hour and the half hour, sets the demonstration clock to show the time, and writes the digital time on the chalkboard.

coin cup

- Ask your child to put the pennies in groups of 10 and trade groups of 10 pennies for dimes.

- Ask your child to identify the number of dimes and the number of extra pennies and to record the total amount of money on the meeting strip.

right/left

- Continue to practice left and right once a week. Practice more often, if necessary.

THE LESSON

Writing the Number 83

"The last number we practiced writing was the number 82."

"What number do you think we will learn how to write today?"

- Write the number 83 on the chalkboard.

"What digits do you see in the number 83?"

"How many dimes and pennies will we use to make 83¢?"

- Use dimes and pennies to demonstrate.

"How many groups of 10 are in 83?"

"How many extra 1's do we have?"

"Let's count by 10's and 1's to check."

Adding Ten to a Number

"Today you will learn how to add ten to a number."

"A few days ago we used the hundred number chart to help us add ten to a number."

"Yesterday we learned a rhyme (rap) to help us add ten to a number."

"Today we will use dimes and pennies."

- Put 4 dimes and 6 pennies in a cup.

"I put 46¢ in the cup."

- Write "46¢" on the chalkboard.

480

"I used only dimes and pennies."

"I used the fewest number of pennies possible."

"How many dimes do you think are in the cup?"

"How many pennies do you think are in the cup?"

- Record the following on the chalkboard:

	dimes	pennies
46¢ =	4	6

"Let's check."

- Show your child the yellow/white mat.

"We will put the dimes on the yellow half of the paper and the pennies on the white half of the paper."

- Ask your child to sort the coins on the mat.

"Let's add ten more cents to 46¢."

- Record the following on the chalkboard:

$$46¢ + 10¢ =$$

"What could I put on the mat to show ten more cents?"   10 pennies or 1 dime

"I could add ten pennies to my mat to show the 10¢."

"What is another way that I can add ten more cents?"   add a dime

"I will add a dime because it is the quickest way to show 10¢."

- Add a dime to the yellow side of the mat.

"Did I change the number of pennies?"   no

"Did I change the number of dimes?"   yes

"How much money do you think we have now?"

"Let's count it to check."

- Record the following on the chalkboard:

$$46¢ + 10¢ = 56¢$$

"Adding ten more is just like counting by 10's."

"Which digit changed when we added ten?"   the digit on the left

"What happened to it?"   it became one more

"We can write this example another way."

- Record the following on the chalkboard:

$$46¢ + 10¢ = 56¢$$

$$\begin{array}{r} 46¢ \\ + 10¢ \\ \hline 56¢ \end{array}$$

- Put 7 dimes and 2 pennies in a cup.

"I put 72¢ in this cup."

- Write "72¢" on the chalkboard.

"I used only dimes and pennies."

"I used the fewest number of pennies possible."

"How many dimes do you think are in the cup?"

"How many pennies do you think are in the cup?"

- Record the following on the chalkboard:

	dimes	pennies
72¢ =	7	2

"Let's check."

"We will put the dimes on the yellow half of the paper and the pennies on the white half of the paper."

- Ask your child to sort the coins on the mat.

"Let's add ten more cents to 72¢."

- Record the following on the chalkboard:

$$72¢ + 10¢ =$$

"What could I put on the mat to show ten more cents?"   10 pennies or 1 dime

"I will add a dime because it is the quickest way to show 10¢."

- Add a dime to the yellow side of the mat.

"Did I change the number of pennies?"   no

"Did I change the number of dimes?"   yes

"How much money do you think we have now?"

"Let's count it to check."

- Record the following on the chalkboard:

$$72¢ + 10¢ = 82¢$$

"Adding ten more is just like counting by 10's."

"Which digit changed when we added ten?"   the digit on the left

"What happened to it?"   it became one more

"We can write this example another way."

- Record the following on the chalkboard:

$$72¢ + 10¢ = 82¢ \qquad \begin{array}{r} 72¢ \\ + 10¢ \\ \hline 82¢ \end{array}$$

- Write the following amounts on the chalkboard:

35¢   41¢   18¢   69¢

"Let's add ten cents to each of these amounts."

"How much money will we have if we add ten cents to each amount?"

- Ask your child to add mentally.
- Write your child's answer below the examples.
- Write the following on the chalkboard:

  65 + 10 =   48 + 10 =   10 + 87 =   36
                                                   + 10

  What is 10 more than 74?

  What is 10 more than 29?

- Ask your child to read the first example.

  "What is the answer?"

- Write your child's answer next to or below the example.
- Repeat with each example.

CLASS PRACTICE

"Use your individual fact cards to practice the subtraction facts."

- Give your child **Fact Sheet S 3.4**.

  "What number facts do you see?"

  "What strategies will you use to find the answers?"

- Correct the fact sheet with your child.

WRITTEN PRACTICE

- Complete **Worksheet 92A** with your child.
- Complete **Worksheet 92B** with your child later in the day.

LESSON 92A
Math 1

Name

Date

Day of the Week

1. Write the number eighty-three three more times. How many digits did you use? ___6___

   83 83

2. Write a number word that has exactly two vowels. _____

   Write another number word that has exactly two vowels. _____
   Write a number sentence to show how many letters you wrote.

   Number sentence _____

   How many letters is that? _____ letters

3. Color the pennies brown. How much money is this? ___35¢___

4. Circle the shapes that are divided into fourths (four equal pieces).

5. Show the number of lights in your classroom using tally marks.

   How many tally marks did you draw? _____

6. Add 10 to each number.

37		15		63¢	29¢	16¢
47		25		+ 10¢	+ 10¢	+ 10¢
				73¢	39¢	26¢

1-92Wa

LESSON 92B
Math 1

Name

1. Circle the largest number.
   Put an X on the smallest number.   (53) 42 50 37

2. Use the words on this side of the paper.
   Write a word that has exactly two vowels. _____

   Write another word that has exactly two vowels. _____
   Write a number sentence to show how many letters you wrote.

   Number sentence _____

   How many letters is that? _____ letters

3. Color the pennies brown. How much money is this? ___14¢___

4. Circle the shapes that are divided into halves (two equal pieces).

5. Show the number of chairs in your house using tally marks.

   How many tally marks did you draw? _____

6. Add 10 to each number.

77		11		54¢	38¢	14¢
87		21		+ 10¢	+ 10¢	+ 10¢
				64¢	48¢	24¢

1-92Wb

esson 93

writing the number 84
ordering numbers to fifty

---

lesson preparation

materials

twenty-five 3" × 5" cards

individual fact cards (addition)

Fact Sheet A 5.2

the night before

• Cut the 3" × 5" cards in half. Number the cards from 1 to 50.

in the morning

• Write the following number pattern on the meeting strip:

| ___, ___, ___, 6, 4, 2 |

Answer: 12, 10, 8, 6, 4, 2

• Put **13 pennies** in the coin cup.

THE MEETING

calendar

- Ask your child to identify the following:

  year

  month

  shapes on the calendar

  today's shape

  shape pattern for the month

- Ask your child to write the date on the calendar.

- Ask your child to do the following:

  identify today's day of the week, yesterday's day of the week, and tomorrow's day of the week

  read the days of the week

  identify the weekdays

identify the number of days in a week

- Ask your child to write the full date on the meeting strip.

weather graph

- Ask your child to report and graph the weather.

- Ask questions about the graph.

counting

- Say the "Counting by 10's Rap" on **Master 1-91** together. Point to the numbers on the hundred number chart as your child counts.

- Count by 5's to 50.

- Count by 10's to 100.

- Count backward from 100 by 10's.

- Count by 2's to 20.

- Count backward from 20 by 2's.

- Say the odd numbers to 19.

- Say the odd numbers backward from 19.

- Add another number to the number line.

   "We will count numbers on the number line by 10's as far as we can and then count by 1's."

- Point to the multiples of 10 as you count together.

   "How many 10's did we count?"

- Point to the digit in the tens' place.

   "And how many more did we count?"

- Point to the digit in the ones' place.

   "What number is _____ tens and _____ more?"

number pattern

- Ask your child to identify and fill in the missing numbers.

- Read the number pattern together.

clock

- Ask your child to set the morning/afternoon/evening/night clock.

- Throughout the day, your child announces the time on the hour and the half hour, sets the demonstration clock to show the time, and writes the digital time on the chalkboard.

coin cup

- Ask your child to put the pennies in groups of 10 and trade groups of 10 pennies for dimes.

- Ask your child to identify the number of dimes and the number of extra pennies and to record the total amount of money on the meeting strip.

right/left

- Continue to practice left and right once a week. Practice more often, if necessary.

THE LESSON

Writing the Number 84

"The last number we practiced writing was the number 83."

"What number do you think we will learn how to write today?"

- Write the number 84 on the chalkboard.

"What digits do you see in the number 84?"

"How many dimes and pennies will we use to make 84¢?"

- Use dimes and pennies to demonstrate.

"How many groups of 10 are in 84?"

"How many extra 1's do we have?"

"Let's count by 10's and 1's to check."

Ordering Numbers to Fifty

"Today you will learn how to order numbers to fifty."

- Show your child the number cards.

"I wrote the numbers from one to fifty on these cards and mixed them up."

- Give your child 2 randomly selected number cards.

"Which is the smaller number?"

"Which is the larger number?"

"Put the smaller number here and the larger number here."

- Indicate locations on the table so that at least 3 other number cards can be placed between.

- Give your child another number card.

"Where will you put this number card?"

"How do you know?"

- Ask your child to place the card in the correct location on the table.

    "Are the cards in the correct order?"

    "Let's read the numbers to check."

- Repeat with two more cards.

    "Point to a number greater than 34."

    "Point to a number less than 21."

    "Point to a number card between 20 and 35."

    "Point to the least or smallest number."

- Put these 5 cards aside.

- Repeat this activity several times using groups of 5–8 cards.

- Put the number cards in a pile.

    "Our number cards are all mixed up."

    "Let's try to put them in order."

- Allow time for your child to do this. Assist your child if necessary.

CLASS PRACTICE

"Use your individual fact cards to practice the addition facts."

- Allow time for your child to practice the addition number facts independently.

- Give your child **Fact Sheet A 5.2**.

    "What number facts do you see?"

    "What strategies will you use to find the answers?"

- Correct the fact sheet with your child.

WRITTEN PRACTICE

- Complete **Worksheet 93A** with your child.

- Complete **Worksheet 93B** with your child later in the day.

Name _____ **LESSON 93A**
Date _____ Math 1
Day of the Week _____

1. Write the number eighty-four four more times. How many digits did you use? __8__

84 84

2. Julie put five pairs of socks in the washing machine.
Draw the socks in the washing machine.
When she took the socks out of the washing machine,
she counted eight socks. What happened?
_____ She lost two socks. _____

3. Put these number cards in order from least to greatest.

| 25 | 42 | 13 | 31 |

| 13 | 25 | 31 | 42 |
least   greatest

4. Color the pennies brown. How much money is this? __16¢__

5. Draw a triangle in the second square.
Draw a circle around the sixth square.
Put an X in the middle square.
Divide the third square into halves.
Divide the fifth square into fourths.

6. Show half past eleven on the clock.

7. Write the answers.

5	3	12	7	5	9	4	7	8
+4	−1	−6	+8	+2	−0	+3	−7	+9
9	2	6	15	7	9	7	0	17

1-93Wa

Name _____ **LESSON 93B**
Math 1

1. Fill in the missing numbers.

10, 20, 30, __40__, __50__, __60__, __70__, 80, __90__, 100

2, 4, 6, __8__, __10__, __12__, __14__, __16__, __18__, __20__

2. Corrine put four pairs of socks in the washing machine.
Draw the socks in the washing machine.
When she took the socks out of the washing machine,
she counted seven socks. What happened?
_____ She lost one sock. _____

3. Put these number cards in order from least to greatest.

| 49 | 21 | 50 | 35 |

| 21 | 35 | 49 | 50 |
least   greatest

4. Color the pennies brown. How much money is this? __52¢__

5. Draw a triangle in the last square.
Draw a circle around the second square.
Put an X below the fourth square.
Divide the sixth square into fourths.
Divide the middle square into halves.

6. Show half past one on the clock.

7. Write the answers.

6	7	10	8	9	3	5	6	7
+5	−1	−5	+7	+2	−0	+4	−6	+6
11	6	5	15	11	3	9	0	13

1-93Wb

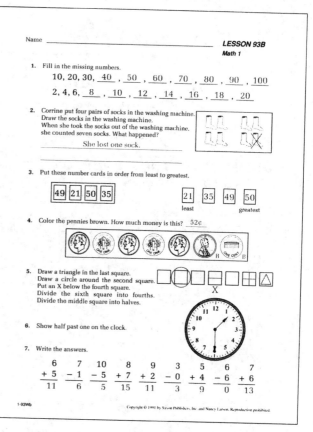

Lesson 94

writing the number 85
addition facts—sums of ten

---

lesson preparation

materials

four 3" × 5" cards
cup of 10 pennies
piece of paper
addition fact cards — blue
Fact Sheet MA 6.0

the night before

• Use the 3" × 5" cards to make a large set of fact cards for the sums of ten facts. Write them in the following way:

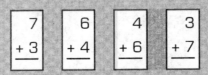

• Separate the blue addition fact cards.

in the morning

• Write the following number pattern on the meeting strip:

> 25, 30, 35, __, __, __

Answer: *25, 30, 35, 40, 45, 50*

• Put **36 pennies** in the coin cup.

THE MEETING

calendar

• Ask your child to identify the following:

year

month

shapes on the calendar

today's shape

shape pattern for the month

• Ask your child to write the date on the calendar.

• Ask your child to do the following:

> identify today's day of the week, yesterday's day of the week, and tomorrow's day of the week
>
> read the days of the week
>
> identify the weekdays
>
> identify the number of days in a week

• Ask your child to write the full date on the meeting strip.

weather graph

• Ask your child to report and graph the weather.

• Ask questions about the graph.

counting

• Say the "Counting by 10's Rap" on **Master 1-91** together. Point to the numbers on the hundred number chart as your child counts.

• Count by 5's to 50.

• Count by 10's to 100.

• Count backward from 100 by 10's.

• Count by 2's to 20.

• Count backward from 20 by 2's.

• Say the odd numbers to 19.

• Say the odd numbers backward from 19.

• Add another number to the number line.

"We will count numbers on the number line by 10's as far as we can and then count by 1's."

• Point to the multiples of 10 as you count together.

"How many 10's did we count?"

• Point to the digit in the tens' place.

"And how many more did we count?"

• Point to the digit in the ones' place.

"What number is _____ tens and _____ more?"

number pattern

• Ask your child to identify and fill in the missing numbers.

• Read the number pattern together.

clock

- Ask your child to set the morning/afternoon/evening/night clock.

- Throughout the day, your child announces the time on the hour and the half hour, sets the demonstration clock to show the time, and writes the digital time on the chalkboard.

coin cup

- Ask your child to put the pennies in groups of 10 and trade groups of 10 pennies for dimes.

- Ask your child to identify the number of dimes and the number of extra pennies and to record the total amount of money on the meeting strip.

right/left

- Continue to practice left and right once a week. Practice more often, if necessary.

THE LESSON

Writing the Number 85

"The last number we practiced writing was the number 84."

"What number do you think we will learn how to write today?"

- Write the number 85 on the chalkboard.

"What digits do you see in the number 85?"

"How many dimes and pennies will we use to make 85¢?"

- Use dimes and pennies to demonstrate.

"How many groups of 10 are in 85?"

"How many extra 1's do we have?"

"Let's count by 10's and 1's to check."

Addition Facts — Sums of Ten

"What addition number fact strategies have we learned?"   doubles, *adding one, adding two, adding zero, doubles plus one*

"Today you will learn the addition facts called the sums of ten facts."

"We will use a paper that has two equal parts."

- Give your child a piece of paper.

"Fold this paper to make two equal parts."

- Ask your child to do this.

- Put the paper on the table like this:

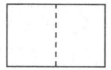

"Put the pennies from your cup on the paper."

"Count them to make sure that you have exactly ten pennies."

"We can arrange the pennies on the paper in different ways."

"Put some of the pennies on the left half of the paper and some of the pennies on the right half of the paper."

"How many pennies are on each half of your paper?"

"Let's try to make an organized list of all of the ways we could put ten pennies on the paper."

"We will begin by putting no pennies on the left half of the paper and all of the rest of the pennies on the right half."

- Allow time for your child to do this.

"How many pennies are on the left half of your paper?"   *0*

"How many pennies are on the right half of your paper?"   *10*

"How will we write a number sentence to show what you have on your paper?"

- Record "0 + 10 = 10" on the chalkboard.

"Now put one penny on the left half of the paper and all of the rest of the pennies on the right half."

- Allow time for your child to do this.

"How many pennies are on the right half of your paper now?"   *9*

"How will we write a number sentence to show what you have on your paper?"

- Record "1 + 9 = 10" on the chalkboard.

"Now put two pennies on the left half of the paper and all of the rest of the pennies on the right half."

- Allow time for your child to do this.

"How many pennies are on the right half of your paper now?"   *8*

"What number sentence will we write to show what you have on your paper?"   *2 + 8 = 10*

- Repeat, using 3, 4, 5, 6, 7, 8, 9, and 10 pennies on the left half of the mat.

"Which number facts use the same numbers?"   *1 + 9 and 9 + 1, etc.*

"We call these switcharound facts."

"Why do you think we call them that?"   *they use the same numbers, the numbers switch places*

• Put the paper on the table like this:

"Put ten pennies on the top half of the paper and all of the rest of the pennies on the bottom half."

• Allow time for your child to do this.

"How many pennies are on the bottom half of your paper?"   *0*

"How will we write a number sentence to show what you have on your paper?"

• Record the following on the chalkboard:

$$\begin{array}{r} 10 \\ +\ 0 \\ \hline 10 \end{array}$$

"When we write our number sentence like this, we write the plus sign in front of the bottom number and draw a line instead of using an equal sign."

"Now put nine pennies on the top half of the paper and all of the rest of the pennies on the bottom half."

• Allow time for your child to do this.

"How many pennies are on the bottom half of your paper now?"   *1*

"What number sentence will we write to show what you have on your paper?"

• Write the following on the chalkboard:

$$\begin{array}{r} 9 \\ +\ 1 \\ \hline 10 \end{array}$$

"Now put eight pennies on the top half of the paper and all of the rest of the pennies on the bottom half."

"How many pennies are on the bottom half of your paper now?"   *2*

"What number sentence will we write to show what you have on your paper now?"

• Write the following on the chalkboard:

$$\begin{array}{r} 8 \\ +\ 2 \\ \hline 10 \end{array}$$

• Repeat, using 7, 6, 5, 4, 3, 2, 1, and 0 pennies on the top half of the paper.

"Which facts look the same?"

"What do we call these facts?"   *switcharound facts*

"Mathematicians say that the switcharound facts are examples of the commutative property of addition."

- Write the following on the chalkboard:

$$\begin{array}{r} 4 \\ + \square \\ \hline 10 \end{array}$$

   "This means four plus some number is ten."

   "What is the missing number?"

   "Let's use the pennies to check."

   "Begin with ten pennies."

   "Put four pennies on the top half of your paper."

   "Put all the other pennies on the bottom half of the paper."

- Allow time for your child to do this.

   "How many pennies do you think are on the bottom half of the paper?"

   "Let's count to check."

- Fill in the missing number on the chalkboard problem.

- Write the following on the chalkboard:

$$\begin{array}{r} \square \\ + 1 \\ \hline 10 \end{array}$$

   "What is the missing number?"

   "Let's use the pennies to check."

   "How will we do that?"

   "Begin with ten pennies."

   "Put one penny on the bottom half of your paper."

   "Put all the other pennies on the top half of the paper."

- Allow time for your child to do this.

   "How many pennies do you think are on the top half of the paper?"

   "Let's count to check."

- Fill in the missing number on the chalkboard problem.

- Write the following on the chalkboard:

$$\square + 3 = 10$$

   "What is the missing number?"

   "Let's use the pennies to check."

   "Begin with ten pennies."

   "Put three pennies on the right half of the paper."

   "Put all the other pennies on the left half of the paper."

- Allow time for your child to do this.

   "How many pennies do you think are on the left half of the paper?"

   "Let's count to check."

- Fill in the missing number on the chalkboard problem.

- Write the following on the chalkboard:

$$8 + \square = 10$$

"What is the missing number?"

"Let's use the pennies to check."

"How will we do that?"

"Begin with ten pennies."

"Put eight pennies on the left half of your paper."

"Put all the other pennies on the right half of the paper."

- Allow time for your child to do this.

"How many pennies do you think are on the right half of the paper?"

"Let's count to check."

- Fill in the missing number on the chalkboard problem.

- Repeat with the following:

$$2 + \boxed{} = 10 \qquad \boxed{} + 6 = 10$$

$$\begin{array}{r} 9 \\ + \boxed{} \\ \hline 10 \end{array} \qquad \begin{array}{r} \boxed{} \\ + 5 \\ \hline 10 \end{array}$$

"Put the pennies in your cup."

- Give your child the blue addition fact cards.

"What are the answers for all of these addition facts?"   *10*

"The answer for an addition problem is called the sum."

"We will call these the sums of ten facts because the answers are always ten."

"Write the answer on the back of each card."

"Put these fact cards with your other fact cards."

CLASS PRACTICE

- Give your child **Fact Sheet MA 6.0**.

"This is a different type of fact sheet."

"We know that all the answers are ten."

"Fill in each missing number to make a sum of ten."

- If necessary, allow your child to use a cup of 10 pennies to find the missing numbers.

- Correct the fact sheet with your child.

WRITTEN PRACTICE

- Complete **Worksheet 94A** with your child.

- Complete **Worksheet 94B** with your child later in the day.

LESSON 94A
Math 1

Name _____

Date _____

Day of the Week _____

1. Write the number eighty-five three more times. How many digits did you use? __6__

85 ̶3̶5̶ _____

2. Christa had 41¢. Show this using the fewest number of dimes and pennies.
Color the pennies brown.

(D) (D) (D) (D) (P)ᴮ (D)

She found another dime. Draw the dime.
How much money does Christa have now? __51¢__

3. Someone made a mistake when they put these number cards in order. Circle a number card that you would move so that the number cards will be in order.

[7] [12] [16] [24] [21] [27] [35]
 Y   Y   Y

answers may vary

4. Color the even numbers yellow in Problem 3.

5. Fill in the missing numbers.

$\begin{array}{r} 2 \\ +\boxed{8} \\ \hline 10 \end{array}$ $\begin{array}{r} \boxed{3} \\ +7 \\ \hline 10 \end{array}$ $\begin{array}{r} 5 \\ +\boxed{5} \\ \hline 10 \end{array}$ $\begin{array}{r} \boxed{9} \\ +1 \\ \hline 10 \end{array}$ $\begin{array}{r} \boxed{6} \\ +4 \\ \hline 10 \end{array}$ $\begin{array}{r} 10 \\ +\boxed{0} \\ \hline 10 \end{array}$

6. Ask exactly 10 people whether they like the color red or the color blue better. Show their choice on this graph.

red
blue

Which color did most of the people you asked like better? _____

1-94Wa

LESSON 94B
Math 1

Name _____

1. Write a number that is between 29 and 35 when you count by 1's.

29 [ ] 35   answers may vary

2. Dan had 32¢. Show this using the fewest number of dimes and pennies.
Color the pennies brown.

(D) (D) (D) (P)ᴮ (P)ᴮ (D)

He found another dime. Draw the dime.
How much money does Dan have now? __42¢__

3. Someone made a mistake when they put these number cards in order. Circle the number card that you would move so that the number cards will be in order.

[8] [14] [18] (17) [23] [29] [34]
 Y   Y   Y   Y

4. Color the even numbers yellow in Problem 3.

5. Fill in the missing numbers.

$\begin{array}{r} 2 \\ +8 \\ \hline 10 \end{array}$ $\begin{array}{r} 3 \\ +\boxed{7} \\ \hline 10 \end{array}$ $\begin{array}{r} \boxed{5} \\ +5 \\ \hline 10 \end{array}$ $\begin{array}{r} 9 \\ +\boxed{1} \\ \hline 10 \end{array}$ $\begin{array}{r} 6 \\ +4 \\ \hline 10 \end{array}$ $\begin{array}{r} \boxed{10} \\ +0 \\ \hline 10 \end{array}$

6. Ask exactly 10 people whether they like cats or dogs better. Show their choice on this graph.

dogs
cats

Which pet did most of the people you asked like better? _____

1-94Wb

esson 95

writing the number 86
counting by 100's

---

lesson preparation ————————————————

materials

Written Assessment #18

5 bags of 100 pennies (save for Lesson 111)

Masters 1-84A and 1-84B (from Lesson 84)

Meeting Book

Fact Sheet MA 6.0

in the morning

• Write the following number pattern on the meeting strip:

> ___, ___, ___, 15, 16, 17

Answer: *12, 13, 14, 15, 16, 17*

• Put **31 pennies** in the coin cup.

THE MEETING

calendar

• Ask your child to identify the following:

  year

  month

  shapes on the calendar

  today's shape

  shape pattern for the month

• Ask your child to write the date on the calendar.

• Ask your child to do the following:

  identify today's day of the week, yesterday's day of the week, and tomorrow's day of the week

  read the days of the week

  identify the weekdays

identify the number of days in a week

- Ask your child to write the full date on the meeting strip.

weather graph

- Ask your child to report and graph the weather.

- Ask questions about the graph.

counting

- Say the "Counting by 10's Rap" on **Master 1-91** together. Point to the numbers on the hundred number chart as your child counts.

- Count by 5's to 50.

- Count by 10's to 100.

- Count backward from 100 by 10's.

- Count by 2's to 20.

- Count backward from 20 by 2's.

- Say the odd numbers to 19.

- Say the odd numbers backward from 19.

- Add another number to the number line.

    "We will count numbers on the number line by 10's as far as we can and then count by 1's."

- Point to the multiples of 10 as you count together.

    "How many 10's did we count?"

- Point to the digit in the tens' place.

    "And how many more did we count?"

- Point to the digit in the ones' place.

    "What number is _____ tens and _____ more?"

number pattern

- Ask your child to identify and fill in the missing numbers.

- Read the number pattern together.

clock

- Ask your child to set the morning/afternoon/evening/night clock.

- Throughout the day, your child announces the time on the hour and the half hour, sets the demonstration clock to show the time, and writes the digital time on the chalkboard.

coin cup

- Ask your child to put the pennies in groups of 10 and trade groups of 10 pennies for dimes.

- Ask your child to identify the number of dimes and the number of extra pennies and to record the total amount of money on the meeting strip.

right/left

- Continue to practice left and right once a week. Practice more often, if necessary.

ASSESSMENT

Written Assessment

- Give your child **Written Assessment #18**.

- Read the directions for each problem. Allow time for your child to complete each problem before continuing to the next.

- Correct the paper, noting your child's mistakes on the **Individual Recording Form**. Review the errors with your child.

THE LESSON

Writing the Number 86

"The last number we practiced writing was the number 85."

"What number do you think we will learn how to write today?"

- Write the number 86 on the chalkboard.

"What digits do you see in the number 86?"

"How many dimes and pennies will we use to make 86¢?"

- Use dimes and pennies to demonstrate.

"How many groups of 10 are in 86?"

"How many extra 1's do we have?"

"Let's count by 10's and 1's to check."

Counting by 100's

"Today you will learn how to count by 100's."

- Show your child 5 bags of 100 pennies each.

"I have some bags of pennies."

"All the bags have the same number of pennies."

"How many pennies do you think are in each of these bags?"

"Let's count one bag to check."

- Give your child a bag of pennies and **Masters 1-84A** and **1-84B** to use to group the pennies.

- Allow time for your child to group and count the pennies.

"Put the pennies back in the bag."

- Allow time for your child to do this.

"Each of these bags has 100 pennies."

"I will put a tag on each bag that says 100 pennies."

- Put a tag or piece of tape labeled with the number 100 on each bag.

"When we count groups of 100, we say that we are counting by 100's."

"Let's count by 100's to find out how many pennies we have altogether."

- Count by 100's with your child as you point to each bag of pennies.

"Each morning we will practice counting by 100's."

"Let's count by 100's together slowly."

"I will write the numbers we say on a counting strip in the Meeting Book."

- Write the numbers from 0 to 1,000 as you count by 100's. Begin at the bottom of the strip and work upward.

"Instead of saying 'ten hundred,' we say 'one thousand.' "

- Write the number 1,000 at the top of the counting strip.

- Hold up 3 bags of pennies.

"How many pennies do I have altogether?" 300

"Let's count to check."

- Count by 100's as you point to each bag of pennies.

- Write "200" on the chalkboard.

"How will we show 200 pennies?" use two bags of pennies

- Hold up 2 bags of pennies.

"Let's count by 100's to check."

- Count by 100's as you point to each bag of pennies.

"How many bags of 100 pennies did we use to show 200 pennies?" 2

- Repeat with 500, 300, and 400.

- Save the bags of pennies for use in Lessons 111 and 126.

CLASS PRACTICE

"Let's practice the sums of ten facts."

"I will write a number from zero to ten on the chalkboard."

"Tell me the number we will add to it to equal ten."

• Practice until each number has been used several times.

• Give your child **Fact Sheet MA 6.0**.

"All of these answers are ten."

"Fill in each missing number to make a sum of ten."

• Correct the fact sheet with your child.

WRITTEN PRACTICE

• Complete **Worksheet 95A** with your child.

• Complete **Worksheet 95B** with your child later in the day.

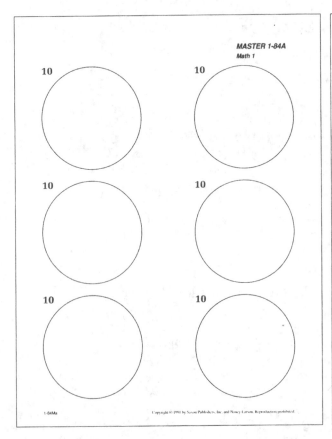

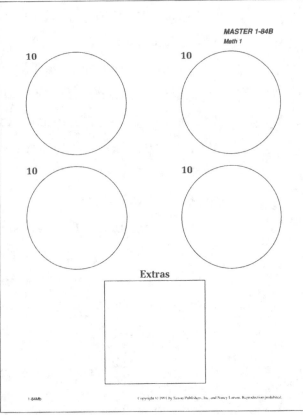

Name _____ **ASSESSMENT 18**
Date _____ **LESSON 95**
                                Math 1

1. There were four books on the table. Patty put three of the books in the closet. Draw a picture and write a number sentence to show how many books are on the table now.

Number sentence _____ 4 − 3 = 1 _____
How many books are on the table now? __1__ book

2. How many more children cut out pink hearts than red hearts?

___2___ children

Hearts

red
pink

3. Julie put her pennies in groups of 10.

How many pennies does she have? __32__

How much money is this? __32¢__

Extras

4. Fill in the answers.

6 + 5 = __11__   9 + 8 = __17__   6 + 7 = __13__
4 + 5 = __9__   8 + 7 = __15__   3 + 4 = __7__

5. Tim's receipt at the classroom store looked like this.
How much money did he spend for the two items? __56¢__
How many dimes is that? __5__
How many pennies is that? __6__

eggs		43	¢
rolls	+	13	¢
Total		56	¢

1-95Aa

Copyright © 1991 by Saxon Publishers, Inc. and Nancy Larson. Reproduction prohibited.

Name _____ **LESSON 95A**
                                Math 1
Date _____

Day of the Week _____

1. Write the number eighty-six four more times. How many digits are on the line? __12__

86 86

2. Write a story for the number sentence **6 − 2 = 4**.

_____

3. Fill in the missing numbers.

100, 200, 300, _400_, _500_, _600_, _700_, _800_, _900_

45, 44, 43, _42_, _41_, _40_, _39_, _38_, _37_

5, 10, 15, _20_, _25_, _30_, _35_, _40_, _45_

4. Color the congruent shapes blue.

B   B

5. Find the total on each receipt.

24	¢
+ 51	¢
75	¢

__7__ dimes __5__ pennies

35	¢
+ 42	¢
77	¢

__7__ dimes __7__ pennies

16	¢
+ 41	¢
57	¢

__5__ dimes __7__ pennies

1-95Wa

Copyright © 1991 by Saxon Publishers, Inc. and Nancy Larson. Reproduction prohibited.

Name _____ **LESSON 95B**
                                Math 1

1. Color the first book red.
Color the sixth book blue.
Color the third book green.
Color the seventh book yellow.
Color the fifth book orange.

R   G   O   B   Y

2. Write a story for the number sentence **9 − 1 = 8**.

_____

3. Fill in the missing numbers.

200, 300, 400, _500_, _600_, _700_, _800_, _900_

26, 27, 28, _29_, _30_, _31_, _32_, _33_, _34_

45, 40, 35, _30_, _25_, _20_, _15_, _10_, _5_

4. Color the congruent shapes blue (same size and shape).

B   B

5. Find the total on each receipt.

60	¢
+ 28	¢
88	¢

__8__ dimes __8__ pennies

16	¢
+ 52	¢
68	¢

__6__ dimes __8__ pennies

43	¢
+ 13	¢
56	¢

__5__ dimes __6__ pennies

1-95Wb

Copyright © 1991 by Saxon Publishers, Inc. and Nancy Larson. Reproduction prohibited.

---

esson 96

writing the number 87
drawing congruent shapes and designs

---

lesson preparation

materials

2 geoboards

7 geobands

Master 1-96A (2 copies)

Fact Sheet MA 6.0

in the morning

• Write the following number pattern on the meeting strip:

> 54, 53, 52, ___, ___, ___

> *Answer: 54, 53, 52, 51, 50, 49*

• Put **15 pennies** in the coin cup.

THE MEETING

calendar

- Ask your child to identify the following:

    year

    month

    shapes on the calendar

    today's shape

    shape pattern for the month

- Ask your child to write the date on the calendar.

- Ask your child to do the following:

    identify today's day of the week, yesterday's day of the week, and tomorrow's day of the week

    read the days of the week

    identify the weekdays

    identify the number of days in a week

• Ask your child to write the full date on the meeting strip.

weather graph

• Ask your child to report and graph the weather.

• Ask questions about the graph.

counting

• Say the "Counting by 10's Rap" on **Master 1-91** together. Point to the numbers on the hundred number chart as your child counts.

"Let's count by 100's to 1000."

• Count by 5's to 50.

• Count by 10's to 100.

• Count backward from 100 by 10's.

• Count by 2's to 20.

• Count backward from 20 by 2's.

• Say the odd numbers to 19.

• Say the odd numbers backward from 19.

• Add another number to the number line.

"We will count numbers on the number line by 10's as far as we can and then count by 1's."

• Point to the multiples of 10 as you count together.

"How many 10's did we count?"

• Point to the digit in the tens' place.

"And how many more did we count?"

• Point to the digit in the ones' place.

"What number is _____ tens and _____ more?"

number pattern

• Ask your child to identify and fill in the missing numbers.

• Read the number pattern together.

clock

• Ask your child to set the morning/afternoon/evening/night clock.

• Throughout the day, your child announces the time on the hour and the half hour, sets the demonstration clock to show the time, and writes the digital time on the chalkboard.

coin cup

- Ask your child to put the pennies in groups of 10 and trade groups of 10 pennies for dimes.

- Ask your child to identify the number of dimes and the number of extra pennies and to record the total amount of money on the meeting strip.

right/left

- Continue to practice left and right once a week. Practice more often, if necessary.

THE LESSON

Writing the Number 87

"The last number we practiced writing was the number 86."

"What number do you think we will learn how to write today?"

- Write the number 87 on the chalkboard.

"What digits do you see in the number 87?"

"How many dimes and pennies will we use to make 87¢?"

- Use dimes and pennies to demonstrate.

"How many groups of 10 are in 87?"

"How many extra 1's do we have?"

"Let's count by 10's and 1's to check."

Drawing Congruent Shapes and Designs

"Today you will learn how to draw congruent shapes and designs."

- Give your child 1 geoboard, 4 geobands, and 2 copies of **Master 1-96A.**

- Make a triangle like the following on your geoboard. Use 3 geobands.

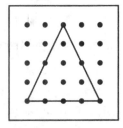

- Show your child the geoboard.

"I made a triangle on my geoboard."

"Make a congruent triangle on your geoboard."

- Allow time for your child to copy the triangle.

"How do you know that the triangles are congruent?" they are exactly the same size and shape

"Now you will draw a congruent triangle on geodot paper."

"How do you think you will do that?"

"Circle the pegs on your geodot paper that are the endpoints of the sides."

- Allow time for your child to do this.

"Now you will draw line segments to show the bands."

- Allow time for your child to draw the line segments. Your child may use a ruler for drawing the line segments, if desired.

"Does your triangle on the geodot paper look just like your geoboard triangle?"

"You have drawn a congruent triangle."

"Take the geobands off your geoboard."

"Make a rectangle on your geoboard using four geobands."

- Allow time for your child to make a rectangle.

"How will you draw a congruent rectangle on your geodot paper?" circle the endpoints and draw line segments

"Draw a congruent rectangle on your geodot paper."

"When you finish, put your geodot paper next to your geoboard so we can see that the rectangles are congruent."

- Allow time for your child to draw the rectangle on the geodot paper.

"Take the geobands off your geoboard."

"Now make any shape or design on your geoboard."

- Allow time for your child to make a shape or design.

"Make a congruent shape or design on your geodot paper."

"When you finish, put your geodot paper next to your geoboard so we can see that the shapes or designs are congruent."

- Provide time for your child to make one more shape or design, if desired.

CLASS PRACTICE

"Let's practice the sums of ten facts."

"I will write a number from zero to ten on the chalkboard."

"Tell me the number we will add to it to equal ten."

- Practice until each number has been used several times.

- Give your child **Fact Sheet MA 6.0**.

  "All of these answers are ten."

  "Fill in each missing number to make a sum of ten."

- Correct the fact sheet with your child.

WRITTEN PRACTICE

- Complete **Worksheet 96A** with your child.

- Complete **Worksheet 96B** with your child later in the day.

MASTER 1-96A
Name _____ **MASTER 1-96A**
Math 1

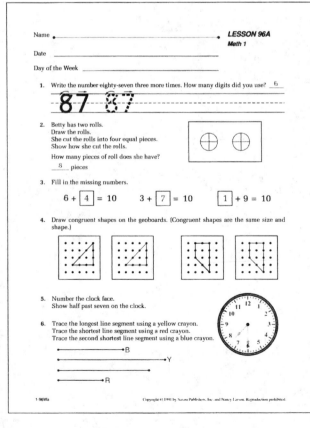

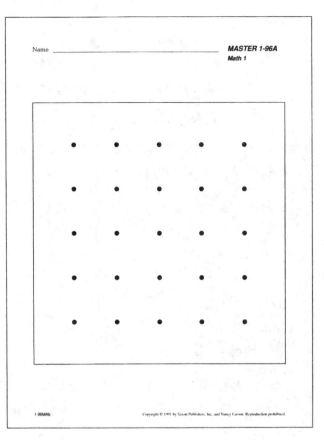

Name _____ **MASTER 1-96A**
Math 1

Name _____ **LESSON 96A**
Math 1

Date _____

Day of the Week _____

1. Write the number eighty-seven three more times. How many digits did you use? __6__

   87 87

2. Betty has two rolls.
   Draw the rolls.
   She cut the rolls into four equal pieces.
   Show how she cut the rolls.

   How many pieces of roll does she have?
   __8__ pieces

3. Fill in the missing numbers.

   $6 + \boxed{4} = 10$ $3 + \boxed{7} = 10$ $\boxed{1} + 9 = 10$

4. Draw congruent shapes on the geoboards. (Congruent shapes are the same size and shape.)

5. Number the clock face.
   Show half past seven on the clock.

6. Trace the longest line segment using a yellow crayon.
   Trace the shortest line segment using a red crayon.
   Trace the second shortest line segment using a blue crayon.

Name _____ **LESSON 96B**
Math 1

1. Fill in the missing numbers.

   25, 24, 23, _22_ , _21_ , _20_ , _19_ , _18_ , _17_ , _16_

   1, 3, 5, _7_ , _9_ , _11_ , _13_ , _15_ , _17_ , _19_

2. Justin has three rolls.
   Draw the rolls.
   He cut the rolls into two equal pieces.
   Show how he cut the rolls.

   How many pieces of roll does he have now?
   __6__ pieces

3. Fill in the missing numbers.

   $\boxed{3} + 7 = 10$ $1 + \boxed{9} = 10$ $\boxed{8} + 2 = 10$

4. Draw congruent shapes on the geoboards.
   (Congruent shapes are the same size and shape.)

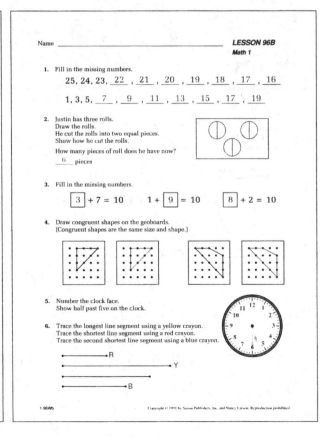

5. Number the clock face.
   Show half past five on the clock.

6. Trace the longest line segment using a yellow crayon.
   Trace the shortest line segment using a red crayon.
   Trace the second shortest line segment using a blue crayon.

L esson 97

writing the number 88
measuring to the nearest inch using a ruler

---

lesson preparation

materials

ruler

Master 1-97

ribbon or string

one 3" × 5" card

tape

Fact Sheet MA 6.0

the night before

• Tape a 1" and a 3" piece of ribbon or string to the 3" × 5" card.

in the morning

• Write the following number pattern on the meeting strip:

> ___, ___, ___, 21, 22, 23

Answer: 18, 19, 20, 21, 22, 23

• Put **32 pennies** in the coin cup.

THE MEETING

calendar

• Ask your child to identify the following:

  year

  month

  shapes on the calendar

  today's shape

  shape pattern for the month

• Ask your child to write the date on the calendar.

- Ask your child to do the following:

    identify today's day of the week, yesterday's day of the week, and tomorrow's day of the week

    read the days of the week

    identify the weekdays

    identify the number of days in a week

- Ask your child to write the full date on the meeting strip.

weather graph

- Ask your child to report and graph the weather.

- Ask questions about the graph.

counting

- Say the "Counting by 10's Rap" on **Master 1-91** together. Point to the numbers on the hundred number chart as your child counts.

    "Let's count by 100's to 1000."

- Count by 5's to 50.

- Count by 10's to 100.

- Count backward from 100 by 10's.

- Count by 2's to 20.

- Count backward from 20 by 2's.

- Say the odd numbers to 19.

- Say the odd numbers backward from 19.

- Add another number to the number line.

    "We will count numbers on the number line by 10's as far as we can and then count by 1's."

- Point to the multiples of 10 as you count together.

    "How many 10's did we count?"

- Point to the digit in the tens' place.

    "And how many more did we count?"

- Point to the digit in the ones' place.

    "What number is _____ tens and _____ more?"

number pattern

- Ask your child to identify and fill in the missing numbers.

- Read the number pattern together.

clock

- Ask your child to set the morning/afternoon/evening/night clock.

- Throughout the day, your child announces the time on the hour and the half hour, sets the demonstration clock to show the time, and writes the digital time on the chalkboard.

coin cup

- Ask your child to put the pennies in groups of 10 and trade groups of 10 pennies for dimes.

- Ask your child to identify the number of dimes and the number of extra pennies and to record the total amount of money on the meeting strip.

right/left

- Continue to practice left and right once a week. Practice more often, if necessary.

THE LESSON

Writing the Number 88

"The last number we practiced writing was the number 87."

"What number do you think we will learn how to write today?"

- Write the number 88 on the chalkboard.

"What digits do you see in the number 88?"

"How many dimes and pennies will we use to make 88¢?"

- Use dimes and pennies to demonstrate.

"How many groups of 10 are in 88?"

"How many extra 1's do we have?"

"Let's count by 10's and 1's to check."

Measuring to the Nearest Inch Using a Ruler

"We have been drawing line segments using a ruler."

"Today you will learn how to measure line segments to the nearest inch using a ruler."

- Give your child an inch/cm ruler.

"What do you see on your ruler?"   numbers

"Are both sides of the ruler the same?"

"How are they different?"

"Today we will use the side of the ruler that has the numbers up to twelve."

"This is called the inch side of the ruler."

"Point to the left end of the ruler."

"Do you see a number at the end?"

"Usually we don't see the zero at the beginning of the ruler."

"Point to the numbers on the inch side of the ruler as we count them together."

- Count by 1's to 12 as your child points to each inch mark on the ruler.

- Give your child the card with the 1" and 3" pieces of ribbon or string.

"Let's measure the shorter ribbon."

"Put the left end of your ruler at the left end of the ribbon."

"Remember that the end of your ruler must be exactly at the end of the ribbon."

"What number on the ruler do you see near the other end of the ribbon?"   *1*

"Each one of the numbers on the ruler tells us one inch."

"We can say that the ribbon is one inch long."

"Let's measure the longer ribbon."

"How will we do this?"

- Ask your child to repeat the steps.

"Put the left end of your ruler at the left end of the ribbon."

"Remember that the end of your ruler must be exactly at the end of the ribbon."

"What number on the ruler do you see near the other end of the ribbon?"   *3*

"How long is this ribbon?"   *3"*

"We say that the ribbon is three inches long."

- Give your child **Master 1-97**.

"Now you will measure these line segments using the inch side of your ruler."

"Find line segment number one."

"Point to the inch side of your ruler."

"Put the left end of the ruler on the endpoint near the one."

"Now look along the ruler until you come to the next endpoint."

"What number do you see on the ruler near the other end of the line segment?"   *2*

"Write the number in the space next to the end of the line segment."

"How many inches long is line segment number one?"   *2*

"Find line segment number two."

"Put the left end of the ruler on the endpoint near the two."

"Now look along the ruler until you come to the next endpoint."

"What number do you see on the ruler near the other end of the line segment?" 5

"Write the number in the space next to the end of the line."

"How many inches long is line segment number two?" 5

- Repeat with line segment numbers 3, 4, and 5. *3", 4", 7"*

"Now you will measure the length of your hand."

"Turn over your paper."

"Trace your hand."

"Draw a line across the bottom where your wrist is."

"We will use the inch side of the ruler."

"Put the beginning of your ruler on your wrist line."

"Now find how long it is to the tip of your longest finger."

"Make sure that you keep the beginning of your ruler on your wrist line."

"The end of your longest finger is closest to what number on the ruler?"

"Write that number next to your hand."

"How many inches long is your hand?"

CLASS PRACTICE

"Let's practice the sums of ten facts."

"I will write a number from zero to ten on the chalkboard."

"Tell me the number we will add to it to equal ten."

- Practice until each number has been used several times.
- Give your child **Fact Sheet MA 6.0**.

"All of these answers are ten."

"Fill in each missing number to make a sum of ten."

- Correct the fact sheet with your child.

WRITTEN PRACTICE

- Complete **Worksheet 97A** with your child.
- Complete **Worksheet 97B** with your child later in the day.

Name _____ **MASTER 1-97**
                                        Math 1

1. •————————• _____ inches

2. •————————————• _____ inches

3. •————————• _____ inches

4. •
         \
          \
           \
            • _____ inches

                              •
                            /
                          /
                        /
                      /
      _____ inches /
                  /
                /
5. •

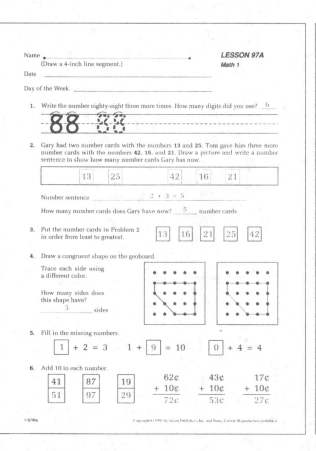

Name •—————————————————• **LESSON 97A**
     (Draw a 4-inch line segment.)   *Math 1*

Date _____

Day of the Week _____

1. Write the number eighty-eight three more times. How many digits did you use? __6__

   88 88 88

2. Gary had two number cards with the numbers **13** and **25**. Tom gave him three more number cards with the numbers **42**, **16**, and **21**. Draw a picture and write a number sentence to show how many number cards Gary has now.

   | 13 | 25 | | 42 | 16 | 21 |

   Number sentence _____2 + 3 = 5_____

   How many number cards does Gary have now? __5__ number cards

3. Put the number cards in Problem 2 in order from least to greatest.   13 16 21 25 42

4. Draw a congruent shape on the geoboard.

   Trace each side using a different color.

   How many sides does this shape have?
   ___5___ sides

5. Fill in the missing numbers.

   1 + 2 = 3   1 + 9 = 10   0 + 4 = 4

6. Add 10 to each number.

   | 41 | 87 | 19 | 62¢   43¢   17¢
   | 51 | 97 | 29 | + 10¢   + 10¢   + 10¢
                         72¢   53¢   27¢

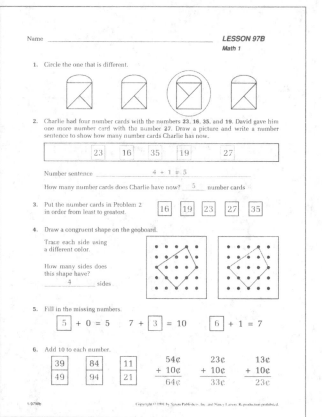

Name _____ **LESSON 97B**
                                        Math 1

1. Circle the one that is different.

2. Charlie had four number cards with the numbers **23**, **16**, **35**, and **19**. David gave him one more number card with the number **27**. Draw a picture and write a number sentence to show how many number cards Charlie has now.

   | 23 | 16 | 35 | 19 | | 27 |

   Number sentence _____4 + 1 = 5_____

   How many number cards does Charlie have now? __5__ number cards

3. Put the number cards in Problem 2 in order from least to greatest.   16 19 23 27 35

4. Draw a congruent shape on the geoboard.

   Trace each side using a different color.

   How many sides does this shape have?
   ___4___ sides

5. Fill in the missing numbers.

   5 + 0 = 5   7 + 3 = 10   6 + 1 = 7

6. Add 10 to each number.

   | 39 | 84 | 11 | 54¢   23¢   13¢
   | 49 | 94 | 21 | + 10¢   + 10¢   + 10¢
                         64¢   33¢   23¢

L esson 98

writing the number 89
subtraction facts—subtracting two from a
number

---

lesson preparation

materials

11 linking cubes

subtraction fact cards — green

Fact Sheet S 4.0

the night before

• Separate the green subtraction fact cards.

in the morning

• Write the following number pattern on the meeting strip:

> ___, ___, ___, 5, 3, 1

Answer: 11, 9, 7, 5, 3, 1

• Put **24 pennies** in the coin cup.

THE MEETING

calendar

- • Ask your child to identify the following:

  year

  month

  shapes on the calendar

  today's shape

  shape pattern for the month

- • Ask your child to write the date on the calendar.

- • Ask your child to do the following:

  identify today's day of the week, yesterday's day of the week, and tomorrow's day of the week

  read the days of the week

identify the weekdays

identify the number of days in a week

- Ask your child to write the full date on the meeting strip.

weather graph

- Ask your child to report and graph the weather.
- Ask questions about the graph.

counting

- Say the "Counting by 10's Rap" on **Master 1-91** together. Point to the numbers on the hundred number chart as your child counts.

    "Let's count by 100's to 1000."

- Count by 5's to 50.
- Count by 10's to 100.
- Count backward from 100 by 10's.
- Count by 2's to 20.
- Count backward from 20 by 2's.
- Say the odd numbers to 19.
- Say the odd numbers backward from 19.
- Add another number to the number line.

    "We will count numbers on the number line by 10's as far as we can and then count by 1's."

- Point to the multiples of 10 as you count together.

    "How many 10's did we count?"

- Point to the digit in the tens' place.

    "And how many more did we count?"

- Point to the digit in the ones' place.

    "What number is _____ tens and _____ more?"

number pattern

- Ask your child to identify and fill in the missing numbers.
- Read the number pattern together.

clock

- Ask your child to set the morning/afternoon/evening/night clock.
- Throughout the day, your child announces the time on the hour and the half hour, sets the demonstration clock to show the time, and writes the digital time on the chalkboard.

coin cup

- Ask your child to put the pennies in groups of 10 and trade groups of 10 pennies for dimes.

- Ask your child to identify the number of dimes and the number of extra pennies and to record the total amount of money on the meeting strip.

right/left

- Continue to practice left and right once a week. Practice more often, if necessary.

THE LESSON

Writing the Number 89

"The last number we practiced writing was the number 88."

"What number do you think we will learn how to write today?"

- Write the number 89 on the chalkboard.

"What digits do you see in the number 89?"

"How many dimes and pennies will we use to make 89¢?"

- Use dimes and pennies to demonstrate.

"How many groups of 10 are in 89?"

"How many extra 1's do we have?"

"Let's count by 10's and 1's to check."

Subtraction Facts—Subtracting Two from a Number

"Today you will learn how to subtract two from a number."

- Give your child 11 linking cubes.

- Write "1 + 2 =" on the chalkboard.

"What does this problem tell us to do?"   *take one linking cube and add two more*

"Show that using your linking cubes."

"How many linking cubes do you have now?"   *3*

- Record the answer on the chalkboard.

"You have three linking cubes."

- Write "3 + 2 =" on the chalkboard.

"What does this problem tell us to do?"   *add two more cubes*

"Add two more."

"How many linking cubes do you have now?"   *5*

- Record the answer on the chalkboard.

"You have five linking cubes."

- Write "5 + 2 =" on the chalkboard.

"What does this problem tell us to do?"   add two more cubes

"Add two more."

"How many linking cubes do you have now?"   7

- Record the answer on the chalkboard.
- Repeat to a sum of 11.
- Circle the first number in each problem.

"What types of numbers are these?"   odd numbers

"What happened when we added two?"   the answer was the next odd number

"You have eleven linking cubes."

- Write "11 − 2 =" on the chalkboard.

"What does this problem tell us to do?"   take away two cubes

"What do you think will happen if we take away two linking cubes from our tower?"

"Subtract, or take away, two linking cubes."

- Allow time for your child to do this.

"How many linking cubes do you have now?"   9

- Record the answer on the chalkboard.

"You have nine linking cubes."

- Write "9 − 2 =" on the chalkboard.

"What does this problem tell us to do?"   take away two cubes

"How many linking cubes do you think you will have if you take away two?"

"Subtract, or take away, two linking cubes."

"How many linking cubes do you have now?"   7

- Record the answer on the chalkboard.
- Repeat until your child has only one cube left.

"What happened when we subtracted two from an odd number?"   the answer was the odd number that comes before

"What do you think will happen if we start with an even number?"

- Repeat the above sequence with the even numbers to 8 + 2 = 10.

"How can we remember how to add two to a number?"   think of the next even or odd number

"Adding two is like saying the next even or odd number."

"How can we remember how to subtract two from a number?" think of the even or odd number that comes before

"Subtracting two is like saying the even or odd numbers backward."

"Do you know another way we could find the answers for subtracting two problems?" counting back two

- Write the following problems on the chalkboard:

$$\begin{array}{cccccc} 8 & 11 & 5 & 9 & 6 & 7 \\ -2 & -2 & -2 & -2 & -2 & -2 \end{array}$$

"What strategy can we use to find each answer?"

"What are the answers for these problems?"

- Write the answers below the problems.

- Give your child the green subtraction fact cards.

"Write the answer on the back of each card."

"Use your linking cubes to check each answer."

"When you finish, snap your cubes together."

- When your child finishes, give the following directions:

"Put your cards in a pile."

"Now read each problem to yourself."

"See if you can remember the answer."

"Turn over the card to check the answer."

"Practice saying the answers to yourself."

- Allow your child to practice independently.

CLASS PRACTICE

"Now you will have a chance to see how many subtracting two facts you remember."

- Give your child **Fact Sheet S 4.0**.

- Correct the fact sheet with your child.

WRITTEN PRACTICE

- Complete **Worksheet 98A** with your child.

- Complete **Worksheet 98B** with your child later in the day.

LESSON 98A
Math 1

Name _____
(Draw a 4-inch line segment.)

Date _____

Day of the Week _____

1. Write the number eighty-nine two more times. How many digits did you use? __4__

   89 89

2. Danielle made six bookmarks. She gave two to Michael. Draw a picture and write a number sentence to show how many bookmarks she has now.

   Number sentence ____6 – 2 = 4____   __4__ bookmarks

3. The children in Miss Walker's class made the following shapes on their geoboards. They turned their geoboards in different directions.

   Circle the shape that is not congruent to the other five shapes.

4. Write the answers.

   $9 - 2 = $ __7__ $6 - 2 = $ __4__ $8 - 2 = $ __6__

5. Show half past ten on the clock.

6. Bob put the linking cubes in trains of 10. How many linking cubes does he have?

   __43__ linking cubes

7. How many tally marks are in the rectangle? __21__ |||| |||| |||| |||| |

LESSON 98B
Math 1

Name _____

1. Fill in the missing numbers.

   5, 10, 15, __20__ , __25__ , __30__ , __35__ , __40__ , __45__ , __50__

   35, 36, 37, __38__ , __39__ , __40__ , __41__ , __42__ , __43__ , __44__

2. Craig made nine bookmarks. He gave two bookmarks to Stephanie. Draw a picture and write a number sentence to show how many bookmarks he has now.

   Number sentence ____9 – 2 = 7____   __7__ bookmarks

3. The children in Mr. Hodge's class made the following shapes on their geoboards. They turned their geoboards in different directions.

   Circle the shape that is not congruent to the other five.

4. Write the answers.

   $7 - 2 = $ __5__ $5 - 2 = $ __3__ $8 - 2 = $ __6__

5. Show half past three on the clock.

6. Jermaine put the linking cubes in trains of 10. How many linking cubes does he have?

   __27__ linking cubes

7. How many tally marks are in the rectangle? __12__ |||| |||| ||

---

esson 99

writing the number 90
counting nickels

---

lesson preparation

materials

ten 3" × 5" cards

cup of 40 pennies

cup of 8 nickels

piece of paper

Fact Sheet S 4.0

the night before

• Use the 3" × 5" cards to make a large set of fact cards for the subtracting two facts.
Write them in the following way:

| 2
 − 2 | 3
 − 2 | 4
 − 2 | 5
 − 2 | 6
 − 2 | 7
 − 2 | 8
 − 2 | 9
 − 2 | 10
 − 2 | 11
 − 2 |

in the morning

• Write the following number pattern on the meeting strip:

50, 45, 40, ___, ___, ___

Answer: 50, 45, 40, 35, 30, 25

• Put **20 pennies** in the coin cup.

THE MEETING

calendar

• Ask your child to identify the following:

year

month

shapes on the calendar

today's shape

shape pattern for the month

- Ask your child to write the date on the calendar.
- Ask your child to do the following:

    identify today's day of the week, yesterday's day of the week, and tomorrow's day of the week

    read the days of the week

    identify the weekdays

    identify the number of days in a week

- Ask your child to write the full date on the meeting strip.

weather graph

- Ask your child to report and graph the weather.
- Ask questions about the graph.

counting

- Say the "Counting by 10's Rap" on **Master 1-91** together. Point to the numbers on the hundred number chart as your child counts.

    "Let's count by 100's to 1000."

- Count by 5's to 50.
- Count by 10's to 100.
- Count backward from 100 by 10's.
- Count by 2's to 20.
- Count backward from 20 by 2's.
- Say the odd numbers to 19.
- Say the odd numbers backward from 19.
- Add another number to the number line.

    "We will count numbers on the number line by 10's as far as we can and then count by 1's."

- Point to the multiples of 10 as you count together.

    "How many 10's did we count?"

- Point to the digit in the tens' place.

    "And how many more did we count?"

- Point to the digit in the ones' place.

    "What number is _____ tens and _____ more?"

number pattern

- Ask your child to identify and fill in the missing numbers.
- Read the number pattern together.

clock

- Ask your child to set the morning/afternoon/evening/night clock.
- Throughout the day, your child announces the time on the hour and the half hour, sets the demonstration clock to show the time, and writes the digital time on the chalkboard.

coin cup

- Ask your child to put the pennies in groups of 10 and trade groups of 10 pennies for dimes.
- Ask your child to identify the number of dimes and the number of extra pennies and to record the total amount of money on the meeting strip.

right/left

- Continue to practice left and right once a week. Practice more often, if necessary.

THE LESSON

Writing the Number 90

"The last number we practiced writing was the number 89."

"What number do you think we will learn how to write today?"

- Write the number 90 on the chalkboard.

"What digits do you see in the number 90?"

"How many dimes and pennies will we use to make 90¢?"

- Use dimes and pennies to demonstrate.

"How many groups of 10 are in 90?"

"How many extra 1's do we have?"

"Let's count by 10's to check."

Counting Nickels

"Today you will learn how to count nickels."

- Write the following tally marks on the chalkboard:

JHT JHT JHT JHT JHT JHT JHT JHT JHT JHT

JHT JHT JHT JHT JHT JHT JHT JHT JHT JHT

"How many tally marks are in each group?"   5

"How can we find out how many tally marks are on the chalkboard altogether?"   count by 5's

"Let's count by 5's together."

"I'll write the numbers we say as we count."

• Write the following below the groups of tally marks as you count by 5's with your child:

| 5 | 10 | 15 | 20 | 25 | 30 | 35 | 40 | 45 | 50 |
| 55 | 60 | 65 | 70 | 75 | 80 | 85 | 90 | 95 | 100 |

"What do you notice about these numbers?"

"Do you see a pattern?"   the digit on the right is a five or a zero

"Let's try counting backward by 5's."

• Point to each number as your child counts.

• Give your child a cup of 40 pennies, a cup of 8 nickels, and a piece of paper.

"Take one coin out of each cup."

"What do we call these coins?"   penny and nickel

"What is a nickel worth?"

"A nickel is the same as five pennies."

"How many pennies do you think are in the penny cup?"

• Ask your child to estimate.

"Put the pennies in piles of five on your paper."

• Allow time for your child to do this.

"Let's count by 5's to see how many pennies you have."

• Count by 5's as your child points to the piles of pennies.

"Point to one group of pennies."

"How many pennies are in the pile?"   5

"We can trade one group of five pennies for one nickel."

"Put a group of five pennies in the penny cup and put a nickel in its place until all the pennies are replaced."

"Each nickel is the same as five pennies."

"Five tally marks in a group are like five pennies in a nickel."

• Repeat with all the groups of pennies.

"When we count nickels, we count by 5's."

"Point to each nickel as we count by 5's."

"Put the nickels back in your cup."

"Now put five nickels on your paper."

"How will we count the nickels?"   by 5's

"Let's count to see how much money we have."

• Repeat with various numbers of nickels.

"Put the nickels in the nickel cup."

CLASS PRACTICE

"Let's practice the subtracting two number facts."

"What strategy will you use to find the answers?"

• Use the large subtracting two fact cards.

• Give your child **Fact Sheet S 4.0**.

• Correct the fact sheet with your child.

WRITTEN PRACTICE

• Complete **Worksheet 99A** with your child.

• Complete **Worksheet 99B** with your child later in the day.

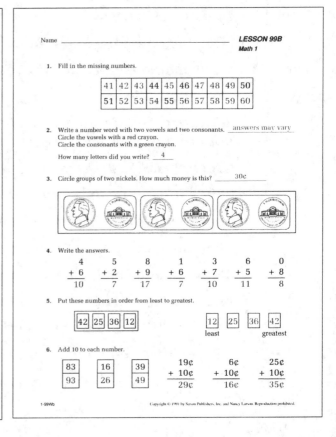

L esson 100

assessment

THE MEETING

calendar

• Ask your child to identify the following:

year

month

shapes on the calendar

today's shape

shape pattern for the month

• Ask your child to write the date on the calendar.

• Ask your child to do the following:

identify today's day of the week, yesterday's day of the week, and tomorrow's day of the week

read the days of the week

identify the weekdays

identify the number of days in a week

• Ask your child to write the full date on the meeting strip.

weather graph

- Ask your child to report and graph the weather.
- Ask questions about the graph.

counting

- Say the "Counting by 10's Rap" on **Master 1-91** together. Point to the numbers on the hundred number chart as your child counts.
- Count by 100's to 1,000.
- Count by 5's to 50.
- Count by 10's to 100.
- Count backward from 100 by 10's.
- Count by 2's to 20.
- Count backward from 20 by 2's.
- Ask your child to identify the digits to use to write the next number on the number line.
- Use an orange crayon to color the square for 100.

   "Now we will use pennies to show how many numbers are on this number line."

   "How many pennies will we need?"

   "Let's count 100 pennies."

- Drop each penny into a container as your child counts to 100. Cover the container.

   "There are 100 pennies in this covered container."

- The covered container of 100 pennies will be used for all the remaining lessons.

number pattern

- Ask your child to identify and fill in the missing numbers.
- Read the number pattern together.

clock

- Ask your child to set the morning/afternoon/evening/night clock.
- Throughout the day, your child announces the time on the hour and the half hour, sets the demonstration clock to show the time, and writes the digital time on the chalkboard.

coin cup

- Ask your child to put the pennies in groups of 10 and trade groups of 10 pennies for dimes.

- Ask your child to identify the number of dimes and the number of extra pennies and to record the total amount of money on the meeting strip.

right/left

- Continue to practice left and right once a week. Practice more often, if necessary.

ASSESSMENT

- All of the questions on the assessment are based on concepts and skills presented at least five lessons ago. If your child is having difficulty with a specific concept, reteach the concept the following day.

Written Assessment

- Give your child **Written Assessment #19**.

- Read the directions for each problem. Allow time for your child to complete each problem before continuing to the next.

- Correct the paper, noting your child's mistakes on the **Individual Recording Form**. Review the errors with your child.

Oral Assessment

- Record your child's responses to the oral interview on the interview sheet.

Name _____ **ASSESSMENT 19**
(Draw a line segment for your name.) **LESSON 100**
Date _____ **Math 1**
Day of the Week _____

1. Lucy drew ten pictures. She sent two pictures to her grandmother. Draw the pictures and write a number sentence to show how many pictures Lucy has left.

Number sentence _____ $10 - 2 = 8$
How many pictures does Lucy have left? __8__ pictures

2. Color the congruent shapes red.

3. Divide the squares into fourths in two different ways. Color one fourth of each square.

4. Color the pennies brown. How much money is this? _____ 17¢

5. Fill in the missing numbers.

35, 34, 33, _32_ , _31_ , _30_ , _29_ , _28_

2, 4, 6, _8_ , _10_ , _12_ , _14_ , _16_ , _18_ , _20_

5, 10, 15, _20_ , _25_ , _30_ , _35_ , _40_ , _45_ , _50_

1-100Aa   Copyright © 1991 by Saxon Publishers, Inc. and Nancy Larson. Reproduction prohibited.

Teacher _____
Date _____

MATH 1 LESSON 100
Oral Assessment # 10 Recording Form

Materials:
2 geoboard
4 geoband

•Make shape A on a geoboard.
"Make a congruent shape on your geoboard."
•Repeat with shape B.

Students	Shape A	Shape B	•Reassess children on items missed on previous assessments. Reassessment

1-100La   Copyright © 1991 by Saxon Publishers, Inc. and Nancy Larson. Reproduction prohibited.

Lesson 101

writing the number 91
counting nickels and pennies

---

lesson preparation

materials

cup of 10 pennies

cup of 8 nickels

piece of paper

large fact cards (subtracting two facts)

Fact Sheet S 4.0

in the morning

• Write the following number pattern on the meeting strip:

___, ___, ___, 20, 25, 30

Answer: 5, 10, 15, 20, 25, 30

• Put **40 pennies** in the coin cup.

THE MEETING

calendar

• Ask your child to identify the following:

    year

    month

    shapes on the calendar

    today's shape

    shape pattern for the month

• Ask your child to write the date on the calendar.

• Ask your child to do the following:

    identify today's day of the week, yesterday's day of the week, and tomorrow's day of the week

    read the days of the week

    identify the weekdays

    identify the number of days in a week

Copyright © 1994 by Saxon Publishers, Inc. and Nancy Larson. Reproduction prohibited.

- Ask your child to write the full date on the meeting strip.

weather graph

- Ask your child to report and graph the weather.

- Ask questions about the graph.

counting

- Say the "Counting by 10's Rap" on **Master 1-91** together. Point to the numbers on the hundred number chart as your child counts.

- Count by 100's to 1,000.

- Count by 5's to 50.

- Count by 10's to 100.

- Count backward from 100 by 10's.

- Say the odd numbers to 19.

- Say the odd numbers backward from 19.

- Ask your child to identify the digits to use to write the next number on the number line.

- Ask your child to identify the total number of pennies needed to show this number.

  "We have 100 pennies in this covered container."

  "How many more pennies do we need?"

  "Put the extra penny in a cup."

  "We have one hundred one pennies."

- Do not say the word "and" between the word "hundred" and the number of pennies. The word "and" is said only when reading a decimal point in a number.

number pattern

- Ask your child to identify and fill in the missing numbers.

- Read the number pattern together.

clock

- Ask your child to set the morning/afternoon/evening/night clock.

- Throughout the day, your child announces the time on the hour and the half hour, sets the demonstration clock to show the time, and writes the digital time on the chalkboard.

coin cup

"Today you will trade the pennies for nickels."

"How many pennies are the same as one nickel?"

> *"Put the pennies in stacks of five."*

• Allow time for your child to do this.

> *"Let's trade the pennies for nickels."*
>
> *"How many nickels will you need?"*
>
> *"Trade the pennies for nickels."*
>
> *"Let's count the nickels together."*

• Ask your child to record the amount of money on the meeting strip.

right/left

• Continue to practice left and right once a week. Practice more often, if necessary.

THE LESSON

Writing the Number 91

> *"The last number we practiced writing was the number 90."*
>
> *"What number do you think we will learn how to write today?"*

• Write the number 91 on the chalkboard.

> *"What digits do you see in the number 91?"*
>
> *"How many dimes and pennies will we use to make 91¢?"*

• Use dimes and pennies to demonstrate.

> *"How many groups of 10 are in 91?"*
>
> *"How many extra 1's do we have?"*
>
> *"Let's count by 10's and 1's to check."*

Counting Nickels and Pennies

> *"Yesterday you learned how to count nickels."*
>
> *"Today you will learn how to count nickels and pennies."*
>
> *"What do we count by when we count nickels?"*   5's

• Give your child a piece of paper, a cup of 8 nickels, and a cup of 10 pennies.

> *"Put six nickels on your paper."*
>
> *"How will you count the nickels?"*   by 5's
>
> *"Let's count to see how much money you have."*

• Repeat with various numbers of nickels.

> *"Put two nickels and four pennies on your paper."*

• Allow time for your child to do this.

"When we count nickels and pennies, we count the nickels first."

"We will count by 5's as you slide the nickels, and then we will count by 1's as you slide the pennies."

- Count the money with your child.

"How much money do you have on your paper?"   14¢

"Put three nickels and two pennies on your paper."

- Allow time for your child to do this.

"How will we count the money?"   count the nickels first and then the pennies

"We will count by 5's as you slide the nickels, and then we will count by 1's as you slide the pennies."

- Count the money with your child.

"How much money do you have on your paper?"   17¢

- Repeat with 5 nickels, 3 pennies; 6 nickels, 1 penny; 8 nickels, 2 pennies; 1 nickel, 8 pennies; and 7 nickles, 0 pennies.

"Show seven cents using the fewest number of coins."

- Allow time for your child to do this.

"What coins did you use?"   1 nickel, 2 pennies

- Count the money together.

"Show twenty cents using the fewest number of coins."

- Allow time for your child to do this.

"What coins did you use?"   4 nickels

- Count the money together.

- Repeat with 16¢ and 34¢.

"Put the nickels in the nickel cup and the pennies in the penny cup."

CLASS PRACTICE

"Let's practice the subtracting two number facts."

"What strategy will you use to find the answers?"

- Use the large subtracting two fact cards.

- Give your child **Fact Sheet S 4.0**.

- Correct the fact sheet with your child.

WRITTEN PRACTICE

- Complete **Worksheet 101A** with your child.
- Complete **Worksheet 101B** with your child later in the day.

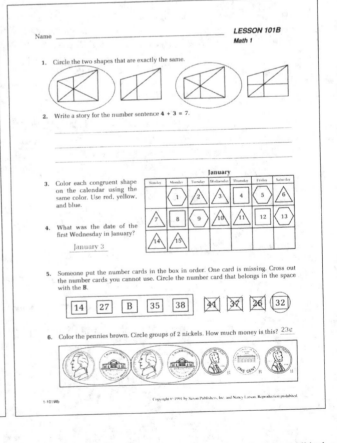

Lesson **102**

writing the number 92
identifying geometric solids (cones and spheres)

---

lesson preparation

materials

ball

ice-cream cone

1 large piece of construction paper

scissors

stapler or tape

large fact cards (subtraction facts)

Fact Sheet S 4.4

in the morning

• Write the following number pattern on the meeting strip:

> —, —, —, 64, 65, 66

Answer: 61, 62, 63, 64, 65, 66

• Put **5 nickels** and **1 penny** in the coin cup.

THE MEETING

calendar

- Ask your child to identify the following:

    year

    month

    shapes on the calendar

    today's shape

    shape pattern for the month

- Ask your child to write the date on the calendar.

- Ask your child to do the following:

    identify today's day of the week, yesterday's day of the week, and tomorrow's day of the week

    read the days of the week

identify the weekdays

identify the number of days in a week

- Ask your child to write the full date on the meeting strip.

weather graph

- Ask your child to report and graph the weather.

- Ask questions about the graph.

counting

- Say the "Counting by 10's Rap" on **Master 1-91** together. Point to the numbers on the hundred number chart as your child counts.

- Count by 100's to 1,000.

- Count by 5's to 50.

- Count by 10's to 100.

- Count backward from 100 by 10's.

- Count by 2's to 20.

- Count backward from 20 by 2's.

- Ask your child to identify the digits to use to write the next number on the number line.

- Ask your child to identify the total number of pennies needed to show this number.

  "We have 100 pennies in this covered container."

  "How many more pennies do we need?"

  "Put the extra pennies in this cup."

  "Let's count the pennies."

- Say "One hundred" as you point to the container of pennies and then "One hundred one, one hundred two" as you point to each extra penny.

number pattern

- Ask your child to identify and fill in the missing numbers.

- Read the number pattern together.

clock

- Ask your child to set the morning/afternoon/evening/night clock.

- Throughout the day, your child announces the time on the hour and the half hour, sets the demonstration clock to show the time, and writes the digital time on the chalkboard.

coin cup

"Today there are only nickels and pennies in the coin cup."

"How many nickels are there?"

"How many pennies are there?"

"When we count money, we begin with the coin that is worth the most."

"Which coin will you count first?"   nickel

- Ask your child to count the nickels and pennies and record the amount of money on the meeting strip.

right/left

- Continue to practice left and right once a week. Practice more often, if necessary.

THE LESSON

Writing the Number 92

"The last number we practiced writing was the number 91."

"What number do you think we will learn how to write today?"

- Write the number 92 on the chalkboard.

"What digits do you see in the number 92?"

"How many dimes and pennies will we use to make 92¢?"

- Use dimes and pennies to demonstrate.

"How many groups of 10 are in 92?"

"How many extra 1's do we have?"

"Let's count by 10's and 1's to check."

Identifying Geometric Solids (Cones and Spheres)

"Today you will learn the special names of two geometric solids."

- Hold up a ball (or other spherical object) and an ice-cream cone (or other conical object).

"What are these?"

- Ask your child to identify the objects.

"Mathematicians have special names for objects with these shapes."

- Hold up the ball.

"Things that are shaped like this are called spheres."

"We can touch and hold a sphere."

"We can roll it."

"Let's look around our house to find other spheres."

- Walk through the house and identify other spheres.

- Hold up the cone.

"Things that are shaped like this are called cones."

"Sometimes people make hats that look like cones."

- Use a large piece of construction paper.

"I can make a cone out of this piece of paper."

"Watch how I will do that."

"First I will fold the piece of paper in half."

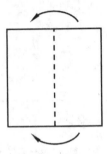

"Now I will fold it in half again."

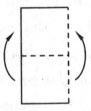

"Now I will cut along a curve."

"What do you think this will look like when I open the paper?"   circle

- Open the paper.

"What shape is this?"   circle

"Where is the center of my circle?"

- Ask your child to point to the center.

"Now I will cut along one of the lines until I reach the center."

"I will make a cone out of my piece of paper."

- Slide the cut edges over each other and staple or tape the paper into the shape of a cone.

   "How is a cone different from a sphere?"

- Allow time for your child to discuss the differences.

   "A cone has a point."

- Demonstrate, using the paper cone.

   "We can roll a cone."

- Demonstrate, using the paper cone.

   "We can also make it sit on its flat side."

- Demonstrate, using the paper cone.

   "Let's look around our house to find another cone."

- Walk through the house and try to identify another cone.

   "During the next week we will look for more spheres and cones."

   "Remember that a sphere will need to look like this ball and a cone will need to look like this hat."

- Optional: Put a sphere of ice cream in the cone as a special snack for your child.

CLASS PRACTICE

   "Let's review the subtraction number facts."

- Use the large subtraction fact cards.
- Give your child **Fact Sheet S 4.4**.

   "What number facts do you see?"

   "What strategies will you use to find the answers?"

- Correct the fact sheet with your child.

WRITTEN PRACTICE

- Complete **Worksheet 102A** with your child.
- Complete **Worksheet 102B** with your child later in the day.

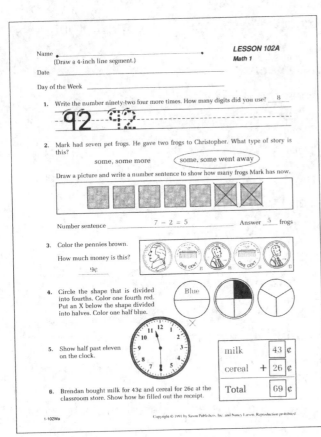

Name ●_____●
(Draw a 4-inch line segment.)

Date _____

Day of the Week _____

1. Write the number ninety-two four more times. How many digits did you use? __8__

    92 92 - - - - - - - - - - - - - - - -

2. Mark had seven pet frogs. He gave two frogs to Christopher. What type of story is this?

    some, some more   (some, some went away)

    Draw a picture and write a number sentence to show how many frogs Mark has now.

    Number sentence _____ 7 – 2 = 5 _____   Answer __5__ frogs

3. Color the pennies brown.

    How much money is this?
    __9¢__

4. Circle the shape that is divided into fourths. Color one fourth red. Put an X below the shape divided into halves. Color one half blue.

    Blue

5. Show half past eleven on the clock.

6. Brendan bought milk for 43¢ and cereal for 26¢ at the classroom store. Show how he filled out the receipt.

    | milk | | 43 | ¢ |
    | cereal | + | 26 | ¢ |
    | Total | | 69 | ¢ |

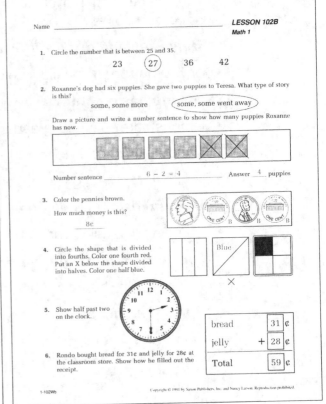

Name _____

1. Circle the number that is between 25 and 35.

    23   (27)   36   42

2. Roxanne's dog had six puppies. She gave two puppies to Teresa. What type of story is this?

    some, some more   (some, some went away)

    Draw a picture and write a number sentence to show how many puppies Roxanne has now.

    Number sentence _____ 6 – 2 = 4 _____   Answer __4__ puppies

3. Color the pennies brown.

    How much money is this?
    __8¢__

4. Circle the shape that is divided into fourths. Color one fourth red. Put an X below the shape divided into halves. Color one half blue.

    Blue

    X

5. Show half past two on the clock.

6. Rondo bought bread for 31¢ and jelly for 28¢ at the classroom store. Show how he filled out the receipt.

    | bread | | 31 | ¢ |
    | jelly | + | 28 | ¢ |
    | Total | | 59 | ¢ |

Lesson 103

writing the number 93
dividing a set of objects by sharing

lesson preparation

materials

21 wrapped chocolate candies in a small bag (other objects can be substituted)

4 small plastic bags

5 small plates

15 linking cubes

large fact cards (subtraction facts)

Fact Sheet S 4.4

in the morning

• Write the following number pattern on the meeting strip:

3, 6, 9, ___, ___, ___

Answer: 3, 6, 9, 12, 15, 18

• Put **2 nickels** and **4 pennies** in the coin cup.

THE MEETING

calendar

• Ask your child to identify the following:

year

month

shapes on the calendar

today's shape

shape pattern for the month

• Ask your child to write the date on the calendar.

• Ask your child to do the following:

identify today's day of the week, yesterday's day of the week, and tomorrow's day of the week

read the days of the week

    identify the weekdays

    identify the number of days in a week

- Ask your child to write the full date on the meeting strip.

weather graph

- Ask your child to report and graph the weather.
- Ask questions about the graph.

counting

- Say the "Counting by 10's Rap" on **Master 1-91** together. Point to the numbers on the hundred number chart as your child counts.
- Count by 100's to 1,000.
- Count by 5's to 50.
- Count by 10's to 100.
- Count backward from 100 by 10's.
- Say the odd numbers to 19.
- Say the odd numbers backward from 19.
- Ask your child to identify the digits to use to write the next number on the number line.
- Ask your child to identify the total number of pennies needed to show this number.

    "We have 100 pennies in this covered container."

    "How many more pennies do we need?"

    "Put the extra pennies in this cup."

- Count on from 100 to count the total number of pennies with your child.

number pattern

- Ask your child to identify and fill in the missing numbers.
- Read the number pattern together.

clock

- Ask your child to set the morning/afternoon/evening/night clock.
- Throughout the day, your child announces the time on the hour and the half hour, sets the demonstration clock to show the time, and writes the digital time on the chalkboard.

coin cup

    "Today there are only nickels and pennies in the coin cup."

    "How many nickels are there?"

"How many pennies are there?"

"When we count money, we begin with the coin that is worth the most."

"Which coin will you count first?"   nickel

- Ask your child to count the nickels and pennies and record the amount of money on the meeting strip.

right/left

- Continue to practice left and right once a week. Practice more often, if necessary.

THE LESSON

Writing the Number 93

"The last number we practiced writing was the number 92."

"What number do you think we will learn how to write today?"

- Write the number 93 on the chalkboard.

"What digits do you see in the number 93?"

"How many dimes and pennies will we use to make 93¢?"

- Use dimes and pennies to demonstrate.

"How many groups of 10 are in 93?"

"How many extra 1's do we have?"

"Let's count by 10's and 1's to check."

Dividing a Set of Objects by Sharing

- Hold up the bag of candies.

"I have a bag of candies."

"Today you will learn how to divide these candies by sharing."

"You will share the candies with _____, _____, and _____."

- Name 3 children.

"Everyone will need a fair share."

"What does it mean to have a fair share?"   everyone has the same number

"I will give you a plate for each child's candies."

- Give your child 4 small plates.

"Share the candies equally."

"Put the same number of candies on each plate."

- When your child finishes, continue.

"How did you divide the candies?"

"How do you know that it's fair?"

"How many candies did you put on each plate?"

"What should we do about the extra candy?"

- Put each child's candy in a separate plastic bag.
- Allow your child to eat his/her candy, if desired.

"Now you will have a chance to practice dividing pretend candies into equal groups."

- Give your child a tower of 15 linking cubes and 1 more small plate.

"We will pretend that each of the linking cubes is a piece of candy."

"Give each plate the same number of pieces of candy."

- Allow time for your child to do this.

"Does each plate have the same number of candies?"

"How many candies did you put on each plate?"

- Remove 1 plate.

"Now give each plate the same number of pieces of candy."

- Allow time for your child to do this.

"Does each plate have the same number of candies?"

"How many candies did you put on each plate?"

"How many extra candies do you have?"

- Repeat, using 3 plates and 2 plates.

Class Practice

"Let's review the subtraction number facts."

- Use the large subtraction fact cards.
- Give your child **Fact Sheet S 4.4.**

"What number facts do you see?"

"What strategies will you use to find the answers?"

- Correct the fact sheet with your child.

Written Practice

- Complete **Worksheet 103A** with your child.
- Complete **Worksheet 103B** with your child later in the day.

Name _____

(Draw a 3-inch line segment.)

Date _____

Day of the Week _____

LESSON 103A
Math 1

1. Write the number ninety-three two more times. How many digits did you use? __4__

93   93

2. On Tuesday, Cerina counted eight fish in the fish tank. Mrs. O' Connor put two more fish in the tank on Wednesday. What type of story is this?

(some, some more)   some, some went away

Draw a picture and write a number sentence to show how many fish are in the tank now.

Number sentence _____ 8 + 2 = 10 _____   Answer __10__ fish

3. There are 8 candies in the bag. Show how Brian and Michael will share the candies.

candies   Brian   Michael

How many candies will each boy have? __4__ candies

4. Count by 10's from 4. | 4 | 14 | 24 | 34 | 44 | 54 | 64 | 74 | 84 | 94 |

5. Write six different examples with a sum of 10.

+ ☐   + ☐   + ☐   + ☐   + ☐   + ☐
10   10   10   10   10   10

1-103Wa

Name _____

Date _____

LESSON 103B
Math 1

1. Fill in the missing numbers.

10, 12, 14, __16__ , __18__ , __20__

34, 33, 32, __31__ , __30__ , __29__ , __28__ , __27__

100, 200, 300, __400__ , __500__ , __600__ , __700__ , __800__

2. On Thursday, Roger counted seven stickers on the chart. Ms. Treat put two more stickers on the chart on Friday. What type of story is this?

(some, some more)   some, some went away

Draw a picture and write a number sentence to show how many stickers are on the chart now.

★ ★ ★ ★ ★ ★ ★   ★ ★

Number sentence _____ 7 + 2 = 9 _____   Answer __9__ stickers

3. There are 10 candies in the bag. Show how Rosa and Pam will share the candies.

candies   Rosa   Pam

How many candies will each girl have? __5__ candies

4. Count by 10's from 3. | 3 | 13 | 23 | 33 | 43 | 53 | 63 | 73 | 83 | 93 |

5. Fill in the missing numbers.

6   3   2   9   5   7
+ 4   + 7   + 8   + 1   + 5   + 3
10   10   10   10   10   10

1-103Wb

esson 104

writing the number 94
identifying a dozen and half dozen

---

lesson preparation ———————————————————

materials

2 egg cartons

6 red and 6 blue linking cubes

2 towers of 10 linking cubes (2 different colors)

large fact cards (subtraction facts)

Fact Sheet S 4.4

in the morning

• Write the following number pattern on the meeting strip:

> 77, 76, 75, ___, ___, ___

> *Answer: 77, 76, 75, 74, 73, 72*

• Put **4 nickels** and **3 pennies** in the coin cup.

THE MEETING

calendar

- • Ask your child to identify the following:

  year

  month

  shapes on the calendar

  today's shape

  shape pattern for the month

- • Ask your child to write the date on the calendar.

- • Ask your child to do the following:

  identify today's day of the week, yesterday's day of the week, and tomorrow's day of the week

  read the days of the week

  identify the weekdays

identify the number of days in a week

- Ask your child to write the full date on the meeting strip.

weather graph

- Ask your child to report and graph the weather.
- Ask questions about the graph.

counting

- Say the "Counting by 10's Rap" on **Master 1-91** together. Point to the numbers on the hundred number chart as your child counts.
- Count by 100's to 1,000.
- Count by 5's to 50.
- Count by 10's to 100.
- Count backward from 100 by 10's.
- Count by 2's to 20.
- Count backward from 20 by 2's.
- Ask your child to identify the digits to use to write the next number on the number line.
- Ask your child to identify the total number of pennies needed to show this number.

"We have 100 pennies in this covered container."

"How many more pennies do we need?"

"Put the extra pennies in this cup."

- Count on from 100 to count the total number of pennies with your child.

number pattern

- Ask your child to identify and fill in the missing numbers.
- Read the number pattern together.

clock

- Ask your child to set the morning/afternoon/evening/night clock.
- Throughout the day, your child announces the time on the hour and the half hour, sets the demonstration clock to show the time, and writes the digital time on the chalkboard.

coin cup

"Today there are only nickels and pennies in the coin cup."

"How many nickels are there?"

"How many pennies are there?"

"When we count money, we begin with the coin that is worth the most."

"Which coin will you count first?"   nickel

- Ask your child to count the nickels and pennies and record the amount of money on the meeting strip.

right/left

- Continue to practice left and right once a week. Practice more often, if necessary.

THE LESSON

Writing the Number 94

"The last number we practiced writing was the number 93."

"What number do you think we will learn how to write today?"

- Write the number 94 on the chalkboard.

"What digits do you see in the number 94?"

"How many dimes and pennies will we use to make 94¢?"

- Use dimes and pennies to demonstrate.

"How many groups of 10 are in 94?"

"How many extra 1's do we have?"

"Let's count by 10's and 1's to check."

Identifying a Dozen and Half Dozen

- Show your child an egg carton (for 12 eggs).

"What do we buy that comes in this type of container?"

"Where would you find eggs in a store?"   usually in a cooler with dairy products

"Do you know how many eggs would be in an egg carton like this?"

- Give your child an egg carton.

"Count the number of eggs you will need to fill this carton."

- Ask your child to count the eggs.

"Today we are going to fill our egg cartons with pretend eggs."

"Why do you think we won't use real eggs?"

"What do you think we could use for pretend eggs?"

"Today we will pretend that our linking cubes are eggs."

"How many linking cubes will we need to fill an egg carton?"   12

"Do you know another name for twelve of something?" dozen

"When we have twelve of something, we say that we have a dozen."

"When I give you the linking cubes, fill your egg carton with a dozen pretend eggs."

- Give your child 2 towers of linking cubes. Use two different colors.

"How many eggs are in a dozen?"

"Count your eggs by 2's to check."

- Fill half of your egg container with red linking cubes and the other half with blue linking cubes in the following way:

R	R	R	B	B	B
R	R	R	B	B	B

- Show your child your carton.

"What do you notice about the eggs in my carton?"

- Allow time for your child to offer observations.

"How many red linking cubes did I use?" 6

"How many blue linking cubes did I use?" 6

- Close the lid and break the egg carton in half.

"What did I do to my egg carton?"

"I divided my egg carton in half."

- Hold up one half of the carton.

"We call this a half dozen."

"When people want only a few eggs, they buy a half dozen."

"How many eggs do you think are in each half dozen?"

- Open the cartons for your child to check.

"Fill your egg carton with a half dozen eggs of each color."

"How many eggs of each color will you need?" 6

"Arrange the eggs in the carton so that they will look attractive to a customer."

- Allow time for your child to do this.

"How many [color] eggs do you have?"

"How many [color] eggs do you have?"

CLASS PRACTICE

"Let's review the subtraction number facts."

- Use the large subtraction fact cards.
- Give your child **Fact Sheet S 4.4**.

  "What number facts do you see?"

  "What strategies will you use to find the answers?"

- Correct the fact sheet with your child.

WRITTEN PRACTICE

- Complete **Worksheet 104A** with your child.
- Complete **Worksheet 104B** with your child later in the day.

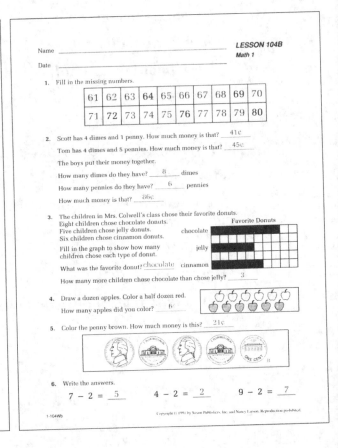

L esson 105

writing the number 95
subtraction facts—subtracting a number from ten

---

lesson preparation ────────────────────

materials

Written Assessment #20

six 3" × 5" cards

cup of 10 pennies

Master 1-105

subtraction fact cards — blue

Fact Sheet S 6.0

the night before

• Use the 3" × 5" cards to make a large set of fact cards for the subtracting a number from ten facts. Write them in the following way:

$$\begin{array}{cc} 10 \\ -3 \end{array} \quad \begin{array}{cc} 10 \\ -4 \end{array} \quad \begin{array}{cc} 10 \\ -6 \end{array} \quad \begin{array}{cc} 10 \\ -7 \end{array} \quad \begin{array}{cc} 10 \\ -8 \end{array} \quad \begin{array}{cc} 10 \\ -9 \end{array}$$

• Separate the blue subtraction fact cards.

in the morning

• Write the following number pattern on the meeting strip:

15, 20, 25, __, __, __

Answer: 15, 20, 25, 30, 35, 40

• Put **7 nickels** and **3 pennies** in the coin cup.

THE MEETING

calendar

• Ask your child to identify the following:

year

month

shapes on the calendar

today's shape

shape pattern for the month

- Ask your child to write the date on the calendar.

- Ask your child to do the following:

  identify today's day of the week, yesterday's day of the week, and tomorrow's day of the week

  read the days of the week

  identify the weekdays

  identify the number of days in a week

- Ask your child to write the full date on the meeting strip.

weather graph

- Ask your child to report and graph the weather.

- Ask questions about the graph.

counting

- Say the "Counting by 10's Rap" on **Master 1-91** together. Point to the numbers on the hundred number chart as your child counts.

- Count by 100's to 1,000.

- Count by 5's to 50.

- Count by 10's to 100.

- Count backward from 100 by 10's.

- Say the odd numbers to 19.

- Say the odd numbers backward from 19.

- Ask your child to identify the digits to use to write the next number on the number line.

- Ask your child to identify the total number of pennies needed to show this number.

  "We have 100 pennies in this covered container."

  "How many more pennies do we need?"

  "Put the extra pennies in this cup."

- Count on from 100 to count the total number of pennies with your child.

number pattern

- Ask your child to identify and fill in the missing numbers.

- Read the number pattern together.

clock

- Ask your child to set the morning/afternoon/evening/night clock.
- Throughout the day, your child announces the time on the hour and the half hour, sets the demonstration clock to show the time, and writes the digital time on the chalkboard.

coin cup

"Today there are only nickels and pennies in the coin cup."

"How many nickels are there?"

"How many pennies are there?"

"When we count money, we begin with the coin that is worth the most."

"Which coin will you count first?"   nickel

- Ask your child to count the nickels and pennies and record the amount of money on the meeting strip.

right/left

- Continue to practice left and right once a week. Practice more often, if necessary.

ASSESSMENT

Written Assessment

- Pass out **Written Assessment #20**.
- Read the directions for each problem. Allow time for your child to complete each problem before continuing to the next.
- Correct the paper, noting your child's mistakes on the **Individual Recording Form**. Review the errors with your child.

THE LESSON

Writing the Number 95

"The last number we practiced writing was the number 94."

"What number do you think we will learn how to write today?"

- Write the number 95 on the chalkboard.

"What digits do you see in the number 95?"

"How many dimes and pennies will we use to make 95¢?"

- Use dimes and pennies to demonstrate.

"How many groups of 10 are in 95?"

"How many extra 1's do we have?"

"Let's count by 10's and 1's to check."

Subtraction Facts—Subtracting a Number from Ten

"What are two numbers that can be added together to equal ten?"

- Write the combinations on the chalkboard in the following way:

0 + 10 = 10	6 + 4 = 10
1 + 9 = 10	7 + 3 = 10
2 + 8 = 10	8 + 2 = 10
3 + 7 = 10	9 + 1 = 10
4 + 6 = 10	10 + 0 = 10
5 + 5 = 10	

"Today you will learn how to subtract a number from ten."

- Give your child **Master 1-105** and a cup of 10 pennies.

"How many small squares are on this paper?"

"Put a penny in each square."

"How many pennies do you have?"

"We will use our pennies to act out stories."

"Mary had ten pennies."

"She spent one penny."

"How will we show that she spent one penny?"   put 1 penny in the penny cup

"What kind of story is this?"   some, some went away

"How many pennies does she have left?"   **9**

"How can we write a number sentence on the chalkboard to show what happened?"

- Write the number sentence "10 − 1 = 9" on the chalkboard.

"Put the penny back on your paper."

"How many pennies do you have now?"   **10**

"Let's act out another story."

"Steve had ten pennies."

"He spent two pennies."

"How will we show that he spent two pennies?"   put 2 pennies in the cup

"What kind of story is this?"   some, some went away

"How many pennies does he have left?"   **8**

"How can we write a number sentence on the chalkboard to show what happened?"

- Write the number sentence "10 – 2 = 8" on the chalkboard.

"Put the pennies back on your paper."

"How many pennies do you have now?"   10

- Repeat with all combinations in random order.

"We can write our subtraction problems a different way."

- Write the following on the chalkboard:

$$\begin{array}{ccccccccccc} 10 & 10 & 10 & 10 & 10 & 10 & 10 & 10 & 10 & 10 & 10 \\ -0 & -1 & -2 & -3 & -4 & -5 & -6 & -7 & -8 & -9 & -10 \end{array}$$

- Point to the first problem.

"If we have ten pennies and take away zero pennies, how many pennies do we have left?"

- Record the answer below the problem.

- Point to the second problem.

"If we have ten pennies and take away one, how many pennies do we have left?"

- Record the answer below the problem.

- Repeat with each problem.

"There is a trick mathematicians use to make sure that their subtraction answer is right."

- Point to the 9 in the problem 10 – 1 = 9. Slowly move your finger upward.

"What do you notice about these numbers?"   nine plus one is ten

- Repeat with 10 – 2 = 8, 10 – 3 = 7, etc.

"We can always check our subtraction answers by adding up."

- Give your child the blue subtraction fact cards.

"Write the answer on the back of each card."

"Use your pennies to check the answers."

CLASS PRACTICE

"Let's practice the subtracting a number from ten facts together."

- Use the large subtraction fact cards. Include 10 – 0, 10 – 1, 10 – 2, and 10 – 5 fact cards also.

- Give your child **Fact Sheet S 6.0.**

- Correct the fact sheet with your child.

WRITTEN PRACTICE

- Complete **Worksheet 105A** with your child.
- Complete **Worksheet 105B** with your child later in the day.

Name _____
(Draw a line segment for your name.)

Date _____

Day of the Week _____

ASSESSMENT 20
LESSON 105
Math 1

1. Bonnie had 26¢. Show this using the fewest number of dimes and pennies. Color the pennies brown.

(D) (D) (P) (P) (P) (P) (P) (P) (D)

She found another dime. Draw the dime.

How much money does Bonnie have now? ___36¢___

2. Put the number cards in the box in order from least to greatest.

[31] [16] [47] [25]   [16] [25] [31] [47]
                             least   greatest

3. Circle the even numbers.

1 (2) 3 (4) 5 (6) 7 (8) 9 (10)

4. Find the answers.

$$\begin{array}{cccccc} 5 & 6 & 1 & 7 & 6 & 3 & 5 \\ +2 & +5 & +8 & +3 & -1 & -3 & -0 \\ \hline 7 & 11 & 9 & 10 & 5 & 0 & 5 \end{array}$$

5. Show half past seven on the clock.

6. Add 10 to each number.

[29]   [18]   34¢   22¢
[39]   [28]   + 10¢   + 10¢
                 ------   ------
                  44¢   32¢

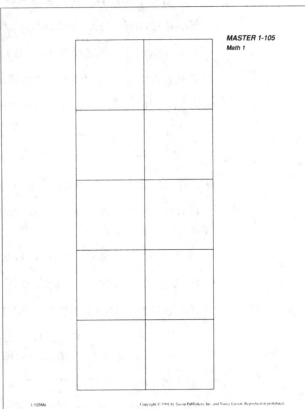

MASTER 1-105
Math 1

Name _____
(Draw a 4-inch line segment.)

Date _____

Day of the Week _____

LESSON 105A
Math 1

1. Write the number ninety-five four more times. How many digits did you use? __8__

95 ~~95~~

2. James and his brother made a dozen cupcakes.
   Draw the cupcakes.
   They put green frosting on a half dozen.
   Use a green crayon to show that.
   How many cupcakes have green frosting? __6__

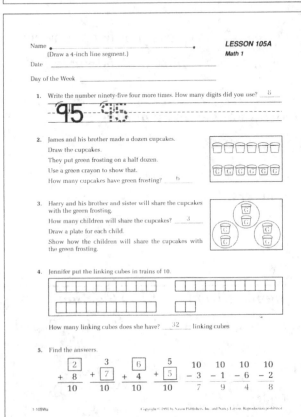

3. Harry and his brother and sister will share the cupcakes with the green frosting.
   How many children will share the cupcakes? __3__
   Draw a plate for each child.
   Show how the children will share the cupcakes with the green frosting.

4. Jennifer put the linking cubes in trains of 10.

How many linking cubes does she have? __32__ linking cubes

5. Find the answers.

$$\begin{array}{cccccccc} [2] & 3 & [6] & 5 & 10 & 10 & 10 & 10 \\ +8 & +[7] & +4 & +[5] & -3 & -1 & -6 & -2 \\ \hline 10 & 10 & 10 & 10 & 7 & 9 & 4 & 8 \end{array}$$

Name _____

Date _____

LESSON 105B
Math 1

1. Circle the two designs that are exactly the same.

2. Vickie and her sister boiled a dozen eggs to make hard-boiled eggs.
   Draw the eggs.
   They dyed a half dozen red.
   Use a red crayon to show that.
   How many eggs are red? __6__

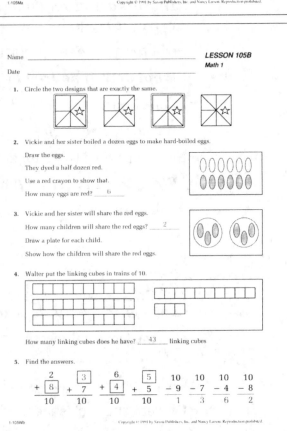

3. Vickie and her sister will share the red eggs.
   How many children will share the red eggs? __2__
   Draw a plate for each child.
   Show how the children will share the red eggs.

4. Walter put the linking cubes in trains of 10.

How many linking cubes does he have? __43__ linking cubes

5. Find the answers.

$$\begin{array}{cccccccc} 2 & [3] & 6 & [5] & 10 & 10 & 10 & 10 \\ +[8] & +7 & +[4] & +5 & -9 & -7 & -4 & -8 \\ \hline 10 & 10 & 10 & 10 & 1 & 3 & 6 & 2 \end{array}$$

556

esson 106

writing the number 96
measuring using feet

---

lesson preparation

materials

2 rulers

large fact cards (subtracting a number from ten facts)

Fact Sheet S 6.0

in the morning

• Write the following number pattern on the meeting strip:

> __, __, __, 50, 60, 70

> *Answer: 20, 30, 40, 50, 60, 70*

• Put **8 nickels** and **1 penny** in the coin cup.

THE MEETING

calendar

- • Ask your child to identify the following:

    year

    month

    shapes on the calendar

    today's shape

    shape pattern for the month

- • Ask your child to write the date on the calendar.

- • Ask your child to do the following:

    identify today's day of the week, yesterday's day of the week, and tomorrow's day of the week

    read the days of the week

    identify the weekdays

    identify the number of days in a week

- • Ask your child to write the full date on the meeting strip.

weather graph

- Ask your child to report and graph the weather.
- Ask questions about the graph.

counting

- Say the "Counting by 10's Rap" on **Master 1-91** together. Point to the numbers on the hundred number chart as your child counts.
- Count by 100's to 1,000.
- Count by 5's to 50.
- Count by 10's to 100.
- Count backward from 100 by 10's.
- Count by 2's to 20.
- Count backward from 20 by 2's.
- Ask your child to identify the digits to use to write the next number on the number line.
- Ask your child to identify the total number of pennies needed to show this number.

    "We have 100 pennies in this covered container."

    "How many more pennies do we need?"

    "Put the extra pennies in this cup."

- Count on from 100 to count the total number of pennies with your child.

number pattern

- Ask your child to identify and fill in the missing numbers.
- Read the number pattern together.

clock

- Ask your child to set the morning/afternoon/evening/night clock.
- Throughout the day, your child announces the time on the hour and the half hour, sets the demonstration clock to show the time, and writes the digital time on the chalkboard.

coin cup

"Today there are only nickels and pennies in the coin cup."

"How many nickels are there?"

"How many pennies are there?"

"When we count money, we begin with the coin that is worth the most."

"Which coin will you count first?" nickel

- Ask your child to count the nickels and pennies and record the amount of money on the meeting strip.

right/left

- Continue to practice left and right once a week. Practice more often, if necessary.

THE LESSON

Writing the Number 96

"The last number we practiced writing was the number 95."

"What number do you think we will learn how to write today?"

- Write the number 96 on the chalkboard.

"What digits do you see in the number 96?"

"How many dimes and pennies will we use to make 96¢?"

- Use dimes and pennies to demonstrate.

"How many groups of 10 are in 96?"

"How many extra 1's do we have?"

"Let's count by 10's and 1's to check."

Measuring Using Feet

"I would like to know how far it is from this side of the room to the other."

"How could we find out?"

- Ask your child for suggestions.

"Today you will learn how to measure the room."

"We can measure how long this room is by using our feet."

"I will try it first."

"Both of my feet are the same size so I can use them together."

- Show that your feet are the same size.

"Count with me as I measure the room using my feet."

"I will begin by putting my back and my heels against one wall."

"Now I will walk straight ahead."

"Each time I take a step, I will put the heel of one foot in front of the toe of my other foot."

"Count with me as I measure the length of the room with my feet."

- Walk across the room in a heel, toe, heel, toe manner, counting with your child.

"I will record the length of the room on the chalkboard."

• Record your name and the number of feet on the chalkboard.

Name	Feet
_____	_____ feet

"Now you will have a chance to measure the length of the room using your feet."

"Do you think that the number of feet you use will be the same as the number of feet I used?"

"Why not?"

"Let's try it."

"What will you do first?"   put his/her back and heels against the wall

"What will you do next?"   walk straight ahead putting the heel of one foot in front of the toe of the other foot

"Let's count together as you measure the length of the room using your feet."

• Ask your child to walk across the room in a heel, toe, heel, toe manner as you count together.

• Record your child's name and the number of feet on the chalkboard.

"Are the answers the same?"

"Why not?"   the parent's feet are longer

"When we measure something, we want to be able to tell someone else how long it is."

"If we tell them it is three feet long, they will need to know whose feet we used to measure the three feet."

"They will want to know if we used my feet or your feet or _____'s feet."

"About 600 years ago someone decided that we should have an exact way to measure inches and feet."

• Hold up a 12-inch ruler.

"It was decided that this is the official length of one foot, not any shorter and not any longer."

• Give your child a ruler.

"How many inches are in one official foot?"

"Is your foot as long as the official foot?"

"Is it shorter or longer than the ruler foot?"

"From now on, we will use the ruler foot whenever we want to measure something using feet."

"Let's work together to measure the distance across the room using ruler feet."

"How many official feet long do you think the room is?"

"We will write 'ruler' on the chalkboard and measure the length of the room using our rulers."

"How could we do this?"

"How did we measure with our feet?"

"We will do the same thing with our rulers."

"Put your ruler against the wall."

• Ask your child to position his/her ruler against the wall.

"I will put my ruler next."

"What will I have to remember to do?" make sure the ends of the rulers touch, and that the rulers make a straight line

• Put your ruler at the end of your child's ruler.

"How many ruler feet have we used so far?" 2

"Now you will put your ruler next."

"What will you have to remember to do?" make sure the ends of the rulers touch, and that the rulers make a straight line

"How many ruler feet have we used so far?" 3

• Repeat across the room.

"How many feet long is our room?"

• Record the answer on the chalkboard.

"This is the length of our room in official feet."

CLASS PRACTICE

"Let's practice the subtracting a number from ten facts together."

• Use the large subtraction fact cards. Include 10 – 0, 10 – 1, 10 – 2, and 10 – 5 fact cards also.

• Give your child **Fact Sheet S 6.0.**

• Correct the fact sheet with your child.

WRITTEN PRACTICE

• Complete **Worksheet 106A** with your child.

• Complete **Worksheet 106B** with your child later in the day.

Name _____
(Draw a 3-inch line segment.)

Date _____

Day of the Week _____

1. Write the number ninety-six three more times. How many digits did you use? __6__

   96 96

2. Glenna had a half dozen pencils. She gave two pencils to Nancy. Draw a picture and write a number sentence to show what happened.

   What type of story is this? some, some more (some, some went away)

   Number sentence _____ 6 − 2 = 4

   How many pencils does Glenna have now? ___4___ pencils

3. Circle the geoboard shape that is not congruent to the others.

4. Find the answers.

   10 − 3 = __7__   10 − 6 = __4__   10 − 2 = __8__

5. Mark has 6 stickers. Show how he will share the stickers with his friend Renee.

   Mark   Renee
   ★ ★ ★   ★ ★ ★

6. Use your ruler to measure something in the classroom that is about 1 foot long.

   What did you measure? _____

Name _____

Date _____

1. Finish the number patterns.

   5, 10, 15, __20__ , __25__ , __30__ , __35__ , __40__

   15, 13, 11, __9__ , __7__ , __5__ , __3__ , __1__

2. Carol had a half dozen stuffed animals. She gave one stuffed animal to her younger brother. Draw a picture and write a number sentence to show what happened.

   Number sentence _____ 6 − 1 = 5

   How many stuffed animals does Carol have now? ___5___ stuffed animals

3. Circle the geoboard shape that is not congruent to the others.

4. Find the answers.

   10 − 7 = __3__   10 − 4 = __6__   10 − 8 = __2__

5. Jessica has 8 toy cars. Show how she will share the cars with her friend Joel.

   Jessica   Joel

6. Use your ruler to measure something at home that is about 1 foot long.

   What did you measure? _____

esson 107

writing the number 97
identifying one half, one third, and one sixth

---

lesson preparation

materials

pattern blocks

large fact cards (subtracting a number from ten facts)

Fact Sheet S 6.0

in the morning

• Write the following number pattern on the meeting strip:

> ___, ___, ___, 42, 43, 44

> *Answer: 39, 40, 41, 42, 43, 44*

• Put **3 nickels** and **2 pennies** in the coin cup.

THE MEETING

calendar

- Ask your child to identify the following:

  year

  month

  shapes on the calendar

  today's shape

  shape pattern for the month

- Ask your child to write the date on the calendar.

- Ask your child to do the following:

  identify today's day of the week, yesterday's day of the week, and tomorrow's day of the week

  read the days of the week

  identify the weekdays

  identify the number of days in a week

- Ask your child to write the full date on the meeting strip.

weather graph

- Ask your child to report and graph the weather.
- Ask questions about the graph.

counting

- Say the "Counting by 10's Rap" on **Master 1-91** together. Point to the numbers on the hundred number chart as your child counts.
- Count by 100's to 1,000.
- Count by 5's to 50.
- Count by 10's to 100.
- Count backward from 100 by 10's.
- Say the odd numbers to 19.
- Say the odd numbers backward from 19.
- Ask your child to identify the digits to use to write the next number on the number line.
- Ask your child to identify the total number of pennies needed to show this number.

  "We have 100 pennies in this covered container."

  "How many more pennies do we need?"

  "Put the extra pennies in this cup."

- Count on from 100 to count the total number of pennies with your child.

number pattern

- Ask your child to identify and fill in the missing numbers.
- Read the number pattern together.

clock

- Ask your child to set the morning/afternoon/evening/night clock.
- Throughout the day, your child announces the time on the hour and the half hour, sets the demonstration clock to show the time, and writes the digital time on the chalkboard.

coin cup

"Today there are only nickels and pennies in the coin cup."

"How many nickels are there?"

"How many pennies are there?"

"When we count money, we begin with the coin that is worth the most."

"Which coin will you count first?"   nickel

• Ask your child to count the nickels and pennies and record the amount of money on the meeting strip.

right/left

• Continue to practice left and right once a week. Practice more often, if necessary.

The Lesson

Writing the Number 97

"The last number we practiced writing was the number 96."

"What number do you think we will learn how to write today?"

• Write the number 97 on the chalkboard.

"What digits do you see in the number 97?"

"How many dimes and pennies will we use to make 97¢?"

• Use dimes and pennies to demonstrate.

"How many groups of 10 are in 97?"

"How many extra 1's do we have?"

"Let's count by 10's and 1's to check."

Identifying One Half, One Third, and One Sixth

"Today you will learn how to identify one half, one third, and one sixth."

• Hold up the yellow pattern block.

"We will pretend that this is a cake."

"The other color pattern blocks are the frosting."

"What color pattern blocks do you think we can use to completely cover the top of the cake with frosting without having any frosting drip over the sides?"

"Let's try it to see."

"Take three yellow cakes."

"Try to cover each cake with frosting of only one color."

"Remember, you can not have empty spaces or frosting dripping over the edges."

• Give your child a basket of pattern blocks.

"What color frosting did you use on your cakes?"

"Do you see the lines on your cakes?"

"Trace the lines on one of your cakes with your finger."

"We'll pretend that the lines show where you cut your cake."

"Do you have a cake with exactly two pieces?"

"What color frosting does the cake have?"   red

"We call each piece one half."

"Do you have a cake with exactly three pieces?"

"What color frosting does the cake have?"   blue

"We call each piece one third because the cake has been cut into three equal pieces."

"Do you have a cake with exactly six pieces?"

"What color frosting does the cake have?"   green

"We call each piece one sixth because the cake has been cut into six equal pieces."

"Wipe the frosting off your cakes."

- Hold up a yellow pattern block covered by one red pattern block.

  "How much of my cake did I frost?"   one half

  "Frost one half of your cake."

- Allow time for your child to cover the yellow pattern block with a red pattern block.

  "Now frost the other half of your cake."

  "How much of the cake is frosted?"   one whole or two halves

  "Wipe the frosting off your cake."

- Hold up a yellow pattern block covered by one blue pattern block.

  "I frosted one third of my cake."

  "Frost one third of your cake."

- Allow time for your child to cover the yellow pattern block with a blue pattern block.

  "Frost another third of your cake."

  "How many thirds of your cake are frosted now?"   two thirds

  "Frost another third of your cake."

  "How many thirds of your cake are frosted now?"   three thirds

  "Now the whole cake is frosted."

  "Wipe the frosting off your cake."

- Hold up a yellow pattern block covered by one green pattern block.

  "I frosted one sixth of my cake."

  "Frost one sixth of your cake."

- Allow time for your child to cover the yellow pattern block with a green pattern block.

"Frost another sixth of your cake."

"How many sixths of your cake are frosted now?"   two sixths

- Repeat, adding one sixth at a time.

"If a cake has two equal pieces, what will we call each piece?"   one half

"If a cake has three equal pieces, what will we call each piece?"   one third

"If a cake has six equal pieces, what will we call each piece?"   one sixth

"Put the pattern blocks in the basket."

CLASS PRACTICE

"Let's practice the subtracting a number from ten facts together."

- Use the large subtraction fact cards. Include 10 – 0, 10 – 1, 10 – 2, and 10 – 5 fact cards also.

- Give your child **Fact Sheet S 6.0.**

- Correct the fact sheet with your child.

WRITTEN PRACTICE

- Complete **Worksheet 107A** with your child.

- Complete **Worksheet 107B** with your child later in the day.

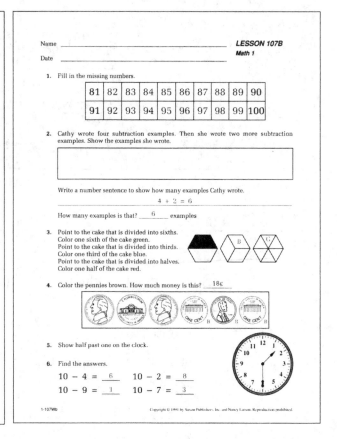

Lesson 108

writing the number 98
addition facts—adding nine to a number

---

lesson preparation

materials

ten 3" × 5" cards

addition fact cards — yellow

Master 1-108

Fact Sheet AA 7.1

the night before

• Use the 3" × 5" cards to make a large set of fact cards for the adding nine facts. Write them in the following way:

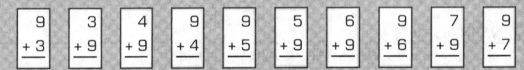

| 9
+ 3 | 3
+ 9 | 4
+ 9 | 9
+ 4 | 9
+ 5 | 5
+ 9 | 6
+ 9 | 9
+ 6 | 7
+ 9 | 9
+ 7 |

• Separate the yellow addition fact cards.

in the morning

• Write the following number pattern on the meeting strip:

66, 67, 68, ___, ___, ___

Answer: 66, 67, 68, 69, 70, 71

• Put **9 nickels** and **4 pennies** in the coin cup.

THE MEETING

calendar

• Ask your child to identify the following:

  year

  month

  shapes on the calendar

  today's shape

  shape pattern for the month

- Ask your child to write the date on the calendar.
- Ask your child to do the following:

    identify today's day of the week, yesterday's day of the week, and tomorrow's day of the week

    read the days of the week

    identify the weekdays

    identify the number of days in a week

- Ask your child to write the full date on the meeting strip.

weather graph

- Ask your child to report and graph the weather.
- Ask questions about the graph.

counting

- Say the "Counting by 10's Rap" on **Master 1-91** together. Point to the numbers on the hundred number chart as your child counts.
- Count by 100's to 1,000.
- Count by 5's to 50.
- Count by 10's to 100.
- Count backward from 100 by 10's.
- Count by 2's to 20.
- Count backward from 20 by 2's.
- Ask your child to identify the digits to use to write the next number on the number line.
- Ask your child to identify the total number of pennies needed to show this number.

    "We have 100 pennies in this covered container."

    "How many more pennies do we need?"

    "Put the extra pennies in this cup."

- Count on from 100 to count the total number of pennies with your child.

number pattern

- Ask your child to identify and fill in the missing numbers.
- Read the number pattern together.

clock

- Ask your child to set the morning/afternoon/evening/night clock.

- Throughout the day, your child announces the time on the hour and the half hour, sets the demonstration clock to show the time, and writes the digital time on the chalkboard.

coin cup

"Today there are only nickels and pennies in the coin cup."

"How many nickels are there?"

"How many pennies are there?"

"When we count money, we begin with the coin that is worth the most."

"Which coin will you count first?"   nickel

- Ask your child to count the nickels and pennies and record the amount of money on the meeting strip.

right/left

- Continue to practice left and right once a week. Practice more often, if necessary.

THE LESSON

Writing the Number 98

"The last number we practiced writing was the number 97."

"What number do you think we will learn how to write today?"

- Write the number 98 on the chalkboard.

"What digits do you see in the number 98?"

"How many dimes and pennies will we use to make 98¢?"

- Use dimes and pennies to demonstrate.

"How many groups of 10 are in 98?"

"How many extra 1's do we have?"

"Let's count by 10's and 1's to check."

Addition Facts—Adding Nine to a Number

"Today you will learn the addition facts called the adding nine facts."

- Write the following on the chalkboard:

$$\begin{array}{r} 4¢ \\ + \ 10¢ \\ \hline \end{array}$$

"How much money is this?"   14¢

- Record "14¢" on the chalkboard.

• Write the following on the chalkboard next to the first problem:

$$4¢$$
$$+\ 9¢$$

"What's different about this problem?"   *adding nine instead of adding ten*

"Will this be the same amount of money as four cents and ten cents?" *no*

"Will this be more money than four cents and ten cents?"   *no*

"How much money do you think this is?"   *13¢*

"How do you know?"   *it is one cent less*

• Write the following problems on the chalkboard:

$$10 \qquad\qquad 9$$
$$+\ 7 \qquad\qquad +\ 7$$

"What is the same about these problems?"

"What is different?"

"If there is one less in the problem, then there is one less in the answer."

"Ten plus seven is seventeen."

"Nine plus seven is sixteen."

• Record each answer below the problem.

• Write the following problems on the chalkboard:

$$5 \qquad\qquad 5$$
$$+\ 10 \qquad\qquad +\ 9$$

"What is the same about these problems?"

"What is different?"

"If there is one less in the problem, then there is one less in the answer."

"What is five plus ten?"   *15*

"What is five plus nine?"   *14*

• Record each answer below the problem.

• Write the following problems on the chalkboard:

$$10 \qquad\qquad 9$$
$$+\ 3 \qquad\qquad +\ 3$$

"What is the same about these problems?"

"What is different?"

"What is ten plus three?"   *13*

"If there is one less in the problem, then there is one less in the answer."

"What is nine plus three?"   12

- Record each answer below the problem.

- Repeat with 6 + 10 and 6 + 9.

- Give your child **Master 1-108**.

  "Write your name at the top of the paper."

  "Fold your paper in half along the dotted line."

- Allow time for your child to do this.

  "Put your paper on your desk so that you can see your name."

  "What kind of problems are these?"   *adding ten problems*

  "Write the answers on your paper as quickly as you can."

- When your child finishes, continue.

  "Let's read the problems and the answers together."

- Read the problems and the answers with your child.

  "Now turn to the other half of your paper."

  "Look at the first row."

  "Read the problems in this row."

  "Are they the same?"

  "How are they different?"

- Repeat with the second, third, and fourth rows.

  "The first problem in each row is an adding ten fact."

  "The second problem in each row is an adding nine fact."

  "How will we find the answers for the adding nine facts?"

  "To find the answer for an adding nine fact, we add ten to the other number and count back one."

  "Write the answers for the problems on this paper."

- When your child finishes, continue.

  "Let's read the problems and the answers together."

- Give your child the yellow addition fact cards.

  "Write the answer on the back of each card."

  "When you finish, read each problem to yourself."

  "See if you can remember the answer."

  "Turn over the card to check the answer."

- Allow time for your child to practice using the fact cards independently.

CLASS PRACTICE

- Give your child **Fact Sheet AA 7.1**.

  "What number facts do you see?"

  "What strategy will you use to find the answers?"

- Correct the fact sheet with your child.

WRITTEN PRACTICE

- Complete **Worksheet 108A** with your child.
- Complete **Worksheet 108B** with your child later in the day.

6 + 10	6 + 10	6 + 9
3 + 10	3 + 10	3 + 9
5 + 10	5 + 10	5 + 9
7 + 10	7 + 10	7 + 9
4 + 10	4 + 10	4 + 9
10 + 3	10 + 3	9 + 3
10 + 5	10 + 5	9 + 5
10 + 7	10 + 7	9 + 7
10 + 4	10 + 4	9 + 4
10 + 6	10 + 6	9 + 6

---

1. Write the number ninety-eight four more times. How many digits did you use? __8__

98

2. Billy's dad made a dozen muffins for breakfast. Billy's family ate ten muffins. Draw a picture and write a number sentence to show what happened.

Number sentence _____ $12 - 10 = 2$ _____

How many muffins are left? __2__ muffins

3. Point to the circle that is divided into thirds.
Color one third blue.

Point to the circle that is divided into halves.
Color one half red.

Point to the circle that is divided into sixths.
Color one sixth green.

Point to the circle that is divided into fourths.
Color one fourth orange.

4. Find the answers.

6 + 10 16	6 + 9 15	4 + 10 14	4 + 9 13	7 + 10 17	7 + 9 16

5. Work with a partner to measure the distance from the floor to the doorknob of your classroom door.

About how many feet from the floor is the doorknob? _____ feet

---

1. Write the numbers that are one more than each number.

9, __10__ 17, __18__ 26, __27__

2. Jessie's mom poured a dozen glasses of orange juice. The children drank nine glasses of juice. Draw a picture and write a number sentence to show what happened.

Number sentence _____ $12 - 9 = 3$ _____

How many glasses of juice are left? __3__ glasses of juice

3. Point to the square that is divided into thirds.
Color one third blue.

Point to the square that is divided into halves.
Color one half red.

Point to the square that is divided into sixths.
Color one sixth green.

Point to the square that is divided into fourths.
Color one fourth orange.

4. Find the answers.

5 + 10 15	5 + 9 14	3 + 10 13	3 + 9 12	8 + 10 18	8 + 9 17

5. Measure the length of your bed from the head of the bed to the foot of the bed.

About how many feet long is your bed? _____ feet

L esson 109

writing the number 99
identifying a quart, gallon, and liter
estimating and measuring the capacity of a
container in cups

---

lesson preparation

materials

unbreakable liter (soda or pop bottle), quart (milk, juice, or cream), and gallon (milk or juice) containers

labels for containers

waterproof marker

unbreakable measuring cup (1 cup)

funnel (optional)

newspapers or plastic drop cloth

large containers for water

food coloring (optional)

Master 1-109

3 plastic containers

large fact cards (adding nine facts)

Fact Sheet AA 7.1

in the morning

• Write the following number pattern on the meeting strip:

> 20, 22, 24, ___, ___, ___

Answer: 20, 22, 24, 26, 28, 30

• Put **6 nickels** and **4 pennies** in the coin cup.
• Write the following on the chalkboard:

Container	Estimate	Actual
	___ cups	___ cups
	___ cups	___ cups
	___ cups	___ cups

THE MEETING

calendar

- Ask your child to identify the following:

  year

  month

  shapes on the calendar

  today's shape

  shape pattern for the month

- Ask your child to write the date on the calendar.

- Ask your child to do the following:

  identify today's day of the week, yesterday's day of the week, and tomorrow's day of the week

  read the days of the week

  identify the weekdays

  identify the number of days in a week

- Ask your child to write the full date on the meeting strip.

weather graph

- Ask your child to report and graph the weather.

- Ask questions about the graph.

counting

- Say the "Counting by 10's Rap" on **Master 1-91** together. Point to the numbers on the hundred number chart as your child counts.

- Count by 100's to 1,000.

- Count by 5's to 50.

- Count by 10's to 100.

- Count backward from 100 by 10's.

- Say the odd numbers to 19.

- Say the odd numbers backward from 19.

- Ask your child to identify the digits to use to write the next number on the number line.

- Ask your child to identify the total number of pennies needed to show this number.

  "We have 100 pennies in this covered container."

  "How many more pennies do we need?"

"Put the extra pennies in this cup."

- Count on from 100 to count the total number of pennies with your child.

number pattern

- Ask your child to identify and fill in the missing numbers.
- Read the number pattern together.

clock

- Ask your child to set the morning/afternoon/evening/night clock.
- Throughout the day, your child announces the time on the hour and the half hour, sets the demonstration clock to show the time, and writes the digital time on the chalkboard.

coin cup

"Today there are only nickels and pennies in the coin cup."

"How many nickels are there?"

"How many pennies are there?"

"When we count money, we begin with the coin that is worth the most."

"Which coin will you count first?"   nickel

- Ask your child to count the nickels and pennies and record the amount of money on the meeting strip.

right/left

- Continue to practice left and right once a week. Practice more often, if necessary.

THE LESSON

Writing the Number 99

"The last number we practiced writing was the number 98."

"What number do you think we will learn how to write today?"

- Write the number 99 on the chalkboard.

"What digits do you see in the number 99?"

"How many dimes and pennies will we use to make 99¢?"

- Use dimes and pennies to demonstrate.

"How many groups of 10 are in 99?"

"How many extra 1's do we have?"

"Let's count by 10's and 1's to check."

Identifying a Quart, Gallon, and Liter
Estimating and Measuring the Capacity of a Container in Cups

- Spread newspapers or a plastic drop cloth on the floor. Fill large containers with water. You will need at least a gallon of water. Add food coloring to the water, if desired.

- Hold up the one-cup measuring cup.

  "We used this before when we were baking."

  "It has a special name."

  "What do we call this?"   a one-cup measuring cup

  "I have some containers."

  "Today you will learn the special names of these containers."

  "You also will learn how to estimate the capacity and fill each of these containers."

- Hold up a gallon container.

  "What do you think was in this container?"

  "How do you know?"

- Repeat with the quart and the liter containers.

- Hold up the gallon container.

  "There is a special word that tells us how much (milk) this container holds."

  "Do you know what that special word is?"   gallon

  "This is called a gallon container."

- Attach a tag with the word "gallon" to the container.

- Hold up the liter container.

  "There is a special word that tells us how much (soda or pop) this container holds."

  "Do you know what that special word is?"   liter

  "This is called a liter container."

- Attach a tag with the word "liter" to the container.

- Hold up the quart container.

  "There is a special word that tells us how much (juice) this container holds."

  "Do you know what that special word is?"   quart

  "This is called a quart container."

- Attach a tag with the word "quart" to the container.

"How many cups of water do you think it will take to fill the quart container?"

- Write your child's estimate on the chalkboard.

"Let's try it."

"I will fill the cup with water and pour it into the quart container."

"We will count together to see how many cups it will take to fill the quart container."

- Fill the container as your child counts.

- Record "4 cups" on the chalkboard.

"Do you think the liter container will hold more or less water than the quart container?"

"How many cups of water do you think it will hold?"

- Write your child's estimate on the chalkboard.

"Let's check it by pouring in cups of water."

- Ask your child to tally the cups as you pour them in the liter container.

"Did the liter container hold more or less water than the quart container?"

"About how many cups did it take to fill the liter container?"

- Record "4 + a little" on the chart.

"Now let's try the gallon container."

"Will it take more or less water to fill the gallon container than it took to fill the quart container?"

"How many cups of water do you think it will take to fill the gallon container?"

- Write your child's estimate on the chalkboard.

"Let's check it by pouring in cups of water."

- Ask your child to tally the cups as you pour them in the gallon container.

"How many cups did it take to fill the gallon container?"

- Record "16 cups" on the chalkboard.

"Now you will have a chance to practice estimating capacity and filling some containers with water."

- Give your child **Master 1-109** and 3 containers of various sizes.

"Choose one container."

"Write the name of the container in the first box."

"How many cups of water do you think it will take to fill this container?"

"Write that in the box under the word 'estimate.' "

"Now use the measuring cup to fill the container."

- Allow time for your child to do this.

"How many cups of water did you use?"

"Write this in the box under the word 'actual.'"

- Repeat with the other 2 containers.

CLASS PRACTICE

- Use the large fact cards to practice the adding nine facts with your child.

- Give your child **Fact Sheet AA 7.1.**

"What number facts do you see?"

"What strategies will you use to find the answers?"

- Correct the fact sheet with your child.

WRITTEN PRACTICE

- Complete **Worksheet 109A** with your child.

- Complete **Worksheet 109B** with your child later in the day.

Name _____ **MASTER 1-109**
Math 1

Container	Estimate	Actual
	_____ cups	_____ cups
	_____ cups	_____ cups
	_____ cups	_____ cups

1-109Ma

Name •_____•   **LESSON 109A**
(Draw a 3-inch line segment.)   Math 1
Date _____

Day of the Week _____

1. Write the number ninety-nine three more times. How many digits did you use? __6__

    99 99 99

2. Ronisha had eight pieces of banana on her cereal. She ate four pieces. Draw a picture and write a number sentence to show what happened.

    ○ ○ ○ ○ ⊗ ⊗ ⊗ ⊗

    What type of story is this? some, some more (some, some went away)
    Number sentence ___8 – 4 = 4___
    How many pieces of banana does she have left to eat? __4__ pieces

3. Sharon had 34 pennies. She put them in groups of 10 on this mat. Draw the pennies to show what she did.

4. Someone spilled paint on one of my number cards and covered the digit on the right.
    Which number card has paint on it? __28__

    24 26 23 29 20 21 25 2● 22 27

5. Choose four even numbers. Add 9 to each number.

    □ + 9 = □   □ + 9 = □   □ + 9 = □   □ + 9 = □

1-109Wa

Name _____   **LESSON 109B**
Math 1
Date _____

1. Write the number that is one less than each number.

    __6__ , 7   __14__ , 15   __22__ , 23

2. Gina put 6 strawberries on her cereal. She ate 3 strawberries. Draw a picture and write a number sentence to show what happened.

    What type of story is this? some, some more (some, some went away)
    Number sentence ___6 – 3 = 3___
    How many strawberries does she have left to eat? __3__ strawberries

3. Harry had 43 pennies. He put them in groups of 10 on this mat. Draw the pennies to show what he did.

4. Someone spilled paint on one of my number cards and covered the digit on the right.
    Which number card has paint on it? __37__

    39 32 35 31 3● 33 36 30 38 34

5. Choose four odd numbers. Add 9 to each number.

    □ + 9 = □   □ + 9 = □   □ + 9 = □   □ + 9 = □

    Parent: Ask your child to find a gallon, liter, and quart container at home. If possible, allow them to count the number of cups of water needed to fill each container.

1-109Wb

Lesson 110

assessment

---

lesson preparation

materials

2 quarters, 3 dimes, 4 nickels, and 5 pennies

graphing grid (Master 1-38)

Written Assessment #21

Oral Assessment #11

in the morning

• Write the following number pattern on the meeting strip:

> 15, 20, 25, __, __, __

> *Answer: 15, 20, 25, 30, 35, 40*

• Put **5 nickels** and **2 pennies** in the coin cup.

THE MEETING

calendar

- Ask your child to identify the following:

    year

    month

    shapes on the calendar

    today's shape

    shape pattern for the month

- Ask your child to write the date on the calendar.

- Ask your child to do the following:

    identify today's day of the week, yesterday's day of the week, and tomorrow's day of the week

    read the days of the week

    identify the weekdays

    identify the number of days in a week

- Ask your child to write the full date on the meeting strip.

weather graph

- Ask your child to report and graph the weather.
- Ask questions about the graph.

counting

- Say the "Counting by 10's Rap" on **Master 1-91** together. Point to the numbers on the hundred number chart as your child counts.
- Count by 100's to 1,000.
- Count by 5's to 50.
- Count by 10's to 100.
- Count backward from 100 by 10's.
- Count by 2's to 20.
- Count backward from 20 by 2's.
- Ask your child to identify the digits to use to write the next number on the number line.
- Use an orange crayon to color the square for 110.
- Ask your child to identify the total number of pennies needed to show this number.

  "We have 100 pennies in this covered container."

  "How many more pennies do we need?"

  "Put the extra pennies in this cup."
- Count on from 100 to count the total number of pennies with your child.

number pattern

- Ask your child to identify and fill in the missing numbers.
- Read the number pattern together.

clock

- Ask your child to set the morning/afternoon/evening/night clock.
- Throughout the day, your child announces the time on the hour and the half hour, sets the demonstration clock to show the time, and writes the digital time on the chalkboard.

coin cup

"Today there are only nickels and pennies in the coin cup."

"How many nickels are there?"

"How many pennies are there?"

"When we count money, we begin with the coin that is worth the most."

"Which coin will you count first?" nickel

- Ask your child to count the nickels and pennies and record the amount of money on the meeting strip.

right/left

- Continue to practice left and right once a week. Practice more often, if necessary.

ASSESSMENT

- All of the questions on the assessment are based on concepts and skills presented at least five lessons ago. If your child is having difficulty with a specific concept, reteach the concept the following day.

Written Assessment

- Give your child **Written Assessment #21**.

- Read the directions for each problem. Allow time for your child to complete each problem before continuing to the next.

- Correct the paper, noting your child's mistakes on the **Individual Recording Form**. Review the errors with your child.

Oral Assessment

- Record your child's responses to the oral interview on the interview sheet.

Name _____

Date _____

ASSESSMENT 21
LESSON 110
Math 1

1. Ms. Allen bought a dozen eggs. She used three eggs to make a cake for her class. Draw a picture and write a number sentence to show how many eggs she has left.

$$O\ O\ O\ O\ O\ O\ O\ O\ O\ \cancel{O}\ \cancel{O}\ \cancel{O}$$

Number sentence _____ $12 - 3 = 9$

How many eggs does she have left? __9__ eggs

2. Draw a 4-inch line segment.

3. How much money is this? 35¢

4. Fill in the missing numbers.

$$\begin{array}{r} 6 \\ + \boxed{4} \\ \hline 10 \end{array} \qquad \begin{array}{r} \boxed{8} \\ + 2 \\ \hline 10 \end{array} \qquad \begin{array}{r} 3 \\ + 7 \\ \hline 10 \end{array} \qquad \begin{array}{r} 1 \\ + \boxed{9} \\ \hline 10 \end{array} \qquad \begin{array}{r} 5 \\ + \boxed{5} \\ \hline 10 \end{array}$$

5. Draw congruent shapes on the geoboards.

Teacher _____

Date _____

MATH 1   LESSON 110
Oral Assessment # 11 Recording Form

Materials:
2 quarters
3 dimes
4 nickels
5 pennies
graphing grid
(Master 1-38)

Students	*Give the child the coins.* "Sort these coins."	"Graph these coins."	"How many dimes do you have?" "How many pennies do you have?" "How many more pennies do you have than dimes?"		
			A.	B.	C.

esson 111

writing the number 100
identifying one dollar

---

lesson preparation

materials

1 bag of 100 pennies

Masters 1-84A and 1-84B (from Lesson 84)

1 one-dollar bill

scrap paper

large fact cards (adding nine facts)

Fact Sheet A 7.1

in the morning

• Write the following number pattern on the meeting strip:

> 61, 63, 65, ___, ___, ___

Answer: 61, 63, 65, 67, 69, 71

• Put **3 nickels** and **4 pennies** in the coin cup.

THE MEETING

calendar

   • Ask your child to identify the following:

   year

   month

   shapes on the calendar

   today's shape

   shape pattern for the month

• Ask your child to write the date on the calendar.

• Ask your child to do the following:

   identify today's day of the week, yesterday's day of the week, and tomorrow's day of the week

   read the days of the week

   identify the weekdays

identify the number of days in a week

- Ask your child to write the full date on the meeting strip.

weather graph

- Ask your child to report and graph the weather.
- Ask questions about the graph.

counting

- Say the "Counting by 10's Rap" on **Master 1-91** together. Point to the numbers on the hundred number chart as your child counts.
- Count by 100's to 1,000.
- Count by 5's to 50.
- Count by 10's to 100.
- Count backward from 100 by 10's.
- Say the odd numbers to 19.
- Say the odd numbers backward from 19.
- Ask your child to identify the digits to use to write the next number on the number line.
- Ask your child to identify the total number of pennies needed to show this number.

"We have 100 pennies in this covered container."

"How many more pennies do we need?"

"Put the extra pennies in this cup."

- Count on from 100 to count the total number of pennies with your child.

number pattern

- Ask your child to identify and fill in the missing numbers.
- Read the number pattern together.

clock

- Ask your child to set the morning/afternoon/evening/night clock.
- Throughout the day, your child announces the time on the hour and the half hour, sets the demonstration clock to show the time, and writes the digital time on the chalkboard.

coin cup

"Today there are nickels and pennies in the coin cup."

"Today you will learn a new way to count the nickels from our coin cup."

"Put the nickels in stacks of two."

- Allow time for your child to stack the nickels.

"Two nickels are the same as one dime."

"Five cents plus five cents is ten cents."

"We can count the stacks of two nickels like we count dimes."

"Let's count the money together as I point to each stack of nickels and the extra pennies."

- Ask your child to record the amount of money on the meeting strip.

right/left

- Continue to practice left and right once a week. Practice more often, if necessary.

THE LESSON

Writing the Number 100

"The last number we practiced writing was the number 99."

"What number do you think we will learn how to write today?"

- Write the number 100 on the chalkboard.

"What digits do you see in the number 100?"

Identifying One Dollar

"Today you will learn how to identify a different unit of money."

- Hold up the bags of pennies.

"A few weeks ago we counted the pennies in these bags."

"How many pennies were in each bag?"

- Hold up a one-dollar bill.

"This is a one-dollar bill."

"The '1' in each corner tells us that it is worth one dollar."

"One hundred pennies is the same as one dollar."

"We can trade a one-dollar bill for a bag of pennies."

- Give your child a one-dollar bill.

"Study your dollar bill very carefully."

- Allow time for your child to inspect the one-dollar bill.

"What do you notice about your one-dollar bill?"

- Allow time for your child to offer as many observations as possible.

"There is a picture of a man on the front."

"Do you know who this is?"

"This is George Washington, the first president of the United States."

"A dollar bill is worth the same as 100 pennies."

"Why do you think people use dollar bills instead of pennies?"   they are easier to carry and count

"We write 'one dollar' like this."

- Write the following on the chalkboard:

$1.00

- Circle the dollar sign.

"This symbol is called a dollar sign."

"We can make a dollar sign by writing a capital S with a '1' on top of it."

- Demonstrate on the chalkboard.

"Let's try that."

- Give your child a piece of scrap paper.

"Write a capital S on your paper."

"Now write a '1' on top of it to make a dollar sign."

"Practice making some more dollar signs."

- Allow time for your child to practice drawing dollar signs.

"Let's write the symbol for one dollar."

- Demonstrate on the chalkboard as you describe each step.

"Draw a dollar sign."

"Now write a '1.'"

"After the '1' we will put a decimal point."

"We always write a decimal point after the dollars."

"Now we will write two zeros to show that we have no extra pennies."

"Write the two zeros after your decimal point."

- Allow time for your child to do this.

"How will we write 'two dollars'?"

- Ask your child to describe how to write "$2.00."

- Write the following on the chalkboard:

$2.00

"Write 'two dollars' on your paper."

- Allow time for your child to do this.

"How will we write 'five dollars'?"

- Ask your child to describe how to write "$5.00."

"Write 'five dollars' on your paper."

- Allow time for your child to do this.

  "If we have 300 pennies, how many dollars will we have?" 3

  "Write 'three dollars' on your paper."

- Allow time for your child to do this.

- Save the bag of pennies.

CLASS PRACTICE

"Let's review the adding nine number facts."

"What strategy will you use to find the answers?"

- Use the large fact cards.

- Give your child **Fact Sheet A 7.1**.

- Correct the fact sheet with your child.

WRITTEN PRACTICE

- Complete **Worksheet 111A** with your child.

- Complete **Worksheet 111B** with your child later in the day.

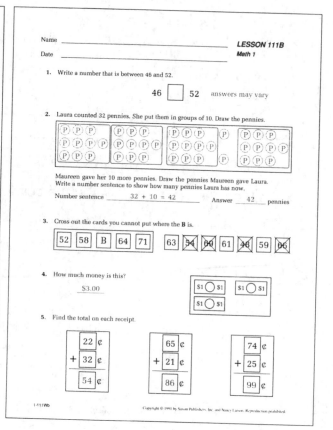

esson 112

writing the number 101
identifying fractional parts of a whole

---

lesson preparation

materials

one-dollar bill

13 small envelopes

13 1" construction paper tags in 6 different colors

6 cherry tomatoes, 3 mushrooms, 2 celery stalks, 2 carrots, 2 cucumbers, and 4 green beans

6 paper plates

cutting board and knife

napkins

large fact cards (adding nine facts)

Fact Sheet A 7.1

the night before

- Cut out thirteen 1" tags of each of the following colors: red, tan, green, orange, light green, and yellow.
- Put one tag of each color in each envelope.

in the morning

- Write the following number pattern on the meeting strip:

> ___, ___, ___, 8, 10, 12

Answer: *2, 4, 6, 8, 10, 12*

- Put **6 nickels** and **2 pennies** in the coin cup.

THE MEETING

calendar

- Ask your child to identify the following:

  year

  month

  shapes on the calendar

today's shape

shape pattern for the month

- Ask your child to write the date on the calendar.

- Ask your child to do the following:

  identify today's day of the week, yesterday's day of the week, and tomorrow's day of the week

  read the days of the week

  identify the weekdays

  identify the number of days in a week

"Let's say the names of the months of the year together."

- Point to the names of the months of the year as you read them with your child.

- Ask your child to write the full date on the meeting strip.

weather graph

- Ask your child to report and graph the weather.

- Ask questions about the graph.

counting

- Say the "Counting by 10's Rap" on **Master 1-91** together once a week.

- Count by 100's to 1,000.

- Count by 5's to 50.

- Count by 10's to 100.

- Count backward from 100 by 10's.

- Count by 2's to 20.

- Count backward from 20 by 2's.

- Ask your child to identify the digits to use to write the next number on the number line.

- Ask your child to identify the total number of pennies needed to show this number.

"We have 100 pennies in this covered container."

- Show your child a one-dollar bill.

"This one-dollar bill is the same as 100 pennies."

"We will use this one-dollar bill instead of this container of 100 pennies."

"How many more pennies do we need to show 112 pennies?"

"Let's use dimes and pennies instead of just pennies."

"How many dimes and pennies will we use?"

- Ask your child to count out that number of dimes and pennies.
- Count the money with your child.

number pattern

- Ask your child to identify and fill in the missing numbers.
- Read the number pattern together.

clock

- Ask your child to set the morning/afternoon/evening/night clock.
- Throughout the day, your child announces the time on the hour and the half hour, sets the demonstration clock to show the time, and writes the digital time on the chalkboard.

coin cup

"Today there are nickels and pennies in the coin cup."

"Put the nickels in stacks of two."

- Allow time for your child to stack the nickels.

"Two nickels are the same as one dime."

"We can count the stacks of two nickels like we count dimes."

"Let's count the money together as I point to each stack of nickels and the extra pennies."

- Ask your child to record the amount of money on the meeting strip.

right/left

- Continue to practice left and right once a week. Practice more often, if necessary.

THE LESSON

Writing the Number 101

"The last number we practiced writing was the number 100."

"What number do you think we will learn how to write today?"

- Write the number 101 on the chalkboard.

"What digits do you see in the number 101?"

Identifying Fractional Parts of a Whole

- Put each type of vegetable on a separate plate.

"Today you will learn how to identify fractional parts of a whole."

"We will use vegetables for our math lesson."

"Do you know the name of any of these vegetables?"

- Ask your child to identify the vegetables he/she knows.

"Where do vegetables grow?"

"Do we know someone who has grown vegetables?"

"Who was it? What did they grow?"

"Today we will taste some vegetables to see which ones we like."

"We will also ask some friends, family members, and neighbors to taste the vegetables to see which ones they like."

"All of these vegetables are safe to eat and can be eaten raw."

"What does the word 'raw' mean?"   not cooked

"We do not have enough of each vegetable so that everyone can have a whole carrot or a whole tomato to eat."

"What can we do if we want everyone to taste each vegetable?"   cut them into pieces

- Point to the plate of tomatoes.

"What is this vegetable called?"

"I would like everyone to have an equal share of tomato to taste."

"I will cut each tomato in half."

- Cut one tomato in half.

"How many pieces did I get from one tomato?"   2

"When we cut something into two equal parts, we call each part one half."

"Count by 2's as I cut the tomatoes in half."

- Cut all the tomatoes in half as your child counts by 2's.
- Point to the plate of mushrooms.

"What is this vegetable called?"

"I would like everyone to have an equal share of mushroom to taste."

"I will cut each mushroom into four equal parts."

- Cut one mushroom into fourths.

"How many pieces did I get from one mushroom?"   4

"When we cut something into four equal parts, we call each part one fourth."

- Cut the other mushrooms into fourths.
- Point to the plate of green beans.

"What is this vegetable called?"

"I would like everyone to have an equal share of green bean to taste."

"I will cut each green bean into three equal parts."

- Cut one green bean into thirds.

"How many pieces did I get from one green bean?" three

"When we cut something into three equal parts, we call each part one third."

- Cut the other green beans into thirds.

- Point to the plate of carrots.

"What is this vegetable called?"

"I would like everyone to have an equal share of carrot to taste."

"I will cut each carrot into six equal parts."

- Cut one carrot into sixths.

"How many pieces did I get from one carrot?" 6

"When we cut something into six equal parts, we call each part one sixth."

- Cut the other carrot into sixths.

- Point to the plate of celery.

"What is this vegetable called?"

"I would like everyone to have an equal share of celery to taste."

"I will cut each stalk of celery into eight equal parts."

- Cut one celery stalk into eighths.

"How many pieces did I get from one stalk of celery?" 8

"What do you think we will call each part when we cut something into eight equal parts?" one eighth

- Cut the other stalk of celery into eighths.

- Point to the plate of cucumbers.

"What is this vegetable called?"

"I would like everyone to have an equal share of cucumber to taste."

"I will cut each cucumber into ten equal parts."

- Cut one cucumber into tenths.

"How many pieces did I get from one cucumber?" 10

"What do you think we will call each part when we cut something into ten equal parts?" one tenth

- Cut the other cucumber into tenths.

"Now you will have a chance to taste each of the vegetables."

"Later we will ask some friends, family members, or neighbors to taste our vegetables."

"After everyone has tasted each vegetable, we will make a graph to show the vegetables that we like."

- Give your child an envelope of tags. The following colors will represent each vegetable:

red	tomato	orange	carrot
tan	mushroom	light green	celery
green	green bean	yellow	cucumber

"Take the tags out of the envelope and put them on the table."

"Write your name on the envelope."

"Now I will give you one half of a cherry tomato."

"When I give you your half of a tomato, take a bite of it."

"If you like the tomato, put the red tag in the envelope."

"If you do not like the tomato, leave the tag on the table and put the tomato on your napkin."

"You will only put the tags of the vegetables you like in the envelope."

- Give your child a piece of cherry tomato on a napkin.

"Do you like the taste of the tomato?"

"If you do, put the red tag in the envelope."

"Now you will try the mushroom."

"I will give you one fourth of a mushroom to try."

- Give your child a piece of mushroom.

"Do you like the taste of the mushroom?"

"If you do, put the tan tag in the envelope."

"Now you will try the green bean."

"I will give you one third of a green bean to try."

- Give your child a piece of green bean.

"Do you like the taste of the green bean?"

"If you do, put the green tag in the envelope."

"Now you will try the carrot."

"I will give you one sixth of a carrot to try."

- Give your child a piece of carrot.

"Do you like the taste of the carrot?"

"If you do, put the orange tag in the envelope."

"Now you will try the celery."

"I will give you one eighth of a piece of celery to try."

- Give your child a piece of celery.

"Do you like the taste of the celery?"

"If you do, put the light green tag in the envelope."

"Now you will try the cucumber."

"I will give you one tenth of a piece of cucumber to try."

- Give your child a piece of cucumber.

"Do you like the taste of the cucumber?"

"If you do, put the yellow tag in the envelope."

"We will use these tags tomorrow to make a graph."

- Save your child's envelope of tags.
- Repeat this tasting activity with 8–10 friends, family members, or neighbors.
- Save one set of tags for use in Lesson 113.

CLASS PRACTICE

"Let's review the adding nine number facts."

"What strategy will you use to find the answers?"

- Use the large fact cards.
- Give your child **Fact Sheet A 7.1**.
- Correct the fact sheet with your child.

WRITTEN PRACTICE

- Complete **Worksheet 112A** with your child.
- Complete **Worksheet 112B** with your child later in the day.

Name ●————————————————————●   **LESSON 112A**
  (Draw a 4-inch line segment.)   *Math 1*

Date ————————————————————————

Day of the Week ————————————————————

1. Write the number one hundred one 4 more times.

$\boxed{101}$ $\boxed{101}$ ——————————

2. Evie read 21 pages of her book on Monday. On Tuesday, she read 10 more pages.
What kind of story is this? (some, some more)   some, some went away
Write a number sentence to find how many pages she read altogether.
Number sentence ___ $21 + 10 = 31$ ___   Answer __31__ pages

3. Each vegetable is cut into how many pieces?

__6__ pieces   __2__ pieces   __4__ pieces

4. Circle a dozen donuts.
Color a half dozen brown
to show that they are chocolate.

5. Use the classroom calendar to answer these questions.
What was the date of the first Tuesday of this month? _____
What was yesterday's date? _____
What day of the week will it be tomorrow? _____

6. Find the answers.
$59 + 10 = $ __69__ $74 + 10 = $ __84__ $16 + 10 = $ __26__

7. Find the answers.

$\begin{array}{r} 7 \\ +9 \\ \hline 16 \end{array}$ $\begin{array}{r} 4 \\ +9 \\ \hline 13 \end{array}$ $\begin{array}{r} 5 \\ +9 \\ \hline 14 \end{array}$ $\begin{array}{r} 8 \\ -2 \\ \hline 6 \end{array}$ $\begin{array}{r} 5 \\ -2 \\ \hline 3 \end{array}$ $\begin{array}{r} 9 \\ -2 \\ \hline 7 \end{array}$

Name —————————————————————   **LESSON 112B**
                                      Math 1

Date ——————————————————————

1. Write the numbers that are one less and one more than each number.

__18__ , 19, __20__   __39__ , 40, __41__

2. Curtis read 36 pages of his book on Saturday. On Sunday, he read 10 more pages.
What kind of story is this? (some, some more)   some, some went away
Write a number sentence to find how many pages he read altogether.
Number sentence ___ $36 + 10 = 46$ ___   Answer __46__ pages

3. Each shape is divided into how many pieces?

__8__ pieces   __4__ pieces   __4__ pieces

4. Circle a dozen cupcakes.
Color a half dozen brown
to show that they are chocolate.

5. What will be the date tomorrow? _____

6. Find the answers.
$62 + 10 = $ __72__ $36 + 10 = $ __46__ $11 + 10 = $ __21__

7. Find the answers.

$\begin{array}{r} 6 \\ +9 \\ \hline 15 \end{array}$ $\begin{array}{r} 8 \\ +9 \\ \hline 17 \end{array}$ $\begin{array}{r} 3 \\ +9 \\ \hline 12 \end{array}$ $\begin{array}{r} 7 \\ -2 \\ \hline 5 \end{array}$ $\begin{array}{r} 10 \\ -2 \\ \hline 8 \end{array}$ $\begin{array}{r} 6 \\ -2 \\ \hline 4 \end{array}$

esson **113**

writing the number 102
graphing tags on a bar graph
writing observations about a graph

---

lesson preparation

materials

graphing grid (see *the night before*)

1 tag of each color from Lesson 112

envelopes with tags (from Lesson 112)

glue stick

paper

large fact cards (addition facts)

Fact Sheet A 7.2

the night before

• Prepare the following graphing grid prior to the lesson:

tomato											
mushroom											
green bean											
carrot											
celery											
cucumber											

in the morning

• Write the following number pattern on the meeting strip:

40, 50, 60, ___, ___, ___

Answer: 40, 50, 60, 70, 80, 90

• Put **7 nickels** and **1 penny** in the coin cup.

THE MEETING

calendar

- Ask your child to identify the following:

    year

    month

    shapes on the calendar

    today's shape

    shape pattern for the month

- Ask your child to write the date on the calendar.

- Ask your child to do the following:

    identify today's day of the week, yesterday's day of the week, and tomorrow's day of the week

    read the days of the week

    identify the weekdays

    identify the number of days in a week

    "Let's say the names of the months of the year together."

- Point to the names of the months of the year as you read them with your child.

- Ask your child to write the full date on the meeting strip.

weather graph

- Ask your child to report and graph the weather.

- Ask questions about the graph.

counting

- Say the "Counting by 10's Rap" on **Master 1-91** together once a week.

- Count by 100's to 1,000.

- Count by 5's to 50.

- Count by 10's to 100.

- Count backward from 100 by 10's.

- Say the odd numbers to 19.

- Say the odd numbers backward from 19.

- Ask your child to identify the digits to use to write the next number on the number line.

- Ask your child to identify the total number of pennies needed to show this number.

"We have 100 pennies in this covered container."

• Show your child a one-dollar bill.

"This one-dollar bill is the same as 100 pennies."

"We will use this one-dollar bill instead of this container of 100 pennies."

"How many more pennies do we need to show 113 pennies?"

"Let's use dimes and pennies instead of just pennies."

"How many dimes and pennies will we use?"

• Ask your child to count out that number of dimes and pennies.

• Count the money with your child.

number pattern

• Ask your child to identify and fill in the missing numbers.

• Read the number pattern together.

clock

• Ask your child to set the morning/afternoon/evening/night clock.

• Throughout the day, your child announces the time on the hour and the half hour, sets the demonstration clock to show the time, and writes the digital time on the chalkboard.

coin cup

"Today there are nickels and pennies in the coin cup."

"Put the nickels in stacks of two."

• Allow time for your child to stack the nickels.

"Two nickels are the same as one dime."

"We can count the stacks of two nickels like we count dimes."

"Let's count the money together as I point to each stack of nickels and the extra pennies."

• Ask your child to record the amount of money on the meeting strip.

right/left

• Continue to practice left and right once a week. Practice more often, if necessary.

THE LESSON

Writing the Number 102

> *"The last number we practiced writing was the number 101."*

> *"What number do you think we will learn how to write today?"*

- Write the number 102 on the chalkboard.

> *"What digits do you see in the number 102?"*

Graphing Tags on a Bar Graph
Writing Observations about a Graph

- Place the graph in the center of the table.

> *"Yesterday we cut vegetables into fractional parts and tasted them to find out which ones we liked."*

> *"What vegetables did we taste?"* tomato, mushroom, green bean, carrot, celery, and cucumber

> *"What did we do after we tasted each vegetable?"* we put a colored tag in our envelope if we liked the vegetable

- Display one tag of each color.

> *"Which color tag did we use for each vegetable?"*

- Place or tape the correct color tag to the left of each vegetable name on the graph.

> *"What do you think we are going to do today?"* graph our tags

> *"Today you will learn how to graph your tags on a bar graph."*

> *"You also will learn how to write observations about a graph."*

> *"What kinds of things do you think we will find out when we graph our tags?"* the favorite vegetable, the least favorite vegetable, how many people liked each vegetable

- Give your child his/her envelope of tags.

> *"Which tag would you like to graph first?"*

> *"Where will you put the tag?"*

- Glue the tag to the graph.

- Repeat with the other tags.

- Ask your child to graph the tags in all the envelopes in the same way.

> *"Let's write some things that we know by looking at this graph."*

- Record your child's observations on paper. Encourage your child to offer as many observations as possible.

> *"How many people liked tomatoes?"*

> *"How many people liked cucumbers?"*

"How many people liked celery?"

"Which vegetable was the favorite?"

"Which vegetable did the fewest people like?"

"How many more people liked _____ than liked _____?"

"How many fewer people liked _____ than liked _____?"

"Which three vegetables were the most well liked?"

"Which vegetables were chosen more often than green beans?"

"Which vegetables were chosen less often than carrots?"

CLASS PRACTICE

- Use the fact cards to practice the addition facts.
- Give your child **Fact Sheet A 7.2.**

  "What number facts do you see?"

  "What strategies will you use to find the answers?"

- Correct the fact sheet with your child.

WRITTEN PRACTICE

- Complete **Worksheet 113A** with your child.
- Complete **Worksheet 113B** with your child later in the day.

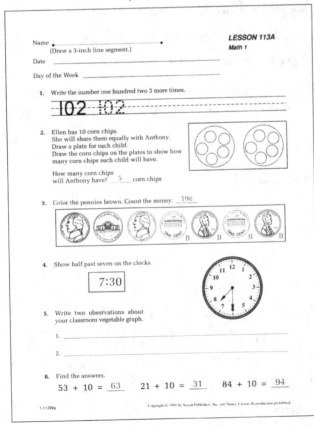

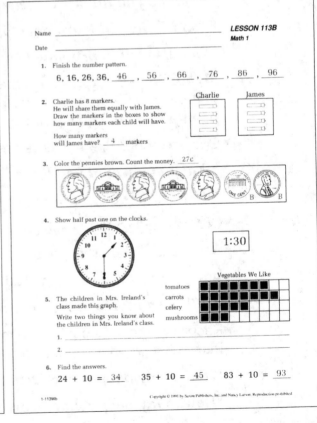

Lesson 114

writing the number 103
counting dimes, nickels, and pennies

lesson preparation

materials

1 cup of 5 dimes, 8 nickels, and 10 pennies

piece of paper

Fact Sheet A 7.2

in the morning

• Write the following number pattern on the meeting strip:

> 4, 14, 24, ___, ___, ___

Answer: 4, 14, 24, 34, 44, 54

• Put **8 nickels** and **3 pennies** in the coin cup.

THE MEETING

calendar

• Ask your child to identify the following:

　year

　month

　shapes on the calendar

　today's shape

　shape pattern for the month

• Ask your child to write the date on the calendar.

• Ask your child to do the following:

　identify today's day of the week, yesterday's day of the week, and tomorrow's day of the week

　read the days of the week

　identify the weekdays

　identify the number of days in a week

"Let's say the names of the months of the year together."

- Point to the names of the months of the year as you read them with your child.
- Ask your child to write the full date on the meeting strip.

weather graph

- Ask your child to report and graph the weather.
- Ask questions about the graph.

counting

- Say the "Counting by 10's Rap" on **Master 1-91** together once a week.
- Count by 100's to 1,000.
- Count by 5's to 50.
- Count by 10's to 100.
- Count backward from 100 by 10's.
- Count by 2's to 20.
- Count backward from 20 by 2's.
- Ask your child to identify the digits to use to write the next number on the number line.
- Ask your child to identify the total number of pennies needed to show this number.

   "We have 100 pennies in this covered container."

- Show your child a one-dollar bill.

   "This one-dollar bill is the same as 100 pennies."

   "We will use this one-dollar bill instead of this container of 100 pennies."

   "How many more pennies do we need to show 114 pennies?"

   "Let's use dimes and pennies instead of just pennies."

   "How many dimes and pennies will we use?"

- Ask your child to count out that number of dimes and pennies.
- Count the money with your child.

number pattern

- Ask your child to identify and fill in the missing numbers.
- Read the number pattern together.

clock

- Ask your child to set the morning/afternoon/evening/night clock.

• Throughout the day, your child announces the time on the hour and the half hour, sets the demonstration clock to show the time, and writes the digital time on the chalkboard.

coin cup

"Today there are nickels and pennies in the coin cup."

"Put the nickels in stacks of two."

• Allow time for your child to stack the nickels.

"Two nickels are the same as one dime."

"We can count the stacks of two nickels like we count dimes."

"Let's count the money together as I point to each stack of nickels and the extra pennies."

• Ask your child to record the amount of money on the meeting strip.

right/left

• Continue to practice left and right once a week. Practice more often, if necessary.

THE LESSON

Writing the Number 103

"The last number we practiced writing was the number 102."

"What number do you think we will learn how to write today?"

• Write the number 103 on the chalkboard.

"What digits do you see in the number 103?"

Counting Dimes, Nickels, and Pennies

"Today you will learn how to count dimes, nickels, and pennies."

• Put 2 dimes, 6 nickels, and 3 pennies on a piece of paper.

"What coins do I have on my paper?"

"Let's count to see how much money this is."

"First I will sort the coins."

• Sort the coins.

"When we count coins, we begin with the coin that is worth the most."

"Which coins will we count first?"   dimes

"Which coins will we count next?"   nickels

"Which coins will we count last?"   pennies

"Before we begin, I will put the nickels in stacks of two."

- Stack the nickels.

"Two nickels are the same as one dime."

"Five cents plus five cents is ten cents."

"When we count the stacks of two nickels, we count them like we count dimes."

"Let's count the money together."

- Point to the dimes, stacks of nickels, and pennies as you count the money with your child.

"Now you will have a chance to count some money."

- Give your child the paper and a cup containing 5 dimes, 8 nickels, and 10 pennies.

"Sort your coins on the paper."

- Allow time for your child to sort the coins.

"How many dimes do you have?"   5

"How many nickels do you have?"   8

"How many pennies do you have?"   10

"What is a dime worth?"   10¢

"What is a nickel worth?"   5¢

"Two nickels are the same as one dime."

"Put your nickels on the paper in stacks of two."

- Allow time for your child to stack the nickels.

"When we count the stacks of two nickels, we count them like we count dimes."

"What is a penny worth?"   1¢

"Put your pennies in a stack of ten."

"If you can't make a stack of ten pennies, leave your pennies flat on the paper."

- Allow time for your child to stack the pennies.

"Each stack of coins is equal to ten cents."

"Let's count the money together."

"Point to each stack as we count by 10's."

- Count the money with your child.

"How much money is this?"   one dollar

"Now we will practice counting different amounts of money."

"Put three dimes, four nickels, and two pennies on your paper."

- Allow time for your child to do this.

  "Put the nickels in stacks of two."

- Allow time for your child to do this.

  "Do you have enough pennies to put them in a pile of ten?" no

  "Let's count the money together."

  "Which coins will we count first?" dimes

  "Which coins will we count next?" nickels

  "Which coins will we count last?" pennies

  "We will begin with the dimes, then we will count the nickels, and then the pennies."

- Count the money with your child.

  "Put two dimes, five nickels, and one penny on your paper."

- Allow time for your child to do this.

  "Put the nickels in stacks of two."

- Allow time for your child to do this.

  "Can you put all the nickels in stacks of two?" no

  "Point to the extra nickel."

  "Can we count this nickel by 10's?" no

  "What is the nickel worth?" 5¢

  "When we count an extra nickel, we add on five cents."

  "Let's count the money together."

  "We will begin with the dimes and the stacks of two nickels."

  "How will we count these?" by 10's

  "Let's count the money together."

- Count the money with your child.

  "Put four dimes, three nickels, and two pennies on your paper."

- Allow time for your child to do this.

  "Put the nickels in stacks of two."

- Allow time for your child to do this.

  "Can you put all the nickels in stacks of two?" no

  "Point to the extra nickel."

  "Can we count this nickel by 10's?" no

  "What is the nickel worth?" 5¢

  "When we count an extra nickel, we add on five cents."

  "Let's count the money together."

"We will begin with the dimes and the stacks of two nickels."

"How will we count these?"   by 10's

- Count the money with your child.

"Put one dime, seven nickels, and three pennies on your paper."

- Allow time for your child to do this.

"Put the nickels in stacks of two."

- Allow time for your child to do this.

"Let's count the money together."

"We will begin with the dimes, then we will count the nickels, and then the pennies."

- Count the money with your child.
- Repeat with 5 dimes, 5 nickels, and 2 pennies.

"Put the coins in the cup."

CLASS PRACTICE

"Use your individual fact cards to practice the addition facts."

- Allow time for your child to practice the addition number facts independently.
- Give your child **Fact Sheet A 7.2.**

"What number facts do you see?"

"What strategies will you use to find the answers?"

- Correct the fact sheet with your child.

WRITTEN PRACTICE

- Complete **Worksheet 114A** with your child.
- Complete **Worksheet 114B** with your child later in the day.

Name ●——————————●   **LESSON 114A**
  (Draw a 3-inch line segment.)   *Math 1*

Date ——————————————

Day of the Week ————————————————

1. Write the number one hundred three 2 more times.

103 103

2. The children in Room 2 had five frogs.
They gave one frog to the children in Room 3.
Draw a picture and write a number sentence to show what happened.

☐ ☐ ☐ ☐ ☒

Number sentence ——————— 5 – 1 = 4 ———————

How many frogs do the children in Room 2 have now?   4   frogs

3. Color the pennies brown. Count the money.   24¢

4. Finish the number pattern.

4, 14, 24, _34_ , _44_ , _54_ , _64_ , _74_ , _84_ , _94_

5. Find the answers.

6	9	10	10	9	6
+ 9	+ 4	– 6	– 3	– 2	– 2
15	13	4	7	7	4

1-114Wa

Name —————————————————   **LESSON 114B**

Date —————————————————   *Math 1*

1. Fill in the missing numbers.

71	72	73	74	75	76	77	78	79	80
81	82	83	84	85	86	87	88	89	90

2. The children in Room 4 had seven fish.
They gave two fish to the children in Room 1.
Draw a picture and write a number sentence to show what happened.

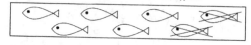

Number sentence ——————— 7 – 2 = 5 ———————

How many fish do the children in Room 4 have now?   5   fish

3. Color the pennies brown. Count the money.   28¢

4. Finish the number pattern.

8, 18, 28, _38_ , _48_ , _58_ , _68_ , _78_ , _88_ , _98_

5. Find the answers.

5	9	10	10	5	7
+ 9	+ 7	– 4	– 7	– 2	– 2
14	16	6	3	3	5

1-114Wb

esson 115

writing the number 104
identifying the season—spring

---

lesson preparation

---

materials

Written Assessment #22

Meeting Book

crayons

large fact cards (addition facts)

Fact Sheet A 7.2

in the morning

• Write the following number pattern on the meeting strip:

> 20, 22, 24, ___, ___, ___

Answer: 20, 22, 24, 26, 28, 30

• Put **5 dimes** and **4 nickels** in the coin cup.

THE MEETING

calendar

• Ask your child to identify the following:

> year
>
> month
>
> shapes on the calendar
>
> today's shape
>
> shape pattern for the month

• Ask your child to write the date on the calendar.

• Ask your child to do the following:

> identify today's day of the week, yesterday's day of the week, and tomorrow's day of the week
>
> read the days of the week
>
> identify the weekdays

identify the number of days in a week

"Let's say the names of the months of the year together."

- Point to the names of the months of the year as you read them with your child.

- Ask your child to write the full date on the meeting strip.

weather graph

- Ask your child to report and graph the weather.

- Ask questions about the graph.

counting

- Say the "Counting by 10's Rap" on **Master 1-91** together once a week.

- Count by 100's to 1,000.

- Count by 5's to 50.

- Count by 10's to 100.

- Count backward from 100 by 10's.

- Say the odd numbers to 19.

- Say the odd numbers backward from 19.

- Ask your child to identify the digits to use to write the next number on the number line.

- Ask your child to identify the total number of pennies needed to show this number.

"We have 100 pennies in this covered container."

- Show your child a one-dollar bill.

"This one-dollar bill is the same as 100 pennies."

"We will use this one-dollar bill instead of this container of 100 pennies."

"How many more pennies do we need to show 115 pennies?"

"Let's use dimes and pennies instead of just pennies."

"How many dimes and pennies will we use?"

- Ask your child to count out that number of dimes and pennies.

- Count the money with your child.

number pattern

- Ask your child to identify and fill in the missing numbers.

- Read the number pattern together.

clock

- Ask your child to set the morning/afternoon/evening/night clock.
- Throughout the day, your child announces the time on the hour and the half hour, sets the demonstration clock to show the time, and writes the digital time on the chalkboard.

coin cup

"Today we have dimes and nickels in the coin cup."

"Put the nickels in stacks of two."

- Allow time for your child to stack the nickels.

"Two nickels are the same as one dime."

"Five cents plus five cents is ten cents."

"We can count the stacks of two nickels like we count dimes."

"Let's count the money together as I point to each dime and each stack of nickels."

- Ask your child to record the amount of money on the meeting strip.

right/left

- Continue to practice left and right once a week. Practice more often, if necessary.

ASSESSMENT

Written Assessment

- Pass out **Written Assessment #22**.
- Read the directions for each problem. Allow time for your child to complete each problem before continuing to the next.
- Correct the paper, noting your child's mistakes on the **Individual Recording Form**. Review the errors with your child.

THE LESSON

Writing the Number 104

"The last number we practiced writing was the number 103."

"What number do you think we will learn how to write today?"

- Write the number 104 on the chalkboard.

"What digits do you see in the number 104?"

Identifying the Season—Spring

- If this lesson takes place before the official beginning of spring, adjust the following dialogue accordingly:

  "Today you will learn about a new season."

  "On March _____ , a new season began."

  Note: The actual date varies from year to year.

  "What season is it now?"   spring

  "How is spring different from fall and winter?"   temperature, amount of daylight, clothing worn, plants and trees are different, etc.

  "What do you do differently in the spring?"

  "Today we will look at the tree (or plant) we chose in the fall."

  "What did it look like then?"

  "We will go outside to see it again today."

- Open the Meeting Book to page 30.

  "You will draw a picture of the tree in the Meeting Book."

  "You will also write about how the tree looks in spring."

- Go outside and observe the tree.

  "What does the tree look like now?"

  "How is this different from when we saw it in the winter?"

  "What does it feel like outside in spring?"

  "How is this different from when we were outside in the winter?"

  "Draw a picture and write about our tree in the spring."

- Encourage your child to write about his/her observations using approximate spelling. Do not correct your child's writing, but rather let this be an example of how your child's writing develops throughout the year.

- Optional: Take a picture of your child next to the tree (plant).

CLASS PRACTICE

"Use your individual fact cards to practice the addition facts."

- Allow time for your child to practice the addition number facts independently.

- Give your child **Fact Sheet A 7.2**.

  "What number facts do you see?"

  "What strategies will you use to find the answers?"

- Correct the fact sheet with your child.

WRITTEN PRACTICE

- Complete **Worksheet 115A** with your child.

- Complete **Worksheet 115B** with your child later in the day.

Name _____
(Draw a 4-inch line segment.)

Date _____

Day of the Week _____

ASSESSMENT 22
LESSON 115
Math 1

1. Maurice had 9 rocks in his collection. He found 2 more rocks for his collection. Draw a picture and write a number sentence to show the rocks in his collection.

Number sentence ___9 + 2 = 11___

How many rocks are in his collection now? ___11___ rocks

2. Danny has 6 dimes. He will share them equally with Tricia. Draw the dimes in the boxes to show how many dimes each child will have.

Danny   Tricia

How many dimes will Tricia have? ___3___ dimes

3. Color the pennies brown. Count the money. ___28¢___

4. Finish the patterns.

6, 8, 10, _12_ , _14_ , _16_ , _18_ , _20_

24, 23, 22, _21_ , _20_ , _19_ , _18_ , _17_

5. Find the answers.

6	9	7	6	10	7	6
+ 2	− 1	+ 7	+ 9	− 4	− 2	+ 5
8	8	14	15	6	5	11

1-115Aa

Copyright © 1991 by Saxon Publishers, Inc. and Nancy Larson. Reproduction prohibited.

Name _____
(Draw a 2-inch line segment.)

Date _____

Day of the Week _____

LESSON 115A
Math 1

1. Write the number one hundred four 2 more times.

104 104

2. Michelle wrote a two-digit number on a piece of paper. She gave the children the following clues to help them guess her secret number. Michelle said. "The digits I used are 5 and 3."

Write the two possible numbers. __(35)__ __53__

Michelle said. "The number is between 29 and 41." Circle Michelle's secret number.

3. Circle the coins Frank can use to pay for the pencil. *answers may vary*

17¢

4. Krista put the linking cubes in trains of 10. How many linking cubes does she have?

___44___ linking cubes

5. Draw tally marks to show the number of chairs in your classroom.

How many chairs are there? _____

6. Find the answers.

79 + 10 = _89_   8 + 10 = _18_   22 + 10 = _32_

1-115Wa

Copyright © 1991 by Saxon Publishers, Inc. and Nancy Larson. Reproduction prohibited.

Name _____

Date _____

LESSON 115B
Math 1

1. Fill in the missing numbers.

45, 44, 43, _42_ , _41_ , _40_ , _39_ , _38_

5, 10, 15, _20_ , _25_ , _30_ , _35_ , _40_

2. Sam wrote a two-digit number on a piece of paper. He gave the children the following clues to help them guess his secret number. Sam said. "The digits I used are 7 and 2."

Write the two possible numbers. __(27)__ __72__

Sam said. "The number is between 18 and 28." Circle Sam's secret number.

3. Circle the coins Paula can use to pay for the ruler. *answers may vary*

23¢

4. Martha put the linking cubes in trains of 10. How many linking cubes does she have?

___62___ linking cubes

5. Draw tally marks to show the number of chairs in your home.

How many chairs are there? _____

6. Find the answers.

88 + 10 = _98_   6 + 10 = _16_   45 + 10 = _55_

1-115Wb

Copyright © 1991 by Saxon Publishers, Inc. and Nancy Larson. Reproduction prohibited.

---

esson 116

writing the number 105
addition facts—the last eight facts

---

lesson preparation

materials

2 towers of linking cubes (10 each of two colors)

Master 1-116

crayons

addition fact cards — white

sixteen 3" × 5" cards

Fact Sheet A 8.1

the night before

• Use the 3" × 5" cards to make a large set of fact cards for the last eight addition facts. Write them in the following way:

$\begin{array}{r} 5 \\ +\,3 \\ \hline \end{array}$	$\begin{array}{r} 6 \\ +\,3 \\ \hline \end{array}$	$\begin{array}{r} 8 \\ +\,3 \\ \hline \end{array}$	$\begin{array}{r} 7 \\ +\,4 \\ \hline \end{array}$	$\begin{array}{r} 7 \\ +\,5 \\ \hline \end{array}$	$\begin{array}{r} 8 \\ +\,4 \\ \hline \end{array}$	$\begin{array}{r} 8 \\ +\,5 \\ \hline \end{array}$	$\begin{array}{r} 8 \\ +\,6 \\ \hline \end{array}$
$\begin{array}{r} 3 \\ +\,5 \\ \hline \end{array}$	$\begin{array}{r} 3 \\ +\,6 \\ \hline \end{array}$	$\begin{array}{r} 3 \\ +\,8 \\ \hline \end{array}$	$\begin{array}{r} 4 \\ +\,7 \\ \hline \end{array}$	$\begin{array}{r} 5 \\ +\,7 \\ \hline \end{array}$	$\begin{array}{r} 4 \\ +\,8 \\ \hline \end{array}$	$\begin{array}{r} 5 \\ +\,8 \\ \hline \end{array}$	$\begin{array}{r} 6 \\ +\,8 \\ \hline \end{array}$

• Separate the white addition fact cards.

in the morning

• Write the following number pattern on the meeting strip:

> ___, ___, ___, 51, 52, 53

Answer: 48, 49, 50, 51, 52, 53

• Put **4 dimes** and **3 nickels** in the coin cup.

THE MEETING

calendar

- Ask your child to identify the following:

  year

  month

  shapes on the calendar

  today's shape

  shape pattern for the month

- Ask your child to write the date on the calendar.

- Ask your child to do the following:

  identify today's day of the week, yesterday's day of the week, and tomorrow's day of the week

  read the days of the week

  identify the weekdays

  identify the number of days in a week

  "Let's say the names of the months of the year together."

- Point to the names of the months of the year as you read them with your child.

- Ask your child to write the full date on the meeting strip.

weather graph

- Ask your child to report and graph the weather.

- Ask questions about the graph.

counting

- Say the "Counting by 10's Rap" on **Master 1-91** together once a week.

- Count by 100's to 1,000.

- Count by 5's to 50.

- Count by 10's to 100.

- Count backward from 100 by 10's.

- Count by 2's to 20.

- Count backward from 20 by 2's.

- Ask your child to identify the digits to use to write the next number on the number line.

- Ask your child to identify the total number of pennies needed to show this number.

"We have 100 pennies in this covered container."

• Show your child a one-dollar bill.

"This one-dollar bill is the same as 100 pennies."

"We will use this one-dollar bill instead of this container of 100 pennies."

"How many more pennies do we need to show 116 pennies?"

"Let's use dimes and pennies instead of just pennies."

"How many dimes and pennies will we use?"

• Ask your child to count out that number of dimes and pennies.

• Count the money with your child.

number pattern

• Ask your child to identify and fill in the missing numbers.

• Read the number pattern together.

clock

• Ask your child to set the morning/afternoon/evening/night clock.

• Throughout the day, your child announces the time on the hour and the half hour, sets the demonstration clock to show the time, and writes the digital time on the chalkboard.

coin cup

"Today we have dimes and nickels in the coin cup."

"Put the nickels in stacks of two."

• Allow time for your child to stack the nickels.

"Two nickels are the same as one dime."

"Five cents plus five cents is ten cents."

"We can count the stacks of two nickels like we count dimes."

"Let's count the money together as I point to each dime and each stack of nickels."

• Ask your child to record the amount of money on the meeting strip.

right/left

• Continue to practice left and right once a week. Practice more often, if necessary.

THE LESSON

Writing the Number 105

"The last number we practiced writing was the number 104."

"What number do you think we will learn how to write today?"

• Write the number 105 on the chalkboard.

"What digits do you see in the number 105?"

Addition Facts—The Last Eight Facts

"Today you will learn the last eight addition facts."

"Some people call these the oddball facts because they don't follow a pattern."

• Give your child **Master 1-116**, 2 towers of linking cubes, and crayons.

"Use the two crayons that match the colors of your linking cubes."

"Today you will use linking cubes to find the answers for the oddball addition facts."

"You will use the cubes of one color to show the first number and the cubes of the other color to show the second number."

"How many cubes do you think you will use altogether to show five plus three?"

"Will you use more than ten cubes?"   no

"How do you know?"   5 + 5 = 10

"Make a train of five cubes of one color."

"Now add on three cubes of the other color."

• Allow time for your child to snap together the cubes.

"Let's count the cars in the train."

"Start with the larger number, and then count the extra cars."

• Encourage your child to say "five, six, seven, eight."

"How many cars does the train have?"   8

"Now you will draw a picture to show the cars on the train."

"Each box on this paper is one car."

"Point to the first train on your paper."

"Point to the left end of the train."

"Color the boxes on your paper to show five cars of one color plus three cars of the other color."

"Be careful not to skip any cars."

• Allow time for your child to color the boxes.

"How many boxes did you color?"   8

"Write '8' next to the '5 + 3 ='."

"How many cubes do you think you will use altogether to show six plus three?"

"Will you use more than ten cubes?"   no

"How do you know?"   6 + 4 = 10

"Make a train of six cubes of one color."

"Now add on three cubes of the other color."

• Allow time for your child to snap together the cubes.

"Let's count the cars in the train."

"Start with the larger number, and then count the extra cars."

"How many cars does the train have?"   9

"Now you will draw a picture to show the cars on the train."

"Point to the second train on your paper."

"Point to the left end of the train."

"Color the boxes on your paper to show six cars of one color plus three cars of the other color."

"Be careful not to skip any cars."

• Allow time for your child to color the boxes.

"How many boxes did you color?"   9

"Write '9' next to the '6 + 3 ='."

"How many cubes do you think you will use altogether to show eight plus three?"

"Will you use more than ten cubes?"   yes

"How do you know?"   8 + 2 = 10

"Make a train of eight cubes of one color."

"Now add on three cubes of the other color."

• Allow time for your child to snap together the cubes.

"Let's count the cars in the train."

"Start with the larger number, and then count the extra cars."

"How many cars does the train have?"   11

"Now you will draw a picture to show the cars on the train."

"Each box on this paper is one car."

"Point to the third train."

"Point to the left end of the train."

"Color the boxes on your paper to show eight cars of one color plus three cars of the other color."

"Be careful not to skip any cars."

- Allow time for your child to color the boxes.

"How many boxes did you color?"   11

"Write '11' next to the '8 + 3 ='."

- Repeat with each of the remaining fact combinations.

"Each day you will choose one oddball fact that will be the oddball fact of the day."

"We will practice this fact as many times as we can during the day."

"During the day I will say, 'What is the oddball fact for today?'."

"We will say the oddball fact of the day together."

- Give your child the white addition fact cards.

"Can you find two facts that are switcharound facts?"

"What facts did you find?"

- Ask your child to name two facts, such as 5 + 8 and 8 + 5.

"Put these cards next to each other."

"What is the answer?"

"Write the answer on the back of each card."

- Repeat until all the fact cards are paired.

"When you finish, practice saying the facts and the answers to yourself."

"See how many answers you can remember."

- Allow time for your child to practice independently.

CLASS PRACTICE

- Give your child **Fact Sheet A 8.1**.
- Correct the fact sheet with your child.

WRITTEN PRACTICE

- Complete **Worksheet 116A** with your child.
- Complete **Worksheet 116B** with your child later in the day.

Name _____ **MASTER 1-116**
_____ Math 1

5 + 3 = _____ ☐☐☐☐☐|☐☐☐☐☐

6 + 3 = _____ ☐☐☐☐☐|☐☐☐☐☐

8 + 3 = _____ ☐☐☐☐☐|☐☐☐☐☐

7 + 4 = _____ ☐☐☐☐☐|☐☐☐☐☐

7 + 5 = _____ ☐☐☐☐☐|☐☐☐☐☐

8 + 4 = _____ ☐☐☐☐☐|☐☐☐☐☐

8 + 5 = _____ ☐☐☐☐☐|☐☐☐☐☐

8 + 6 = _____ ☐☐☐☐☐|☐☐☐☐☐

1-116Ma

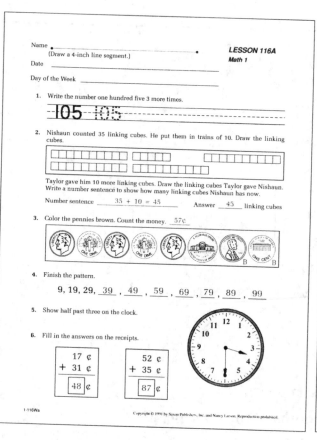

Name •_____• **LESSON 116A**
(Draw a 4-inch line segment.) Math 1
Date _____

Day of the Week _____

1. Write the number one hundred five 3 more times.

   105 105

2. Nishaun counted 35 linking cubes. He put them in trains of 10. Draw the linking cubes.

   Taylor gave him 10 more linking cubes. Draw the linking cubes Taylor gave Nishaun. Write a number sentence to show how many linking cubes Nishaun has now.

   Number sentence ___35 + 10 = 45___   Answer ___45___ linking cubes

3. Color the pennies brown. Count the money. ___57¢___

4. Finish the pattern.

   9, 19, 29, _39_ , _49_ , _59_ , _69_ , _79_ , _89_ , _99_

5. Show half past three on the clock.

6. Fill in the answers on the receipts.

17 ¢		52 ¢
+ 31 ¢		+ 35 ¢
48 ¢		87 ¢

1-116Wa

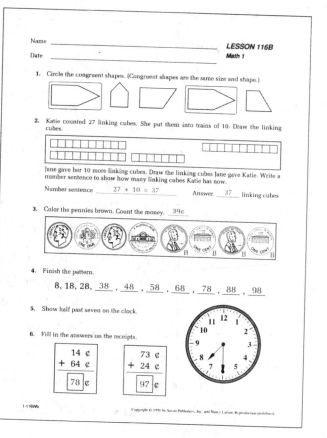

Name _____ **LESSON 116B**
Date _____ Math 1

1. Circle the congruent shapes. (Congruent shapes are the same size and shape.)

2. Katie counted 27 linking cubes. She put them into trains of 10. Draw the linking cubes.

   Jane gave her 10 more linking cubes. Draw the linking cubes Jane gave Katie. Write a number sentence to show how many linking cubes Katie has now.

   Number sentence ___27 + 10 = 37___   Answer ___37___ linking cubes

3. Color the pennies brown. Count the money. ___39¢___

4. Finish the pattern.

   8, 18, 28, _38_ , _48_ , _58_ , _68_ , _78_ , _88_ , _98_

5. Show half past seven on the clock.

6. Fill in the answers on the receipts.

14 ¢		73 ¢
+ 64 ¢		+ 24 ¢
78 ¢		97 ¢

1-116Wb

L esson 117

writing the number 106
measuring line segments using centimeters

---

lesson preparation

materials

ruler

Master 1-117

Fact Sheet A 8.1

in the morning

• Write the following number pattern on the meeting strip:

> 6, 16, 26, ___, ___, ___

Answer: 6, 16, 26, 36, 46, 56

• Put **3 dimes** and **5 nickels** in the coin cup.

THE MEETING

calendar

• Ask your child to identify the following:

> year
>
> month
>
> shapes on the calendar
>
> today's shape
>
> shape pattern for the month

• Ask your child to write the date on the calendar.

• Ask your child to do the following:

> identify today's day of the week, yesterday's day of the week, and tomorrow's day of the week
>
> read the days of the week
>
> identify the weekdays
>
> identify the number of days in a week

"Let's say the names of the months of the year together."

- Point to the names of the months of the year as you read them with your child.
- Ask your child to write the full date on the meeting strip.

weather graph

- Ask your child to report and graph the weather.
- Ask questions about the graph.

counting

- Say the "Counting by 10's Rap" on **Master 1-91** together once a week.
- Count by 100's to 1,000.
- Count by 5's to 50.
- Count by 10's to 100.
- Count backward from 100 by 10's.
- Say the odd numbers to 19.
- Say the odd numbers backward from 19.
- Ask your child to identify the digits to use to write the next number on the number line.
- Ask your child to identify the total number of pennies needed to show this number.

   "We have 100 pennies in this covered container."

- Show your child a one-dollar bill.

   "This one-dollar bill is the same as 100 pennies."

   "We will use this one-dollar bill instead of this container of 100 pennies."

   "How many more pennies do we need to show 117 pennies?"

   "Let's use dimes and pennies instead of just pennies."

   "How many dimes and pennies will we use?"

- Ask your child to count out that number of dimes and pennies.
- Count the money with your child.

number pattern

- Ask your child to identify and fill in the missing numbers.
- Read the number pattern together.

clock

- Ask your child to set the morning/afternoon/evening/night clock.

- Throughout the day, your child announces the time on the hour and the half hour, sets the demonstration clock to show the time, and writes the digital time on the chalkboard.

coin cup

"Today we have dimes and nickels in the coin cup."

"Put the nickels in stacks of two."

- Allow time for your child to stack the nickels.

"Two nickels are the same as one dime."

"Five cents plus five cents is ten cents."

"We can count the stacks of two nickels like we count dimes."

"Let's count the money together as I point to each dime and each stack of nickels."

- Ask your child to record the amount of money on the meeting strip.

right/left

- Continue to practice left and right once a week. Practice more often, if necessary.

number fact of the day

- Ask your child to choose a number fact (one of the oddball facts) to practice for the day.

"Let's practice number facts."

"Hip, hip, hooray!"

"What is the oddball fact for today?"

- Write the number fact on the chalkboard. Frequently during the day, ask your child the following question:

"What is our oddball fact for today?"

THE LESSON

Writing the Number 106

"The last number we practiced writing was the number 105."

"What number do you think we will learn how to write today?"

- Write the number 106 on the chalkboard.

"What digits do you see in the number 106?"

Measuring Line Segments Using Centimeters

"We have been measuring and drawing line segments using inches."

"Today you will learn how to measure line segments using centimeters."

• Give your child an inch/cm ruler.

"Point to the inch side of your ruler."

"How many inches are there on your ruler?"   12

"Now look at the other edge of the ruler."

"Does this edge of the ruler look the same as the edge with the inches?"

"How is it different?"

• Allow time for your child to offer observations.

"When we use this side of the ruler, we are measuring using centimeters."

"Many people use centimeters instead of inches for measuring."

"About how many centimeters long is your ruler?"   30

"Let's measure some line segments using centimeters."

• Give your child **Master 1-117**.

"You will measure these line segments using the centimeter edge of your ruler."

"Point to line segment number one."

"Put the centimeter edge of your ruler next to line segment one."

"Put the left end of the ruler (the zero) on the endpoint near the one."

"Now look along the ruler until you come to the other endpoint."

"What number on the ruler is near the other end of the line segment?"

"Write this number in the space below the line segment."

"How many centimeters long is line segment one?"   13 cm

"Point to line segment number two."

"Put the left end of the ruler (the zero) on the endpoint near the two."

"Now look along the ruler until you come to the next endpoint."

"What number on the ruler is near the other end of the line segment?"

"Write this number in the space below the line segment."

"How many centimeters long is line segment two?"   7 cm

• Repeat with line segment numbers 3, 4, 5, and 6.   *15 cm, 14 cm, 3 cm, 6 cm*

"Now you will measure the length of your feet."

"Turn over your paper."

"Put your paper on the floor and trace your foot."

- Assist your child with the tracing, if necessary.

"Put your paper on the table."

"Now you will use the centimeter edge of the ruler to measure the length of your foot."

"Put the end of your ruler (the zero) at the end of your heel."

"The end of your longest toe is closest to what number on the ruler?"

"Write that number next to your toe."

CLASS PRACTICE

"Practice the addition facts on your white addition fact cards."

- Allow time for your child to do this.
- Give your child **Fact Sheet A 8.1**.
- Correct the fact sheet with your child.

WRITTEN PRACTICE

- Complete **Worksheet 117A** with your child.
- Complete **Worksheet 117B** with your child later in the day.

Name _____ **MASTER 1-117**
Math 1

1. _____ centimeters

2. _____ centimeters

3. _____ centimeters

4. _____ centimeters

5. _____ centimeters

6. _____ centimeters

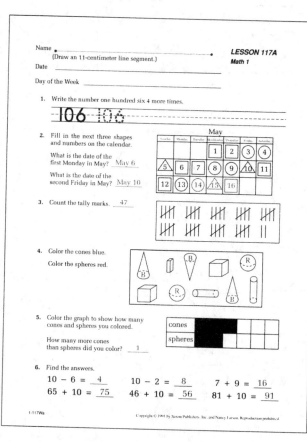

Name _____ **LESSON 117A**
(Draw an 11-centimeter line segment.)   **Math 1**

Date _____

Day of the Week _____

1. Write the number one hundred six 4 more times.

   106 106

2. Fill in the next three shapes
   and numbers on the calendar.

   May

   What is the date of the
   first Monday in May? May 6

   What is the date of the
   second Friday in May? May 10

3. Count the tally marks. 47

4. Color the cones blue.

   Color the spheres red.

5. Color the graph to show how many
   cones and spheres you colored.

   How many more cones
   than spheres did you color? 1

6. Find the answers.

   $10 - 6 = \underline{4}$ $10 - 2 = \underline{8}$ $7 + 9 = \underline{16}$

   $65 + 10 = \underline{75}$ $46 + 10 = \underline{56}$ $81 + 10 = \underline{91}$

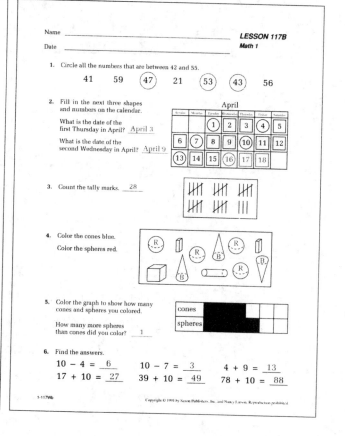

Name _____ **LESSON 117B**
Math 1

Date _____

1. Circle all the numbers that are between 42 and 55.

   41   59   (47)   21   (53)   (43)   56

2. Fill in the next three shapes
   and numbers on the calendar.

   April

   What is the date of the
   first Thursday in April? April 3

   What is the date of the
   second Wednesday in April? April 9

3. Count the tally marks. 28

4. Color the cones blue.

   Color the spheres red.

5. Color the graph to show how many
   cones and spheres you colored.

   How many more spheres
   than cones did you color? 1

6. Find the answers.

   $10 - 4 = \underline{6}$ $10 - 7 = \underline{3}$ $4 + 9 = \underline{13}$

   $17 + 10 = \underline{27}$ $39 + 10 = \underline{49}$ $78 + 10 = \underline{88}$

L esson 118

writing the number 107
identifying geometric solids (cylinders and cubes)

---

lesson preparation

materials

1 linking cube (other cubes can be used as models)

2 cans of food

scissors

two 6" × 9" pieces of construction paper

tape

Fact Sheet A 8.1

in the morning

• Write the following number pattern on the meeting strip:

> ___, ___, ___, 25, 30, 35

Answer: 10, 15, 20, 25, 30, 35

• Put **5 dimes** and **7 nickels** in the coin cup.

THE MEETING

calendar

• Ask your child to identify the following:

year

month

shapes on the calendar

today's shape

shape pattern for the month

• Ask your child to write the date on the calendar.

• Ask your child to do the following:

identify today's day of the week, yesterday's day of the week, and tomorrow's day of the week

read the days of the week

identify the weekdays

identify the number of days in a week

> *"Let's say the names of the months of the year together."*

- Point to the names of the months of the year as you read them with your child.

- Ask your child to write the full date on the meeting strip.

weather graph

- Ask your child to report and graph the weather.

- Ask questions about the graph.

counting

- Say the "Counting by 10's Rap" on **Master 1-91** together once a week.

- Count by 100's to 1,000.

- Count by 5's to 50.

- Count by 10's to 100.

- Count backward from 100 by 10's.

- Count by 2's to 20.

- Count backward from 20 by 2's.

- Ask your child to identify the digits to use to write the next number on the number line.

- Ask your child to identify the total number of pennies needed to show this number.

> *"We have 100 pennies in this covered container."*

- Show your child a one-dollar bill.

> *"This one-dollar bill is the same as 100 pennies."*

> *"We will use this one-dollar bill instead of this container of 100 pennies."*

> *"How many more pennies do we need to show 118 pennies?"*

> *"Let's use dimes and pennies instead of just pennies."*

> *"How many dimes and pennies will we use?"*

- Ask your child to count out that number of dimes and pennies.

- Count the money with your child.

number pattern

- Ask your child to identify and fill in the missing numbers.

- Read the number pattern together.

clock

- Ask your child to set the morning/afternoon/evening/night clock.
- Throughout the day, your child announces the time on the hour and the half hour, sets the demonstration clock to show the time, and writes the digital time on the chalkboard.

coin cup

"Today we have dimes and nickels in the coin cup."

"Put the nickels in stacks of two."

- Allow time for your child to stack the nickels.

"Two nickels are the same as one dime."

"Five cents plus five cents is ten cents."

"We can count the stacks of two nickels like we count dimes."

"Let's count the money together as I point to each dime and each stack of nickels."

- Ask your child to record the amount of money on the meeting strip.

right/left

- Continue to practice left and right once a week. Practice more often, if necessary.

number fact of the day

- Ask your child to choose a number fact (one of the oddball facts) to practice for the day.

"Let's practice number facts."

"Hip, hip, hooray!"

"What is the oddball fact for today?"

- Write the number fact on the chalkboard. Frequently during the day, ask your child the following question:

"What is our oddball fact for today?"

THE LESSON

Writing the Number 107

"The last number we practiced writing was the number 106."

"What number do you think we will learn how to write today?"

- Write the number 107 on the chalkboard.

"What digits do you see in the number 107?"

Identifying Geometric Solids (Cylinders and Cubes)

"A few weeks ago you learned the special names for two geometric solids."

"Do you remember what they were?"   cone and sphere

"Today you will learn about the special names for two more geometric solids."

- Hold up a linking cube (or other cube) and a can of food (or other cylindrical object).

"What are these?"

"Mathematicians have special names for objects with these shapes."

- Hold up the linking cube.

"Things that are shaped like this are called cubes."

- Give your child the linking cube.

"All the sides of a cube are the same size."

"Put your cube on the table in front of you."

"Look at it carefully."

"How many sides does a cube have?"   6

"Let's count them together."

"There is one side facing you, one side on the back, one side facing right, one side facing left, one on the top, and one on the bottom."

"Put a different side of the cube on the table."

"Does your cube look the same?"   yes

"Let's look around the house to find other cubes."

- Walk through the house and identify other cubes.

- Hold up the 2 cans of food.

"Things that are shaped like these cans are called cylinders."

- Stand one can on its base and lay the other can on its side.

"What do you notice about a cylinder?"

"Can we always roll a cylinder?"   no, not when it's standing on a base

"What is the shape of each end of a cylinder?"   circle

"How many circles does a cylinder have?"   2

"If I take the label off a can, what shape do you think it will be?"

"Let's try it to see."

- Carefully cut the label off the can.

"What shape is this?"   rectangle

"Now I will put the label back on the can so I will know what is in the can."

- Tape the label on the can.
- Remind your child not to take the labels off cans without your permission.

"I can make a cylinder using a piece of paper."

- Show your child the two rectangular pieces of paper.

"Both of these pieces of paper are the same size."

- Show your child that they are the same.

"Now I will roll these pieces of construction paper to make cylinders."

- Roll one 6" × 9" piece of construction paper horizontally and the other vertically and tape the edges.

"I used the same size piece of construction paper to make both of these cylinders."

"Do they look the same?" no

"What did I do to make them look different?" rolled them along different sides

"Let's look around our house to find other cylinders."

- Walk through the house and identify other cylinders.

"During the next week we will look for more cubes and cylinders."

"Remember that a cube will need to look like this linking cube and a cylinder will need to look like this can."

CLASS PRACTICE

"Practice the addition facts on your white addition fact cards."

- Allow time for your child to do this.
- Give your child **Fact Sheet A 8.1.**
- Correct the fact sheet with your child.

WRITTEN PRACTICE

- Complete **Worksheet 118A** with your child.
- Complete **Worksheet 118B** with your child later in the day.

Name _____ LESSON 118A
(Draw a 9-centimeter line segment.) *Math 1*

Date _____

Day of the Week _____

1. Write the number one hundred seven 2 more times.

   107 107

2. Harvey cut out a half dozen paper hearts. Then he cut out two more paper hearts.
   Draw a picture and write a number sentence to show the hearts.

   ♡ ♡ ♡ ♡ ♡ ♡   ♡ ♡

   Number sentence _____ 6 + 2 = 8 _____

   How many paper hearts did Harvey cut out altogether? __8__ hearts

3. Circle the coins that Melinda can use to pay for the donut.   answers may vary

4. Circle the clock that shows half past one.

5. Measure this line segment using centimeters.   __14__ cm

6. Find the answers.

   5 + 7 = __12__   4 + 7 = __11__   6 + 8 = __14__
   3 + 8 = __11__   5 + 3 = __8__   8 + 5 = __13__

1-118Wa

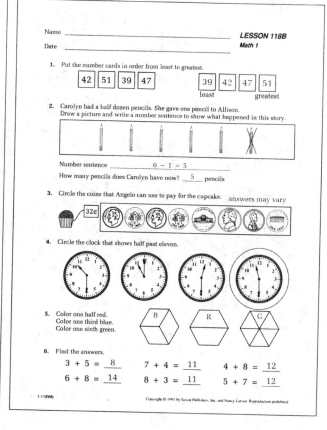

Name _____ LESSON 118B
Math 1

Date _____

1. Put the number cards in order from least to greatest.

   [42] [51] [39] [47]   [39] [42] [47] [51]
                           least   greatest

2. Carolyn had a half dozen pencils. She gave one pencil to Allison.
   Draw a picture and write a number sentence to show what happened in this story.

   Number sentence _____ 6 − 1 = 5 _____

   How many pencils does Carolyn have now? __5__ pencils

3. Circle the coins that Angelo can use to pay for the cupcake.   answers may vary

4. Circle the clock that shows half past eleven.

5. Color one half red.
   Color one third blue.
   Color one sixth green.

   B   R   G

6. Find the answers.

   3 + 5 = __8__   7 + 4 = __11__   4 + 8 = __12__
   6 + 8 = __14__   8 + 3 = __11__   5 + 7 = __12__

1-118Wb

esson 119

writing the number 108
subtracting ten from a number

---

lesson preparation

materials

scrap paper

large fact cards (oddball addition facts)

Fact Sheet A 8.2

in the morning

• Write the following number pattern on the meeting strip:

> 13, 15, 17, __, __, __

> *Answer: 13, 15, 17, 19, 21, 23*

• Put **2 dimes, 6 nickels,** and **4 pennies** in the coin cup.

THE MEETING

calendar

• Ask your child to identify the following:

> year

> month

> shapes on the calendar

> today's shape

> shape pattern for the month

• Ask your child to write the date on the calendar.

• Ask your child to do the following:

> identify today's day of the week, yesterday's day of the week, and tomorrow's day of the week

> read the days of the week

> identify the weekdays

> identify the number of days in a week

"Let's say the names of the months of the year together."

- Point to the names of the months of the year as you read them with your child.

- Ask your child to write the full date on the meeting strip.

weather graph

- Ask your child to report and graph the weather.

- Ask questions about the graph.

counting

- Say the "Counting by 10's Rap" on **Master 1-91** together once a week.

- Count by 100's to 1,000.

- Count by 5's to 50.

- Count by 10's to 100.

- Count backward from 100 by 10's.

- Say the odd numbers to 19.

- Say the odd numbers backward from 19.

- Ask your child to identify the digits to use to write the next number on the number line.

- Ask your child to identify the total number of pennies needed to show this number.

  "We have 100 pennies in this covered container."

- Show your child a one-dollar bill.

  "This one-dollar bill is the same as 100 pennies."

  "We will use this one-dollar bill instead of this container of 100 pennies."

  "How many more pennies do we need to show 119 pennies?"

  "Let's use dimes and pennies instead of just pennies."

  "How many dimes and pennies will we use?"

- Ask your child to count out that number of dimes and pennies.

- Count the money with your child.

number pattern

- Ask your child to identify and fill in the missing numbers.

- Read the number pattern together.

clock

- Ask your child to set the morning/afternoon/evening/night clock.

- Throughout the day, your child announces the time on the hour and the half hour, sets the demonstration clock to show the time, and writes the digital time on the chalkboard.

coin cup

"Today there are dimes, nickels, and pennies in the coin cup."

"Put the nickels in stacks of two."

- Allow time for your child to stack the nickels.

"Two nickels are the same as one dime."

"Let's count the money together as I point to each dime, stack of nickels, and penny."

- Ask your child to record the amount of money on the meeting strip.

right/left

- Continue to practice left and right once a week. Practice more often, if necessary.

number fact of the day

- Ask your child to choose a number fact (one of the oddball facts) to practice for the day.

"Let's practice number facts."

"Hip, hip, hooray!"

"What is the oddball fact for today?"

- Write the number fact on the chalkboard. Frequently during the day, ask your child the following question:

"What is our oddball fact for today?"

THE LESSON

Writing the Number 108

"The last number we practiced writing was the number 107."

"What number do you think we will learn how to write today?"

- Write the number 108 on the chalkboard.

"What digits do you see in the number 108?"

Subtracting Ten from a Number

"Today you will learn how to subtract ten from a number."

"Subtracting ten from a number is like counting backward by 10's."

"Let's try counting backward by 10's."

"When we count backward by 10's, which way will I move my finger on the hundred number chart?" up

"Choose a number in the last row of the hundred number chart for us to begin with."

• Point to the numbers on the hundred number chart as you count backward by 10's with your child.

"Let's try that again."

"Choose a different number from which to begin counting backward by 10's."

• Point to the numbers on the hundred number chart as you count together.

• Write "84 – 10 =" on the chalkboard.

"The minus sign tells us to count backward."

"This means count backward one ten from 84."

"What number is ten less than 84?" 74

"Let's count backward to check."

• Point to the numbers on the hundred number chart.

• Write "26 – 10 =" on the chalkboard.

"The minus sign tells us to count backward."

"This means count backward one ten from 26."

"What number is ten less than 26?" 16

"Let's count backward to check."

• Point to the numbers on the hundred number chart.

• Write "71 – 10 =" on the chalkboard.

"What does the minus sign tell us to do?" count backward

"At what number will we start?" 71

"What number is ten less than 71?" 61

• Move your finger up from 71 to 61 on the hundred number chart.

• Write "29 – 10 =" on the chalkboard.

"What does the minus sign tell us to do?" count backward

"At what number will we start?" 29

"What number is ten less than 29?" 19

• Move your finger up from 29 to 19 on the hundred number chart.

• Write "16 – 10 =" on the chalkboard.

"Read this problem."

"What does the minus sign tell us to do?" count backward

"At what number will we start?" 16

"How much are we taking away?" 10

"What number is ten less than 16?" 6

- Move your finger up from 16 to 6 on the hundred number chart.

- Write "53 – 10 =" on the chalkboard.

"Read this problem."

"What does the minus sign tell us to do?" count backward

"At what number will we start?" 53

"How much are we taking away?" 10

"What number is ten less than 53?" 43

- Move your finger up from 53 to 43 on the hundred number chart.

- Give your child a piece of scrap paper (or use the back of the fact sheet).

"Now I will write an adding ten or a subtracting ten problem on the chalkboard."

- Write the following problem on the chalkboard:

$$82 - 10 =$$

"Write just the answer for this problem on your paper."

"What is the answer?" 72

- Record the answer on the chalkboard.

- Repeat, using the following problems. Write the problems on the chalkboard one at a time.

17 – 10 =	46 + 10 =	75 – 10 =
15 + 10 =	38 – 10 =	77 + 10 =

"Do you see a pattern?"

"Which digit changes when we add or subtract ten?"

"We call the digit on the left in a two-digit number the tens' digit."

- Repeat with several more problems, if desired.

CLASS PRACTICE

"Let's practice the oddball addition number facts."

- Use the large fact cards to practice the oddball addition facts.

- Give your child **Fact Sheet A 8.2.**

- Correct the fact sheet with your child.

WRITTEN PRACTICE

- Complete **Worksheet 119A** with your child.
- Complete **Worksheet 119B** with your child later in the day.

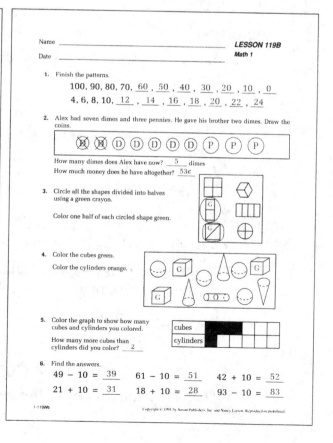

Worksheet 119A:

Name _____ (Draw a 10-centimeter line segment.)
LESSON 119A
Math 1

Date _____

Day of the Week _____

1. Write the number one hundred eight 3 more times.

   108 108

2. Amy had six dimes and two pennies. Her sister gave her three more dimes. Draw the coins.

   (D) (D) (D) (D) (D) (D) (P) (P)   (D) (D) (D)

   How many dimes does Amy have now? __9__ dimes
   How much money does she have altogether? __92¢__

3. Circle all the shapes divided into fourths using an orange crayon.

   Color one fourth of each circled shape orange.

4. Color the cubes green.
   Color the cylinders orange.

5. Color the graph to show how many cubes and cylinders you colored.
   How many more cubes than cylinders did you color? __1__

   | cubes |
   | cylinders |

6. Find the answers.

   63 − 10 = __53__   62 + 10 = __72__   48 − 10 = __38__

   14 + 10 = __24__   79 − 10 = __69__   36 + 10 = __46__

1-119Wa

Copyright © 1991 by Saxon Publishers, Inc. and Nancy Larson. Reproduction prohibited.

Worksheet 119B:

Name _____
LESSON 119B
Math 1

Date _____

1. Finish the patterns.

   100, 90, 80, 70, _60_ , _50_ , _40_ , _30_ , _20_ , _10_ , _0_

   4, 6, 8, 10, _12_ , _14_ , _16_ , _18_ , _20_ , _22_ , _24_

2. Alex had seven dimes and three pennies. He gave his brother two dimes. Draw the coins.

   (⊗) (⊗) (D) (D) (D) (D) (D) (P) (P) (P)

   How many dimes does Alex have now? __5__ dimes
   How much money does he have altogether? __53¢__

3. Circle all the shapes divided into halves using a green crayon.

   Color one half of each circled shape green.

4. Color the cubes green.
   Color the cylinders orange.

5. Color the graph to show how many cubes and cylinders you colored.
   How many more cubes than cylinders did you color? __2__

   | cubes |
   | cylinders |

6. Find the answers.

   49 − 10 = __39__   61 − 10 = __51__   42 + 10 = __52__

   21 + 10 = __31__   18 + 10 = __28__   93 − 10 = __83__

1-119Wb

Copyright © 1991 by Saxon Publishers, Inc. and Nancy Larson. Reproduction prohibited.

Lesson 120

assessment

lesson preparation

materials

50 pennies

5 dimes

Written Assessment #23

Oral Assessment #12

in the morning

• Write the following number pattern on the meeting strip:

27, 37, 47, ___, ___, ___

Answer: 27, 37, 47, 57, 67, 77

• Put **3 dimes**, **4 nickels**, and **2 pennies** in the coin cup.

THE MEETING

calendar

• Ask your child to identify the following:

year

month

shapes on the calendar

today's shape

shape pattern for the month

• Ask your child to write the date on the calendar.

• Ask your child to do the following:

identify today's day of the week, yesterday's day of the week, and tomorrow's day of the week

read the days of the week

identify the weekdays

identify the number of days in a week

"Let's say the names of the months of the year together."

- Point to the names of the months of the year as you read them with your child.
- Ask your child to write the full date on the meeting strip.

weather graph

- Ask your child to report and graph the weather.
- Ask questions about the graph.

counting

- Say the "Counting by 10's Rap" on **Master 1-91** together once a week.
- Count by 100's to 1,000.
- Count by 5's to 50.
- Count by 10's to 100.
- Count backward from 100 by 10's.
- Count by 2's to 20.
- Count backward from 20 by 2's.
- Ask your child to identify the digits to use to write the next number on the number line.
- Use an orange crayon to color the square for 120.
- Ask your child to identify the total number of pennies needed to show this number.

  "Let's show this amount of money using dollars, dimes, and pennies."

  "How many dollar bills will we use?"

  "How many dimes will we use?"

  "How many pennies will we use?"

- Ask your child to show that amount of money.

  "Let's count the money together."

- Count the money with your child.

  "Which digit in the number _____ tells us the number of dollar bills?"

  "Which digit in the number _____ tells us the number of dimes?"

  "Which digit in the number _____ tells us the number of pennies?"

number pattern

- Ask your child to identify and fill in the missing numbers.
- Read the number pattern together.

clock

- Ask your child to set the morning/afternoon/evening/night clock.

- Throughout the day, your child announces the time on the hour and the half hour, sets the demonstration clock to show the time, and writes the digital time on the chalkboard.

coin cup

"Today there are dimes, nickels, and pennies in the coin cup."

"Put the nickels in stacks of two."

- Allow time for your child to stack the nickels.

"Two nickels are the same as one dime."

"Let's count the money together as I point to each dime, stack of nickels, and penny."

- Ask your child to record the amount of money on the meeting strip.

right/left

- Continue to practice left and right once a week. Practice more often, if necessary.

number fact of the day

- Ask your child to choose a number fact (one of the oddball facts) to practice for the day.

"Let's practice number facts."

"Hip, hip, hooray!"

"What is the oddball fact for today?"

- Write the number fact on the chalkboard. Frequently during the day, ask your child the following question:

"What is our oddball fact for today?"

ASSESSMENT

- All of the questions on the assessment are based on concepts and skills presented at least five lessons ago. If your child is having difficulty with a specific concept, reteach the concept the following day.

Written Assessment

- Give your child **Written Assessment #23**.

- Read the directions for each problem. Allow time for your child to complete each problem before continuing to the next.

- Correct the paper, noting your child's mistakes on the **Individual Recording Form**. Review the errors with your child.

Oral Assessment

- Record your child's responses to the oral interview on the interview sheet.

Name _____

Date _____

ASSESSMENT 23
LESSON 120
Math 1

1. Randy counted 24 pennies. He put them in groups of 10. Draw the pennies.

Philip gave him 10 more pennies. Draw the pennies Philip gave Randy.
Write a number sentence to show how many pennies Randy has now.

Number sentence ____24 + 10 = 34____   Answer ___34___ pennies

2. Cross out the cards you cannot put where the X is.

| 17 | 26 | X | 34 | 49 | | 46̸ | 33 | 2̸5̸ | 28 | 3̸7̸ | 30 |

3. Point to the hexagon that is divided into thirds. Color one third blue.

Point to the hexagon that is divided in half. Color one half red.

Point to the hexagon that is divided into sixths. Color one sixth green.

B   R   G

4. Find the answers.

35 + 10 = ___45___   14 + 10 = ___24___   83 + 10 = ___93___

5. Use the classroom calendar to answer these questions.

What was the date of the first Monday of this month? _____

What day of the week will it be tomorrow? _____

How many days are there in one week? ___Seven___

1-120Aa

Teacher _____

Date _____

Materials:
50 pennies
5 dimes

MATH 1   LESSON 120
Oral Assessment # 12 Recording Form

Students	*Give the child 30-50 pennies [Vary the amount.] "How much money did I give you?"	"If I tell you to trade as many pennies for dimes as possible, how many dimes will you need?"	"Trade the pennies for dimes."	"How much money do you have?" Recounts	Knows

1-120La

Lesson 121

writing the number 109
adding three single-digit numbers

---

lesson preparation

materials

Master 1-121

cup of 20 pennies

large fact cards (oddball addition facts)

Fact Sheet A 8.2

in the morning

• Write the following number pattern on the meeting strip:

> 50, 45, 40, __, __, __

Answer: 50, 45, 40, 35, 30, 25

• Put **5 dimes**, **2 nickels**, and **3 pennies** in the coin cup.

THE MEETING

calendar

• Ask your child to identify the following:

  year

  month

  shapes on the calendar

  today's shape

  shape pattern for the month

• Ask your child to write the date on the calendar.

• Ask your child to do the following:

  identify today's day of the week, yesterday's day of the week, and tomorrow's day of the week

  read the days of the week

  identify the weekdays

  identify the number of days in a week

"Let's say the names of the months of the year together."

- Point to the names of the months of the year as you read them with your child.

- Ask your child to write the full date on the meeting strip.

weather graph

- Ask your child to report and graph the weather.

- Ask questions about the graph.

counting

- Say the "Counting by 10's Rap" on **Master 1-91** together once a week.

- Count by 100's to 1,000.

- Count by 5's to 50.

- Count by 10's to 100.

- Count backward from 100 by 10's.

- Say the odd numbers to 19.

- Say the odd numbers backward from 19.

- Ask your child to identify the digits to use to write the next number on the number line.

- Ask your child to identify the total number of pennies needed to show this number.

"Let's show this amount of money using dollars, dimes, and pennies."

"How many dollar bills will we use?"

"How many dimes will we use?"

"How many pennies will we use?"

- Ask your child to show that amount of money.

"Let's count the money together."

- Count the money with your child.

"Which digit in the number _____ tells us the number of dollar bills?"

"Which digit in the number _____ tells us the number of dimes?"

"Which digit in the number _____ tells us the number of pennies?"

number pattern

- Ask your child to identify and fill in the missing numbers.

- Read the number pattern together.

clock

- Ask your child to set the morning/afternoon/evening/night clock.

- Throughout the day, your child announces the time on the hour and the half hour, sets the demonstration clock to show the time, and writes the digital time on the chalkboard.

coin cup

"Today there are dimes, nickels, and pennies in the coin cup."

"Put the nickels in stacks of two."

- Allow time for your child to stack the nickels.

"Two nickels are the same as one dime."

"Let's count the money together as I point to each dime, stack of nickels, and penny."

- Ask your child to record the amount of money on the meeting strip.

right/left

- Continue to practice left and right once a week. Practice more often, if necessary.

number fact of the day

- Ask your child to choose a number fact (one of the oddball facts) to practice for the day.

"Let's practice number facts."

"Hip, hip, hooray!"

"What is the oddball fact for today?"

- Write the number fact on the chalkboard. Frequently during the day, ask your child the following question:

"What is our oddball fact for today?"

THE LESSON

Writing the Number 109

"The last number we practiced writing was the number 108."

"What number do you think we will learn how to write today?"

- Write the number 109 on the chalkboard.

"What digits do you see in the number 109?"

Adding Three Single-Digit Numbers

"Today you will learn how to add three single-digit numbers."

- Give your child a cup of 20 pennies and a copy of **Master 1-121**.

- Position **Master 1-121** horizontally on the table.

"Take eight pennies out of the cup."

"Put some of the pennies in each of the circles on your paper."

- Allow time for your child to do this.

"How many pennies did you put in each circle?"

"We can write a number sentence for that like this."

- Write the addition problem horizontally on the chalkboard.

"Put the pennies in the circles in a different way."

- Allow time for your child to do this.

"How many pennies did you put in each circle?"

"We can write a number sentence for that like this."

- Write the addition problem horizontally on the chalkboard.

- Write "4 + 1 + 5 =" on the chalkboard.

"Put the pennies on your paper to show this problem."

- Allow time for your child to put the pennies on the paper.

"How many pennies did you use altogether?"   10

"We can find the answer for this problem without using pennies."

"We will add two of these numbers first."

"Then we will add the last number."

"We can add our two favorite numbers first."

"What are your two favorite numbers in this problem?"

- Ask your child to choose 2 numbers in the problem.

"I will put a dot below each of these numbers to help us remember the numbers we used."

- Put a dot on the chalkboard below each of the chosen numbers.

"Let's add these numbers together."

"What is the answer?"

"Now we will add the extra number."

"What is the answer?"

- Write the answer next to the equal sign.

- Erase the dots under the problem.

"My two favorite numbers are _____ and _____."

- Choose 2 different numbers in the problem.

"I will put a dot below each of these numbers to help us remember the numbers I chose."

- Put a dot on the chalkboard below each of the chosen numbers.

"Let's add these numbers together."

"What is the answer?"

"Now we will add the extra number."

"What is the answer?"

"Point to problem A in the upper left-hand corner of your paper."

"Put a dot under the two numbers that you would like to add first."

• Allow time for your child to do this.

"Add these numbers in your head."

"Now add the extra number."

"Write your answer in the box."

• Allow time for your child to do this.

"Put pennies in the circles to check your answer."

• Allow time for your child to do this.

"How many pennies did you use?"

• Repeat with problems B and C.

"Now we will turn the paper."

• Position **Master 1-121** vertically on the table.

• Write the following problem on the chalkboard:
$$\begin{array}{r} 2 \\ 4 \\ + 3 \\ \hline \end{array}$$

"Put the pennies on your paper to show this problem."

• Allow time for your child to put the pennies on the paper.

"How many pennies did you use altogether?"   9

"We can find the answer for this problem without using pennies."

"We will add two of these numbers first."

"Then we will add the extra number."

"We can add our two favorite numbers first."

"What are your two favorite numbers in this problem?"

• Ask your child to choose 2 numbers in the problem.

"I will put a dot next to each of these numbers to help us remember the numbers we used."

• Put a dot on the chalkboard next to each of the chosen numbers.

"Let's add these numbers together."

"What is the answer?"

"Now we will add the extra number."

"What is the answer?"

- Write the answer below the problem.
- Erase the dots next to the numbers.

"My two favorite numbers are _____ and _____."

- Choose 2 different numbers in the problem.

"I will put a dot next to each of these numbers to help us remember the numbers I chose."

- Put a dot on the chalkboard next to each of the chosen numbers.

"Let's add these numbers together."

"What is the answer?"

"Now we will add the extra number."

"What is the answer?"

"Point to problem D in the upper right-hand corner of your paper."

"Put a dot next to the two numbers that you would like to add first."

- Allow time for your child to do this.

"Add these numbers in your head."

"Now add the extra number."

"Write your answer in the box."

- Allow time for your child to do this.

"Put pennies in the circles to check your answer."

- Allow time for your child to do this.

"How many pennies did you use?"

- Repeat with problems E and F.

CLASS PRACTICE

"Let's practice the oddball addition number facts."

- Use the large fact cards to practice the oddball addition facts.
- Give your child **Fact Sheet A 8.2**.
- Correct the fact sheet with your child.

WRITTEN PRACTICE

- Complete **Worksheet 121A** with your child.
- Complete **Worksheet 121B** with your child later in the day.

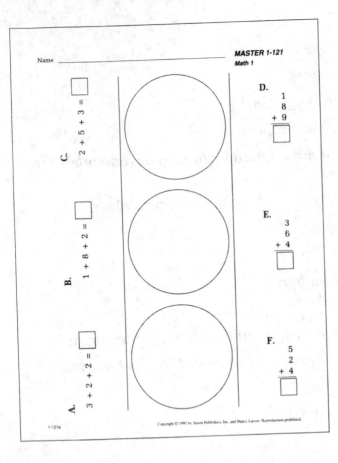

Name _____ **MASTER 1-121**
Math 1

C. 2 + 5 + 3 = ☐

B. 1 + 8 + 2 = ☐

A. 3 + 2 + 2 = ☐

D.
```
  1
  8
+ 9
```
☐

E.
```
  3
  6
+ 4
```
☐

F.
```
  5
  2
+ 4
```
☐

1-121a

Name _____ **LESSON 121A**
(Draw an 8-centimeter line segment.)   Math 1

Date _____

Day of the Week _____

1. Write the number one hundred nine 3 more times.

   -109-109--------------------------

2. Colette had 7 pencils and 3 erasers. She gave Steven 2 pencils. Draw the pencils and erasers. Write a number sentence to show how many pencils she has now.

   Number sentence _____

   How many pencils does Colette have now? _____ pencils

3. Measure these line segments using centimeters.

   •———————————————• ___ cm

   •—————————• ___ cm

4. Draw lines to show how to divide the squares into fourths in two different ways. Color two fourths of each square.

5. Find the answers.

   39 − 10 = ___   61 − 10 = ___   15 − 10 = ___

6. Find the answers.

   6 + 1 + 6 = ___   3 + 5 + 7 = ___

1-121Wa

Name _____ **LESSON 121B**
Math 1

1. Write the numbers that are 10 more than each number.

   5, ___   24, ___   73, ___

2. Dana had 6 markers and 2 pencils. She gave her brother Josh 3 markers. Draw a picture and write a number sentence to show how many markers she has now.

   Number sentence _____

   How many markers does Dana have now? ___ markers

3. The line segment below is 10 centimeters long.

   •———————————————————————•

   Find something at home that is about 10 centimeters long. What did you find?

   _____

4. Draw lines to show how to divide the squares into fourths in two different ways. Color one fourth of each square.

5. Find the answers.

   62 − 10 = ___   47 − 10 = ___   13 − 10 = ___

6. Find the answers.

   4 + 3 + 6 = ___   2 + 1 + 8 = ___

1-121Wb

Lesson 122

writing the number 110
subtraction facts—differences of one

---

lesson preparation

materials

seven 3" × 5" cards

1 tower of 10 linking cubes

subtraction fact cards — yellow

large fact cards (subtraction facts)

Fact Sheet S 2.2

the night before

• Use the 3" × 5" cards to make a large set of fact cards for the differences of one subtraction facts. Write them in the following way:

3	4	5	6	7	8	9
− 2	− 3	− 4	− 5	− 6	− 7	− 8

• Separate the yellow subtraction fact cards.

in the morning

• Write the following number pattern on the meeting strip:

> 49, 59, 69, __, __, __

Answer: 49, 59, 69, 79, 89, 99

• Put **1 dime, 6 nickels,** and **4 pennies** in the coin cup.

THE MEETING

calendar

• Ask your child to identify the following:

  year

  month

  shapes on the calendar

  today's shape

---

shape pattern for the month

- Ask your child to write the date on the calendar.
- Ask your child to do the following:

  identify today's day of the week, yesterday's day of the week, and tomorrow's day of the week

  read the days of the week

  identify the weekdays

  identify the number of days in a week

  "Let's say the names of the months of the year together."

- Point to the names of the months of the year as you read them with your child.
- Ask your child to write the full date on the meeting strip.

weather graph

- Ask your child to report and graph the weather.
- Ask questions about the graph.

counting

- Say the "Counting by 10's Rap" on **Master 1-91** together once a week.
- Count by 100's to 1,000.
- Count by 5's to 50.
- Count by 10's to 100.
- Count backward from 100 by 10's.
- Count by 2's to 20.
- Count backward from 20 by 2's.
- Ask your child to identify the digits to use to write the next number on the number line.
- Ask your child to identify the total number of pennies needed to show this number.

  "Let's show this amount of money using dollars, dimes, and pennies."

  "How many dollar bills will we use?"

  "How many dimes will we use?"

  "How many pennies will we use?"

- Ask your child to show that amount of money.

  "Let's count the money together."

- Count the money with your child.

  "Which digit in the number _____ tells us the number of dollar bills?"

> *"Which digit in the number _____ tells us the number of dimes?"*
>
> *"Which digit in the number _____ tells us the number of pennies?"*

number pattern

- Ask your child to identify and fill in the missing numbers.
- Read the number pattern together.

clock

- Ask your child to set the morning/afternoon/evening/night clock.
- Throughout the day, your child announces the time on the hour and the half hour, sets the demonstration clock to show the time, and writes the digital time on the chalkboard.

coin cup

> *"Today there are dimes, nickels, and pennies in the coin cup."*
>
> *"Put the nickels in stacks of two."*

- Allow time for your child to stack the nickels.

> *"Two nickels are the same as one dime."*
>
> *"Let's count the money together as I point to each dime, stack of nickels, and penny."*

- Ask your child to record the amount of money on the meeting strip.

right/left

- Continue to practice left and right once a week. Practice more often, if necessary.

number fact of the day

- Ask your child to choose a number fact (one of the oddball facts) to practice for the day.

> *"Let's practice number facts."*
>
> *"Hip, hip, hooray!"*
>
> *"What is the oddball fact for today?"*

- Write the number fact on the chalkboard. Frequently during the day, ask your child the following question:

> *"What is our oddball fact for today?"*

THE LESSON

Writing the Number 110

"The last number we practiced writing was the number 109."

"What number do you think we will learn how to write today?"

- Write the number 110 on the chalkboard.

"What digits do you see in the number 110?"

Subtraction Facts—Differences of One

"Today you will learn the subtraction facts called the difference of one facts."

"What are some subtraction facts that have an answer of zero?"

- List 5–10 facts on the chalkboard.

"Let's check these problems using linking cubes."

- Choose one problem.

"How many do we have to begin with?"

- Hold up that number of linking cubes.

"How many are we taking away?"

"How many do we have left?"

- Repeat with several problems.

"These subtraction facts have an answer of zero."

"Let's try to write some subtraction facts that have an answer of one."

- Write several problems on the chalkboard vertically and horizontally.

"Let's check one of these problems using linking cubes."

- Choose one problem.

"How many linking cubes does this problem tell us to begin with?"

- Hold up that number of linking cubes.

"How many linking cubes does this problem tell us to take away?"

- Break off that number of cubes.

"How many linking cubes do we have left?"   *1*

- Repeat with each problem.

"What do you notice about the numbers we subtracted to get an answer of one?"   *they are next to each other when we count by 1's*

- Allow time for your child to offer observations.

"Let's try to find as many subtraction problems as possible with an answer of one."

- Write your child's suggested problems on the chalkboard.

- Ask your child to use linking cubes to show a problem, if necessary.

"Now I will give you fact cards for the difference of one subtraction facts."

- Give your child the yellow subtraction fact cards.

"Write the answer on the back of each card."

CLASS PRACTICE

"Let's practice all the subtraction facts."

- Use the large subtraction fact cards.

- Give your child **Fact Sheet S 2.2**.

- Correct the fact sheet with your child.

WRITTEN PRACTICE

- Complete **Worksheet 122A** with your child.

- Complete **Worksheet 122B** with your child later in the day.

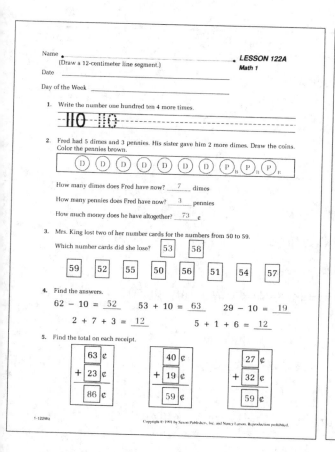

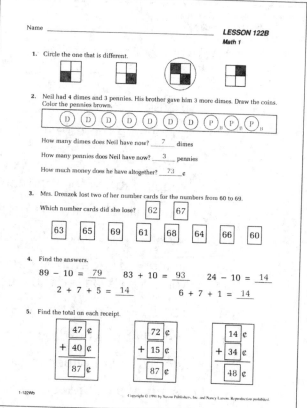

Lesson 123

writing the number 111
drawing polygons

THE MEETING

calendar

- Ask your child to identify the following:

  year

  month

  shapes on the calendar

  today's shape

  shape pattern for the month

- Ask your child to write the date on the calendar.

- Ask your child to do the following:

  identify today's day of the week, yesterday's day of the week, and tomorrow's day of the week

  read the days of the week

  identify the weekdays

  identify the number of days in a week

"Let's say the names of the months of the year together."

- Point to the names of the months of the year as you read them with your child.

- Ask your child to write the full date on the meeting strip.

weather graph

- Ask your child to report and graph the weather.

- Ask questions about the graph.

counting

- Say the "Counting by 10's Rap" on **Master 1-91** together once a week.

- Count by 100's to 1,000.

- Count by 5's to 50.

- Count by 10's to 100.

- Count backward from 100 by 10's.

- Say the odd numbers to 19.

- Say the odd numbers backward from 19.

- Ask your child to identify the digits to use to write the next number on the number line.

- Ask your child to identify the total number of pennies needed to show this number.

    "Let's show this amount of money using dollars, dimes, and pennies."

    "How many dollar bills will we use?"

    "How many dimes will we use?"

    "How many pennies will we use?"

- Ask your child to show that amount of money.

    "Let's count the money together."

- Count the money with your child.

    "Which digit in the number _____ tells us the number of dollar bills?"

    "Which digit in the number _____ tells us the number of dimes?"

    "Which digit in the number _____ tells us the number of pennies?"

number pattern

- Ask your child to identify and fill in the missing numbers.

- Read the number pattern together.

clock

- Ask your child to set the morning/afternoon/evening/night clock.

• Throughout the day, your child announces the time on the hour and the half hour, sets the demonstration clock to show the time, and writes the digital time on the chalkboard.

coin cup

"Today there are dimes, nickels, and pennies in the coin cup."

"Put the nickels in stacks of two."

• Allow time for your child to stack the nickels.

"Two nickels are the same as one dime."

"Let's count the money together as I point to each dime, stack of nickels, and penny."

• Ask your child to record the amount of money on the meeting strip.

right/left

• Continue to practice left and right once a week. Practice more often, if necessary.

number fact of the day

• Ask your child to choose a number fact (one of the oddball facts) to practice for the day.

"Let's practice number facts."

"Hip, hip, hooray!"

"What is the oddball fact for today?"

• Write the number fact on the chalkboard. Frequently during the day, ask your child the following question:

"What is our oddball fact for today?"

THE LESSON

Writing the Number 111

"The last number we practiced writing was the number 110."

"What number do you think we will learn how to write today?"

• Write the number 111 on the chalkboard.

"What digits do you see in the number 111?"

Drawing Polygons

- Draw the following shapes on the chalkboard:

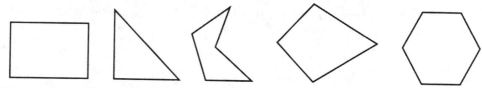

"These are all polygons."

- Write the word "polygon" on the chalkboard.

"Polygons look like little pens or cages for animals."

"They always have straight sides with no openings."

"Some polygons have special names."

"Do you know the special name of any of the polygons I drew?"   rectangle, triangle, hexagon

"Today you will learn how to draw polygons."

"I will show you how to draw a polygon with three sides."

"First I will draw three points on the chalkboard."

"This will show the points where the sides meet."

- Draw 3 points on the chalkboard.

"Now I will connect the points just like you did when you copied your geoboard shapes."

- Connect the points of the triangle.

"I have drawn a three-sided polygon."

"What is the special name for this polygon?"   triangle

"Now I will draw a polygon with four sides."

"First I will draw four points on the chalkboard."

"This will show the points where the sides meet."

- Draw 4 points on the chalkboard in the following way:

"Now I will connect the points just like you did when you copied your geoboard shapes."

- Connect the points of the square.

"I have drawn a four-sided polygon."

"What is the special name for this polygon?"   square

"Let's draw a different four-sided polygon."

"What should I do first?"   **draw four points on the chalkboard**

• Draw 4 points on the chalkboard in the following way:

    •   •

    •   •

"What will I do next?"   **connect the points**

• Connect the points of the rectangle.

"I have drawn a four-sided polygon."

"What is the special name for this polygon?"   **rectangle**

"Now I will draw a different four-sided polygon."

• Draw 4 points and connect the points to make a parallelogram on the chalkboard.

      •   •

   •   •

"What is the special name for this polygon?"   **parallelogram**

"Now I will draw a polygon with six sides."

"First I will draw six points on the chalkboard."

• Draw 6 points on the chalkboard.

    • •

   •   •

    • •

"Now I will connect the points."

• Connect the points of the hexagon.

"I have drawn a six-sided polygon."

"What is the special name for this polygon?"   **hexagon**

"Now I will draw a polygon with five sides."

"How will I do that?"

• Draw 5 points on the chalkboard and connect the points.

    • •

   •   •

    •

"I have drawn a five-sided polygon."

"Now you will have a chance to draw some polygons."

• Give your child **Master 1-123**.

"You will draw a three-sided polygon in the first box."

"Draw three points to show where the sides meet."

"The three points cannot be in a straight line."

- Demonstrate on the chalkboard, if necessary.

"Now connect the points just like you did when you copied your geoboard triangle onto geodot paper."

"Try to make the line between two points as straight as you can."

- Demonstrate on the chalkboard, if necessary.

"Let's count the sides."

"Now you will draw a four-sided polygon in the second box."

"How many points will you draw to make a four-sided polygon?"   4

"Draw four points to show where the sides will meet."

- Demonstrate on the chalkboard, if necessary.

"Connect the points."

- Demonstrate on the chalkboard, if necessary.

"Let's count the sides."

"Now you will draw a five-sided polygon in the next box."

"How many points will you draw to make a five-sided polygon?"   5

"Draw five points to show where the sides will meet."

- Demonstrate on the chalkboard, if necessary.

"Connect the points."

- Demonstrate on the chalkboard, if necessary.

"Let's count the sides."

- Repeat with a six-sided polygon.

CLASS PRACTICE

"Let's practice all the subtraction facts."

- Use the large subtraction fact cards.
- Give your child **Fact Sheet S 2.2**.
- Correct the fact sheet with your child.

WRITTEN PRACTICE

- Complete **Worksheet 123A** with your child.
- Complete **Worksheet 123B** with your child later in the day.

Polygons

3 sides	4 sides
5 sides	**6 sides**

Name _____   **MASTER 1-123**
                                              Math 1

Name ●_____   **LESSON 123A**
     (Draw an 11-centimeter line segment.)   Math 1

Date _____

Day of the Week _____

1. Write the number one hundred eleven 5 more times.

2. While she was away Shannon wrote four letters to her parents, four letters to her Aunt Debby, and two letters to her brother Billy. Draw a picture and write a number sentence to show the letters Shannon wrote.

   Number sentence _____ 4 + 4 + 2 = 10 _____

   How many letters did Shannon write? __10__ letters

3. The children in Mrs. Mathew's class made this graph about their favorite ice cream.

vanilla	🍦🍦🍦🍦🍦🍦🍦🍦🍦 🍦🍦
chocolate	🍦🍦🍦🍦🍦🍦🍦🍦🍦 🍦

   Write two things you know about the children in Mrs. Matthew's class.
   (It's okay to use approximate spelling.)

   1)_____

   2)_____

4. Draw a four-sided polygon in the box.

5. Find the answers.

5	4	6
2	1	5
+ 3	+ 4	+ 4
10	9	15

Name _____   **LESSON 123B**
                                              Math 1

1. Circle the two that are exactly the same.

2. While he was away, Billy wrote five letters to his parents, one letter to his Aunt Debby, and three letters to his sister Shannon. Draw a picture and write a number sentence to show the letters Billy wrote.

   Number sentence _____ 5 + 1 + 3 = 9 _____

   How many letters did Billy write? __9__ letters

3. The children in Mrs. Brereton's class made this graph about their favorite fruit.

orange	◯◯◯◯◯◯◯◯◯◯
apple	🍎🍎🍎🍎🍎🍎

   Write two things you know about the children in Mrs. Brereton's class.
   (It's okay to use approximate spelling.)

   1)_____

   2)_____

4. Draw a three-sided polygon in the box.

5. Find the answers.

9	3	4
9	2	3
+ 1	+ 7	+ 6
19	12	13

Lesson **124**

writing the number 112
identifying and counting quarters

---

lesson preparation

materials

25 pennies, 6 nickels, and 2 dimes

3 small plastic bags

16–20 quarters

5 small cups

large fact cards (oddball addition facts)

Fact Sheet A 8.2

the night before

• Put 25 pennies in a small plastic bag and label the bag "A." Put 5 nickels in another small plastic bag and label the bag "B." Put 2 dimes and 1 nickel in another small plastic bag and label the bag "C."

in the morning

• Write the following number pattern on the meeting strip:

> 29, 27, 25, __, __, __

Answer: 29, 27, 25, 23, 21, 19

• Put **7 dimes**, **1 nickel**, and **3 pennies** in the coin cup.

THE MEETING

calendar

  • Ask your child to identify the following:

    year

    month

    shapes on the calendar

    today's shape

    shape pattern for the month

  • Ask your child to write the date on the calendar.

- Ask your child to do the following:

  identify today's day of the week, yesterday's day of the week, and tomorrow's day of the week

  read the days of the week

  identify the weekdays

  identify the number of days in a week

  "Let's say the names of the months of the year together."

- Point to the names of the months of the year as you read them with your child.

- Ask your child to write the full date on the meeting strip.

weather graph

- Ask your child to report and graph the weather.

- Ask questions about the graph.

counting

- Say the "Counting by 10's Rap" on **Master 1-91** together once a week.

- Count by 100's to 1,000.

- Count by 5's to 50.

- Count by 10's to 100.

- Count backward from 100 by 10's.

- Count by 2's to 20.

- Count backward from 20 by 2's.

- Ask your child to identify the digits to use to write the next number on the number line.

- Ask your child to identify the total number of pennies needed to show this number.

  "Let's show this amount of money using dollars, dimes, and pennies."

  "How many dollar bills will we use?"

  "How many dimes will we use?"

  "How many pennies will we use?"

- Ask your child to show that amount of money.

  "Let's count the money together."

- Count the money with your child.

  "Which digit in the number _____ tells us the number of dollar bills?"

  "Which digit in the number _____ tells us the number of dimes?"

  "Which digit in the number _____ tells us the number of pennies?"

number pattern

- Ask your child to identify and fill in the missing numbers.

- Read the number pattern together.

clock

- Ask your child to set the morning/afternoon/evening/night clock.

- Throughout the day, your child announces the time on the hour and the half hour, sets the demonstration clock to show the time, and writes the digital time on the chalkboard.

coin cup

"Today there are dimes, nickels, and pennies in the coin cup."

"Let's count the money together as I point to each dime, nickel, and penny."

- Ask your child to record the amount of money on the meeting strip.

right/left

- Continue to practice left and right once a week. Practice more often, if necessary.

number fact of the day

- Ask your child to choose a number fact (one of the oddball facts) to practice for the day.

"Let's practice number facts."

"Hip, hip, hooray!"

"What is the oddball fact for today?"

- Write the number fact on the chalkboard. Frequently during the day, ask your child the following question:

"What is our oddball fact for today?"

THE LESSON

Writing the Number 112

"The last number we practiced writing was the number 111."

"What number do you think we will learn how to write today?"

- Write the number 112 on the chalkboard.

"What digits do you see in the number 112?"

Identifying and Counting Quarters

"Today you will learn how to identify and count a new coin."

• Show your child the 3 bags of coins.

"Which bag do you think has the most money?"

"Why?"

"Bag A has twenty-five pennies."

"How much money is that?"

"Bag B has five nickels."

"How much money is that?"

"Let's count it together."

• Slide each nickel as your child counts the money.

"Bag C has two dimes and one nickel."

"How much money is that?"

"Let's count it together."

• Slide each coin as your child counts the money.

"Each of these bags has twenty-five cents."

"There is another coin that is worth the same as twenty-five pennies, the same as five nickels, and the same as two dimes and one nickel."

"Do you know what that coin is?"   quarter

"A quarter is the same as twenty-five pennies."

"I will give you a quarter to look at."

• Give your child a quarter to examine.

"Look at both sides of the quarter."

• Allow time for your child to examine the quarter.

"Are the sides the same?"

"What do you see?"

"One side is called the heads side."

"Which side do you think that is?"

"What else do you see on the heads side of a quarter?"

• Allow time for your child to offer as many observations as possible.

"What do we call the other side of a quarter?"   the tails side

"What do you see on the tails side of a quarter?"

• Allow time for your child to offer as many observations as possible.

"Today you will learn how to count quarters."

"When we count quarters, we count by 25's."

"We count by 25's like this."

- Write "25, 50, 75, 100" on the chalkboard as you say each number.

"Let's count by 25's together."

- Point to each number as you count by 25's with your child several times.

"When we count money, we say 'one dollar' instead of '100.' "

"This is because one dollar is the same as one hundred pennies."

- Show your child the small cups.

"I have some small cups."

"You will put four quarters in each cup."

- Give your child 4 quarters.

- Put a cup on the table.

"As you drop each quarter in this cup, we will count by 25's."

- Say "25, 50, 75, one dollar" with your child as he/she drops the quarters in a cup.

- Put this cup aside.

- Repeat with the other cups.

"Each of these cups has one dollar."

"How many dollars do we have altogether?"

CLASS PRACTICE

"Let's practice the oddball addition number facts."

- Use the large fact cards to practice the oddball addition facts.
- Give your child **Fact Sheet A 8.2**.
- Correct the fact sheet with your child.

WRITTEN PRACTICE

- Complete **Worksheet 124A** with your child.
- Complete **Worksheet 124B** with your child later in the day.

LESSON 124A
Math 1

Name _____
(Draw a 9-centimeter line segment.)

Date _____

Day of the Week _____

1. Write the number one hundred twelve 4 more times.

112 112

2. Walter counted the puzzle pieces. He had 2 piles of 10 pieces and 6 extra pieces. Draw a picture to show the 2 piles of 10 pieces and the 6 extra pieces.

How many pieces did Walter count? __26__ pieces

3. Write a story for the number sentence **6 + 9 = 15**.

_____
_____
_____

4. Draw a six-sided polygon in the box.

5. How much money is this? __75¢__

6. Find the answers.

51 − 10 = __41__   34 + 10 = __44__

2 + 7 + 8 = __17__

$$\begin{array}{r} 73¢ \\ +\ 25¢ \\ \hline 98¢ \end{array}$$

LESSON 124B
Math 1

Name _____

1. Fill in the missing numbers.

61	62	63	64	65	66	67	68	69	70
71	72	73	74	75	76	77	78	79	80

2. Christopher counted the candies. He had 3 piles of 10 candies and 7 extra pieces. Draw a picture to show the 3 piles of 10 candies and the 7 extra pieces.

How many candies did Christopher count? __37__ candies

3. Write a story for the number sentence **3 + 4 = 7**.

_____
_____
_____

4. Draw a five-sided polygon in the box.

5. How much money is this? __50¢__

6. Find the answers.

62 − 10 = __52__   17 + 10 = __27__

9 + 6 + 1 = __16__

$$\begin{array}{r} 16¢ \\ +\ 43¢ \\ \hline 59¢ \end{array}$$

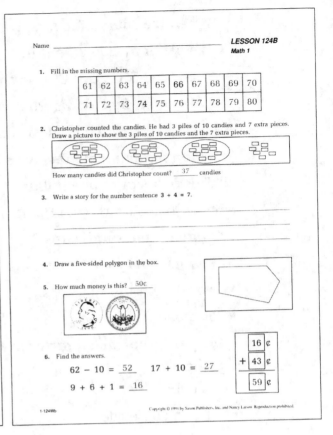

esson 125

writing the number 113
subtraction facts—subtracting using the
doubles plus one addition facts

---

lesson preparation

materials

Written Assessment #24

eight 3" × 5" cards

11 linking cubes

subtraction fact cards — pink

Fact Sheet S 5.0

the night before

• Use the 3" × 5" cards to make a large set of fact cards for the subtracting using the doubles plus one addition facts. Write them in the following way:

| $\begin{array}{r} 5 \\ -2 \\ \hline \end{array}$ | $\begin{array}{r} 5 \\ -3 \\ \hline \end{array}$ | $\begin{array}{r} 7 \\ -3 \\ \hline \end{array}$ | $\begin{array}{r} 7 \\ -4 \\ \hline \end{array}$ | $\begin{array}{r} 9 \\ -4 \\ \hline \end{array}$ | $\begin{array}{r} 9 \\ -5 \\ \hline \end{array}$ | $\begin{array}{r} 11 \\ -5 \\ \hline \end{array}$ | $\begin{array}{r} 11 \\ -6 \\ \hline \end{array}$ |

• Separate the pink subtraction fact cards.

in the morning

• Write the following number pattern on the meeting strip:

> 13, 15, 17, __, __, __

Answer: 13, 15, 17, 19, 21, 23

• Put **3 quarters** in the coin cup.

THE MEETING

calendar

• Ask your child to identify the following:

year

month

shapes on the calendar

---

today's shape

shape pattern for the month

- Ask your child to write the date on the calendar.

- Ask your child to do the following:

  identify today's day of the week, yesterday's day of the week, and tomorrow's day of the week

  read the days of the week

  identify the weekdays

  identify the number of days in a week

"Let's say the names of the months of the year together."

- Point to the names of the months of the year as you read them with your child.

- Ask your child to write the full date on the meeting strip.

weather graph

- Ask your child to report and graph the weather.

- Ask questions about the graph.

counting

- Say the "Counting by 10's Rap" on **Master 1-91** together once a week.

- Count by 100's to 1,000.

- Count by 5's to 50.

- Count by 10's to 100.

- Count backward from 100 by 10's.

- Say the odd numbers to 19.

- Say the odd numbers backward from 19.

- Ask your child to identify the digits to use to write the next number on the number line.

- Ask your child to identify the total number of pennies needed to show this number.

"Let's show this amount of money using dollars, dimes, and pennies."

"How many dollar bills will we use?"

"How many dimes will we use?"

"How many pennies will we use?"

- Ask your child to show that amount of money.

"Let's count the money together."

- Count the money with your child.

"Which digit in the number _____ tells us the number of dollar bills?"

"Which digit in the number _____ tells us the number of dimes?"

"Which digit in the number _____ tells us the number of pennies?"

number pattern

- Ask your child to identify and fill in the missing numbers.
- Read the number pattern together.

clock

- Ask your child to set the morning/afternoon/evening/night clock.
- Throughout the day, your child announces the time on the hour and the half hour, sets the demonstration clock to show the time, and writes the digital time on the chalkboard.

coin cup

"What coins do we have in the coin cup?"

"Let's count the money together."

- Ask your child to record the amount of money on the meeting strip.

right/left

- Continue to practice left and right once a week. Practice more often, if necessary.

number fact of the day

- Ask your child to choose a number fact (one of the oddball facts) to practice for the day.

"Let's practice number facts."

"Hip, hip, hooray!"

"What is the oddball fact for today?"

- Write the number fact on the chalkboard. Frequently during the day, ask your child the following question:

"What is our oddball fact for today?"

ASSESSMENT

Written Assessment

- Pass out **Written Assessment #24**.
- Read the directions for each problem. Allow time for your child to complete each problem before continuing to the next.

- Correct the paper, noting your child's mistakes on the **Individual Recording Form.** Review the errors with your child.

THE LESSON

Writing the Number 113

"*The last number we practiced writing was the number 112.*"

"*What number do you think we will learn how to write today?*"

- Write the number 113 on the chalkboard.

"*What digits do you see in the number 113?*"

Subtraction Facts—Subtracting Using the Doubles Plus One Addition Facts

- Write the following addition facts on the chalkboard:

$$
\begin{array}{cc} 2 \\ +3 \end{array} \quad \begin{array}{cc} 3 \\ +2 \end{array} \qquad \begin{array}{cc} 3 \\ +4 \end{array} \quad \begin{array}{cc} 4 \\ +3 \end{array} \qquad \begin{array}{cc} 4 \\ +5 \end{array} \quad \begin{array}{cc} 5 \\ +4 \end{array} \qquad \begin{array}{cc} 5 \\ +6 \end{array} \quad \begin{array}{cc} 6 \\ +5 \end{array}
$$

"*What type of addition problems are these?*"   *doubles plus one facts*

"*Let's fill in the answers.*"

"*What strategy can we use to find the answers?*"   *double the smaller number and add one*

"*What is two plus three?*"

"*What is three plus two?*"

- Fill in the answers on the chalkboard problems.

- Repeat with each doubles plus one fact on the chalkboard.

"*Today you will learn the answers to some new subtraction facts.*"

"*We will use the doubles plus one addition facts to help us find these answers.*"

"*We can write two subtraction facts for each pair of doubles plus one problems.*"

- Below the 2 + 3 problems, write the following:

$$
\begin{array}{cc} 5 \\ -2 \end{array} \qquad \begin{array}{cc} 5 \\ -3 \end{array}
$$

"*Let's use linking cubes to help us find these answers.*"

- Give your child 11 linking cubes.

"*Make a tower of five linking cubes.*"

- Allow time for your child to do this.

"Now break off two cubes."

"How many cubes are left?" 3

• Record the answer on the chalkboard problem.

"Put the cubes together to make a tower of five cubes."

• Allow time for your child to do this.

"Now break off three cubes."

"How many cubes are left?" 2

• Record the answer on the chalkboard problem.

"What do you notice about these problems?"

• Repeat with the following problems:

$$\begin{array}{cc} 7 & 7 \\ -3 & -4 \end{array} \qquad \begin{array}{cc} 9 & 9 \\ -4 & -5 \end{array} \qquad \begin{array}{cc} 11 & 11 \\ -5 & -6 \end{array}$$

"Now I will give you fact cards for the doubles plus one subtraction facts."

• Give your child the pink subtraction fact cards.

"Use the linking cubes to help you find the answers for these facts."

"Write each answer on the back of the card."

"When you finish, practice saying the facts and the answers to yourself."

"See how many answers you can remember."

CLASS PRACTICE

"Let's practice the new subtraction facts together."

• Use the large subtraction fact cards.

• Give your child **Fact Sheet S 5.0.**

"What number facts do you see?"

"What strategy will you use to find the answers?"

• Correct the fact sheet with your child.

WRITTEN PRACTICE

• Complete **Worksheet 125A** with your child.

• Complete **Worksheet 125B** with your child later in the day.

Name _____   ASSESSMENT 24
Date _____   LESSON 125
                                        Math 1

1. Write a story for the number sentence **6 + 4 = 10.**

   _____
   _____
   _____

2. How much money is this? _32¢_

3. Color the spheres green.
   Color the cubes yellow.
   Color the cones red.
   Color the cylinders blue.

4. Color the graph to show how many cubes and cylinders you colored.

Cubes				
Cylinders				

   How many more cylinders than cubes are there? _2_

5. Count by 10's from 6. Fill in the numbers you say.

6	16	26	36	46	56	66	76	86	96

6. Fill in the answers.

   5 − 2 = _3_   10 − 3 = _7_   6 + 9 = _15_   5 + 3 = _8_

1-125Aa   Copyright © 1991 by Saxon Publishers, Inc. and Nancy Larson. Reproduction prohibited.

Name • _____   LESSON 125A
   (Draw an 8-centimeter line segment.)   Math 1
Date _____

Day of the Week _____

1. Write the number one hundred thirteen 3 more times.

   113 113

2. Elizabeth has 2 dimes and 4 pennies. Stephanie has 1 penny and 5 dimes. Draw the coins. Color the pennies brown.

   Ⓓ Ⓓ Ⓓ Ⓓ Ⓓ Ⓓ Ⓓ Ⓟ Ⓟ Ⓟ Ⓟ Ⓟ

   How many dimes do the girls have altogether? _7_ dimes
   How many pennies do the girls have altogether? _5_ pennies
   How much money is that? _75¢_

3. The children in Mrs. Burton's class made this graph about their favorite colors.

   Write two things you know about the children in Mrs. Burton's class.

   1) _____
   _____

   2) _____

   FAVORITE COLORS
   red blue green yellow

4. Measure this line segment using inches.
   _3_ inches

5. Measure this line segment using centimeters.
   _8_ centimeters

6. Find the answers.

   7 + 2 + 3 = _12_
   5 + 1 + 6 = _12_

   $\begin{array}{r} 9 \\ -4 \\ \hline 5 \end{array}$ $\begin{array}{r} 7 \\ -3 \\ \hline 4 \end{array}$ $\begin{array}{r} 11 \\ -6 \\ \hline 5 \end{array}$ $\begin{array}{r} 5 \\ -2 \\ \hline 3 \end{array}$

1-125Wa   Copyright © 1991 by Saxon Publishers, Inc. and Nancy Larson. Reproduction prohibited.

Name _____   LESSON 125B
                                        Math 1

1. Circle all the numbers that are between 38 and 51.

   ⟨43⟩ 55 ⟨50⟩ 35 ⟨47⟩ ⟨39⟩

2. Lesley has 3 dimes and 2 pennies. Theresa has 3 pennies and 1 dime. Draw the coins. Color the pennies brown.

   Ⓓ Ⓓ Ⓓ Ⓓ Ⓟ Ⓟ Ⓟ Ⓟ Ⓟ

   How many dimes do the girls have altogether? _4_ dimes
   How many pennies do the girls have altogether? _5_ pennies
   How much money is that? _45¢_

3. The children in Mrs. Trembley's class made this graph about their favorite colors.

   Write two things you know about the children in Mrs. Trembley's class.

   _____
   _____
   _____

   FAVORITE COLORS
   red blue green yellow

4. Finish the patterns.

   100 , 200 , _300_ , 400, 500, 600, _700_ , _800_ , _900_
   23, 33, 43, _53_ , _63_ , _73_ , _83_ , _93_
   50, 45, 40, _35_ , _30_ , _25_ , _20_ , _15_

5. Find the answers.

   6 + 3 + 4 = _13_
   3 + 1 + 4 = _8_

   $\begin{array}{r} 5 \\ -3 \\ \hline 2 \end{array}$ $\begin{array}{r} 9 \\ -5 \\ \hline 4 \end{array}$ $\begin{array}{r} 7 \\ -4 \\ \hline 3 \end{array}$ $\begin{array}{r} 11 \\ -5 \\ \hline 6 \end{array}$

1-125Wb   Copyright © 1991 by Saxon Publishers, Inc. and Nancy Larson. Reproduction prohibited.

Lesson 126

writing the number 114
identifying and counting hundreds, tens, and ones

---

lesson preparation

materials

5 bags of 100 pennies plus 50 extra pennies

Masters 1-84A and 1-84B (from Lesson 84)

Master 1-126 (2 copies)

1 small plastic bag

scissors

large fact cards (subtraction using the doubles plus one facts)

Fact Sheet S 5.0

in the morning

• Write the following number pattern on the meeting strip:

> 100, 200, 300, ___, ___, ___

Answer: 100, 200, 300, 400, 500, 600

• Put **3 dimes, 5 nickels,** and **1 penny** in the coin cup.

THE MEETING

calendar

• Ask your child to identify the following:

    year

    month

    shapes on the calendar

    today's shape

    shape pattern for the month

• Ask your child to write the date on the calendar.

- Ask your child to do the following:

    identify today's day of the week, yesterday's day of the week, and tomorrow's day of the week

    read the days of the week

    identify the weekdays

    identify the number of days in a week

  "Let's say the names of the months of the year together."

- Point to the names of the months of the year as you read them with your child.

- Ask your child to write the full date on the meeting strip.

weather graph

- Ask your child to report and graph the weather.

- Ask questions about the graph.

counting

- Say the "Counting by 10's Rap" on **Master 1-91** together once a week.

- Count by 100's to 1,000.

- Count by 5's to 50.

- Count by 10's to 100.

- Count backward from 100 by 10's.

- Count by 2's to 20.

- Count backward from 20 by 2's.

- Ask your child to identify the digits to use to write the next number on the number line.

- Ask your child to identify the total number of pennies needed to show this number.

  "Let's show this amount of money using dollars, dimes, and pennies."

  "How many dollar bills will we use?"

  "How many dimes will we use?"

  "How many pennies will we use?"

- Ask your child to show that amount of money.

  "Let's count the money together."

- Count the money with your child.

  "Which digit in the number _____ tells us the number of dollar bills?"

  "Which digit in the number _____ tells us the number of dimes?"

  "Which digit in the number _____ tells us the number of pennies?"

number pattern

- Ask your child to identify and fill in the missing numbers.
- Read the number pattern together.

clock

- Ask your child to set the morning/afternoon/evening/night clock.
- Throughout the day, your child announces the time on the hour and the half hour, sets the demonstration clock to show the time, and writes the digital time on the chalkboard.

coin cup

"Today there are dimes, nickels, and pennies in the coin cup."

"Put the nickels in stacks of two."

- Allow time for your child to stack the nickels.

"Let's count the money together as I point to each dime, stack of nickels, extra nickel, and penny."

- Ask your child to record the amount of money on the meeting strip.

right/left

- Continue to practice left and right once a week. Practice more often, if necessary.

number fact of the day

- Ask your child to choose a number fact (one of the oddball facts) to practice for the day.

"Let's practice number facts."

"Hip, hip, hooray!"

"What is the oddball fact for today?"

- Write the number fact on the chalkboard. Frequently during the day, ask your child the following question:

"What is our oddball fact for today?"

THE LESSON

Writing the Number 114

"The last number we practiced writing was the number 113."

"What number do you think we will learn how to write today?"

- Write the number 114 on the chalkboard.

"What digits do you see in the number 114?"

Identifying and Counting Hundreds, Tens, and Ones

"Today you will learn how to identify the number of hundreds, tens, and ones in a number."

"You also will learn how to count hundreds, tens, and ones."

• Hold up 3 bags of 100 pennies.

"How many pennies do I have altogether?" *300*

• Turn over **Master 1-84A** and put 1 bag of 100 pennies on the back of the paper. Put 4 groups of 10 pennies and 3 extra pennies on **Master 1-84B**.

"How many groups of one hundred pennies do we have?" *1*

"How many groups of ten pennies do we have?" *4*

"How many extra ones do we have?" *3*

"Let's count to see how many pennies there are altogether."

• Point to each group of pennies as you count by 100's, 10's, and 1's with your child.

"We write 'one hundred forty-three' like this."

• Say "one hundred forty-three" slowly as you write "143" on the chalkboard.

• Put 3 bags of 100 pennies on the back of **Master 1-84A**. Put 2 groups of 10 pennies and 6 extra pennies on **Master 1-84B**.

"Let's count to see how many pennies there are altogether."

• Point to each group of pennies as you count by 100's, 10's, and 1's with your child.

"We write 'three hundred twenty-six' like this."

• Say "three hundred twenty-six" slowly as you write "326" on the chalkboard.

"How many groups of one hundred do we have?" *3*

"How many groups of ten do we have?" *2*

"How many extra ones do we have?" *6*

• Put 4 bags of 100 pennies on the back of **Master 1-84A**. Put 5 groups of 10 pennies on **Master 1-84B**.

"How many groups of one hundred do we have?" *4*

"How many groups of ten do we have?" *5*

"How many extra ones do we have?" *0*

"How many pennies do you think there are altogether?"

"Let's count to check."

• Point to each group of pennies as you count by 100's and 10's with your child.

"We write 'four hundred fifty' like this."

- Say "four hundred fifty" slowly as you write "450" on the chalkboard.

  "Which digit tells us the number of hundreds?" 4

  "Which digit tells us the number of tens?" 5

  "Which digit tells us the number of extra pennies?" 0

- Put 5 bags of 100 pennies on the back of **Master 1-84A**. Put 3 groups of 10 pennies and 6 extra pennies on **Master 1-84B**.

  "How many groups of one hundred pennies do we have?" 5

  "How many groups of ten pennies do we have?" 3

  "How many extra ones do we have?" 6

  "How many pennies do you think there are altogether?"

  "Let's count to check."

- Point to each group of pennies as you count by 100's, 10's, and 1's with your child.

  "We write 'five hundred thirty-six' like this."

- Say "five hundred thirty-six" slowly as you write "536" on the chalkboard.

  "Which digit tells us the number of hundreds?" 5

  "Which digit tells us the number of tens?" 3

  "Which digit tells us the number of extra pennies?" 6

- Put 2 bags of 100 pennies on the back of **Master 1-84A**. Put 5 extra pennies on **Master 1-84B**.

  "How many groups of one hundred do we have?" 2

  "How many groups of ten do we have?" 0

  "How many extra ones do we have?" 5

  "How many pennies do you think there are altogether?"

  "Let's count to check."

- Point to each group of pennies as you count by 100's and 1's with your child.

  "We write 'two hundred five' like this."

- Say "two hundred five" slowly as you write "205" on the chalkboard.

  "Which digit tells us the number of hundreds?" 2

  "Which digit tells us the number of tens?" 0

  "Which digit tells us the number of extra pennies?" 5

  "Tomorrow you will learn how to show numbers using pictures of groups of pennies."

- Cut out the groups of 100 pennies, 10 pennies, and individual pennies on **Masters 1-26**. Put the pieces in a small plastic bag for use in Lesson 127.

CLASS PRACTICE

"Let's practice the subtraction using the doubles plus one facts."

"What strategy will you use to find the answers?"

- Use the large fact cards.
- Give your child **Fact Sheet S 5.0.**
- Correct the fact sheet with your child.

WRITTEN PRACTICE

- Complete **Worksheet 126A** with your child.
- Complete **Worksheet 126B** with your child later in the day.

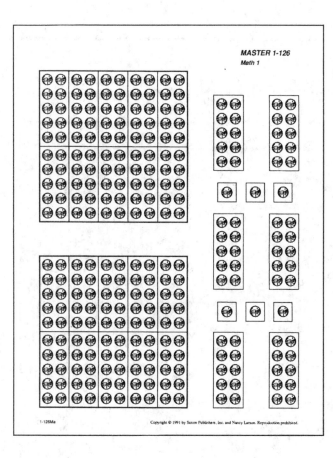

Name _____   **LESSON 126A**
(Draw a 4-inch line segment.)   Math 1

Date _____

Day of the Week _____

1. Write the number one hundred fourteen 3 more times.

    ‖4   ‖4 ‖4

2. Five children from Room 4 went to the nurse's office to have their eyes checked. Six children from Room 5 went to the nurse's office to have their eyes checked. Draw a picture and write a number sentence to show the children at the nurse's office.

    Number sentence _____ 5 + 6 = 11 _____

    How many children are at the nurse's office? __11__ children

3. The children in Mrs. Flinter's class made this graph about their favorite insects. Write two things you know about the children in Mrs. Flinter's class.

    1)_____

    2)_____

    FAVORITE INSECTS

    Ladybug ▓▓▓▓▓□
    Firefly ▓▓▓▓▓▓
    Ant ▓▓▓□□□

4. Color the pennies brown. How much money is this? __41¢__

5. Find the answers.

    $2 + 2 + 7 = \underline{11}$ $\begin{array}{r} 9 \\ -8 \\ \hline 1 \end{array}$ $\begin{array}{r} 8 \\ -1 \\ \hline 7 \end{array}$ $\begin{array}{r} 5 \\ -2 \\ \hline 3 \end{array}$ $\begin{array}{r} 6 \\ -5 \\ \hline 1 \end{array}$ $\begin{array}{r} 8 \\ -2 \\ \hline 6 \end{array}$

    $5 + 4 + 4 = \underline{13}$

Name _____   **LESSON 126B**
                                       Math 1

1. Finish the number patterns.

    100, 200, 300, __400__ , __500__ , __600__ , __700__ , __800__

    19, 17, 15, __13__ , __11__ , __9__ , __7__ , __5__

2. Six children from Room 5 went to the library to return books. Seven children from Room 4 went to the library to return books. Draw a picture and write a number sentence to show the children in the library.

    Number sentence _____ 6 + 7 = 13 _____

    How many children are in the library? __13__ children

3. The children in Miss Rocco's class made this graph about their favorite insects. Write two things you know about the children in Miss Rocco's class.

    1)_____

    2)_____

    FAVORITE INSECTS

    Ladybug ▓▓▓▓▓□
    Firefly ▓▓▓▓▓▓
    Ant ▓▓▓□□□

4. Color the pennies brown. How much money is this? __36¢__

5. Find the answers.

    $3 + 3 + 6 = \underline{12}$ $\begin{array}{r} 7 \\ -1 \\ \hline 6 \end{array}$ $\begin{array}{r} 5 \\ -4 \\ \hline 1 \end{array}$ $\begin{array}{r} 9 \\ -2 \\ \hline 7 \end{array}$ $\begin{array}{r} 7 \\ -6 \\ \hline 1 \end{array}$ $\begin{array}{r} 6 \\ -2 \\ \hline 4 \end{array}$

    $2 + 5 + 5 = \underline{12}$

esson 127

writing the number 115
representing numbers to 500 using pictures

---

lesson preparation

materials

bag of pieces from Master 1-126

cup of 10 pennies

1 piece of paper

large fact cards (subtraction using the doubles plus one facts)

Fact Sheet S 5.0

in the morning

• Write the following number pattern on the meeting strip:

> 800, 700, 600, __, __, __

Answer: 800, 700, 600, 500, 400, 300

• Put **4 quarters** in the coin cup.

THE MEETING

calendar

• Ask your child to identify the following:

    year

    month

    shapes on the calendar

    today's shape

    shape pattern for the month

• Ask your child to write the date on the calendar.

• Ask your child to do the following:

    identify today's day of the week, yesterday's day of the week, and tomorrow's day of the week

    read the days of the week

    identify the weekdays

---

identify the number of days in a week

"Let's say the names of the months of the year together."

- Point to the names of the months of the year as you read them with your child.

- Ask your child to write the full date on the meeting strip.

weather graph

- Ask your child to report and graph the weather.

- Ask questions about the graph.

counting

- Say the "Counting by 10's Rap" on **Master 1-91** together once a week.

- Count by 100's to 1,000.

- Count by 5's to 50.

- Count by 10's to 100.

- Count backward from 100 by 10's.

- Say the odd numbers to 19.

- Say the odd numbers backward from 19.

- Ask your child to identify the digits to use to write the next number on the number line.

- Ask your child to identify the total number of pennies needed to show this number.

  "Let's show this amount of money using dollars, dimes, and pennies."

  "How many dollar bills will we use?"

  "How many dimes will we use?"

  "How many pennies will we use?"

- Ask your child to show that amount of money.

  "Let's count the money together."

- Count the money with your child.

  "Which digit in the number _____ tells us the number of dollar bills?"

  "Which digit in the number _____ tells us the number of dimes?"

  "Which digit in the number _____ tells us the number of pennies?"

number pattern

- Ask your child to identify and fill in the missing numbers.

- Read the number pattern together.

clock

- Ask your child to set the morning/afternoon/evening/night clock.

- Throughout the day, your child announces the time on the hour and the half hour, sets the demonstration clock to show the time, and writes the digital time on the chalkboard.

coin cup

"Today there are four quarters in the coin cup."

"Let's count the money together."

- Ask your child to record the amount of money on the meeting strip.

right/left

- Continue to practice left and right once a week. Practice more often, if necessary.

number fact of the day

- Ask your child to choose a number fact (one of the oddball facts) to practice for the day.

"Let's practice number facts."

"Hip, hip, hooray!"

"What is the oddball fact for today?"

- Write the number fact on the chalkboard. Frequently during the day, ask your child the following question:

"What is our oddball fact for today?"

THE LESSON

Writing the Number 115

"The last number we practiced writing was the number 114."

"What number do you think we will learn how to write today?"

- Write the number 115 on the chalkboard.

"What digits do you see in the number 115?"

Representing Numbers to 500 Using Pictures

"Today you will learn how to show numbers using pictures of pennies."

- Give your child the bag of pieces from **Master 1-126** and a piece of paper.

"Take the pictures of pennies out of the bag and sort them."

- Allow time for your child to do this.

"How many pennies are on each small rectangle?" 10

"Let's count them to check."

"How many pennies are on the large square?" 100

"Let's count them by 10's to check."

"How many hundreds do you have?" 4

"Put three pictures of one hundred pennies on your paper."

- Allow time for your child to do this.

"Put five pictures of ten pennies on your paper."

- Allow time for your child to do this.

"Put two extra pennies on your paper."

- Allow time for your child to do this.

"Let's count to see how many pennies this is altogether."

"How many hundreds do we have?" 3

"Let's count by 100's."

- Count by 100's with your child.

"We have three hundred pennies."

"How many tens do we have?" 5

"Let's count by 10's."

- Count by 10's with your child.

"Now we have three hundred fifty pennies."

"Now we will count the extra pennies."

"How many extra pennies do we have?" 2

"We have three hundred fifty-two pennies."

"What digits do you think I will write to show how much this is?"

- Write "352" on the chalkboard.

- Point to each digit as you say the following:

"We have three hundreds, five tens, and two ones."

"Show two groups of one hundred, six groups of ten, and eight extra ones."

- Allow time for your child to do this.

"Let's count to see how many pennies this is altogether."

"How many hundreds do we have?" 2

"Let's count by 100's."

- Count by 100's with your child.

"We have two hundred pennies."

"How many tens do we have?"   6

"How many pennies is that?"   sixty

"Let's count by 10's to check."

- Count by 10's with your child.

   "Now we have two hundred sixty pennies."

   "How many extra pennies do we have?"   8

   "We have two hundred sixty-eight pennies."

   "What digits do you think I will write to show how much this is?"

- Write "268" on the chalkboard.

- Point to each digit as you say the following:

   "We have two hundreds, six tens, and eight ones."

   "Show one hundred, no tens, and six ones."

- Allow time for your child to do this.

   "Let's count to see how many pennies this is altogether."

   "How many hundreds do we have?"   1

   "We have one hundred pennies."

   "How many tens do we have?"   0

   "How many extra pennies do we have?"   6

   "We have one hundred six pennies."

- Write "106" on the chalkboard.

- Point to each digit as you say the following:

   "We have one hundred, zero tens, and six ones."

   "I wrote a zero to show that we do not have any tens."

   "Show three hundreds, seven tens, and four ones."

- Allow time for your child to do this.

   "Let's count to see how many pennies this is altogether."

   "How many hundreds do we have?"   3

   "How many pennies is that?"   three hundred

   "How many tens do we have?"   7

   "How many pennies is that?"   seventy

   "How many extra pennies do we have?"   4

   "How many pennies is this altogether?"   374

   "Let's count by 100's, 10's, and 1's to check."

- Count by 100's, 10's, and 1's with your child.

   "We have three hundred seventy-four pennies."

"What digits do you think I will write to show how much this is?"

• Write "374" on the chalkboard.

• Point to each digit as you say the following:

"We have three hundreds, seven tens, and four ones."

"Show four hundreds and three tens."

• Allow time for your child to do this.

"Let's count to see how many pennies this is altogether."

"How many hundreds do we have?" 4

"How many pennies is that?" *four hundred*

"How many tens do we have?" 3

"How many pennies is that?" *thirty*

"How many extra pennies do we have?" 0

"How many pennies is this altogether?" 430

"Let's count by 100's and 10's to check."

• Count by 100's and 10's with your child.

"We have four hundred thirty pennies."

• Write "430" on the chalkboard.

• Point to each digit as you say the following:

"We have four hundreds, three tens, and zero ones."

"I wrote a zero to show that we do not have any ones."

• Write "247" on the chalkboard.

• Ask your child to read the number.

"How many hundreds will we use to show this number?" 2

"How many tens will we use to show this number?" 4

"How many ones will we use to show this number?" 7

"Show this using hundreds, tens, and ones."

• Allow time for your child to do this.

• Repeat, using 182, 453, 204, and 350.

"Put your pieces in the bag."

CLASS PRACTICE

"Let's practice the subtraction using the doubles plus one facts."

"What strategy will you use to find the answers?"

• Use the large fact cards.

• Give your child **Fact Sheet S 5.0.**

• Correct the fact sheet with your child.

WRITTEN PRACTICE

• Complete **Worksheet 127A** with your child.

• Complete **Worksheet 127B** with your child later in the day.

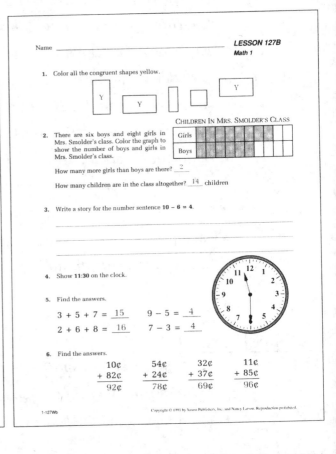

Name _____
(Draw a 12-centimeter line segment.)

LESSON 127A
Math 1

Date _____

Day of the Week _____

1. Write the number one hundred fifteen 4 more times.

   115 115 ------------------------------

2. There are nine boys and seven girls in Mrs. Glenn's class. Color the graph to show the number of boys and girls in Mrs. Glenn's class.

   CHILDREN IN MRS. GLENN'S CLASS

   | Girls | | | | | | | | |
   | Boys | | | | | | | | |

   How many more boys than girls are there? 2

   How many children are in the class altogether? 16 children

3. Write a story for the number sentence **9 – 2 = 7.**
   _____
   _____
   _____

4. Show **8:30** on the clock.

5. Find the answers.

   2 + 6 + 8 = 16   7 – 4 = 3
   1 + 6 + 1 = 8   11 – 5 = 6

6. Find the answers.

79¢	65¢	43¢	30¢
+ 10¢	+ 23¢	+ 41¢	+ 28¢
89¢	88¢	84¢	58¢

1-127Wa

Name _____

LESSON 127B
Math 1

1. Color all the congruent shapes yellow.

   Y   Y   Y

2. There are six boys and eight girls in Mrs. Smolder's class. Color the graph to show the number of boys and girls in Mrs. Smolder's class.

   CHILDREN IN MRS. SMOLDER'S CLASS

   | Girls | | | | | | | | |
   | Boys | | | | | | | | |

   How many more girls than boys are there? 2

   How many children are in the class altogether? 14 children

3. Write a story for the number sentence **10 – 6 = 4.**
   _____
   _____
   _____

4. Show **11:30** on the clock.

5. Find the answers.

   3 + 5 + 7 = 15   9 – 5 = 4
   2 + 6 + 8 = 16   7 – 3 = 4

6. Find the answers.

10¢	54¢	32¢	11¢
+ 82¢	+ 24¢	+ 37¢	+ 85¢
92¢	78¢	69¢	96¢

1-127Wb

L esson **128**

writing the number 116
subtraction facts—the leftover facts

---

lesson preparation

materials

eight 3" × 5" cards

1 tower of 10 linking cubes

subtraction fact cards — white

Fact Sheet S 9.1

the night before

• Use the 3" × 5" cards to make a large set of fact cards for the leftover subtraction facts. Write them in the following way:

6	7	8	9	8	8	9	9
− 4	− 5	− 6	− 7	− 3	− 5	− 3	− 6

• Separate the fact cards.

in the morning

• Write the following number pattern on the meeting strip:

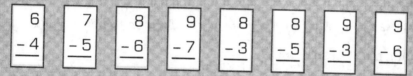

—, —, —, 500, 600, 700

Answer: 200, 300, 400, 500, 600, 700

• Put **2 dimes, 4 nickels,** and **6 pennies** in the coin cup.

THE MEETING

calendar

• Ask your child to identify the following:

year

month

shapes on the calendar

today's shape

shape pattern for the month

- Ask your child to write the date on the calendar.
- Ask your child to do the following:

    identify today's day of the week, yesterday's day of the week, and tomorrow's day of the week

    read the days of the week

    identify the weekdays

    identify the number of days in a week

    "Let's say the names of the months of the year together."

- Point to the names of the months of the year as you read them with your child.
- Ask your child to write the full date on the meeting strip.

weather graph

- Ask your child to report and graph the weather.
- Ask questions about the graph.

counting

- Say the "Counting by 10's Rap" on **Master 1-91** together once a week.
- Count by 100's to 1,000.
- Count by 5's to 50.
- Count by 10's to 100.
- Count backward from 100 by 10's.
- Count by 2's to 20.
- Count backward from 20 by 2's.
- Ask your child to identify the digits to use to write the next number on the number line.
- Ask your child to identify the total number of pennies needed to show this number.

    "Let's show this amount of money using dollars, dimes, and pennies."

    "How many dollar bills will we use?"

    "How many dimes will we use?"

    "How many pennies will we use?"

- Ask your child to show that amount of money.

    "Let's count the money together."

- Count the money with your child.

    "Which digit in the number _____ tells us the number of dollar bills?"

    "Which digit in the number _____ tells us the number of dimes?"

"Which digit in the number _____ tells us the number of pennies?"

number pattern

- Ask your child to identify and fill in the missing numbers.

- Read the number pattern together.

clock

- Ask your child to set the morning/afternoon/evening/night clock.

- Throughout the day, your child announces the time on the hour and the half hour, sets the demonstration clock to show the time, and writes the digital time on the chalkboard.

coin cup

"Today there are dimes, nickels, and pennies in the coin cup."

"Put the nickels in stacks of two."

- Allow time for your child to stack the nickels.

"Let's count the money together as I point to each dime, stack of nickels, and penny."

- Ask your child to record the amount of money on the meeting strip.

right/left

- Continue to practice left and right once a week. Practice more often, if necessary.

number fact of the day

- Ask your child to choose a number fact (one of the oddball facts) to practice for the day.

"Let's practice number facts."

"Hip, hip, hooray!"

"What is the oddball fact for today?"

- Write the number fact on the chalkboard. Frequently during the day, ask your child the following question:

"What is our oddball fact for today?"

The Lesson

Writing the Number 116

"The last number we practiced writing was the number 115."

"What number do you think we will learn how to write today?"

- Write the number 116 on the chalkboard.

"What digits do you see in the number 116?"

Subtraction Facts—The Leftover Facts

"Today you will learn eight new subtraction facts that do not follow a pattern."

"We will call these the leftover facts."

- Write the following problems on the chalkboard:

$$6 - 4 =$$
$$7 - 5 =$$
$$8 - 6 =$$
$$9 - 7 =$$

"What do you think the answers for these problems will be?"

"How do you know?"

"Do you see a pattern in these problems?"

"Let's use linking cubes to help us find the answer for each problem."

- Give your child a tower of 10 linking cubes.

"How will we use linking cubes to show the first problem?" make a tower of six cubes and break off four cubes

"Make a tower of six cubes."

- Allow time for your child to do this.

"Now break off four cubes."

"How many cubes are left?" 2

- Record the answer next to the problem.

"How will you use linking cubes to show the next problem?" make a tower of seven cubes and break off five cubes

"Show seven minus five using your linking cubes."

- Allow time for your child to do this.

"How many cubes are left?" 2

- Record the answer next to the problem.

- Repeat with the last two problems.

"What do you notice about all of these problems?"

- Allow time for your child to offer observations.

- Write the following problems on the chalkboard:

$$\begin{array}{cccc} 8 & 8 & 9 & 9 \\ -3 & -5 & -3 & -6 \end{array}$$

"What do you think the answers for these problems will be?"

"How do you know?"

"Do you see a pattern in these problems?"

"Let's use linking cubes to help find the answer for each problem."

"How will you use linking cubes to show the first problem?"   make a tower of eight cubes and break off three cubes

"Make a tower of eight cubes."

- Allow time for your child to do this.

"Now break off three cubes."

"How many cubes are left?"   5

- Record the answer next to the problem.

"How will we use linking cubes to show the next problem?"   make a tower of eight cubes and break off five cubes

"Show eight minus five using your linking cubes."

- Allow time for your child to do this.

"How many cubes are left?"   3

- Record the answer next to the problem.
- Repeat with the last two problems.

"Now I will give you fact cards for the leftover subtraction facts."

- Give your child the white subtraction fact cards.

"Use the linking cubes to help you find the answers for these facts."

"Write each answer on the back of the card."

"When you finish, practice saying the facts and the answers to yourself."

"See how many answers you can remember."

CLASS PRACTICE

"Let's practice the leftover subtraction facts together."

- Use the large fact cards
- Give your child **Fact Sheet S 9.1.**
- Correct the fact sheet with your child.

WRITTEN PRACTICE

- Complete **Worksheet 128A** with your child.
- Complete **Worksheet 128B** with your child later in the day.

LESSON 128A
Math 1

Name _____
(Draw a 4-inch line segment.)

Date _____

Day of the Week _____

1. Write the number one hundred sixteen 3 more times.

    116 116

2. On Mrs. Barlow's lunch graph, eight children put their tags in the lunch from home row. Six children put their tags in the school lunch row. Draw the tags on the lunch graph.

Lunch from home	H H H H H H H H
School lunch	S S S S S S

   How many more children eat home lunch than eat school lunch? __2__

   How many tags are on the graph? __14__ tags

3. Draw a five-sided polygon in the box.

4. How much money is this? __50¢__

5. Maureen wrote a two-digit number on a piece of paper. She gave the children the following clues to help them guess her secret number. Maureen said, "The digits I used are 4 and 6."

   Write the two possible numbers. 46   64

   Maureen said, "The number is between 48 and 70." Circle Maureen's secret number.

6. Find the answers.

   6 + 7 + 3 = __16__   8 + 1 + 9 = __18__   2 + 7 + 8 = __17__

1-128Wa

LESSON 128B
Math 1

Name _____

1. Circle all the numbers that are between 50 and 75.

   78   43   (61)   (58)   82   (71)

2. On Mrs. York's lunch graph, nine children put their tags in the lunch from home row. Six children put their tags in the school lunch row. Draw the tags on the lunch graph.

Lunch from home	H H H H H H H H H
School lunch	S S S S S S

   How many more children eat home lunch than eat school lunch? __3__

   How many tags are on the graph? __15__ tags

3. Draw a three-sided polygon in the box.

4. How much money is this? __75¢__

5. Sharon wrote a two-digit number on a piece of paper. She gave the children the following clues to help them guess her secret number. Sharon said, "The digits I used are 7 and 9."

   Write the two possible numbers. (79)   97

   Sharon said, "The number is between 75 and 95." Circle Sharon's secret number.

6. Find the answers.

   8 + 2 + 6 = __16__   5 + 4 + 7 = __16__   2 + 9 + 3 = __14__

1-128Wb

694

Lesson 129

writing the number 117
identifying the season—summer

---

lesson preparation

materials

crayons

large fact cards (leftover subtraction facts)

Fact Sheet S 9.1

in the morning

• Write the following number pattern on the meeting strip:

> 79, 77, 75, ___, ___, ___

Answer: *79, 77, 75, 73, 71, 69*

• Put **6 dimes**, **3 nickels**, and **8 pennies** in the coin cup.

THE MEETING

calendar

- • Ask your child to identify the following:

    year

    month

    shapes on the calendar

    today's shape

    shape pattern for the month

- • Ask your child to write the date on the calendar.

- • Ask your child to do the following:

    identify today's day of the week, yesterday's day of the week, and tomorrow's day of the week

    read the days of the week

    identify the weekdays

    identify the number of days in a week

"Let's say the names of the months of the year together."

- Point to the names of the months of the year as you read them with your child.

- Ask your child to write the full date on the meeting strip.

weather graph

- Ask your child to report and graph the weather.

- Ask questions about the graph.

counting

- Say the "Counting by 10's Rap" on **Master 1-91** together once a week.

- Count by 100's to 1,000.

- Count by 5's to 50.

- Count by 10's to 100.

- Count backward from 100 by 10's.

- Say the odd numbers to 19.

- Say the odd numbers backward from 19.

- Ask your child to identify the digits to use to write the next number on the number line.

- Ask your child to identify the total number of pennies needed to show this number.

   "Let's show this amount of money using dollars, dimes, and pennies."

   "How many dollar bills will we use?"

   "How many dimes will we use?"

   "How many pennies will we use?"

- Ask your child to show that amount of money.

   "Let's count the money together."

- Count the money with your child.

   "Which digit in the number _____ tells us the number of dollar bills?"

   "Which digit in the number _____ tells us the number of dimes?"

   "Which digit in the number _____ tells us the number of pennies?"

number pattern

- Ask your child to identify and fill in the missing numbers.

- Read the number pattern together.

clock

- Ask your child to set the morning/afternoon/evening/night clock.

- Throughout the day, your child announces the time on the hour and the half hour, sets the demonstration clock to show the time, and writes the digital time on the chalkboard.

coin cup

"Today there are dimes, nickels, and pennies in the coin cup."

"Put the nickels in stacks of two."

- Allow time for your child to stack the nickels.

"Let's count the money together as I point to each dime, stack of nickels, extra nickel, and penny."

- Ask your child to record the amount of money on the meeting strip.

right/left

- Continue to practice left and right once a week. Practice more often, if necessary.

number fact of the day

- Ask your child to choose a number fact (one of the oddball facts) to practice for the day.

"Let's practice number facts."

"Hip, hip, hooray!"

"What is the oddball fact for today?"

- Write the number fact on the chalkboard. Frequently during the day, ask your child the following question:

"What is our oddball fact for today?"

THE LESSON

Writing the Number 117

"The last number we practiced writing was the number 116."

"What number do you think we will learn how to write today?"

- Write the number 117 on the chalkboard.

"What digits do you see in the number 117?"

Identifying the Season—Summer

"Today you will learn about a new season."

"On June _____ , a new season begins."

Note: The actual date varies from year to year.

"What season is it now?"   spring

"How will summer be different from spring?"   temperature, amount of daylight, plants and trees are different, clothing worn, etc.

"What do you do differently in the summer?"

"Today we will look at the tree (plant) we chose in the fall."

"What did it look like then?"

"We will go outside to see it again today."

- Open the Meeting Book to page 42.

"You will draw a picture of the tree in the Meeting Book."

"You will also write about how the tree looks in summer."

- Go outside and observe the tree.

"What does the tree look like now?"

"How is this different from when we saw it a few weeks ago?"

"What does it feel like outside in summer?"

"How is this different from spring?"

"Draw a picture and write about our tree in the summer."

- Optional: Take a picture of your child next to the tree (plant).

CLASS PRACTICE

"Let's practice the leftover subtraction facts together."

- Use the large fact cards
- Give your child **Fact Sheet S 9.1**.
- Correct the fact sheet with your child.

WRITTEN PRACTICE

- Complete **Worksheet 129A** with your child.
- Complete **Worksheet 129B** with your child later in the day.

Name _____
(Draw a 10-centimeter line segment.)

LESSON 129A
Math 1

Date _____

Day of the Week _____

1. Write the number one hundred seventeen 4 more times.

    117 117 _____

2. In Room 9, ten children wore long sleeve shirts and seven children wore short sleeve shirts. Color the graph to show the shirts the children wore.

    | Short sleeves | ████ | | | |
    | Long sleeves | ████████ | | |

    How many more children wore long sleeves than wore short sleeves? __3__

    How many children are in Room 9? __17__ children

3. Measure this line segment using centimeters.

    •————————————————————• __12__ centimeters

4. Measure this line segment using inches.

    •————————• __2__ inches

5. Circle all of the shapes divided into fourths. Color two fourths of each circled shape blue.

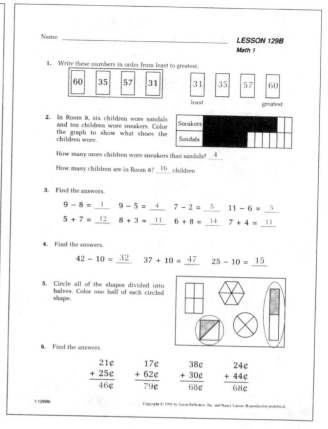

6. Find the answers.

    | 52¢ | 10¢ | 25¢ | 13¢ |
    | + 34¢ | + 89¢ | + 42¢ | + 73¢ |
    | 86¢ | 99¢ | 67¢ | 86¢ |

Name _____

LESSON 129B
Math 1

1. Write these numbers in order from least to greatest.

    | 60 | 35 | 57 | 31 | | 31 | 35 | 57 | 60 |
                                   least   greatest

2. In Room 8, six children wore sandals and ten children wore sneakers. Color the graph to show what shoes the children wore.

    | Sneakers | ████████ | | |
    | Sandals | ████ | | | |

    How many more children wore sneakers than sandals? __4__

    How many children are in Room 8? __16__ children

3. Find the answers.

    $9 - 8 =$ __1__ $9 - 5 =$ __4__ $7 - 2 =$ __5__ $11 - 6 =$ __5__

    $5 + 7 =$ __12__ $8 + 3 =$ __11__ $6 + 8 =$ __14__ $7 + 4 =$ __11__

4. Find the answers.

    $42 - 10 =$ __32__ $37 + 10 =$ __47__ $25 - 10 =$ __15__

5. Circle all of the shapes divided into halves. Color one half of each circled shape.

6. Find the answers.

    | 21¢ | 17¢ | 38¢ | 24¢ |
    | + 25¢ | + 62¢ | + 30¢ | + 44¢ |
    | 46¢ | 79¢ | 68¢ | 68¢ |

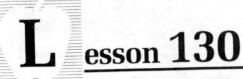esson 130

assessment

---

lesson preparation ————————————————

materials

individual clock

Written Assessment #25

Oral Assessment #13

in the morning

- Write the following number pattern on the meeting strip:

25, 20, 15, __, __, __

Answer: 25, 20, 15, 10, 5, 0

- Put **5 dimes**, **3 nickels**, and **7 pennies** in the coin cup.

THE MEETING

calendar

- Ask your child to identify the following:

    year

    month

    shapes on the calendar

    today's shape

    shape pattern for the month

- Ask your child to write the date on the calendar.

- Ask your child to do the following:

    identify today's day of the week, yesterday's day of the week, and tomorrow's day of the week

    read the days of the week

    identify the weekdays

    identify the number of days in a week

"Let's say the names of the months of the year together."

- Point to the names of the months of the year as you read them with your child.

• Ask your child to write the full date on the meeting strip.

weather graph

• Ask your child to report and graph the weather.

• Ask questions about the graph.

counting

• Say the "Counting by 10's Rap" on **Master 1-91** together once a week.

• Count by 100's to 1,000.

• Count by 5's to 50.

• Count by 10's to 100.

• Count backward from 100 by 10's.

• Count by 2's to 20.

• Count backward from 20 by 2's.

• Ask your child to identify the digits to use to write the next number on the number line.

• Use an orange crayon to color the square for 130.

• Ask your child to identify the total number of pennies needed to show this number.

"Let's show this amount of money using dollars, dimes, and pennies."

"How many dollar bills will we use?"

"How many dimes will we use?"

"How many pennies will we use?"

• Ask your child to show that amount of money.

"Let's count the money together."

• Count the money with your child.

"Which digit in the number _____ tells us the number of dollar bills?"

"Which digit in the number _____ tells us the number of dimes?"

"Which digit in the number _____ tells us the number of pennies?"

number pattern

• Ask your child to identify and fill in the missing numbers.

• Read the number pattern together.

clock

• Ask your child to set the morning/afternoon/evening/night clock.

- Throughout the day, your child announces the time on the hour and the half hour, sets the demonstration clock to show the time, and writes the digital time on the chalkboard.

coin cup

"Today there are dimes, nickels, and pennies in the coin cup."

"Put the nickels in stacks of two."

- Allow time for your child to stack the nickels.

"Let's count the money together as I point to each dime, stack of nickels, extra nickel, and penny."

- Ask your child to record the amount of money on the meeting strip.

right/left

- Continue to practice left and right once a week. Practice more often, if necessary.

number fact of the day

- Ask your child to choose a number fact (one of the oddball facts) to practice for the day.

"Let's practice number facts."

"Hip, hip, hooray!"

"What is the oddball fact for today?"

- Write the number fact on the chalkboard. Frequently during the day, ask your child the following question:

"What is our oddball fact for today?"

ASSESSMENT

- All of the questions on the assessment are based on concepts and skills presented at least five lessons ago. If your child is having difficulty with a specific concept, reteach the concept the following day.

Written Assessment

- Give your child **Written Assessment #25**.

- Read the directions for each problem. Allow time for your child to complete each problem before continuing to the next.

- Correct the paper, noting your child's mistakes on the **Individual Recording Form**. Review the errors with your child.

Oral Assessment

- Record your child's responses to the oral interview on the interview sheet.

Name _____   **ASSESSMENT 25**

Date _____   **LESSON 130**

                                                            Math 1

1. Two children from Room 1 went to the library. Six children from Room 3 went to the library. Draw a picture and write a number sentence to show the children in the library.

Number sentence _____ $2 + 6 = 8$

How many children are at the library now? __8__ children

2. Draw a five-sided polygon in the box.

3. How much money is this? 50¢

4. Find the answers.

$$25 - 10 = \underline{15} \qquad 49 - 10 = \underline{39}$$

$$2 + 6 + 8 = \underline{16} \qquad 3 + 2 + 7 = \underline{12}$$

5. Measure this line segment using centimeters. __9__ centimeters

6. The children in Mrs. Castellon's class made this graph about their favorite juice. Write two things that you know about the children in Mrs. Castellon's class.

FAVORITE JUICE

1) _____

_____

2) _____

_____

1-130Aa

Teacher _____

Date _____

MATH 1   LESSON 130

Oral Assessment # 13 Recording Form

Materials:
Individual clock

Students	A •Show half past 2 on an individual clock *"What time is it?"*	B •Move the hands on the clock •Give the child the individual clock *"Show half past eight."*	•Reassess children on items missed on previous assessments

1-130La

SUMMERTIME
FUN
COOKBOOK

Volume II

GREAT AMERICAN OPPORTUNITIES, INC./ FAVORITE RECIPES® PRESS

President: Thomas F. McDow III
Editorial Manager: Mary Jane Blount
Design and Marketing Manager:
  Karen Bird
Editors: Georgia Brazil, Jane Hinshaw,
  Linda Jones, Carolyn King,
  Debbie Van Mol, Mary Wilson
Typographers: Jessie Anglin,
  Sara Anglin, Pam Newsome
Essayist: Carolyn King

Summertime Fun II is a collection of our favorite recipes, which are not necessarily original recipes.

Published by:
Favorite Recipes® Press, a division of Great American Opportunities, Inc.
P.O. Box 305142
Nashville, Tennessee 37230
1-800-251-1542

Copyright© 1994
by Great American Opportunities, Inc.

Library of Congress Number: 94-61832
ISBN: 0-87197-806-7

Manufactured in the United States of America
First Printing 1994   30,000 copies
Second Printing 1995   55,000 copies

*That night I dreamed in peaceful
sleep of shady summertime
Of old dogs and children and
watermelon "vines."*

Lyrics adapted from
Old Dogs, Children and Watermelon Wine
Tom T. Hall (BMI)

CONTENTS

WATERMELON, WATERMELON EVERYWHERE

Summertime—a time when the living is easy and the winter-jaded senses reawaken. A time for new-mown grass, daisies and goldenrod, dewy cobwebs and butterflies. A time to eat grapes in an arbor, pick juicy berries off the vine, roam through orchards with the hum of bees on the fruit-scented air. A time for splashing in pools, running through sprinklers, sloshing through puddles in pepperings of rain. A time for boat rides and beach fun.

And watermelon, watermelon everywhere . . . at roadside stands, in fields, in markets. Consumed in every imaginable way—split jagged and warm in the patch, the juice trickling down the chin; chilled in a mountain stream, the cold rind sending shivers down the sun-drenched arm; cooled and eaten sliced or in fanciful presentations on patios, decks and porches—as a respite from the heat or as fruitbasket confections for parties. Opening every chapter in *Summertime Fun* is a watermelon-theme recipe. Nothing need be wasted. The rind can be pickled and preserved or carved into baskets to hold a bounty of fruits, the melon used in something as whimsical as melonsicles or as satisfying as a cake. Even the seeds can be projectiles in games of propulsion prowess.

Who could resist a bite from the slice on the cover of our slim tall book? Just as tempting, and as full of ideas to give you maximum fun time with minimum preparation, are the categories. Pack a basket with **Picnic Fun** fare, or bring out the grill for **Cookout Fun** foods. Desserts can be delicious as well as quick to fix, as you'll find in **Munchy Fun**, and those cool refreshing beverages come right off the pages and into your hand from our **Chill Out Fun** section. And when the okra and cucumbers become proliferous, thumb to **Garden Patch Fun**, bring out the pint jars and preserve the best of summer to enjoy all year-round. *Summertime Fun*—a book where the cooking is easy and the eating is fun.

Chill Out Fun

Watermelon Bombe

1 pint lime sherbet,
partially softened

1 pint pineapple sherbet,
partially softened

1 pint raspberry sherbet,
partially softened

1/4 cup semisweet chocolate chips

Line 1 1/2-quart bowl with 12x15-inch piece of foil. Spread lime sherbet over bottom and side of prepared bowl. Freeze for 1 hour or until firm. Press and shape pineapple sherbet over lime sherbet layer. Freeze for 30 minutes. Pack raspberry sherbet into center, smoothing top to resemble cut watermelon. Freeze, covered, for 8 hours or until firm. Unmold onto serving plate; remove foil. Cut into wedges. Press chocolate chips into wedges to resemble seeds. Serve immediately.
Yield: 8 servings.

Banana Ice Cream

4 egg yolks
1 cup sugar
2 cups milk
1 teaspoon salt
4 cups mashed bananas
3 tablespoons lemon juice
4 cups whipping cream
1 tablespoon vanilla extract
4 egg whites

Combine egg yolks, sugar, milk and salt in double boiler; mix well. Cook over boiling water until mixture coats spoon, stirring constantly. Chill in refrigerator. Combine bananas, lemon juice, whipping cream and vanilla in bowl; mix well. Add cooled custard; mix well. Beat egg whites in mixer bowl until stiff peaks form. Fold into custard. Pour into ice cream freezer container. Freeze using manufacturer's instructions. Yield: 16 servings.

Chocolate and Cherry Ice Cream

3 eggs, slightly beaten
1 cup sugar
4 cups milk
2 cups whipping cream
1 (10-ounce) jar maraschino cherries, drained
1 cup chocolate syrup
3 (2-ounce) milk chocolate candy bars, chopped
1 tablespoon vanilla extract

Combine eggs, sugar, milk, whipping cream, maraschino cherries, chocolate syrup, candy bars and vanilla in large bowl; mix well. Pour into 1-gallon ice cream freezer container. Freeze using manufacturer's instructions. Yield: 3 quarts.

Fresh Fruit Ice Cream

1 (4-ounce) package vanilla instant
    pudding mix
1 (12-ounce) can evaporated milk
2 to 4 cups half and half
2 cups sugar
1 teaspoon vanilla extract
2 cups chopped fruit
Milk

Combine pudding mix, evaporated milk, half and half, sugar and vanilla in bowl; mix well. Pour into ice cream freezer container. Add fruit and milk to fill line. Freeze using manufacturer's instructions. Yield: 2 quarts.

Low-Fat Ice Cream

2 cups nonfat yogurt
1 cup strawberry jam

Combine yogurt and jam in mixer bowl. Beat until smooth. Freeze until partially frozen. Beat again. Repeat process until desired consistency is reached.
Yield: 6 servings.

Milky Way Ice Cream

12 (2-ounce) Milky Way candy bars,
    chopped
1 cup milk
1 (14-ounce) can sweetened condensed
    milk
1 (5-ounce) can chocolate syrup
11 cups milk

Combine candy bars and 1 cup milk in double boiler. Cook over hot water until smooth, stirring constantly. Cool. Pour candy mixture, condensed milk, chocolate syrup and 11 cups milk into ice cream freezer container; mix well. Freeze using manufacturer's instructions.
Yield: 16 servings.

CHILL OUT FUN

Pineapple and Mint Frozen Yogurt

1 (8-ounce) can juice-pack crushed
  pineapple
1 cup plain yogurt
1/3 cup frozen apple juice concentrate
1 1/2 teaspoons lemon juice
1/2 teaspoon vanilla extract
1/8 teaspoon salt
1/4 teaspoon mint extract
4 to 6 drops of green food coloring

Drain pineapple, reserving juice. Combine reserved juice, yogurt, apple juice concentrate and lemon juice in saucepan. Cook over low heat for 2 to 3 minutes or until yogurt dissolves, stirring frequently. Cool. Combine cooled mixture with pineapple, vanilla, salt, mint extract and food coloring in bowl; mix well. Pour into freezer tray. Freeze until very thick but not hard. Place in mixer bowl; beat until smooth and fluffy. Pour into covered freezer container. Freeze, covered, for 4 hours or until firm. Let stand at room temperature for 10 minutes before serving. Yield: 5 servings.

Old-Fashioned Vanilla Custard Ice Cream

1 quart milk
4 egg yolks
1/2 cup honey
1 teaspoon arrowroot
2 teaspoons vanilla extract
4 egg whites, stiffly beaten

Scald milk in heavy saucepan. Beat egg yolks in mixer bowl until light and fluffy. Add honey gradually, beating well after each addition. Add arrowroot; mix well. Stir a small amount of hot milk into egg mixture; stir egg mixture into hot milk. Cook over medium heat until thickened, stirring frequently. Cool to room temperature. Chill in refrigerator. Add vanilla; mix well. Fold in egg whites. Pour into ice cream freezer container. Freeze using manufacturer's instructions.
Yield: 6 servings.

Peanut Butter Fudge Sauce

1/2 cup whipping cream
2/3 cup semisweet chocolate chips
2 tablespoons creamy peanut butter

Combine whipping cream and chocolate chips in 1-quart microwave-safe dish. Microwave on High for 1 to 1 1/2 minutes or until mixture boils vigorously, stirring 2 or 3 times. Add peanut butter, stirring until smooth. Microwave for 30 seconds. Serve over ice cream, frozen yogurt or strawberries. Yield: 1 cup.

Old-Fashioned Sherbet

1 1/2 cups sugar
3 1/2 cups freshly squeezed orange juice
Juice of 3 lemons
1 (12-ounce) can evaporated milk
1 cup coffee cream
6 cups half and half

Combine sugar, orange juice and lemon juice in large bowl; mix well. Add mixture of evaporated milk, cream and half and half; mix well. Pour into ice cream freezer container. Freeze using manufacturer's instructions. Yield: 3 quarts.

Cranberry Ice

1 (16-ounce) package fresh cranberries
3 cups water
2 cups sugar
Juice of 2 lemons, strained

Combine cranberries and water in saucepan. Cook over medium heat until cranberries stop popping, stirring occasionally. Strain, reserving liquid. Discard cranberries. Add sugar to reserved liquid in saucepan. Cook until sugar dissolves, stirring frequently. Add lemon juice; mix well. Pour into 2-quart container. Freeze, covered, in freezer. Beat with mixer or whisk 2 times before mixture freezes. Yield: 6 servings.

Pear Sorbet

1 cup sugar
1 cup water
Juice of 1 lemon
1¹/₂ cups pear purée

Combine sugar, water and lemon juice in saucepan; mix well. Heat until sugar dissolves; do not boil. Add pear purée; mix well. Pour into freezer container. Freeze until firm, stirring occasionally.
Yield: 3 cups.

Banana Pops

2 medium bananas, cut into halves
¹/₄ cup crisp rice cereal
1 tablespoon toasted coconut
1 tablespoon finely chopped peanuts
¹/₄ teaspoon nutmeg
2 teaspoons maple syrup

Insert a wooden popsicle stick into the cut end of each banana half. Place on baking sheet. Freeze for 1 hour or until firm. Combine cereal, coconut, peanuts and nutmeg in shallow dish. Brush frozen bananas with maple syrup; roll in cereal mixture. Freeze, individually wrapped in plastic wrap, for 2 hours or longer. Yield: 4 servings.

Summer Frozen Delight

1 (16-ounce) can sliced peaches
1 (15-ounce) can apricots
1 (10-ounce) package frozen
   strawberries, thawed
2 medium bananas, sliced
1 cup pineapple juice
1 (6-ounce) can frozen orange juice
   concentrate, thawed
¹/₄ cup lemon juice

Combine undrained peaches, undrained apricots and undrained strawberries in large bowl. Add bananas, pineapple juice, orange juice concentrate and lemon juice; mix well. Ladle into 5¹/₂-ounce paper cups; cover tightly with foil and place on tray. Freeze until firm. Peel paper cup from frozen treat as you eat. Yield: 12 servings.

Summer Popsicles

3 medium bananas
3 cups water
1 (6-ounce) can frozen orange juice
  concentrate
1 (6-ounce) can frozen guava juice
  concentrate
1 (28-ounce) can pineapple juice

Process bananas, water, orange juice concentrate, guava juice concentrate and pineapple juice in blender until smooth. Pour into ice cube tray. Freeze until firm. Yield: 9 servings.

Watermelon Frozen Treats

1 small watermelon, seeded
Popsicle sticks

Process watermelon in blender until puréed. Pour into popsicle molds; insert popsicle sticks. Freeze until firm. Yield: variable.

Baked Alaska

6 egg yolks
1/2 cup water
1 (2-layer) package devil's food cake mix
1/2 gallon vanilla ice cream, softened
6 egg whites
1/2 teaspoon cream of tartar
1 cup sugar

Combine egg yolks, water and cake mix in bowl. Mix just until moistened; batter will be stiff and lumpy. Spread in greased and floured 9x13-inch baking pan. Bake at 350 degrees for 20 minutes. Cool. Chill in freezer for 1 hour or longer. Spread with ice cream to within 1/2 inch of edges. Freeze. Beat egg whites with cream of tartar in mixer bowl until foamy. Add sugar 1 tablespoon at a time, beating constantly until stiff peaks form. Spread over ice cream, sealing to edges. Bake at 500 degrees for 3 minutes or until brown. Freeze until firm. Yield: 12 servings.

CHILL OUT FUN

Caramel Delight

1 cup margarine, softened
2 cups flour
1/2 cup packed light brown sugar
1/2 cup rolled oats
1/2 cup chopped pecans
1 (12-ounce) jar caramel ice cream
    topping
1/2 gallon butter brickle or vanilla ice
    cream, softened

Combine margarine, flour and brown sugar in bowl; mix well. Stir in oats and pecans. Spread as flat as possible on large baking sheet. Bake at 350 degrees for 20 minutes. Let stand to cool. Crumble baked mixture. Layer half the crumbs, half the ice cream topping, ice cream, remaining crumbs and remaining topping in 9x13-inch pan. Freeze until firm. Yield: 16 to 20 servings.

Butter Brickle
Ice Cream Sandwiches

1/2 cup melted butter or margarine
1/2 cup packed light brown sugar
1 teaspoon vanilla extract
Dash of salt
2 cups flaked coconut
1 cup chopped nuts
3 cups crisp rice cereal
1/2 gallon butter brickle ice cream

Combine butter and brown sugar in skillet; heat until melted. Add vanilla, salt, coconut, nuts and cereal; mix well. Press 1/2 of the mixture into bottom of 9x13-inch pan. Slice ice cream; arrange in even layer over mixture. Top with remaining mixture. Freeze. Cut into squares. Yield: 12 servings.

Crispy Ice Cream Roll

1/4 cup melted margarine
1 (16-ounce) can vanilla frosting
1/4 cup light corn syrup
5 cups crisp rice cereal
1 quart ice cream, softened

Combine margarine, frosting and corn syrup in bowl; mix well. Stir in cereal; coat well. Press into waxed paper-lined 10x15-inch pan. Chill for 30 minutes. Spread ice cream over cereal mixture. Roll as for jelly roll. Freeze until firm. Yield: 10 servings.

Double Chocolate Crunch

12 ounces chocolate sandwich cookies, crushed
1/4 cup melted butter or margarine
2/3 cup chocolate chips
2 cups confectioners' sugar
1 1/2 cups evaporated milk
1/2 cup butter or margarine
1 teaspoon vanilla extract
1/2 gallon vanilla ice cream
1 cup chopped Spanish peanuts
Whipped cream or whipped topping (optional)

Mix cookie crumbs and 1/4 cup melted butter in bowl. Press mixture into 9x13-inch pan. Combine chocolate chips, confectioners' sugar, evaporated milk and 1/2 cup butter in saucepan. Bring to a boil over medium heat. Cook for 8 minutes, stirring frequently. Let stand until cool. Stir in vanilla. Slice ice cream onto prepared layer. Sprinkle with peanuts. Pour chocolate mixture over peanuts. Freeze. Serve with whipped cream. Yield: 15 servings.

CHILL OUT FUN

Fried Mexican Ice Cream

1 pint ice cream
1/2 cup crushed corn flakes or cookie
    crumbs
1 teaspoon cinnamon
2 teaspoons sugar
1 egg, beaten
Oil for deep frying
Honey
Whipped cream

Scoop 4 or 5 balls of ice cream into bowl.
Place in freezer. Mix corn flake crumbs,
cinnamon and sugar in bowl. Roll ice cream
balls in half the crumb mixture; return to
freezer. Dip ice cream balls in egg; roll in
remaining crumb mixture. Return to
freezer. Preheat oil to 350 degrees in deep-
fryer. Cook ice cream balls 1 at a time in
fryer basket or slotted spoon for 1 minute.
Remove to dessert compote. Drizzle with
honey; top with whipped cream.
Yield: 4 to 5 servings.

Frozen Cream

8 ounces cream cheese, softened
1 cup sifted confectioners' sugar
1 cup half and half
1/2 teaspoon vanilla extract
2 cups fresh or frozen strawberries

Beat cream cheese in small mixer bowl
until light and fluffy. Add sifted confectioners' sugar, half and half and vanilla
gradually, beating until smooth. Spoon into
paper-lined muffin cups. Freeze for 2 hours
or until firm. Remove paper liners; place on
individual dessert plates. Let stand until
slightly thawed. Spoon strawberries over
top. May substitute raspberries, blueberries
or peaches for strawberries.
Yield: 8 servings.

CHILL OUT FUN

Frozen Fruitcake

¼ cup flour
½ cup sugar
¼ teaspoon salt
2 cups milk, scalded
2 eggs, beaten
1 cup golden raisins
1 cup pecan pieces
2 cups macaroon pieces
½ cup chopped candied red and green
   cherries
1 teaspoon vanilla extract
1 cup whipping cream, whipped

Mix flour, sugar, salt and a small amount of milk in bowl. Combine with remaining milk in double boiler over hot water. Cook for 10 minutes, stirring frequently. Stir a small amount of hot mixture into beaten eggs; stir eggs into hot mixture. Cook until thickened, stirring constantly. Cool. Stir in next 5 ingredients. Fold in whipped cream. Pour into 9x12-inch dish. Freeze until firm. Yield: 10 servings.

Ice Cream Crunch Cake

2 cups chocolate chips
⅔ cup creamy peanut butter
6 cups crisp rice cereal
1 gallon vanilla ice cream, softened

Melt chocolate chips and peanut butter in large saucepan; mix well. Stir in cereal. Spread on cookie sheet. Cool. Break into small pieces. Reserve 1 cup of the cereal mixture. Place ice cream in large bowl. Fold in remaining cereal mixture. Spoon into 10-inch springform pan. Sprinkle with reserved cereal mixture. Freeze. Garnish with whipped cream and strawberries. Yield: 12 servings.

CHILL OUT FUN

Lemon Meringue Dessert

2 cups crushed vanilla wafers
1/3 cup melted margarine
6 egg yolks
1 (14-ounce) can sweetened condensed
  milk
1 (6-ounce) can frozen lemonade
  concentrate, thawed
8 ounces whipped topping
6 egg whites
3/4 cup sugar

Mix vanilla wafer crumbs and melted margarine in bowl. Press into bottom of 9x13-inch baking pan. Beat egg yolks in mixer bowl until lemon-colored. Add condensed milk and lemonade concentrate, stirring until blended. Fold in whipped topping. Pour into prepared pan. Beat egg whites at medium speed in mixer bowl until soft peaks form. Add sugar gradually, beating constantly at high speed until stiff peaks form. Spread over filling, sealing to edge. Broil for 2 to 3 minutes or until meringue is light brown. Freeze until firm. Remove from freezer 10 to 15 minutes before serving. Yield: 24 servings.

Orange Torte

1/2 cup vanilla wafer crumbs
1 quart vanilla ice cream, softened
1 (6-ounce) can frozen orange juice
  concentrate
1/2 cup light corn syrup
1 cup semisweet chocolate chips
1 (5-ounce) can evaporated milk
1 1/2 cups miniature marshmallows

Sprinkle wafer crumbs in 8x8-inch dish. Combine ice cream and orange juice concentrate in bowl. Spread in prepared dish. Freeze until firm. Combine corn syrup, chocolate chips, evaporated milk and marshmallows in double boiler. Cook over hot water until chocolate melts, stirring constantly. Cool. Spread over frozen layer. Freeze until firm. Cut into squares. Yield: 6 servings.

Piña Colada Ice Cream Cake

1 quart vanilla ice cream, softened
1 cup cream of coconut
1 (8-ounce) can crushed pineapple, drained
1/2 cup chopped walnuts
1 cup shredded sweetened coconut

Beat ice cream, cream of coconut and pineapple in mixer bowl until combined. Stir in walnuts. Spoon into 9-inch springform pan. Freeze, covered, overnight. Broil shredded coconut on baking sheet for 1 minute or until light brown. Let stand until cool. Remove cake from freezer; cut into wedges. Sprinkle each serving with toasted coconut. Yield: 12 servings.

Praline Ice Cream Crêpes

1 cup packed brown sugar
1/4 cup butter
1/4 cup whipping cream
1/8 teaspoon rum extract
1/4 cup chopped pecans
1 pint vanilla ice cream
8 dessert crêpes

Combine brown sugar, butter and whipping cream in small saucepan. Bring to a boil; reduce heat. Simmer over low heat for 2 minutes, stirring frequently; remove from heat. Stir in rum extract and pecans; set aside. Spoon 1/4 cup ice cream in center of each crêpe. Fold edges over to enclose ice cream. Place seam side down on dessert plate. Spoon 2 tablespoons praline sauce over each crêpe. May make sauce ahead of time and reheat before serving. Yield: 8 servings.

Indulge yourself with a frozen candy bar on a hot summer day.

CHILL OUT FUN

Raspberry Melon Boats

1 tablespoon cornstarch
1 tablespoon sugar
1/2 cup raspberry syrup
1/2 cup orange juice
1 (10-ounce) package frozen red
  raspberries, thawed, drained
Vanilla ice cream
2 small cantaloupe halves, chilled

Mix cornstarch and sugar in saucepan. Add mixture of raspberry syrup and orange juice. Cook until thickened, stirring constantly. Cool. Stir in raspberries. Scoop ice cream into centers of melon halves. Drizzle with raspberry sauce. Yield: 2 servings.

Frozen Strawberry Pies

2 cups frozen strawberries, thawed
1 cup sugar
2 egg whites
1 cup whipping cream, whipped
2 baked (9-inch) pie shells

Beat strawberries, sugar and egg whites in mixer bowl for 20 minutes. Fold in whipped cream. Spoon into pie shells. Freeze. Yield: 12 servings.

Yogurt Bars

1/2 jar butterscotch ice cream topping
1/2 box low-fat granola cereal without
  raisins
1/2 gallon vanilla frozen yogurt

Spoon in enough ice cream topping to cover bottom of 9x13-inch pan. Sprinkle enough cereal over topping to cover. Spread yogurt over cereal. Top with remaining cereal and remaining ice cream topping. Freeze until firm. Cut into bars.
Yield: 12 to 15 servings.

CHILL OUT FUN

Cherry Shakes

1 cup boiling water
1 (3-ounce) package cherry gelatin
1 (21-ounce) can cherry pie filling
1 quart vanilla ice cream
8 cups milk

Combine boiling water and gelatin in blender container; process until gelatin dissolves. Add pie filling; process until smooth. Chill until serving time. Spoon into twelve 12-ounce glasses. Add 1 scoop ice cream to each glass; mix gently. Fill glasses with milk; mix gently. Garnish with peppermint sticks. Yield: 12 servings.

Fruit Cider

2 (6-ounce) cans frozen grapefruit juice
    concentrate
3 cups water
2 (6-ounce) cans frozen lemonade
    concentrate
3 cups water
1 (6-ounce) can frozen orange juice
    concentrate
6 concentrate cans water
2 quarts apple cider, chilled
4 cups water
2 (10-ounce) packages frozen
    strawberries, thawed, drained
2 quarts ginger ale, chilled

Mix grapefruit juice concentrate with 3 cups water in bowl. Pour into ice cube tray. Freeze until firm. Mix lemonade concentrate with 3 cups water in bowl. Pour into ice cube tray. Freeze until firm. Chill punch bowl. Mix orange juice concentrate and 6 cans water in punch bowl. Add cider, 4 cups water and strawberries; mix well. Add grapefruit juice and lemonade ice cubes to punch 30 minutes before serving. Add ginger ale 10 minutes before serving.
Yield: 56 servings.

Grape Juice Fizzies

1 quart grape juice, chilled
1 quart lemon-lime soda, chilled

Combine grape juice and lemon-lime soda in pitcher; mix well. Serve immediately. Yield: 8 servings.

Minted Limeade

36 to 48 limes
1½ cups sugar
2 quarts water
Mint sprigs

Squeeze enough limes to make 2 cups of lime juice, reserving rinds. Simmer rinds, sugar and water in saucepan for 15 minutes; strain. Chill. Combine sugar mixture, lime juice and mint in pitcher; mix well. Yield: 10 cups.

Orange Brutus

1 quart orange juice
1 (4-ounce) package vanilla pudding mix
1 envelope whipped topping mix

Place orange juice and pudding mix in blender container. Process for 30 seconds. Add topping mix. Process for 15 seconds. Yield: 8 servings.

Pink Lassies

1 cup cranberry juice
¼ cup orange juice
1 cup vanilla ice cream

Process cranberry juice, orange juice and vanilla ice cream in blender until smooth and creamy. Pour into glasses. Yield: 6 servings.

For a quick refreshing drink, mix equal parts cranberry juice and ginger ale together. Serve over crushed ice.

Summer Cooler

1½ cups plain low-fat yogurt
1 cup ice water
1 tablespoon lemon juice
½ teaspoon mint extract
1 cup melon chunks

Process yogurt, ice water, lemon juice, mint extract and melon chunks in blender until smooth. Pour into glass and serve.
Yield: 1 serving.

Smoothie

½ cup vanilla yogurt
½ cup ice
½ cup unsweetened pineapple juice
½ sliced fresh pineapple
½ banana
2 large strawberries or 1 large kiwifruit

Combine yogurt, ice, pineapple juice, pineapple, banana and strawberries in blender container. Process at high speed for 2 minutes. Yield: 4 to 6 servings.

Florida Fizz Punch

2 cups orange juice
1 cup grapefruit juice
1 cup tangerine juice
2 cups chilled ginger ale

Blend orange juice, grapefruit juice and tangerine juice in pitcher. Chill, covered, until serving time. Stir in ginger ale. Pour over ice cubes in glasses. Yield: 6 servings.

Golden Punch

1 (24-ounce) bottle of apple juice
1 (16-ounce) bottle of non-alcoholic sparkling white grape juice
1 (12-ounce) can frozen apple juice concentrate
1 (2-liter) bottle of lemon-lime soda
1 (1-liter) bottle of club soda

Pour bottled apple juice into gelatin mold for ice ring. Freeze. Combine remaining ingredients in punch bowl; mix well. Add ice ring. Yield: 28 servings.

Ice Cream Punch

1½ cups sugar
2 cups water
2 quarts lemonade
¾ cup white grapefruit juice
1 (46-ounce) can pineapple juice
½ gallon vanilla ice cream, softened
½ gallon pineapple sherbet, softened
2 quarts ginger ale, chilled

Dissolve sugar in water in pitcher. Combine with lemonade, grapefruit juice and pineapple juice in punch bowl; mix well. Add ice cream and sherbet; mix gently. Add ginger ale; mix gently. Yield: 40 servings.

Lemon Grape Punch

1 cup lemon juice
12 cups grape juice
16 cups ginger ale
¼ cup sugar

Mix lemon juice, grape juice and ginger ale in punch bowl. Stir in sugar. Garnish with ice ring, cinnamon sticks and orange slices. Yield: 30 servings.

Peppermint Twist Punch

1 (6-ounce) can frozen orange juice
    concentrate
1 (6-ounce) can frozen lemonade
    concentrate
1 (6-ounce) can frozen limeade
    concentrate
1 (46-ounce) can pineapple juice
1 quart peppermint ice cream, softened
1 (10-ounce) package frozen strawberries
1 quart ginger ale, chilled

Combine frozen juices in large punch bowl; mix well. Add 1 tray of ice cubes. Stir in pineapple juice. Blend ice cream in mixer bowl just before serving. Add ice cream, strawberries and ginger ale to punch bowl; mix well. Yield: 24 servings.

Peachy Slush

1 (16-ounce) package frozen peaches,
  slightly thawed
1 (12-ounce) can peach nectar
1 (6-ounce) can frozen orange juice
  concentrate
1 (2-liter) bottle of lemon-lime soda

Combine first 3 ingredients in blender container. Process until smooth. Pour into ice cube trays. Freeze until firm. Let stand at room temperature for 20 minutes or until slightly thawed. Place 2 or 3 cubes in each glass. Fill with lemon-lime soda.
Yield: 8 servings.

Cranberry Tea

4 cups cranberries
8 cups water
1 cup red hot cinnamon candies
2 cups sugar
12 whole cloves
1/2 (6-ounce) can frozen orange juice
  concentrate
1/2 (6-ounce) can frozen lemonade
  concentrate

Combine cranberries with 4 cups of the water in saucepan. Bring to a boil. Cook until cranberries pop, stirring occasionally. Strain, discarding pulp. Combine remaining 4 cups water with next 3 ingredients in saucepan. Cook until candies and sugar dissolve, stirring occasionally. Combine with cranberry liquid in large container. Stir in orange and lemonade concentrates. Chill until serving time. Fill each glass half full with mixture. Fill remainder of glass with water. Yield: 25 servings.

*Freeze orange juice or
lemonade in ice cube trays. Use
as ice cubes for iced tea.*

CHILL OUT FUN

Strawberry Tea

4 tea bags
2 cups boiling water
6 cinnamon sticks
1 teaspoon ground cloves
1 (6-ounce) can frozen orange juice
   concentrate
1 (6-ounce) can frozen lemonade
   concentrate
1 (46-ounce) can pineapple juice
1 (3-ounce) package strawberry gelatin
2 cups water

Steep tea bags in 2 cups boiling water in large saucepan for several minutes. Add cinnamon sticks, cloves, orange juice concentrate, lemonade concentrate, pineapple juice, gelatin and 2 cups water. Bring to a boil, stirring until gelatin dissolves. Keep hot, covered, over low heat or serve from slow cooker. Yield: 20 servings.

Tea Quencher

2 quarts water
1/4 cup tea leaves or 5 tea bags
1 cup sugar
1 cup water
2 (2-inch) cinnamon sticks
1 tablespoon grated lemon rind
2 teaspoons grated orange rind
1/2 cup orange juice
1/4 cup lemon juice
1/2 cup pineapple juice

Bring 2 quarts water to a boil in saucepan; pour over tea leaves in bowl. Steep for 3 to 5 minutes; strain into pitcher, discarding leaves. Combine sugar, 1 cup water, cinnamon sticks, lemon rind and orange rind in saucepan. Simmer for 15 minutes, stirring frequently. Add with remaining juices to tea; mix well. Chill in refrigerator. Serve in punch bowl or in tall ice-filled glasses. Yield: 10 servings.

MUNCHY FUN

Watermelon Cookies

3/4 cup butter, softened

3/4 cup sugar

1 egg

1/2 teaspoon almond extract

1/4 teaspoon baking powder

1/4 teaspoon salt

2 to 2 1/4 cups flour

Green and red paste food coloring

Dried currant bits or sesame seeds

Cream butter, sugar, egg and almond extract in mixer bowl until light and fluffy. Add baking powder, salt and 2 cups flour; mix well. Stir in remaining 1/4 cup flour if dough is too soft. Tint 1/3 cup dough green. Reserve 2/3 cup plain dough. Tint remaining dough red. Shape into roll 3 1/2 inches long. Chill dough, covered, for 2 hours. Roll plain dough into 3 1/2x8 1/2-inch rectangle on floured surface. Place roll of red dough along short edge. Roll up. Roll green dough to 3 1/2x10-inch rectangle. Place roll along short edge; roll up. Chill, covered, overnight. Slice dough 1/8 to 3/16 inch thick. Place on ungreased cookie sheet. Press currant bits or sesame seeds into cookies. Bake at 375 degrees for 6 minutes or until firm but not brown. Cut into halves. Remove to wire rack to cool. Yield: 3 to 5 dozen.

Almond Roca Cookies

1/2 cup butter, softened
1/2 cup sugar
1/2 cup packed brown sugar
1 egg yolk
1 cup flour
1/2 teaspoon salt
1 (4-ounce) chocolate candy bar, melted
1 cup chopped almonds

Cream butter, sugar and brown sugar in mixer bowl until light and fluffy. Add egg yolk; mix well. Add flour and salt; mix well. Spread in nonstick 11x15-inch jelly roll pan. Bake at 350 degrees for 25 minutes. Spread chocolate over baked layer; sprinkle with almonds. Cut into bars. Yield: 2 1/2 dozen.

Yogurt Apple Squares

2 cups flour
2 cups packed light brown sugar
1/2 cup butter, softened
1 cup chopped pecans
2 teaspoons cinnamon
1 teaspoon vanilla extract
1/2 teaspoon salt
1 teaspoon baking soda
1 cup plain yogurt
1 egg
2 cups finely chopped apples

Combine flour, brown sugar and butter in mixer bowl; mix at medium speed until crumbly. Stir in pecans. Press 2 3/4 cups of the mixture into ungreased 9x13-inch baking pan. Combine remaining crumb mixture with cinnamon, vanilla, salt, baking soda, yogurt and egg in bowl. Stir in apples. Spoon evenly over crust. Bake at 350 degrees for 40 minutes. Cool to room temperature. Chill in refrigerator for 1 hour. Cut into squares. Yield: 2 dozen.

Apricot Meringue Bars

1/2 cup margarine, softened
1/2 cup confectioners' sugar
2 egg yolks
1 cup flour
3/4 cup apricot jam
2 egg whites
1/2 cup sugar
1/4 teaspoon cinnamon
1 cup chopped pecans

Cream first 2 ingredients in mixer bowl until light and fluffy. Add egg yolks and flour; mix well. Press mixture into ungreased 9x13-inch pan. Bake at 350 degrees for 10 minutes. Spread with jam. Beat egg whites in mixer bowl until soft peaks form. Add sugar and cinnamon, beating until stiff peaks form. Fold in pecans. Spread over jam. Bake for 20 minutes longer or until meringue is golden brown. Cool to room temperature. Cut into bars.
Yield: 1 1/2 dozen.

Banana Chip Cookies

1 cup shortening
1/2 cup sugar
1 cup packed brown sugar
1 teaspoon vanilla extract
2 eggs
1 teaspoon baking soda
3 cups flour, sifted
1 teaspoon salt
2 very ripe bananas, mashed
2 cups chocolate chips

Cream shortening, sugar, brown sugar, vanilla and eggs in bowl until light and fluffy. Add baking soda, flour, salt, mashed bananas and chocolate chips; mix well. Drop by spoonfuls onto greased cookie sheet. Bake at 350 degrees for 10 to 12 minutes. Yield: 4 dozen.

MUNCHY FUN

Black Tops

1 cup butter, softened
1 cup packed brown sugar
1 egg yolk
1 teaspoon vanilla extract
2 cups flour
1 cup chocolate chips
1/2 cup chopped walnuts

Combine butter, brown sugar, egg yolk, vanilla and flour in mixer bowl; beat until smooth. Spread in greased 10x15-inch baking pan. Bake at 375 degrees for 15 minutes. Melt chocolate chips in double boiler over hot water. Spread over baked layer; sprinkle with walnuts. Let stand until cool. Cut into squares. Yield: 2 dozen.

Butterfinger Crunch Bars

1 (2-layer) package lemon cake mix
1/3 cup melted margarine
1 egg
1 (14-ounce) can sweetened condensed milk
1 egg
1 teaspoon vanilla extract
3 large Butterfinger candy bars, crushed

Combine cake mix, margarine and 1 egg in large mixer bowl. Mix at high speed until crumbly. Press into greased 9x13-inch baking pan. Blend condensed milk, remaining egg and vanilla in small bowl. Stir in crushed candy bars. Spread in prepared pan. Bake at 350 degrees for 30 minutes or until light golden brown; center may appear soft. Cool completely. Cut into bars. May bake in 10x15-inch baking pan for 25 minutes. Yield: 3 dozen.

Use frosting to pipe names of guests on rectangular cookies to use for place cards.

Butterscotch Cheesecake Bars

8 ounces cream cheese, softened
1 (14-ounce) can sweetened condensed
  milk
1 teaspoon vanilla extract
1 egg
2 cups butterscotch chips
1/2 cup margarine
2 cups graham cracker crumbs
1 cup chopped walnuts

Beat cream cheese in mixer bowl until fluffy. Add condensed milk, vanilla and egg; mix well. Melt butterscotch chips and margarine in saucepan. Stir in graham cracker crumbs and walnuts. Pat half the mixture into bottom of greased 9x13-inch baking dish. Spread cream cheese mixture evenly over crumb layer. Top with remaining crumb mixture. Bake at 350 degrees for 25 to 30 minutes or until toothpick inserted near center comes out clean. Let stand until completely cooled. Cut into bars.
Yield: 2 dozen.

New York Brownies

1/4 cup melted margarine
3/4 cup packed light brown sugar
1/4 cup sugar
3 tablespoons baking cocoa
1 egg, beaten
1 teaspoon vanilla extract
1/2 cup self-rising flour
1/4 teaspoon salt
1/2 cup chopped pecans
1 (16-ounce) can chocolate frosting

Combine margarine, brown sugar, sugar, baking cocoa, egg and vanilla in bowl; mix well. Add flour, salt and pecans; mix well. Spread in greased 8x8-inch baking pan. Bake at 350 degrees for 20 minutes or until brownies pull from edge of pan; do not overbake. Let stand until slightly cooled. Frost brownies. Cut into squares.
Yield: 1 dozen.

MUNCHY FUN

Minty Brownies

1 (22-ounce) package brownie mix
1 egg
1 cup chocolate chips
1 cup chopped pecans
1 (16-ounce) can vanilla frosting
2 tablespoons Crème de Menthe syrup
6 ounces semisweet chocolate
2 tablespoons butter

Prepare brownie mix with egg using package directions. Add chocolate chips and pecans. Pour into greased 9x13-inch baking pan. Bake at 350 degrees for 27 to 30 minutes. Blend frosting with syrup. Spread over brownies. Melt chocolate with butter in saucepan over low heat, stirring constantly. Drizzle over frosting. Cool. Cut into squares. Yield: 2 dozen.

Hello Dolly Brownies

10 tablespoons margarine
1½ cups graham cracker crumbs
1 cup chocolate chips
1 cup coconut
1 (14-ounce) can sweetened condensed milk
½ cup chopped pecans

Melt margarine in 9x13-inch baking pan. Press graham cracker crumbs into margarine. Add layer of chocolate chips and coconut. Pour condensed milk over top; sprinkle with pecans. Bake at 350 degrees for 30 minutes. Cut into squares. Yield: 2 dozen.

Praline Brownies

1 (22-ounce) package brownie mix
½ cup packed brown sugar
½ cup chopped pecans
2 tablespoons melted margarine

Prepare brownies using package directions. Spread in greased 9x13-inch baking pan. Combine brown sugar, pecans and margarine in bowl; mix well. Sprinkle over batter. Bake at 350 degrees for 30 minutes. Cool on wire rack. Cut into squares. Frost with fudge frosting if desired. Yield: 2 dozen.

The Ultimate Brownie

1 (2-layer) package chocolate cake mix
1 egg, beaten
1/2 cup butter
1 cup chopped pecans or walnuts
1 tablespoon water
8 ounces cream cheese, softened
3 eggs
1 (1-pound) package confectioners' sugar

Combine cake mix, 1 egg, butter, pecans and water in bowl; mix well. Press into greased 9x13-inch baking pan. Combine cream cheese, 3 eggs and confectioners' sugar in mixer bowl; mix until smooth. Pour over chocolate layer. Bake at 350 degrees for 30 to 45 minutes or until golden brown. May substitute lemon or yellow cake mix for chocolate if preferred.
Yield: 2 dozen.

Zucchini Brownies

2 cups flour
1 1/2 teaspoons baking soda
1 teaspoon salt
1/4 cup baking cocoa
1 1/4 cups sugar
2 cups grated zucchini
1/2 cup vegetable oil
2 teaspoons vanilla extract
1/2 cup chopped pecans

Sift flour, baking soda, salt, cocoa and sugar together. Combine zucchini and oil in mixer bowl. Add sifted dry ingredients; mix well. Stir in vanilla and pecans. Spread batter in greased and floured 10x15-inch baking pan. Bake at 350 degrees for 18 to 20 minutes or until edges pull from sides of pan. Let stand until cool. Cut into bars.
Yield: 2 dozen.

For variety, add peanut butter chips, white chocolate chips, "M & M's" Chocolate Candies or any crushed candy bar to your favorite chocolate brownie recipe.

Buttery Melt-Away Cookies

1 cup butter, softened
¹/2 cup confectioners' sugar
2¹/4 cups sifted cake flour
¹/4 teaspoon salt
1 teaspoon vanilla extract
¹/2 cup confectioners' sugar

Cream butter and ¹/2 cup confectioners' sugar in mixer bowl. Add cake flour, salt and vanilla; mix well. Chill for 1 hour. Drop by spoonfuls 3 inches apart onto cookie sheet lined with foil. Bake at 350 degrees for 10 minutes or until set but not brown. Remove to wire rack. Sift ¹/2 cup confectioners' sugar over tops.
Yield: 3 dozen.

Grand Prize Caramel Chews

1 cup butter, softened
1 (1-pound) package brown sugar
2 tablespoons vanilla extract
2 eggs
1¹/2 cups flour
2¹/2 teaspoons baking powder
1 cup chopped pecans

Combine butter, brown sugar, vanilla and eggs in mixer bowl; mix until smooth. Add flour and baking powder; mix well. Stir in pecans. Spoon into greased and floured 9x13-inch baking pan. Bake at 350 degrees for 30 minutes. Cool on wire rack. Cut into squares. Yield: 2 dozen.

For an easy no-bake cookie, combine ¹/2 cup softened margarine, 4 cups confectioners' sugar, ¹/2 cup chopped pecans, 6 ounces orange juice concentrate and 4 cups vanilla wafer crumbs. Shape into balls and coat with additional crumbs.

Chocolate Toffee Crescent Bars

1 (8-count) can crescent rolls
1 cup packed brown sugar
1 cup margarine
1½ cups chopped pecans
1 cup chocolate chips

Unroll crescent roll dough. Separate into rectangles. Press over bottom of 10x15-inch baking pan; press perforations and edges to seal. Combine brown sugar and margarine in small saucepan. Bring to a boil, stirring constantly. Boil for 1 minute. Pour over dough. Sprinkle with pecans. Bake at 375 degrees for 14 to 18 minutes or until golden brown. Sprinkle with chocolate chips. Let stand for 2 minutes to allow some of the chips to melt; swirl melted and unmelted chocolate over top. Cool. Cut into bars. Yield: 4 dozen.

Coconut Corn Flake Cookies

2 cups sifted flour
1 teaspoon baking soda
½ teaspoon salt
½ teaspoon baking powder
1¼ cups shortening
1 cup sugar
1 cup packed brown sugar
2 eggs, beaten
1 teaspoon vanilla extract
2 cups flaked coconut
2 cups corn flakes

Sift flour, baking soda, salt and baking powder together. Cream shortening, sugar and brown sugar in mixer bowl until light and fluffy. Add eggs and vanilla; beat well. Add dry ingredients; mix well. Stir in coconut and corn flakes. Drop by teaspoonfuls 1½ inches apart onto greased cookie sheet. Bake at 350 degrees for 8 to 10 minutes or until cookies test done. Cool on cookie sheet for several minutes. Remove to wire rack to cool completely. Yield: 8 dozen.

MUNCHY FUN

Easy Coconut Macaroons

⅔ cup sweetened condensed milk
3 cups shredded coconut
1 teaspoon vanilla extract

Combine condensed milk, coconut and vanilla in bowl; mix well. Drop by teaspoonfuls 1 inch apart onto greased cookie sheet. Bake at 350 degrees for 8 to 10 minutes or until delicately browned. Remove macaroons from cookie sheet immediately. Yield: 8 dozen.

Coconut Lemon Squares

2 cups flour
½ cup packed light brown sugar
1 cup butter, softened
½ teaspoon vanilla extract
2 cups sugar
1 teaspoon baking powder
¼ cup flour
3 eggs, beaten
1 cup flaked coconut
⅔ cup lemon juice
Grated zest of 2 lemons

Combine 2 cups flour and brown sugar in bowl. Cut in butter until crumbly. Stir in vanilla. Press into greased 9x13-inch baking pan. Bake at 350 degrees for 15 minutes. Combine sugar, baking powder and ¼ cup flour in bowl. Stir in eggs, coconut, lemon juice and lemon zest. Pour over prepared crust. Bake at 350 degrees for 20 minutes. Cool on wire rack. Cut into squares. Yield: 3 dozen.

If you need an extra cookie sheet, grease the bottom of an inverted 9x13-inch baking pan. Cookies will brown more evenly than in a pan with sides.

MUNCHY FUN

Country Granola Bars

3 cups quick-cooking oats
1/4 cup packed brown sugar
1/4 cup wheat germ
1/2 cup butter, softened
1/4 cup corn syrup
1/4 cup honey
1/2 cup chocolate chips
1/2 cup flaked coconut

Mix oats, brown sugar and wheat germ in bowl. Cut in butter until crumbly. Add corn syrup and honey; mix well. Mix in chocolate chips and coconut. Press into well greased 9x12-inch baking pan. Bake at 350 degrees for 20 to 25 minutes. Cool for 10 minutes. Cut into bars. Yield: 2 dozen.

Gourmet Delights

1 large package refrigerator chocolate chip cookie dough
5 or 6 Snickers candy bars, sliced 1/4 inch thick

Spread cookie dough in 9x11-inch baking pan. Bake using package directions or until almost golden brown. Arrange candy over baked layer. Bake until candy is softened; spread evenly over baked layer. Cool. Cut into squares. Yield: 2 dozen.

I Can't Believe It's a Cookie

1 cup sugar
1 cup peanut butter
1 egg
48 chocolate star candies

Combine sugar, peanut butter and egg in bowl; mix well. Shape into 1-inch balls. Place on cookie sheet; press chocolate star into center of each ball. Bake at 350 degrees for 6 minutes. Cool on wire rack.
Yield: 4 dozen.

MUNCHY FUN

Lime Bars

2 cups flour
1/4 cup sugar
1 cup margarine, softened
1/4 cup flour
2 cups sugar
1 teaspoon baking powder
3 eggs
2/3 cup lime juice
Grated rind of 2 limes

Combine 2 cups flour and 1/4 cup sugar in bowl; mix well. Cut in margarine until crumbly. Pat into 9x13-inch baking pan. Bake at 350 degrees for 15 minutes or until brown. Combine remaining 1/4 cup flour, remaining 2 cups sugar, baking powder, eggs, lime juice and lime rind in mixer bowl; mix well. Pour over baked layer. Bake for 20 minutes longer or until set. Cool on wire rack. Cut into bars. Yield: 2 dozen.

One-Cup Cookies

1 cup margarine, softened
1 cup sugar
1 cup packed brown sugar
3 eggs
1 cup peanut butter
1 cup flour
1 tablespoon baking soda
1 cup rolled oats
1 cup coconut
1 cup chopped walnuts
1 cup raisins
1 cup chocolate chips

Cream margarine, sugar and brown sugar in bowl until light and fluffy. Beat in eggs 1 at a time. Beat in peanut butter. Add mixture of flour and baking soda; mix well. Add oats, coconut, walnuts, raisins and chocolate chips 1 at a time, mixing well after each addition. Drop by heaping teaspoonfuls onto cookie sheet. Bake at 350 degrees for 10 minutes. Yield: 5 dozen.

Easy Peanut Butter Cookies

1 (14-ounce) can sweetened condensed
  milk
1 egg
1 cup peanut butter
1 teaspoon vanilla extract
2 cups baking mix

Combine condensed milk, egg, peanut
butter and vanilla in mixer bowl; beat until
smooth. Add baking mix; mix well. Chill
for 1 hour or longer. Shape into 1-inch
balls; place 2 inches apart on ungreased
cookie sheet. Flatten with fork in crisscross
pattern. Bake at 350 degrees for 6 to 8
minutes or until light brown; do not overbake. Cool on wire rack. Store in tightly
covered container at room temperature.
Yield: 5 dozen.

Carrot Patch Cookies

1/2 cup butter, softened
1/2 cup peanut butter
1/3 cup sugar
1/3 cup packed brown sugar
2 egg whites
1/2 teaspoon vanilla extract
1/2 cup shredded carrot
1 cup flour
1/2 teaspoon baking soda
1 cup rolled oats

Cream butter, peanut butter, sugar and
brown sugar in bowl until light and fluffy.
Add egg whites, vanilla and carrot; mix
well. Mix in flour and baking soda. Stir in
oats. Drop by rounded teaspoonfuls 2
inches apart onto ungreased cookie sheet.
Bake at 375 degrees for 10 minutes. Remove to wire rack to cool. Yield: 4 dozen.

MUNCHY FUN

Peanut Butter Cups

1 (20-ounce) package refrigerator
   peanut butter cookie dough
1 (14-ounce) package miniature peanut
   butter cups

Slice cookie dough; cut slices into quarters. Place each portion in miniature muffin cup. Bake using package directions. Place 1 miniature peanut butter cup in each cookie. Cool in muffin cups. Yield: 3 dozen.

Pecan Dreams

2 cups packed brown sugar
2 egg whites, stiffly beaten
2 tablespoons flour
Salt to taste
2 cups chopped pecans

Beat brown sugar into stiffly beaten egg whites. Fold in flour, salt and pecans. Drop by spoonfuls onto greased cookie sheet. Bake at 325 degrees for 8 to 10 minutes or until light brown. Remove to wire rack to cool. Yield: 2 dozen.

Pecan Pie Bars

2 cups flour
1/2 cup confectioners' sugar
1 cup margarine
1 (14-ounce) can sweetened condensed
   milk
1 egg, beaten
1 teaspoon vanilla extract
1 cup almond brickle chips
1 cup chopped pecans

Combine flour and confectioners' sugar in bowl. Cut in margarine until crumbly. Press into 9x13-inch greased baking pan. Bake at 350 degrees for 15 minutes. Beat condensed milk, egg and vanilla in small bowl. Stir in almond brickle chips and pecans. Spread over baked crust. Bake for 25 minutes longer or until golden brown. Cool on wire rack. Cut into bars. Store, covered, in refrigerator or freezer. Yield: 3 dozen.

Preserve Bars

1 (2-layer) package yellow cake mix
1/3 cup margarine, softened
1 egg
1/2 cup strawberry or apricot preserves
1 cup sugar
3 eggs
2 tablespoons margarine, softened
2 tablespoons flour
1/4 teaspoon baking powder
Salt to taste
1 1/2 cups flaked coconut

Combine cake mix, 1/3 cup margarine and 1 egg in bowl; mix well. Press into greased 10x15-inch baking pan. Bake at 350 degrees for 10 to 12 minutes or until light brown; crust will be soft. Cool slightly in pan. Spread preserves over crust. Cream sugar, remaining 3 eggs and remaining 2 tablespoons margarine in mixer bowl until light and fluffy. Add flour, baking powder and salt; mix well. Stir in coconut. Spread evenly over preserves. Bake for 15 to 20 minutes or until light brown. Cool in pan. Cut into bars. Yield: 3 to 4 dozen.

Raisin Cream Cheese Cookies

1/4 cup butter, softened
8 ounces cream cheese, softened
1 egg yolk
1 teaspoon vanilla extract
1 (2-layer) package yellow cake mix
1 1/4 cups raisins
1/4 cup shredded coconut
1/4 cup chopped walnuts

Cream butter, cream cheese, egg yolk and vanilla in mixer bowl. Blend in cake mix 1/3 at a time, mixing the last portion by hand. Stir in raisins, coconut and walnuts. Drop by level tablespoonfuls 2 inches apart onto greased cookie sheet. Bake at 350 degrees for 15 minutes or until light brown. Cool on wire rack. May substitute margarine for butter and white cake mix for yellow cake mix. Yield: 4 dozen.

Snickerdoodles

1/2 cup margarine, softened
1/2 cup shortening
1 1/2 cups sugar
2 eggs
2 3/4 cups flour
2 teaspoons cream of tartar
1 teaspoon baking soda
1/4 teaspoon salt
2 tablespoons sugar
2 teaspoons cinnamon

Cream margarine, shortening and 1 1/2 cups sugar in mixer bowl until light and fluffy. Beat in eggs. Add flour, cream of tartar, baking soda and salt; mix well. Shape into balls. Roll in mixture of 2 tablespoons sugar and cinnamon; place on cookie sheet. Bake at 400 degrees for 8 to 10 minutes or until light brown. Cool on cookie sheet for 2 minutes. Remove to wire rack to cool completely. Yield: 3 dozen.

Sour Cream Cookies

2 cups sugar
1 cup margarine, softened
1 cup sour cream
2 eggs, beaten
1 teaspoon vanilla extract
1 teaspoon baking soda
2 to 4 cups flour

Cream sugar and margarine in bowl until light and fluffy. Add sour cream and eggs; mix well. Add vanilla; mix well. Add mixture of baking soda and 1 cup of the flour; mix well. Add enough remaining flour to make dough. Knead 1/3 at a time on floured surface, kneading in any remaining flour needed for desired consistency. Roll and cut with cookie cutters. Place on cookie sheet. Bake at 375 degrees for 10 to 12 minutes or until brown. Remove to wire rack to cool. Yield: 9 dozen.

MUNCHY FUN

Chocolate Sugar Cookies

1/2 cup butter, softened
1/2 cup sugar
1 egg
1/2 teaspoon cream of tartar
1/4 teaspoon baking soda
1/4 teaspoon salt
1/2 teaspoon almond extract
1 to 2 teaspoons baking cocoa
1 1/2 cups flour

Cream butter and sugar in mixer bowl until light and fluffy. Beat in egg. Add cream of tartar, baking soda, salt, almond flavoring, cocoa and flour; mix well. Drop by table-spoonfuls onto microwave-safe dish. Microwave on High for 2 1/2 to 3 1/2 minutes, rotating twice. Cool on wire rack. May bake in regular oven at 350 degrees for 8 to 10 minutes. Yield: 1 1/2 dozen.

Cream Cheese Sugar Cookies

1 cup margarine, softened
1 cup sugar
3 ounces cream cheese, softened
1 egg
1/2 teaspoon butter extract
1/2 teaspoon almond extract
1/2 teaspoon vanilla extract
1/2 teaspoon salt
2 1/4 cups flour

Cream margarine, sugar, cream cheese, egg, flavorings and salt in bowl until light and fluffy. Add flour gradually; beating just until moistened. Chill for 2 hours. Roll 1/3 at a time to 1/8-inch thickness on floured surface; cut as desired. Place on ungreased cookie sheet. Bake at 375 degrees for 7 to 10 minutes or until light golden brown. Yield: 3 dozen.

MUNCHY FUN

Old-Fashioned Soft Sugar Cookies

1/2 cup margarine, softened
1 cup sugar
1 egg
1 1/2 teaspoons vanilla extract
1/2 cup sour cream
3 1/4 cups sifted flour
1 teaspoon baking soda
1/2 teaspoon salt

Beat margarine, sugar, egg and vanilla in mixer bowl until light and fluffy. Add sour cream; mix well. Sift flour, baking soda and salt together. Add to sugar mixture gradually, beating well after each addition. Roll 1/4 inch thick on lightly floured surface. Cut with floured cookie cutter. Place on greased cookie sheet. Bake at 350 degrees for 8 minutes. Do not overbake. Cool on wire rack. May frost and decorate as desired. Yield: 4 dozen.

Toffee Cookies

1 cup butter, softened
1 cup packed brown sugar
1 egg yolk
1 cup flour
6 (1.05-ounce) milk chocolate candy bars
2/3 cup finely chopped pecans

Cream butter, brown sugar and egg yolk in bowl until light and fluffy. Add flour gradually, blending well. Spread over bottom of lightly greased 10x15-inch baking pan. Bake at 350 degrees for 15 to 20 minutes or until medium brown. Arrange chocolate candy bars over top of hot baked layer. Let stand until melted. Spread melted chocolate evenly over top; sprinkle with pecans. Cool. Cut into bars. Yield: 6 dozen.

MUNCHY FUN

Chilled Coconut Balls

1 cup creamy peanut butter
1 cup sifted confectioners' sugar
2 tablespoons melted margarine
1/2 cup chopped pecans
1 cup coconut

Combine peanut butter, confectioners' sugar, margarine and pecans in bowl; mix well. Shape into 1/2-inch balls. Roll in coconut, coating well. Chill in refrigerator. Yield: 3 dozen.

Coconut Dainties

4 cups confectioners' sugar
8 ounces cream cheese, softened
1 cup finely shredded coconut
1 (12-ounce) package colored mints

Cream confectioners' sugar and cream cheese in mixer bowl until light and fluffy. Stir in coconut. Shape into small balls; arrange on waxed paper. Press mint into center of each ball. Chill in refrigerator until firm. Freezes well. Yield: 8 dozen.

Graham Cracker Crisps

24 honey graham crackers
6 tablespoons margarine
1/2 cup butter
1/2 cup sugar
3 ounces sliced blanched almonds

Break graham crackers apart. Arrange in single layer in 10x15-inch baking pan. Combine margarine, butter and sugar in saucepan. Bring to a boil, stirring until margarine and butter melt and sugar dissolves. Boil for 2 minutes. Pour over graham crackers. Sprinkle with almonds. Bake at 325 degrees for 10 minutes. Remove immediately to wire rack over waxed paper. Let stand until cool. Store in airtight container. Yield: 24 servings.

MUNCHY FUN

Dipped Pretzels

1 (12-ounce) package almond bark
1 (9-ounce) package small pretzels

Melt almond bark using package directions. Dip pretzels into melted almond bark. Place on waxed paper. Let stand until firm. Yield: 1 pound.

Nothing-Like-It Fudge

1 cup honey
1 cup peanut butter
1 cup carob powder
1 cup unsalted sunflower seeds
$1/2$ cup sesame seeds
$1/2$ cup flaked coconut
$1/2$ cup chopped walnuts
$1/2$ cup raisins

Cook honey and peanut butter in saucepan over low heat, stirring until melted. Remove from heat. Stir in carob powder, sunflower seeds, sesame seeds, coconut, walnuts and raisins. Press into buttered 9-inch square pan. Chill, covered, for several hours. Cut into squares. Yield: 3 dozen.

Peanut Butter Fudge

$1 1/2$ pounds white chocolate
16 ounces chunky peanut butter

Microwave white chocolate on High in large glass bowl until melted. Stir in peanut butter, mixing well. Pour into buttered dish. Cool to room temperature. Cut into squares. Yield: 4 dozen.

Quick Microwave Chocolate Fudge

2 (1-pound) packages confectioners' sugar
1 cup baking cocoa
1/2 cup milk
1 cup butter
1 1/2 cups chopped pecans
2 tablespoons vanilla extract

Mix confectioners' sugar and cocoa in glass dish. Add milk and butter; do not mix. Microwave on High for 4 1/2 to 6 minutes or until butter melts; mix well. Add pecans and vanilla; mix well. Spoon into buttered square dish. Chill until firm. Cut into small squares. May chop pecans coarsely and add 1 cup miniature marshmallows with pecans for Rocky Road Fudge. Yield: 5 dozen.

Velveeta Fudge

8 ounces Velveeta cheese
1 cup butter
1 1/2 teaspoons vanilla extract
1/2 cup baking cocoa
2 (1-pound) packages confectioners' sugar
1/2 cup nuts

Combine cheese and butter in large saucepan over low heat. Heat until melted, stirring constantly; remove from heat. Add vanilla and cocoa; blend well. Add confectioners' sugar and nuts; mix well. Pour into buttered 9x13-inch pan. Chill until serving time. Cut into squares. Yield: 5 dozen.

MUNCHY FUN

Peanut Butter Gems

1 (18-ounce) jar chunky peanut butter
1/2 cup melted butter
1/2 cup packed brown sugar
2 1/2 cups confectioners' sugar
1 teaspoon vanilla extract
1 cup milk chocolate chips
1/3 cup butter

Combine peanut butter, 1/2 cup melted butter, brown sugar, confectioners' sugar and vanilla in bowl; mix well. Press into buttered shallow pan. Melt chocolate chips with 1/3 cup butter in saucepan. Spread over peanut butter mixture. Chill until firm. Cut into squares. Yield: 5 dozen.

Toffee Clusters

1 pound almond bark
2 cups chocolate chips
1 (10-ounce) package butter brickle chips

Place almond bark in glass bowl. Microwave for 5 minutes or until almond bark melts, stirring with wooden spoon frequently. Add chocolate chips. Microwave for 1 to 1 1/2 minutes or until melted. Stir in butter brickle chips. Drop by teaspoonfuls onto waxed paper-lined tray. Yield: 3 dozen.

White Chocolate Brittle

1 pound white chocolate
1 cup Spanish peanuts
1 cup broken pretzel sticks

Melt white chocolate in saucepan. Stir in peanuts and pretzels. Spread in thin layer on large tray. Chill in freezer until firm. Break into pieces. Yield: 16 servings.

White Chocolate Candy

2 pounds white chocolate
1 cup peanut butter
3 cups crisp rice cereal
1 (24-ounce) jar dry-roasted peanuts
1 (10-ounce) package marshmallows

Melt white chocolate and peanut butter in saucepan, stirring to mix well. Combine with cereal, peanuts and marshmallows in large bowl; mix well. Drop by spoonfuls onto waxed paper. Let stand until firm. Store in airtight container. Yield: 2 dozen.

Curried Nibbles

1 cup margarine
1/2 teaspoon garlic salt
1/4 teaspoon minced garlic
1 teaspoon salt
1 teaspoon curry powder
1 teaspoon Worcestershire sauce
Tabasco sauce to taste
5 cups mixed nuts
1 quart popped popcorn
1 (12-ounce) package corn chips
8 ounces small cheese crackers

Melt margarine in roasting pan in oven. Stir in garlic salt, garlic, salt, curry powder, Worcestershire sauce and Tabasco sauce. Add mixed nuts, popcorn, corn chips and crackers; toss gently. Bake at 250 degrees for 1 hour, stirring occasionally. Remove to paper towels to cool. Yield: 25 servings.

For a one-of-a-kind treat, combine your favorite cereal with chopped dried fruit, nuts, chocolate chips, butterscotch chips, sunflower seeds...use your imagination!

MUNCHY FUN

Picnic Mix

4 cups bite-sized shredded wheat cereal
1/2 cup mixed nuts
1/2 cup shredded coconut
1/3 cup butter
1/4 cup frozen orange or pineapple juice
  concentrate
2 tablespoons honey
3/4 teaspoon ginger
1 cup raisins

Combine cereal, mixed nuts and coconut in large bowl; mix well. Combine butter, orange juice concentrate, honey and ginger in saucepan. Cook until butter melts, stirring frequently. Add raisins. Cook for 2 minutes or until raisins are soft, stirring frequently. Add to cereal mixture; toss to coat. Spread on baking sheet. Bake at 350 degrees for 12 to 15 minutes or until cereal is light brown, stirring once. Cool to room temperature. Store in covered container. Yield: 24 servings.

Scramble

1 pound cashews
1 pound mixed nuts
1 pound pecan halves
1 (12-ounce) package wheat Chex
1 (12-ounce) package round oat cereal
2 (8-ounce) packages pretzel sticks
2 cups vegetable oil
1 teaspoon garlic salt
1 tablespoon seasoned salt

Combine cashews, mixed nuts, pecans, cereals, pretzels, oil, garlic salt and seasoned salt in large roasting pan; mix gently with wooden spoon. Bake at 250 degrees for 2 hours, stirring every 15 minutes. Cool to room temperature. Store in airtight container. May substitute sesame sticks for round oat cereal and rice Chex for wheat Chex if preferred. Yield: 50 servings.

*Store crunchy snacks in
an airtight container.*

MUNCHY FUN

Seasoned Oyster Crackers

³/₄ cup canola oil
¹/₄ cup sesame oil
2 (12-ounce) packages oyster crackers
1¹/₂ teaspoons Cavender's Greek seasoning

Blend canola oil and sesame oil in 9x13-inch baking pan. Add oyster crackers. Stir gently to coat crackers on both sides. Sprinkle with seasoning. Bake in preheated 225-degree oven for 10 minutes; stir. Bake for 10 minutes longer or until golden brown. Remove to paper towels to drain. Let stand until cool. Store in airtight container in refrigerator. Yield: 48 servings.

Snack Attack Crackers

1 cup vegetable oil
1 package ranch-style salad dressing mix
2 teaspoons lemon pepper seasoning
1 teaspoon dillweed
1 teaspoon garlic powder
2 (12-ounce) packages oyster crackers

Warm oil in saucepan over medium heat. Add dressing mix, lemon pepper seasoning, dillweed and garlic powder; mix well. Place crackers in large bowl. Pour oil mixture over crackers, tossing gently to coat. Let stand for 1 hour before serving. Yield: 2 pounds.

Quackers

4 cups rice, corn or wheat Chex
16 ounces oyster crackers
2 cups Doo-Dads
2 cups pretzels
2 cups Cheese Ducks
1¹/₂ cups salad oil
2 envelopes buttermilk salad dressing mix
1 teaspoon lemon pepper
1 teaspoon dillweed
1 teaspoon garlic powder

Combine rice Chex, oyster crackers, Doo-Dads, pretzels and Cheese Ducks in bowl. Blend oil and salad dressing mix in small bowl. Add seasonings; mix well. Pour over cereal mixture; mix well. Spread on baking sheets. Bake at 250 degrees for 15 to 20 minutes or until warm. Yield: 50 servings.

Puppy Chow

2 cups chocolate chips
1/2 cup butter
1 cup creamy peanut butter
1 (12-ounce) box Crispix
1 (1-pound) package confectioners' sugar

Melt chocolate chips and butter in saucepan. Blend in peanut butter. Add cereal; toss to coat. Coat mixture with confectioners' sugar. Yield: 3 pounds.

Triple Goodness

6 ounces butterscotch chips
1 1/2 cups golden raisins
1 1/2 cups salted peanuts

Combine butterscotch chips, raisins and peanuts in bowl; mix well. Spoon into 8 small plastic bags. Yield: 8 servings.

Onion Pretzels

1 (18-ounce) package pretzels
1 cup margarine
1 envelope onion soup mix

Break pretzels into bite-sized pieces. Melt margarine in 4-quart saucepan. Add soup mix; mix well. Add pretzels gradually, stirring to coat well. Spread on 10x15-inch baking sheet. Bake at 225 degrees for 45 minutes, stirring every 15 minutes. Yield: 10 servings.

Glazed Pecans

1/2 cup sour cream
1 1/2 teaspoons vanilla extract
1 1/2 cups sugar
4 cups pecan halves

Combine sour cream, vanilla and sugar in saucepan. Cook to 234 to 240 degrees on candy thermometer, soft-ball stage. Add pecan halves; stir until coated. Spread on tray. Let stand until cool and dry. Store in airtight container. Yield: 16 servings.

Spiced Pecans

1 egg white
¼ teaspoon cinnamon
¼ teaspoon cloves
¼ teaspoon allspice
½ teaspoon salt
½ cup sugar
2 tablespoons water
4 cups pecan halves

Combine egg white, cinnamon, cloves, all-spice, salt, sugar and water in bowl; mix well. Let stand for 15 minutes. Stir in pecan halves. Spread on two 10x15-inch baking sheets. Bake at 250 degrees for 1 hour. Remove to waxed paper to cool.
Yield: 8 servings.

Swedish Nuts

1½ cups almonds
2 cups walnuts
½ cup pecans
2 egg whites
1 cup sugar
⅛ teaspoon salt
½ cup melted butter

Spread almonds, walnuts and pecans on baking sheet. Bake at 275 degrees until toasted. Beat egg whites in bowl until foamy. Add sugar 1 tablespoonful at a time, beating constantly until stiff peaks form. Beat in salt. Stir in toasted nuts, coating well. Spoon into melted butter in 10x15-inch baking pan. Bake at 300 degrees for 30 minutes, stirring several times. May turn entire baked layer after 15 minutes or bake without turning if preferred.
Yield: 20 servings.

MUNCHY FUN

One pound of walnuts or pecans in the shell will yield about 2 cups of shelled nuts.

Zesty Pecans

1 tablespoon melted butter
1 pound pecans
Salt to taste
3 tablespoons Worcestershire sauce
Tabasco sauce to taste

Mix butter and pecans in large baking pan. Bake at 300 degrees for 5 minutes. Add salt; mix well. Bake for 10 minutes. Mix Worcestershire sauce and Tabasco sauce in small bowl. Pour over pecans; mix well. Bake for 15 to 20 minutes longer or until done to taste. Yield: 12 servings.

Honey Oven Popcorn

1 cup honey
1 cup packed brown sugar
1 cup margarine
1 teaspoon salt
$1/2$ teaspoon baking soda
1 cup peanuts
5 quarts popped popcorn

Combine honey, brown sugar, margarine and salt in saucepan. Simmer over low heat for 2 minutes, stirring constantly. Remove from heat. Add baking soda. Combine with peanuts and popcorn in large baking dish. Bake at 250 degrees for 1 hour, stirring occasionally. Yield: 20 cups.

White Chocolate Delights

White chocolate
1 package Ritz Bits peanut butter
 crackers

Melt chocolate in double boiler over hot water. Dip crackers into chocolate to coat. Place on waxed paper or wire rack to dry. Yield: variable.

MUNCHY FUN

GARDEN PATCH FUN

Spiced Watermelon Rind

Watermelon rind

5 cups sugar

2 cups cider vinegar

1 cup water

1 tablespoon whole cloves

1 tablespoon whole allspice

1 tablespoon crushed cinnamon stick

1 lemon, sliced

Cut red and green portions from enough rind to yield 3 pounds white portion only; cut into cubes. Let stand in salted water to cover overnight. Drain. Place in large saucepan; add water to cover. Bring to a boil; reduce heat. Simmer until tender; drain. Combine sugar, vinegar and 1 cup water in large saucepan. Add spices and lemon slices tied in cheesecloth bag. Bring to a boil, stirring until sugar dissolves. Boil for 5 minutes. Add watermelon rind. Simmer for 15 minutes or until cubes are transparent. Discard spice bag. Pack rinds into hot sterilized jars. Add hot syrup, leaving 1/4 inch headspace; seal with 2-piece lids. Yield: 3 to 4 pints.

Herb Butter

1 tablespoon minced fresh dill, chives,
    chervil, fennel, marjoram or tarragon
½ cup butter, softened

Combine herb of choice with butter in small bowl; mix until smooth. Let stand, covered, at room temperature for 2 hours to blend flavors. Store in refrigerator for several days. Use in cooking fish or meat, in scrambled eggs or as sandwich spread. Yield: ½ cup.

Tomato Catsup

4 quarts chopped peeled tomatoes
3 cups chopped onions
3 cups chopped green bell peppers
1 hot pepper, chopped
1 cup vinegar
1 cup sugar
2 tablespoons Worcestershire sauce
2 to 3 tablespoons salt

Combine all ingredients in saucepan. Simmer until reduced to desired consistency, stirring frequently. Cool to room temperature. Store in covered container in refrigerator. Yield: 4 to 6 cups.

Blueberry Rhubarb Jam

5 cups finely cut rhubarb
1 cup water
5 cups sugar
1 (21-ounce) can blueberry pie filling
2 (3-ounce) packages raspberry gelatin

Simmer rhubarb in water in saucepan until tender. Add sugar. Cook for 10 minutes, stirring constantly. Add pie filling. Cook for 6 to 8 minutes; remove from heat. Add gelatin, stirring until dissolved. Pour into hot sterilized jelly jars, leaving ¼ inch headspace; seal with 2-piece lids. Store in refrigerator or freezer.
Yield: 6 to 8 (6-ounce) jars.

Microwave Grape Jelly

2 cups grape juice
1 cup water
1 (1¾-ounce) package fruit pectin
3½ cups sugar

Pour juice and water into 2-quart glass bowl. Add pectin; stir well. Cover with plastic wrap. Microwave on High for 8 to 10 minutes or until bubbles appear at edge of bowl, stirring after 3 minutes. Add sugar gradually, mixing well. Microwave, covered, for 6 to 7 minutes or until mixture has boiled at least 1 minute. Skim off foam; stir well. Pour into hot sterilized jelly jar, leaving ¼ inch headspace; seal with 2-piece lids. Cool. Store in refrigerator. May substitute boysenberry, apple or blackberry juice for grape juice. Yield: 4 to 6 (6-ounce) jars.

Pepper Jelly

1½ cups cider vinegar
6 cups sugar
1 or 2 drops of green food coloring
1 cup ground red and green bell peppers
2 pods red and green hot peppers,
    ground
1 bottle of Certo

Heat vinegar, sugar and food coloring in saucepan until sugar dissolves, stirring frequently. Add bell peppers and hot peppers. Bring to a boil. Remove from heat. Let stand for 30 minutes. Bring to a boil again. Cook for 2 minutes. Remove from heat. Let stand for 5 minutes. Add Certo; mix well. Ladle into hot sterilized jars, leaving ¼ inch headspace; seal with 2-piece lids.
Yield: 4 to 6 (6-ounce) jars.

*To reduce the amount of foam
when making jelly, add ½ teaspoon
of butter with the sugar.*

GARDEN PATCH FUN

Frozen Strawberry Jam

2 cups mashed strawberries
4 cups sugar
1 cup water
1 (1³/₄-ounce) package fruit pectin

Combine strawberries and sugar in bowl.
Let stand for 20 minutes, stirring occasionally. Bring water to a boil in saucepan; add
pectin. Boil for 1 minute, stirring constantly; remove from heat. Add
strawberries; stir for 2 minutes. Pour into
hot sterilized jelly jars, leaving ¼ inch
headspace; seal with 2-piece lids. Let stand
for 1 hour. Chill in refrigerator until firm.
Store in freezer. Refrigerate after opening.
Yield: 4 to 6 (6-ounce) jars.

Zucchini Jelly

6 cups shredded zucchini
6 cups sugar
1 (8-ounce) can crushed pineapple
1 (6-ounce) package orange gelatin

Combine zucchini and sugar in saucepan;
mix well. Bring to a boil. Boil for 6 minutes.
Add pineapple and gelatin. Boil for 6 minutes longer, stirring constantly. Pour into
hot sterilized jelly jars, leaving ¼ inch
headspace; seal with 2-piece lids. This resembles orange marmalade—no one will
guess it is zucchini. May substitute any
flavor gelatin for orange gelatin.
Yield: 6 to 8 (6-ounce) jars.

Easy Pickled Beets

2 tablespoons sugar
³/₄ teaspoon salt
¹/₈ teaspoon ground cloves
¹/₃ cup cider vinegar
¹/₃ cup water
2 cups cooked sliced beets, drained
1 medium onion, sliced

Combine sugar, salt and cloves in bowl;
mix well. Stir in vinegar and water. Add
beets and onion; mix well. Spoon into container. Store, covered, in refrigerator,
shaking occasionally. Serve with meat or
fish. Yield: 2 to 3 cups.

Pickled Peaches

3 pounds sugar
2 cups water
1 1/2 cups vinegar
2 to 3 cinnamon sticks
1 teaspoon whole cloves
5 pounds peaches, peeled

Mix sugar, water, vinegar and spices in large saucepan. Bring to a boil. Cook over high heat for 5 minutes. Add peaches. Cook for 5 to 10 minutes or until tender; drain, reserving syrup. Pack into hot sterilized jars. Fill with reserved syrup, leaving 1/2 inch headspace. Seal with 2-piece lids. Yield: 2 to 4 quarts.

Easy and Delicious Pickles

2 cucumbers, thinly sliced
1 onion, thinly sliced
1/2 green bell pepper, thinly sliced
1 cup white vinegar
1 1/2 cups sugar
1 1/2 teaspoons celery seeds
1 tablespoon salt

Pack cucumbers, onion and green pepper into hot sterilized 1-pint jars. Combine vinegar, sugar, celery seeds and salt in saucepan. Heat until sugar dissolves. Pour over cucumbers. Cover with waxed paper; seal. Let stand in refrigerator for 2 to 3 days, shaking occasionally. Store in refrigerator for several months. Yield: 2 pints.

Iodized salt used in pickling will cause pickles to darken.

Pickled Okra

1/4 teaspoon dill
1/4 teaspoon celery seeds
1/4 teaspoon mustard seeds
1 clove of garlic, minced
1 or 2 hot peppers, chopped
3 cups white vinegar
1/2 cup pickling salt
1 1/2 cups water
6 pints okra

Combine dill, celery seeds, mustard seeds, garlic and hot peppers in bowl; mix well. Combine white vinegar, pickling salt and water in saucepan. Boil for several minutes. Add seasoning mixture. Simmer for 10 minutes, stirring occasionally. Wash okra; pack in 6 hot sterilized 1-pint jars. Pour pickling mixture over okra; seal with 2-piece lids. Process in boiling water bath for 10 minutes. Let stand for 4 to 6 weeks before serving. Yield: 6 pints.

Squash Pickles

8 cups sliced squash
2 cups sliced onions
3 green bell peppers, chopped
Salt to taste
3 cups sugar
2 cups vinegar
2 teaspoons mustard seeds
2 teaspoons celery seeds

Combine squash, onions, green peppers and salt in bowl; mix well. Let stand for 1 hour; drain. Combine sugar, vinegar, mustard seeds and celery seeds in large saucepan. Bring to a boil. Remove from heat. Add vegetables; mix well. Ladle into hot sterilized 1-pint jars, leaving 1/4 inch headspace; seal with 2-piece lids. Process in boiling water bath for 10 minutes.
Yield: 5 to 6 pints.

Old-Fashioned Chow Chow

1 quart (or more) vinegar
2 cups sugar
3 large white onions, chopped
1 green bell pepper, chopped
1 red bell pepper, chopped
3 medium cucumbers, chopped
1/4 small head cabbage, finely chopped

Heat vinegar and sugar in large saucepan until sugar is dissolved, stirring frequently. Add onions, bell peppers, cucumbers and cabbage; mix well. Simmer over low heat for 1 1/2 hours. Ladle into 9 hot sterilized 1-pint jars, leaving 1/4 inch headspace; seal with 2-piece lids. Process in boiling water bath for 10 minutes. Let stand overnight before serving. Yield: 9 pints.

Pear Relish

16 cups ground pears
8 cups ground onions
14 red bell peppers, ground
6 hot peppers, ground
2 cups salt
8 cups vinegar
5 cups sugar
2 tablespoons mustard seeds
2 tablespoons turmeric

Combine pears, onions, red peppers and hot peppers in large container. Add salt; mix well. Let stand overnight. Drain and rinse 3 times. Drain well. Combine vinegar, sugar, mustard seeds and turmeric in stockpot. Bring to a boil. Cook for 5 minutes. Add pear mixture. Cook for 10 minutes, stirring frequently. Ladle into 12 to 15 hot sterilized 1-pint jars; seal with 2-piece lids. Process in boiling water bath for 15 minutes. Yield: 12 to 15 pints.

GARDEN PATCH FUN

Zucchini Relish

10 cups ground zucchini
4 cups ground onions
1 cup ground mango peppers
3 tablespoons salt
2½ cups vinegar
1 teaspoon salt
1 teaspoon pepper
1 teaspoon nutmeg
1 teaspoon turmeric
2 tablespoons cornstarch

Mix zucchini, onions, peppers and 3 table-spoons salt in bowl; let stand overnight. Drain and rinse vegetables twice, squeezing to remove liquid. Combine vinegar, 1 tea-spoon salt, pepper, nutmeg, turmeric and cornstarch in large saucepan; mix well. Stir in vegetables. Bring mixture to a boil. Ladle into hot sterilized jars, leaving ½ inch headspace; seal with 2-piece lids.
Yield: 5 pints.

Salsa

4 quarts tomatoes, peeled, chopped
1 cup chopped green bell pepper
2 cups chopped onions
5 jalapeño peppers, seeded, finely
    chopped
¾ cup sugar
3 tablespoons salt
2¼ teaspoons paprika
2 tablespoons garlic powder
2 tablespoons seasoned salt
¼ cup lemon juice

Combine vegetables, sugar, seasonings and lemon juice in large saucepan. Cook over low heat until thickened, stirring occasion-ally. Pour into hot sterilized jars, leaving ½ inch headspace; seal with 2-piece lids. Process in boiling water bath for 10 min-utes. Yield: 6 to 10 (8-ounce) jars.

GARDEN PATCH FUN

COOKOUT FUN

Surprise Watermelon Pie

1 (14-ounce) can sweetened condensed milk

4 ounces whipped topping

1/4 cup lime juice

2 cups watermelon balls

1 (9-inch) graham cracker pie shell

Combine condensed milk and whipped topping in bowl; mix well. Stir in lime juice. Reserve 5 watermelon balls. Fold in remaining watermelon balls gently. Spoon into graham cracker shell. Arrange reserved watermelon balls over top. Chill for 2 hours or longer.
Yield: 6 servings.

Beef and Chicken Fajitas

1½ pounds chicken breast filets
1½ pounds skirt steak
1 (12-ounce) can beer
2 tablespoons olive oil
2 teaspoons lime juice
2 teaspoons minced garlic
Worcestershire sauce to taste
Tequila to taste
½ teaspoon oregano
1 tablespoon coarsely ground pepper
12 flour tortillas
Vegetable Sauté
Toppings such as sour cream, shredded
    Cheddar and Monterey Jack cheeses,
    salsa, shredded lettuce and sliced
    black olives

Rinse chicken and pat dry; trim fat from steak. Combine next 8 ingredients in large bowl; mix well. Pour half over chicken and half over beef in separate bowls. Marinate, covered, in refrigerator overnight. Drain, reserving marinades. Grill chicken and steak on covered grill until cooked through, brushing occasionally with marinade. Slice chicken and steak into strips. Sear in hot skillet. Serve with tortillas, warm Vegetable Sauté and remaining toppings. Yield: 12 servings.

Vegetable Sauté

1 green bell pepper, sliced
2 or 3 tomatoes, chopped
1 red onion, sliced
Garlic salt and pepper to taste
1 or 2 teaspoons butter or margarine

Sauté green pepper, tomatoes and onion with garlic salt and pepper in butter in large skillet until tender. Keep warm.
Yield: 12 servings.

Beef Burgers Hawaiian

1 1/2 pounds lean ground beef
1 teaspoon salt
1/4 teaspoon pepper
1 (13-ounce) can pineapple tidbits,
    drained
2 cloves of garlic, minced
1/4 cup soy sauce
1 tablespoon vinegar
1/4 cup corn oil
2 tablespoons catsup
1/4 teaspoon pepper
6 slices bacon

Combine ground beef with salt and 1/4 teaspoon pepper in bowl; mix well. Shape into 6 patties. Press 5 or 6 pineapple tidbits into each patty; place in glass dish. Combine next 6 ingredients in small bowl; mix well. Pour over patties. Chill, covered, for 1 hour or longer. Drain patties and wrap each with slice of bacon; secure with wooden pick. Grill over hot coals for 8 to 10 minutes on each side or until cooked through.
Yield: 6 servings.

Patio Pot Roast

1 (3-pound to 4-pound) blade-bone pot
    roast, 1 1/2 to 2 inches thick
Salt and pepper to taste
3 tablespoons flour
1 tablespoon light brown sugar
1/2 teaspoon dry mustard
1/2 cup catsup
1 tablespoon Worcestershire sauce
1 tablespoon vinegar
Sliced carrots, celery and onions

Brown roast on grill over medium-hot coals for 30 minutes. Season with salt and pepper. Combine next 7 ingredients in bowl; mix well. Place half the sauce in center of large piece of heavy-duty aluminum foil. Place roast on top of sauce. Top with vegetables; add remaining sauce. Fold foil over and seal tightly. Place on another piece of foil on grill. Cook over medium-hot coals for 1 1/2 to 2 hours or until done to taste.
Yield: 8 servings.

Sesame Seed Steak Teriyaki

1²/₃ cups soy sauce
¹/₃ cup water
2 tablespoons sugar
1 piece of gingerroot, crushed
1 clove of garlic, crushed
3 teaspoons sesame seeds, toasted
1 (3-pound) boneless rump or round
  roast, ¹/₄ to ¹/₃ inch thick

Pour mixture of soy sauce, water, sugar, gingerroot, garlic and sesame seeds over roast in shallow dish, tossing to coat. Marinate, covered, in refrigerator for 2¹/₂ hours, turning occasionally. Grill over hot coals until done to taste. Yield: 8 to 10 servings.

Grilled Pork Roast

1 (2-pound) boneless pork roast, cut
  into ³/₄-inch slices
1 clove of garlic, minced
4 green onions with tops, chopped
¹/₄ cup margarine
2 tablespoons lemon juice
1 teaspoon grated lemon rind
¹/₂ cup packed brown sugar
¹/₄ cup vinegar
¹/₄ cup water
¹/₂ cup catsup
1 tablespoon Worcestershire sauce
2 dashes of hot pepper sauce

Arrange pork in shallow dish. Sauté garlic and green onions in margarine in skillet for 5 minutes. Stir in lemon juice, lemon rind, brown sugar, vinegar, water, catsup, Worcestershire sauce and hot pepper sauce. Bring to a boil, stirring occasionally. Pour over pork. Marinate in refrigerator for 3 hours or longer, turning occasionally. Drain, reserving marinade. Grill pork over medium-hot coals for 30 minutes or until cooked through, basting with reserved marinade frequently. Yield: 6 to 8 servings.

COOKOUT FUN

Marinated Pork Chops

1 (6-ounce) can frozen lemonade
   concentrate, thawed
2/3 cup soy sauce
1/2 teaspoon garlic salt
1/4 teaspoon celery salt
1/4 teaspoon onion salt
4 pork chops

Combine lemonade concentrate, soy sauce, garlic salt, celery salt and onion salt in bowl; mix well. Pour over pork chops in shallow dish. Marinate in refrigerator overnight. Grill pork chops over hot coals for 10 to 15 minutes or until cooked through. Yield: 4 servings.

Chicken Kabobs

6 chicken breast filets
24 green bell pepper wedges
2 tomatoes, cut into wedges
12 ounces mushroom caps
1 cup soy sauce
1/2 cup corn oil
1/4 cup sugar
4 teaspoons lemon juice
1 teaspoon meat tenderizer
2 cloves of garlic, minced

Rinse chicken and pat dry. Cut into 2-inch pieces. Thread chicken alternately with vegetables onto skewers. Combine soy sauce, oil, sugar, lemon juice, meat tenderizer and garlic in bowl; mix well. Arrange skewers on foil-lined grill rack. Grill over hot coals for 30 minutes or until cooked through, basting frequently with soy sauce mixture. Yield: 6 servings.

*Use your favorite Italian salad dressing
for a quick and easy marinade.*

COOKOUT FUN

Greek Chicken

6 to 8 chicken breast filets
1 cup vinegar
1 cup vegetable oil
1/2 teaspoon salt
1/2 teaspoon pepper
2 tablespoons oregano

Rinse chicken and pat dry. Arrange in shallow dish. Pour mixture of vinegar, oil, salt, pepper and oregano over chicken, tossing to coat. Marinate in refrigerator for several hours, turning occasionally. Drain, reserving marinade. Grill chicken over hot coals until cooked through, basting with reserved marinade. Yield: 6 to 8 servings.

Savory Lemon Chicken

1 (3-pound) chicken, cut up
1/3 cup vegetable oil
1/3 cup white cooking wine
2 teaspoons lemon pepper
1 teaspoon prepared mustard
1/2 teaspoon tarragon leaves
1/2 teaspoon onion powder

Rinse chicken and pat dry. Arrange in shallow dish. Pour mixture of remaining ingredients over chicken, tossing to coat. Marinate in refrigerator for 1 hour. Drain, reserving marinade. Grill chicken for 30 to 45 minutes or until cooked through, basting frequently with reserved marinade. Yield: 6 servings.

Sesame and Ginger Chicken

4 (4-ounce) chicken breast filets
1 tablespoon toasted sesame seeds
2 teaspoons grated ginger
2 tablespoons honey
2 tablespoons reduced-sodium soy sauce
Thin green onion strips

Rinse chicken and pat dry. Pound 1/4 inch thick between sheets of waxed paper. Combine next 4 ingredients in bowl; mix well. Spray grill rack with nonstick cooking spray. Grill chicken over hot coals for 4 minutes per side or until cooked through, basting frequently with soy sauce mixture. Top with green onions. Yield: 4 servings.

Grilled Turkey Breast

1/4 cup soy sauce
1/4 cup vegetable oil
1/4 cup wine or sherry
2 tablespoons lemon juice
2 tablespoons dehydrated onion
1/4 teaspoon dry mustard
Pepper to taste
Garlic salt to taste
1 pound turkey breast steaks, 3/4 to 1
    inch thick

Combine soy sauce, oil, wine, lemon juice, onion, dry mustard, pepper and garlic salt in bowl; mix well. Add turkey, tossing to coat. Marinate, covered, in refrigerator for 5 hours or longer, turning occasionally. Drain, reserving marinade. Grill turkey steaks over medium-hot coals for 6 to 8 minutes per side or until cooked through, basting frequently with reserved marinade. Yield: 4 servings.

Sweet and Sour Barbecued Salmon

3 pounds salmon filets
1/2 cup packed light brown sugar
1/4 teaspoon salt
1/4 teaspoon pepper
1/2 cup butter or margarine
1/2 cup mayonnaise
1/4 cup catsup
2 tablespoons white vinegar
1/2 teaspoon Worcestershire sauce

Arrange salmon filets skin side down on double layer of foil slightly larger than fish; pierce holes at 2-inch intervals around fish. Sprinkle with brown sugar, salt and pepper; dot with butter. Spread with mixture of mayonnaise, catsup, white vinegar and Worcestershire sauce. Place foil and fish on grill over hot coals. Cover with additional foil or grill cover. Grill for 20 minutes or until fish flakes easily. Yield: 6 servings.

COOKOUT FUN

Grilled Sole with Lemon

¹/₂ cup freshly squeezed lemon juice
1 teaspoon salt
¹/₂ teaspoon pepper
¹/₂ teaspoon thyme
1¹/₂ pounds sole or cod filets
2 tablespoons melted butter

Combine lemon juice, salt, pepper and thyme in glass dish; mix well. Add fish, turning to coat. Chill, covered, for 1 hour, turning 3 times. Drain, discarding marinade. Brush filets with melted butter. Grill over hot coals for 5 minutes on each side or until fish flakes easily, turning once. Yield: 4 servings.

Favorite Shrimp

1 pound large shrimp, peeled, deveined
1 (16-ounce) bottle of Italian dressing
¹/₃ cup soy sauce
1 tablespoon Tabasco sauce
1 tablespoon lemon juice
¹/₄ teaspoon celery seeds

Arrange shrimp in shallow dish. Pour mixture of Italian dressing, soy sauce, Tabasco sauce, lemon juice and celery seeds over shrimp, tossing to coat. Marinate in refrigerator for 6 hours, tossing occasionally. Drain shrimp, reserving marinade. Thread shrimp on skewers. Grill over medium-hot coals for 3 minutes per side or until shrimp turn pink, basting frequently with reserved marinade. Yield: 6 servings.

*Grill fish for 10 minutes for
each inch of thickness.*

Jumbo Shrimp Kabobs

1 cup French salad dressing
1/4 cup lemon juice
1 tablespoon chopped parsley
18 jumbo shrimp, peeled
6 lemon wedges
12 cherry tomatoes
12 chunks green bell pepper

Combine French dressing, lemon juice and parsley in bowl; add shrimp. Marinate in refrigerator for several hours, tossing occasionally. Drain, reserving marinade. Place 1 lemon wedge on each of 6 metal skewers. Alternate, shrimp, cherry tomatoes and green pepper on skewers. Grill over medium coals for 6 minutes, turning once and brushing with reserved marinade.
Yield: 6 servings.

Gingery Swordfish Steaks

2 tablespoons vegetable oil
2 tablespoons lemon juice
2 tablespoons low-sodium soy sauce
1 teaspoon grated lemon rind
1 tablespoon dry sherry
2 cloves of garlic, minced
1/4 teaspoon pepper
2 teaspoons minced fresh ginger
4 (4-ounce) swordfish steaks

Combine oil, lemon juice, soy sauce, lemon rind, sherry, garlic, pepper and ginger in bowl; mix well. Arrange fish in shallow baking pan. Pour marinade over fish, turning to coat. Marinate, covered, in refrigerator for 2 hours. Place on lightly greased grill 6 inches from hot coals. Grill for 6 minutes or until fish flakes easily, turning once. Yield: 4 servings.

COOKOUT FUN

Barbecued Bluefin Tuna

2 cups fresh orange juice
1/2 cup soy sauce
1 cup red wine vinegar
1/2 cup olive oil
1 onion, chopped
4 cloves of garlic, minced
1 (6-ounce) can tomato paste
1/2 cup sugar
1 teaspoon red pepper flakes
1 tablespoon cumin
1 1/2 tablespoons whole mixed pickling
    spice
1 teaspoon black pepper
6 (6-ounce) bluefin tuna steaks, 1 inch
    thick
2 tablespoons unsalted butter
Black pepper to taste

Whisk orange juice, soy sauce, vinegar, olive oil, onion, garlic, tomato paste, sugar, red pepper flakes, cumin, pickling spice and 1 teaspoon black pepper in bowl. Arrange tuna steaks in single layer in dish. Add orange juice mixture, tossing to coat. Marinate, covered, in refrigerator for 12 to 24 hours, turning occasionally. Drain, reserving marinade. Grill fish on lightly oiled rack 3 to 5 inches from coals for 3 minutes on each side. Place steaks in baking dish. Spoon 1 tablespoon reserved marinade over each steak. Bake at 375 degrees for 4 to 5 minutes or just until fish flakes easily. Top with butter and black pepper.
Yield: 6 servings.

Corn on the Cob

1/2 cup butter, softened
1/4 cup grated Parmesan cheese
1/4 cup mayonnaise
1 tablespoon dried minced onion
1/4 teaspoon garlic powder
1/4 teaspoon white pepper
8 ears of corn

Beat butter, cheese, mayonnaise, onion, garlic powder and white pepper in mixer bowl for 2 to 3 minutes or until light and creamy. Chill, covered, for 1 hour or longer. Spread corn with butter mixture; wrap corn individually in heavy-duty foil. Grill over low coals for 20 minutes, turning frequently. Yield: 8 servings.

Eggplant Parmesan

1 large eggplant
1/2 cup vegetable oil
1/2 teaspoon dried oregano, crushed
1/2 teaspoon dried rosemary, crushed
1/4 teaspoon garlic powder
6 ounces sliced mozzarella cheese
1 cup grated Parmesan cheese
1 (15-ounce) jar Marinara sauce, heated

Rinse eggplant well; do not peel. Slice eggplant crosswise into 1/2-inch slices. Combine next 4 ingredients in bowl. Brush sides of eggplant slices with oil mixture. Cut mozzarella cheese slices to fit eggplant slices; set aside. Grill eggplant on covered grill over medium-hot coals for 5 minutes on each side, turning often and basting with oil. Arrange mozzarella cheese slices on eggplant slices; spoon Parmesan cheese over each. Grill until cheeses melt. Place eggplant on serving dish; spoon Marinara sauce over eggplant before serving.
Yield: 6 to 8 servings.

Grilled Mushrooms

24 large whole mushrooms
24 slices bacon
1 cup margarine, melted
1 cup teriyaki sauce
1/4 cup liquid smoke
1/4 cup packed dark brown sugar
1/4 teaspoon onion powder
1/4 teaspoon garlic powder

Wrap each mushroom with bacon slice, securing end with wooden pick. Combine remaining ingredients in bowl; mix well. Place mushrooms in 9x13-inch baking pan. Pour marinade over mushrooms. Marinate for 30 minutes. Drain, reserving marinade. Grill over medium-hot coals until bacon is crisp, basting occasionally with reserved marinade. Yield: 8 to 10 servings.

COOKOUT FUN

Onioned Potatoes

6 medium baking potatoes
1/2 cup butter, softened
1 envelope onion soup mix

Cut each potato lengthwise into 3 or 4
slices. Spread each slice with mixture of
butter and soup mix. Reassemble potatoes
and wrap with heavy-duty foil; seal tightly.
Grill over low coals for 45 to 60 minutes or
until tender, turning occasionally.
Yield: 6 servings.

Potatoes on the Grill

6 potatoes, peeled, cut into strips
1 small onion, sliced
1 small green bell pepper, diced
1/4 cup butter or margarine
Paprika to taste
Salt and pepper to taste
Garlic salt to taste

Spray a large piece of heavy-duty foil gen-
erously with nonstick cooking spray.
Arrange potatoes, onion and green pepper
on foil; dot with butter. Sprinkle with
paprika, salt, pepper and garlic salt; seal to
enclose vegetables. Grill over medium-hot
coals for 30 minutes on each side.
Yield: 6 servings.

Vegetable Kabobs

1/2 cup fat-free Italian salad dressing
1 tablespoon minced parsley
1 teaspoon basil
2 medium yellow squash, cut into
   1-inch pieces
8 small onions
8 cherry tomatoes
8 medium mushrooms
2 cups cooked rice

Combine salad dressing, parsley and basil
in bowl; mix well. Chill, covered, in refrigerator. Alternate squash, onions, cherry
tomatoes and mushrooms on 8 skewers.
Place on grill sprayed with nonstick cooking spray. Grill for 15 minutes or until
vegetables are tender, basting frequently
with salad dressing mixture. Serve over hot
cooked rice. Yield: 4 servings.

Zucchini Parmesan

1/2 cup grated Parmesan cheese
1 medium zucchini, peeled, cut into
  strips
1/2 cup chopped onion
Salt and pepper to taste

Spray large piece of heavy-duty foil with nonstick cooking spray; sprinkle with 1/4 cup of the Parmesan cheese. Arrange zucchini and onion over cheese; season with remaining cheese, salt and pepper. Seal foil to enclose vegetables. Grill over hot coals for 20 to 30 minutes or until zucchini is tender, turning 1 or 2 times.
Yield: 4 servings.

Peaches with Raspberry Purée

1/2 (10-ounce) package frozen
  raspberries in light syrup, slightly
  thawed
1 1/2 teaspoons lemon juice
2 medium peaches, peeled, cut into
  halves
1 1/2 tablespoons light brown sugar
1/4 teaspoon cinnamon
1 1/2 teaspoons rum extract
1 1/2 teaspoons margarine

Process raspberries and lemon juice in blender until smooth. Strain into small bowl. Chill, covered, in refrigerator. Place peach halves cut side up on 18-inch square piece of foil. Fill centers with mixture of brown sugar and cinnamon. Sprinkle with rum extract; dot with margarine. Seal foil; place packet on grill rack. Grill over medium coals for 15 minutes or until heated through. Place peaches on serving plates; spoon raspberry purée into centers.
Yield: 4 servings.

COOKOUT FUN

*Make a delicious lemon
butter for grilled vegetables of 1/2 cup
softened butter, 1 tablespoon lemon
juice and 1 teasoon salt.*

Cheese and Mushroom Bread

1 (1-pound) loaf French bread
2 (10-ounce) cans mushrooms
10 ounces Swiss cheese, shredded
1 cup melted butter
2 tablespoons finely chopped onion
2 tablespoons poppy seeds
1 teaspoon seasoned salt
1/2 teaspoon lemon juice
1/2 teaspoon dry mustard

Slit bread horizontally down center to but not through bottom. Cut into 20 slices to but not through bottom. Place bread on sheet of foil. Stuff with mixture of mushrooms and cheese. Combine butter, onion, poppy seeds, seasoned salt, lemon juice and mustard in bowl; mix well. Spoon over bread. Wrap tightly with foil. Grill for 20 minutes or until heated through. Serve warm. Yield: 20 servings.

Grilled Corncakes

2 cups cornmeal
1 tablespoon flour
2 tablespoons sugar
1 egg, beaten
1/4 cup chopped onion
1/3 to 1/2 cup buttermilk

Combine cornmeal, flour, sugar, egg and onion in bowl; mix well. Stir in buttermilk until of medium consistency. Drop by large spoonfuls onto preheated greased cast-iron skillet. Grill over hot coals until brown on both sides, turning once; drain.
Yield: 8 to 9 servings.

PICNIC FUN

Watermelon Rind Muffins

1 cup water

1 cup sugar

1/2 cup margarine

1 cup watermelon rind preserves

1 teaspoon cinnamon

2 cups flour

1 teaspoon baking soda

1/4 teaspoon salt

1 egg, beaten

1 teaspoon vanilla extract

1 cup chopped pecans

1/2 cup raisins

Combine water, sugar, margarine, preserves and cinnamon in saucepan. Bring to a boil. Boil for 5 minutes. Mix flour with baking soda and salt. Beat egg with vanilla in bowl. Add flour mixture and egg mixture alternately to sugar mixture in large bowl, mixing well after each addition. Stir in pecans and raisins. Spoon into greased miniature muffin cups. Bake at 350 degrees until golden brown. Yield: 18 servings.

Dill Dip

1 cup mayonnaise
1 cup sour cream
1 tablespoon dried minced onion
1 tablespoon parsley flakes
1 teaspoon seasoned salt
1 teaspoon dillweed or 1 tablespoon
  chopped fresh dillweed
1 teaspoon Worcestershire sauce
1/2 teaspoon MSG
Sliced fresh vegetables

Combine mayonnaise, sour cream, onion, parsley, seasoned salt, dillweed, Worcestershire sauce and MSG in bowl; mix well. Serve with sliced fresh vegetables such as carrots, celery, green onions, broccoli or cauliflower. Yield: 35 servings.

Orange Fruit Dip

1 (6-ounce) can frozen orange juice
  concentrate
1 (3-ounce) package vanilla instant
  pudding mix
1/4 cup milk
1/2 cup sour cream

Combine orange juice concentrate, pudding mix and milk in mixer bowl. Beat for 2 minutes. Stir in sour cream. Chill for 2 hours. Serve with fresh fruit. Yield: 2 cups.

Salsa Supreme

3 large tomatoes, finely chopped
1 large onion, finely chopped
6 tablespoons chopped fresh cilantro
Juice of 2 limes
3 cloves of garlic, crushed
2 teaspoons vegetable oil
1 teaspoon salt
1/2 teaspoon pepper
1 tablespoon chopped jalapeño peppers
2 teaspoons sugar

Combine all ingredients in bowl; mix well. Spoon 1/2 of the undrained tomato mixture into blender container. Process on High until tomatoes and onion are 1/3 original size. Combine with remaining mixture; mix well. Chill, covered, in refrigerator for 2 to 4 hours. Yield: 12 servings.

Texas Caviar

2 (14-ounce) cans jalapeño black-eyed
  peas, drained
1 (16-ounce) can white hominy, drained
2 medium tomatoes, chopped
4 green onions, chopped
2 cloves of garlic, minced
1 medium green bell pepper, chopped
1/2 cup chopped onion
1/2 cup chopped fresh parsley
1 (8-ounce) bottle of Italian salad
  dressing

Combine black-eyed peas, hominy, tomatoes, green onions, garlic, green pepper,
onion and parsley in bowl; mix well. Stir in
salad dressing. Marinate, covered, in refrigerator for 2 hours. Drain. Serve with tortilla
chips. Yield: 48 servings.

Bacon Hors d'Oeuvres

1 (1-pound) package bacon
1 (1-pound) package brown sugar
1 jar sweet pickled watermelon rind

Cut bacon slices into halves; place on
waxed paper. Coat heavily with brown
sugar. Roll watermelon rind with bacon;
secure with toothpicks. Place on rack in
broiler pan. Bake at 425 degrees for 15
minutes or until brown and crisp. Serve
warm. Yield: 32 servings.

*Freeze juice-in-box drinks the night
before going to a picnic. Use to
keep foods cold on the way and enjoy
an icy drink when you arrive.*

PICNIC FUN

Fruit Kabobs

1 cantaloupe, cut into chunks
1/2 honeydew melon, cut into chunks
1 pint strawberries
Sections of 2 oranges
2 bananas, cut into chunks
2 apples, sliced
2 tablespoons lemon juice
Citrus Dip

Brush fruit with lemon juice. Thread onto skewers. Arrange skewers spoke-fashion on tray. Spoon Citrus Dip into bowl in center. Yield: 24 servings.

Citrus Dip

1 tablespoon flour
1/3 cup sugar
1 egg, beaten
1/2 cup canned pineapple juice
1/3 cup strained fresh orange juice
1/4 cup strained fresh lemon juice
1/2 cup whipping cream, whipped

Combine flour and sugar in small saucepan; mix well. Stir in egg and fruit juices. Cook over medium heat for 5 minutes or until thickened, stirring constantly. Chill for 10 minutes. Fold in whipped cream. Chill until serving time. Yield: 2 cups.

New Potato Appetizers

1/2 cup sour cream
2 tablespoons chopped chives
1/3 teaspoon garlic powder
24 small new potatoes, cooked
4 slices bacon, crisp-fried, crumbled

Mix sour cream, chives and garlic powder in bowl; set aside. Cut potatoes into halves; scoop out centers with teaspoon or melon baller. Fill with sour cream mixture; sprinkle with bacon. Chill in refrigerator until serving time. Yield: 24 servings.

Quiche Squares

1 (8-count) package crescent rolls
3/4 cup shredded Swiss cheese
3/4 cup shredded mozzarella cheese
1 tablespoon minced onion
1 egg, beaten
3/4 cup milk
1/2 cup sliced stuffed green olives
1/2 cup mushroom stems and pieces
6 tablespoons bacon bits
1 tablespoon parsley flakes

Unroll crescent roll dough. Separate into 2
rectangles. Place in ungreased 9x13-inch
baking pan; press over bottom and 1/2 inch
up sides of baking pan to form shell. Seal
perforations. Sprinkle cheeses over dough.
Combine onion, egg, milk, olives and
mushrooms in bowl; mix well. Pour over
cheeses. Sprinkle with bacon bits and parsley. Bake at 375 degrees for 22 to 28
minutes or until set. Cool for 5 minutes.
Cut into squares. Yield: 60 servings.

Spinach Pinwheels

1 cup sour cream
8 ounces cream cheese, softened
3 (10-ounce) packages frozen chopped
    spinach, thawed, drained
1 envelope ranch salad dressing mix
3 green onions, finely chopped
1/2 teaspoon dillweed
Garlic powder to taste
1/3 to 1/2 cup bacon bits
1 (10-count) package large flour tortillas

Beat sour cream and cream cheese in mixer
bowl until light and fluffy. Add spinach;
beat well. Add salad dressing mix, green
onions, dillweed, garlic powder and bacon
bits; mix well. Spread over tortillas. Fold in
sides; roll to enclose filling. Wrap individually in waxed paper. Chill or freeze until
serving time. Cut into 1/2-inch to 1-inch
pieces. Place on microwave-safe plate.
Microwave on High for several seconds or
until warm. Yield: 50 servings.

PICNIC FUN

Tuna-Stuffed Eggs

6 hard-boiled eggs
3 to 4 tablespoons mayonnaise
1 (4-ounce) can water-pack tuna, drained
1 teaspoon sweet pickle relish
1 tablespoon prepared mustard
1/2 tablespoon grated onion
1/8 teaspoon salt
Pepper to taste

Slice eggs into halves lengthwise. Combine egg yolks with mayonnaise, tuna, pickle relish, mustard, onion, salt and pepper in bowl; mix well. Stuff mixture into egg whites. Chill until serving time.
Yield: 6 servings.

Zucchini Bars

4 eggs, slightly beaten
1/2 cup vegetable oil
3 cups shredded zucchini
1 cup baking mix
1/2 cup finely chopped onion
1/2 cup grated Parmesan cheese
2 tablespoons parsley
1 teaspoon salt
1/2 teaspoon oregano
1 clove of garlic, minced
1/8 teaspoon pepper

Combine eggs and oil in bowl; mix well. Add zucchini, baking mix, onion, Parmesan cheese, parsley, salt, oregano, garlic and pepper; mix well. Pour into greased 9x13-inch baking pan. Bake at 350 degrees for 30 minutes. Cut into bars. Yield: 48 servings.

Bananawiches

12 tablespoons peanut butter
6 hot dog buns, split
6 bananas
6 tablespoons strawberry preserves

Spread 2 tablespoons peanut butter in each hot dog bun. Place 1 banana inside each bun. Spread 1 tablespoon preserves over each banana. Wrap in colored plastic wrap.
Yield: 6 servings.

Benedictine Cucumber Sandwiches

16 ounces cream cheese, softened
1 1/2 teaspoons garlic powder
1 1/2 teaspoons onion powder
1/2 cup grated cucumber
1 or 2 drops of green food coloring
32 slices white bread, crusts trimmed

Combine cream cheese, garlic powder, onion powder and cucumber in mixer bowl. Beat at medium speed until mixture is creamy. Stir in food coloring. Spread mixture on half the bread; top with remaining bread. Yield: 16 servings.

Finger Sandwiches

1 (4-ounce) can shrimp
3 tablespoons mayonnaise
2 tablespoons finely chopped celery
1/4 teaspoon onion flakes
1 tablespoon chili sauce
2 (4-ounce) cans deviled ham
12 ounces cream cheese, softened
1/4 cup drained crushed pineapple
3 tablespoons minced green bell pepper
1 tablespoon minced onion
1/4 cup raisins
1/2 cup chopped apple
1/4 cup chopped celery
1/4 cup chopped pecans
1/4 cup mayonnaise
1 loaf thinly sliced bread, crusts
    trimmed

Shrimp Finger Sandwiches: Combine shrimp, 3 tablespoons mayonnaise, 2 tablespoons celery, onion flakes and chili sauce in bowl; mix well. **Creamy Ham Finger Sandwiches:** Blend ham and cream cheese in bowl. Add pineapple, green pepper and onion; mix well. **Raisin-Apple Finger Sandwiches:** Mix raisins, apple, 1/4 cup celery, pecans and mayonnaise in bowl. Slice bread into thirds. Spread with fillings. Yield: 5 dozen.

Frankwiches

1 (10-count) package hot dogs, sliced
2 cups shredded mozzarella cheese
2 tablespoons prepared mustard
2 tablespoons pickle relish
1 tablespoon sugar
Catsup
12 to 16 hamburger buns

Combine hot dog slices, cheese, mustard and relish in bowl; mix well. Add sugar and enough catsup to coat hot dog slices. Spoon into buns. Wrap individually in foil. Grill over hot coals for 30 minutes.
Yield: 12 to 16 servings.

Hawaiian Ham Sandwiches

1 cup ground cooked ham
$1/2$ cup drained crushed pineapple
1 tablespoon brown sugar
$1/8$ teaspoon ground cloves
6 raisin-cinnamon bagels, split

Combine ham, pineapple, brown sugar and cloves in bowl; mix well. Spread between bagels. Yield: 6 servings.

Swiss Pita Pockets

1 cup grated Swiss cheese
1 cup cottage cheese
$1/2$ cup chopped green bell pepper
$1/2$ teaspoon dillweed
Salt and pepper to taste
2 tablespoons mayonnaise
2 tablespoons chopped green onion tops
1 package pita bread, cut into halves
Alfalfa sprouts

Combine Swiss cheese, cottage cheese, green pepper, dillweed, salt, pepper, mayonnaise and green onion tops in bowl; mix well. Spoon filling into pita bread pockets; top with sprouts. Yield: 6 to 8 servings.

Oriental Chicken Pitas

4 cups chopped cooked chicken
2 cups grapefruit sections
1 cup orange sections
1 cup chopped celery
1 cup chopped green bell pepper
1/2 cup chopped onion
1/2 cup seedless green grape halves
1/4 cup sliced green olives
1 cup mayonnaise
1/4 cup prepared mustard
1 tablespoon grated orange rind
1 teaspoon ground ginger
1/2 teaspoon salt
1/4 teaspoon pepper
3 (6-count) packages pita bread

Combine chicken, grapefruit sections, orange sections, celery, green pepper, onion, grapes and olives in large bowl; mix well. Combine next 6 ingredients in bowl; mix well. Stir into chicken mixture. Chill in refrigerator. Cut pita bread into halves; open to form pockets. Spoon 1/2 cup chicken mixture into each pocket.
Yield: 18 servings.

Crunchy Vegetable Salad

1 cup vegetable oil
1 cup sugar
1/2 cup vinegar
1 (16-ounce) can cut green beans, drained
1 (16-ounce) can peas, drained
1 (8-ounce) can sliced water chestnuts, drained
4 large stalks celery, finely chopped
1 (4-ounce) jar chopped pimentos
Salt to taste

Combine oil, sugar and vinegar in bowl; stir until sugar dissolves. Add vegetables and salt; mix well. Marinate in refrigerator for 8 hours to overnight. May add mushrooms or cocktail onions. Drain. Serve as vegetable or on lettuce as salad.
Yield: 8 servings.

Fruit and Rice Salad

¹/₄ cup honey
¹/₄ cup vegetable oil
2 tablespoons lemon juice
¹/₄ teaspoon dry mustard
¹/₄ teaspoon celery seeds
¹/₄ teaspoon salt
3 cups cooked rice, chilled
2 cups cantaloupe chunks
8 ounces seedless green grapes, cut into halves
1 medium banana, diced
¹/₂ cup salted peanuts

Combine honey, oil, lemon juice, dry mustard, celery seeds and salt in bowl; mix well. Stir in rice. Add cantaloupe, grapes, banana and peanuts just before serving; toss lightly. Yield: 6 servings.

Pear and Walnut Salad

¹/₂ cup vegetable oil
3 tablespoons vinegar
3 tablespoons sugar
¹/₂ teaspoon celery seeds
¹/₄ teaspoon salt
1 large bunch leaf lettuce, torn into bite-sized pieces
2 fresh pears, peeled, sliced
1 ounce bleu cheese
¹/₂ cup toasted walnuts or pecans

Combine oil, vinegar, sugar, celery seeds and salt in bowl; mix well. Chill, covered, in refrigerator. Toss lettuce, pears, bleu cheese and walnuts in salad bowl. Chill. Pour celery seed dressing over lettuce mixture just before serving; toss lightly. Yield: 4 to 6 servings.

Sunflower Salad

1 to 2 bananas, sliced
1 cup thinly sliced celery
1 cup shredded carrot
1/4 cup golden raisins
1/2 cup dry-roasted sunflower seeds
2 tablespoons vegetable oil
1 tablespoon frozen orange juice
    concentrate
1 tablespoon honey
2 teaspoons lemon juice
1 teaspoon poppy seeds

Combine bananas, celery, carrot, raisins
and sunflower seeds in bowl; mix well.
Combine oil, orange juice concentrate,
honey, lemon juice and poppy seeds in
bowl; mix well. Pour over salad; mix gently.
Yield: 4 servings.

Watermelon Basket

1 large watermelon
2 cups cantaloupe melon balls
1 cups honeydew melon balls
2 cups white grapes
2 cups red grapes
3 cups whole strawberries
2 cups blueberries
2 cups sliced fresh peaches
2 cups chopped fresh pineapple

Cut watermelon into basket with handle.
Scoop enough pulp of watermelon into balls
to measure 4 cups. Combine watermelon
balls, cantaloupe, honeydew, white grapes,
red grapes, strawberries, blueberries,
peaches and pineapple in large bowl; mix
well. Chill fruit and basket overnight. Fill
watermelon basket with fruit.
Yield: 24 servings.

Confetti Salad

Flowerets of 1 head cauliflower
1 (16-ounce) can green beans, drained
1 (16-ounce) can wax beans, drained
1 stalk celery, sliced
1 pint cherry tomatoes
1 (4-ounce) jar pickled yellow corn
1 small bunch carrots, sliced
1 (7-ounce) can black olives, sliced
1 (7-ounce) can stuffed green olives
2 tablespoons dried chives
1 (8-ounce) bottle of Italian salad
    dressing
1 (8-ounce) bottle of buttermilk or
    ranch salad dressing

Combine cauliflowerets, beans, celery, tomatoes, corn, carrots and olives in large bowl; mix well. Mix chives with salad dressings in small bowl. Pour over vegetables; toss to coat well. May store in refrigerator for up to 2 weeks. May substitute any creamy salad dressing for buttermilk or ranch dressing.
Yield: 10 servings.

Mushroom Salad

1 large head cauliflower
1 pound fresh mushrooms
1 (10-ounce) package frozen peas
1 medium onion, chopped
2/3 cup vegetable oil
1/4 cup lemon juice
1 teaspoon dry mustard
1 1/2 teaspoons salt

Chop cauliflower into bite-sized pieces. Combine with mushrooms, peas and onion in serving bowl; mix well. Mix oil, lemon juice, dry mustard and salt in small bowl. Add to vegetables; mix well. Chill, covered, for 3 hours. Garnish with bacon bits.
Yield: 12 servings.

PICNIC FUN

Southwestern Salad

1 (15-ounce) can black beans, drained
1 (15-ounce) can low-sodium whole
  kernel corn, drained
2 cloves of garlic, finely minced
1 bunch green onions, finely sliced
6 cherry tomatoes, cut into quarters,
  seeded
1 small bunch fresh cilantro, finely
  chopped
1/2 cup chopped red and green bell
  pepper
1/3 cup vinegar

Combine black beans and corn in bowl; mix well. Stir in garlic, green onions, cherry tomatoes, cilantro and bell pepper. Add vinegar, tossing to coat. Chill for 1 hour or longer. Yield: 6 to 8 servings.

Spinach Pasta Salad

8 ounces corkscrew spinach rotini,
  cooked
1 (8-ounce) can artichoke hearts,
  drained, chopped
3/4 cup sliced pitted black olives
1 (4-ounce) jar pimentos, drained,
  chopped
1 medium red onion, chopped
2 ounces provolone cheese, cubed
2 ounces Cheddar cheese, cubed
1/3 cup red wine vinegar
1/4 cup vegetable oil
2 tablespoons honey
3/4 teaspoon basil
1/2 teaspoon dillweed
1/2 teaspoon garlic powder
1/2 teaspoon pepper
1/4 teaspoon salt

Combine rotini, artichoke hearts, black olives, pimentos, red onion, provolone cheese and Cheddar cheese in bowl; mix well. Pour mixture of wine vinegar, oil, honey, basil, dillweed, garlic powder, pepper and salt over rotini mixture, tossing to coat. Chill, covered, for several hours to overnight. Yield: 10 to 12 servings.

Tangy Coleslaw

1 head cabbage, shredded
1 medium white onion, chopped
1 medium green bell pepper, chopped
1 small carrot, shredded
1/2 cup sugar
1 cup white vinegar
3/4 cup salad oil
2 teaspoons sugar
1 teaspoon dry mustard
1/2 teaspoon garlic salt
1 teaspoon celery seeds

Layer cabbage, onion, green pepper and carrot in salad bowl, sprinkling 2 tablespoons sugar between each layer. Bring vinegar, oil, 2 teaspoons sugar, dry mustard, garlic salt and celery seeds to a boil in saucepan, stirring occasionally. Pour over vegetables. Let stand at room temperature for 1 hour; stir. Let stand at room temperature for 2 hours; stir. Chill until serving time. May be stored at room temperature for 3 days. Yield: 10 servings.

Herbed Tomatoes

6 tomatoes, peeled, sliced
2/3 cup salad oil
1/4 cup tarragon wine vinegar
1/2 cup snipped fresh parsley
1/4 cup sliced green onions
1/2 teaspoon basil
1/2 teaspoon thyme
1/2 teaspoon marjoram
1 teaspoon salt
1/4 teaspoon pepper
1 clove of garlic, minced

Arrange tomato slices in bowl. Pour mixture of oil, tarragon wine vinegar, parsley, green onions, basil, thyme, marjoram, salt, pepper and garlic over tomatoes. Chill, covered, for several hours to overnight. Drain before serving. Yield: 8 to 10 servings.

Summertime Vegetable Medley Supreme

1 red bell pepper, chopped
1 green bell pepper, chopped
3 cucumbers, chopped
Flowerets of 1 bunch broccoli
Flowerets of 1/2 head cauliflower
1/2 cup tarragon vinegar
1 tablespoon lemon juice
1/4 teaspoon garlic powder
1 tablespoon dry mustard
1 tablespoon Dijon mustard
1/4 teaspoon pepper
1/4 cup sugar
1/3 cup olive oil
1/2 cup chopped fresh parsley

Combine red pepper, green pepper, cucumbers, broccoli and cauliflower in bowl, toss lightly. Pour mixture of tarragon vinegar, lemon juice, garlic powder, dry mustard, Dijon mustard, pepper, sugar, olive oil and parsley over vegetables, tossing to coat. Marinate, covered, in refrigerator for 24 hours, tossing occasionally.
Yield: 8 to 10 servings.

Zesty Brussels Sprouts

1 1/2 cups sugar
1 cup cider vinegar
5 tablespoons hot horseradish
Salt to taste
2 teaspoons dry mustard
2 (10-ounce) packages frozen Brussels
   sprouts, cooked, drained

Combine sugar, vinegar, horseradish, salt and dry mustard in bowl; mix well. Add Brussels sprouts, tossing to coat. Chill for 6 hours to overnight. Yield: 6 servings.

PICNIC FUN

Lemon Poppy Seed Bread

1 (2-layer) package lemon cake mix
1 (4-ounce) package lemon instant
  pudding mix
1 cup water
1 teaspoon lemon extract
1/2 cup vegetable oil
4 eggs
1/4 cup poppy seeds

Combine cake mix, pudding mix, water, lemon extract, oil, eggs and poppy seeds in bowl; mix well. Spoon into 2 greased 5x9-inch loaf pans. Bake at 350 degrees for 45 minutes or until loaves test done.
Yield: 24 servings.

Raspberry Muffins

2 cups sifted flour
1 cup sugar
1 tablespoon baking powder
1/2 teaspoon salt
1 cup half and half
1/2 cup vegetable oil
1 teaspoon lemon extract
2 eggs
1 cup frozen raspberries, thawed,
  drained

Combine flour, sugar, baking powder and salt in large bowl; mix well. Blend half and half, oil, lemon extract and eggs in small bowl. Add to flour mixture, stirring just until moistened. Fold in raspberries. Fill paper-lined muffin cups 3/4 full. Bake at 425 degrees for 18 to 20 minutes or until golden brown. Cool for 5 minutes. Remove to wire rack to cool completely.
Yield: 12 servings.

Strawberry Bread

3 cups flour
1 teaspoon baking soda
1¹/2 teaspoons cinnamon
2 cups sugar
3 eggs, beaten
1 cup vegetable oil
2 (10-ounce) packages frozen sliced
    strawberries, thawed

Mix flour, baking soda, cinnamon and sugar in bowl. Combine eggs, oil and strawberries in large bowl; mix well. Stir in flour mixture. Spoon into 2 greased 5x9-inch loaf pans. Bake at 350 degrees for 1 hour or until loaves test done. Yield: 24 servings.

Tropical Mandarin Bread

¹/2 cup vegetable oil
³/4 cup sugar
2 eggs
¹/2 cup mashed bananas
¹/2 teaspoon almond extract
1 (11-ounce) can mandarin oranges,
    drained, chopped
1¹/2 teaspoons grated orange rind
1³/4 cups flour
¹/2 teaspoon baking powder
¹/2 teaspoon baking soda
³/4 teaspoon salt
¹/2 cup flaked coconut
1 to 2 tablespoons graham cracker
    crumbs

Combine oil and sugar in bowl. Add eggs 1 at a time, mixing well after each addition. Add bananas, almond extract, oranges and orange rind; mix well. Stir in mixture of flour, baking powder, baking soda, salt and coconut; mix well. Grease 5x9-inch loaf pan; dust with graham cracker crumbs. Pour batter into prepared pan. Bake at 325 degrees for 55 minutes. Yield: 12 servings.

Chocolate Applesauce Cake

2 cups applesauce
1/2 cup vegetable oil
2 cups flour
1 1/2 cups sugar
2 eggs
2 tablespoons baking cocoa
1 1/2 teaspoons baking soda
1/2 teaspoon salt
1/2 teaspoon cinnamon
2 tablespoons sugar
1 cup chopped pecans
1 cup chocolate chips

Combine applesauce, oil, flour, 1 1/2 cups sugar, eggs, cocoa, baking soda, salt and cinnamon in mixer bowl. Beat at medium speed for 4 minutes. Spoon into greased and floured 9x13-inch cake pan. Sprinkle with mixture of 2 tablespoons sugar, pecans and chocolate chips. Bake at 340 degrees for 40 to 45 minutes or until cake tests done. Yield: 24 servings.

Festive Watermelon Cake

1 tablespoon flour
1 (2-layer) package white cake mix
1 (3-ounce) package mixed fruit gelatin
3/4 cup vegetable oil
1 cup chopped seeded watermelon
4 eggs
1/2 cup margarine, softened
1 (1-pound) package confectioners' sugar
1/2 to 1 cup chopped seeded watermelon

Sprinkle flour over cake mix in mixer bowl. Add gelatin, oil and 1 cup watermelon; beat well. Add eggs 1 at a time, beating well after each addition. Spoon batter into 2 greased and floured 8-inch cake pans. Bake at 325 degrees for 30 minutes. Remove to wire rack to cool. Cream margarine and confectioners' sugar in small bowl until light and fluffy. Add enough remaining watermelon gradually to make of spreading consistency. Spread between layers and over top and side of cake. May tint frosting with red food coloring if desired. Yield: 10 servings.

INDEX

94

INDEX

INDEX

INDEX